The U-boat

The evolution and technical history of German submarines

Half-title: The commissioning of *U234* (Type XB) on 2 March 1944. Her provisional armament comprised 2cm guns without a protective shield. **Title page:** U-boats of Types VIID, VIIC and XB at GW's fitting-out piers, summer 1942.

The U-boat

The evolution and technical history of German submarines

by Eberhard Rössler. Translated by Harold Erenberg

Arms and Armour Press **a&p** London/Melbourne

Contents

Published in 1981 by
Arms and Armour Press, Lionel Leventhal Limited,
2-6 Hampstead High Street, London NW3 1QQ
and at
4-12 Tattersalls Lane, Melbourne, Victoria 3000,
Australia.

First German-language edition *Geschichte des deutschen
Ubootbaus*, published in 1975 © J. F. Lehmanns Verlag,
Munich, 1975.
First English-language edition, revised and expanded,
© Lionel Leventhal Limited, 1981.

The publishers wish to express their warm appreciation of
much help and advice contributed by Arthur D. Baker
III, Jak P. Mallmann Showell and Antony Preston.
Edited by Michael Boxall, David Gibbons and Tessa
Rose. Designed by David Gibbons. Production: Beryl
Gibbons. Typset by Typesetters (Birmingham) Limited,
Smethwick, Warley, West Midlands; printed on
135gm²Fineblade Cartridge by Clarke, Doble & Brendon,
Plymouth; bound by The Western Book Company,
Maesteg, Glamorgan.

British Library Cataloguing in Publication Data:
Rössler, Eberhard
The U-boat.
1. Submarine boats — History
2. Geschichte des deutschen Ubootbootbaus. *English*
I. Title
623.8′257   V859.G3
ISBN 0—85368—115—5

1 2 3 4 5 6 7 8 9 0

Publisher's note
The drawings included in this book represent the fruit of
many years' diligent research by the author, and have
been compiled from a considerable number of sources.
The publishers regret that a number of these illustrations
fall short of the high standards to be expected in modern
book production: age, rarity and intricacy of detail have,
in such cases, combined to erode clarity of line and
frustrate our efforts to obtain optimum results. We feel
sure, however, that the reader would rather such
drawings be included, in order to complete the story, than
be excluded on grounds of quality. Every effort has also
been made to translate the terms used on the line
drawings; however, in a number of cases, translation of
inboard detail especially would have necessitated the
mutilation or obliteration of parts of the drawings
themselves. In such cases, the reader is invited to consult
the Glossary on page 372.

Below: The new generation of U-boats emerges. *U19* (Class 206) in the process of surfacing.

Foreword
by Ulrich Gabler

The German Navy turned to submarine construction late by comparison with other navies, and it is therefore true to say that when it did make a start a considerable amount of groundwork in diving science had already been carried out. During the First World War, strategic circumstances conspired to make the submarine much more important for the German Navy than for its enemies, which stimulated rapid developments on the German side. In addition to significant improvements in overall construction techniques, further advantageous circumstances were that Germany had developed the diesel engine and had available a very reliable electrical industry.

In the main, submarines in the First World War had tended to travel on the surface and had dived only to carry out an attack or to escape an enemy. The period between the wars saw German submarines being developed in this same direction. Improved technology ushered in electric welding and improved diesel and electrical installations. Further advances were made with the introduction of wakeless torpedoes which left no trail or tell-tale bubbles and provided a strengthening of the submarine's armament. The middle of the Second World War saw a reappraisal of the rôle of the submarine, however: the demand was now for submarines that could carry out all operational functions submerged. The ideal U-boat would have a propulsion system totally independent of an air supply, and the Walter process would have been wholly suitable for this. Although a quick decision was made to install it in U-boats carrying out long voyages submerged, it was never used operationally. Then, U-boats were developed that used large electric battery installations and schnorkels, and these were ready for operational use by the end of the war. Following the cessation of hostilities, these most recent U-boats were the departure points for all submarines in the rest of the world. The first 'true' submarine came into being only with the discovery of the nuclear propulsion unit.

In addition to the development work that had led to actual construction, much research was done on projects that were not realized. All these undertakings, in which almost all aspects of engineering played their part, affected and continue to affect the whole technology. The influence of military submarine construction on the emerging civil underwater science cannot be over-estimated.

Up to now, there has been no comprehensive treatise on this interesting facet of technical history. The author deserves the greatest credit for achieving this in a most all-embracing way and for depicting also the history of unrealized projects. There is no doubt that this volume will be obligatory reading for all those interested in technical development and those who have participated in underwater travel.

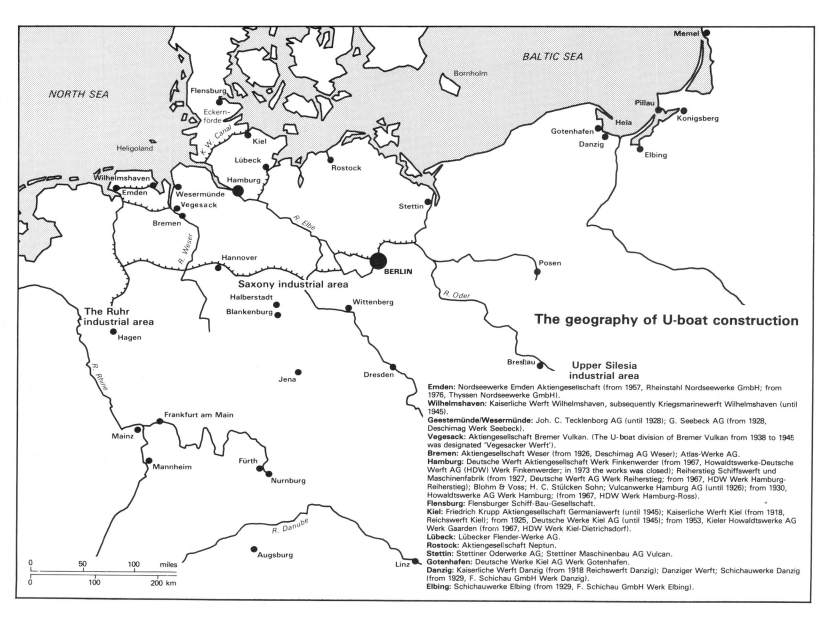

NORTH SEA

BALTIC SEA

Memel

Bornholm

Flensburg

Pillau

Eckern-
förde

Hela

Konigsberg

Heligoland

Kiel

Gotenhafen

K. W. Canal

Danzig

Elbing

Lübeck

Rostock

Wilhelmshaven

Hamburg

Emden

Wesermünde

Vegesack

R. Elbe

Stettin

Bremen

R. Weser

Hannover

BERLIN

Posen

Saxony industrial area

R. Oder

Halberstadt

The Ruhr
industrial area

Blankenburg

Wittenberg

Hagen

The geography of U-boat construction

R. Rhine

Breslau

Upper Silesia
industrial area

Jena

Dresden

Frankfurt am Main

Mainz

Fürth

Mannheim

Nurnburg

R. Danube

50   100   miles

Augsburg

Linz

100   200 km

Emden: Nordseewerke Emden Aktiengesellschaft (from 1957, Rheinstahl Nordseewerke GmbH; from 1976, Thyssen Nordseewerke GmbH).
Wilhelmshaven: Kaiserliche Werft Wilhelmshaven, subsequently Kriegsmarinewerft Wilhelmshaven (until 1945).
Geestemünde/Wesermünde: Joh. C. Tecklenborg AG (until 1928); G. Seebeck AG (from 1928, Deschimag Werk Seebeck).
Vegesack: Aktiengesellschaft Bremer Vulkan. (The U-boat division of Bremer Vulkan from 1938 to 1945 was designated 'Vegesacker Werft').
Bremen: Aktiengesellschaft Weser (from 1926, Deschimag AG Weser); Atlas-Werke AG.
Hamburg: Deutsche Werft Aktiengesellschaft Werk Finkenwerder (from 1967, Howaldtswerke-Deutsche Werft AG (HDW) Werk Finkenwerder; in 1973 the works was closed); Reiherstieg Schiffswerft und Maschinenfabrik (from 1927, Deutsche Werft AG Werk Reiherstieg; from 1967, HDW Werk Hamburg-Reiherstieg); Blohm & Voss; H. C. Stülcken Sohn; Vulcanwerke Hamburg AG (until 1926); from 1930, Howaldtswerke AG Werk Hamburg; (from 1967, HDW Werk Hamburg-Ross).
Flensburg: Flensburger Schiff-Bau-Gesellschaft.
Kiel: Friedrich Krupp Aktiengesellschaft Germaniawerft (until 1945); Kaiserliche Werft Kiel (from 1918, Reichswerft Kiel); from 1925, Deutsche Werke Kiel AG (until 1945); from 1953, Kieler Howaldtswerke AG Werk Gaarden (from 1967, HDW Werk Kiel-Dietrichsdorf).
Lübeck: Lübecker Flender-Werke AG.
Rostock: Aktiengesellschaft Neptun.
Stettin: Stettiner Oderwerke AG; Stettiner Maschinenbau AG Vulcan.
Gotenhafen: Deutsche Werke Kiel AG Werk Gotenhafen.
Danzig: Kaiserliche Werft Danzig (from 1918 Reichswerft Danzig); Danziger Werft; Schichauwerke Danzig (from 1929, F. Schichau GmbH Werk Danzig).
Elbing: Schichauwerke Elbing (from 1929, F. Schichau GmbH Werk Elbing).

Preface

A veil of secrecy has always surrounded submarine development, especially in Germany, and there is no doubt that the concept of the submarine as representing the most advanced technology and demanding the most skilled seamanship has strengthened this. Even though Germany suffered a complete military defeat in 1945, this veil was slow to lift. Those documents and plans relating to U-boats that did survive the war were appropriated by the Allies and, therefore, became inaccessible. They remain largely so to this day.

When the first reliable reports from foreign technical journals concerning the German 'Wonder U-boats' of the last war years reached me, it was not solely technical and historical interest but equally the lure of 'archaeological' research and reconstruction that impelled me to track down the origins and properties of the legendary Type XXI U-boat. The results of my research were presented in 1966 in a first report, the second edition of which (twelve months later) was to usher in a series of articles dealing with aspects of military science. Research then followed into the development of Type XXIII, the Walter U-boats and the closed-cycle propulsion for submersible vessels. Initially, foreign publications and especially private enquiries, sketches and collections formed the basis for this research, but the subsequent return of documents by the British to the Bundesarchiv/ Militärarchiv facilitated matters. A perusal of the unarranged technical data, pertaining mainly to Yards and Naval Service Stations, elicited a mine of information and detail, allowing—even without the most important source, the missing documents and plans from the U-boat departments of the Naval Design office—a mosaic of German submarine development to be put together.

I found that in order to provide a firm foundation for my technical and historical research it was necessary to delve further and further back into the past. But the temporal gap separating historical events multiplied considerabley the problem of finding background material. Similarly, the period preceding 1918, with a few exceptions, was devoid of essential U-boat documentation. And the paucity of material from the Technical Office of the U-boat Inspectorate is the harder to bear in the light of the fact that those involved in U-boat development of that era are no longer alive. Apart from the three famous publications dating back to 1919/20 and

1922 from Dr. Techel, Dr. Werner and Schürer on particular aspects of German submarine construction and the comprehensive work in tabular form of Erich Gröner on German warships, very little additional information on German U-boat development and construction has come from the archives. Nor, with just a few exceptions, has much information been forthcoming from the yards. I therefore had to base my research for this period initially on the available documents put out by the Reichs Naval Office and Imperial Navy Staff, which were in the possession of the Bundesarchiv/ Militärarchiv, but these lean more towards the military-political, strategic and economic aspects rather than to technical data. It was therefore impossible for me to present as complete a picture of all U-boat projects evolved by the Torpedo and U-Boat Inspectorate as I could of the OKM projects of the Navy; nevertheless, one may regard the chain of developments in this period as closed.

Much initial spadework had been done when J. F. Lehmanns Verlag of Munich suggested that, rather than rework my report on Type XXI, I write a complete history of U-boat construction. From the start, I had no illusions about the difficulties of incorporating information on such a wide subject into one manageable volume with the many diagrams and illustrations necessary. As far as was possible, the landmarks in German U-boat development were marked out by quotations, dates, sketches and photographs, around which I attempted a thorough analysis to give the reader an overall and clear picture of the subject. Basic information is given preference over comment. This method of presentation seems to me to be wholly justified, since it is out of the question for most readers to study the multiplicity of different sources. In view of the shortage of background material, in certain of the most complex developments there is considerable variation in the completeness of information—especially in the matter of naming U-boat designers, frequently only the head of a design team being stated. In these cases, his name must stand as representative of the unnamed originators and collaborators but for whose work a creation as complex as a submarine could not be achieved.

The book we now present must not be taken to replace scientific treatises on aspects of U-boat construction, comprehensive reference books and

tabular works or even text books. Standard works such as those by Gröner, Techel, Gabler, Lawrenz and Herzog are earnestly recommended as a complement.

As was the case in my earlier writings, a number of distinguished experts gave their support. Special mention must be made of Dr. Jost Dülffer, Professor Ulrich Gabler, Klaus Herold, Jürgen Friese, Dr. Dieter Jung, Wolf Kaliebe, Hans-Joachim Lawrenz, Lutz Nohse, Franz Selinger, Dr. Bernd Stegemann, Professor Jürgen Rohwer, Berndt Wenzel and Norbert Krüger, Dr. Gert Sandhofer and Wilhelm Wedelich for reading manuscripts, making helpful suggestions and additions. The staff of the Bundesarchiv/Militär-archiv have earned my thanks for their kind aid in sifting through archives. Fritz Köhl redrew and retouched many U-boat plans which he made available for this book. Among those who supplied photographs, special mention must be made of Professor Jürgen Rohwer, Christer Sahlin, Franz Selinger, Udo Ude and the Deutschen Museum in Munich. Finally, I wish to thank especially J. F. Lehmanns Verlag, who made possible the initial production of this comprehensive work.

Sadly, technical history remains the poor relation of history and engineering, even though it should play a key rôle as a lynch-pin between these two disciplines. Many historical events can only be explained within the framework of technical developments, of important inventions and even of large misconceptions, just as technical developments may only be appreciated correctly if one takes account of the historical background. It is my hope that this publication will contribute a little to this appreciation.

Eberhard Rössler, Berlin, 1974 and 1981

1 ORIGINS OF THE U-BOAT

THE EVOLUTION OF GERMAN SUBMARINE CONSTRUCTION

The ingenuity that has enabled man to develop methods of leaving his land-bound environment, to ascend into the skies and plumb the depths of the sea, marks the culmination of centuries of dreaming and theoretical design. The Renaissance, with its burgeoning of science and the technical arts, led to the projection of diving apparati and underwater vehicles that were technically feasible and well thought out. In Germany, as in other countries, inventors had experimented with diving technology, but German participation in its development has been relatively little investigated and documented:

1465 A Nuremberg weapons designer named Kyeser designed a diving boat.

1604 Magnus Pegel (Pegelius), a pedagogue from Rostock, published a technical description of flying machines, and basic ideas for a diving boat.

1691 The French physicist, Denis Papin, a professor at the University of Marburg, was commissioned by the Landgrave Karl von Hessen, to build a diving boat. This elliptical craft was propelled by oars, contained a ballast tank and bilge pump and, significantly, was equipped with a lock chamber and a schnorkel-like air circulation system worked by a centrifugal pump. In 1692, after an unsuccessful attempt in Kassel, he was said to have dived to the bottom of the River Fulda in his boat and returned safely to the surface.

1772 Count Wilhelm of Schaumburg-Lippe commissioned his Chief Engineer and Instructor at the Military Academy, J. Chr. Praetorius, to build a narrow diving boat. This was 10 metres long, had a fish-shaped profile, and was propelled on the surface by two oars. When submerged, it was to be propelled by movements of the 'fish tail'. Armed with a small cannon (a falconet), the boat formed part of the Count's fleet on Lake Steinhuder, but it is not known whether the 'fish' ever made a descent.

1792 J. A. Schultes, a Professor of Medicine at Landshut, published the results of his studies regarding the problem of renewing air in sub-

marines. He suggested that an air chamber or air bottles be installed.

1798 Klingert constructed a diving apparatus. A man wearing a diver's helmet and a watertight suit would stand on a platform, taking in air through tubes from the apparatus. By means of a handle, he could alter the position of a piston in a cylinder to affect the displacement of the apparatus so that ascent and descent could be regulated.

1799 A Surveyor of Mines, Joseph von Baader, published a plan for the construction of a two-man submarine.

The technical breakthrough came in the nineteenth century, with the construction of a fully-functional free-travelling submarine vessel, and the credit for this must go to the Bavarian non-commissioned officer of artillery, Wilhelm Bauer, the first German 'submarine' engineer.

The inventive genius of Wilhelm Bauer

Sebastian Wilhelm Valentin Bauer was born on 23 December 1822, in Dillingen on the Danube. His entire life was devoted to ceaseless invention, with an emphasis on submarines and their propulsion. His ability, ingenuity and iron will, coupled with an unshakeable confidence, ranks him among those nineteenth century inventors who were internationally recognized in their own lifetimes.

In April 1849, during the war over Schleswig-Holstein, the Danish Fleet was blockading the German coast. During the assault of the fortifications at Düppel on 13 April, the idea came to Bauer of using charges from boats to blow up the Sonderburg bridge in an attempt to break the Danish blockade. After the Bavarian troops had withdrawn from Schleswig-Holstein, he experimented with models in Ingolstadt and Munich, and completed the design of a submarine. Neither in his autobiography nor in his memoirs does Bauer give any indication that he was aware of the discoveries of other researchers into the problems of underwater travel, so it is quite possible that the design that emerged — *Brandtaucher* (literally 'Diving Incendiary') — was entirely his own concept.

In January 1850, he left the Bavarian Army, entered that of Schleswig-Holstein as a non-commissioned officer of artillery, and immediately placed his plans for a submarine before his new commanders. The project was passed to the Ministry of Marine from whom Bauer was allocated

30 Prussian talers from the naval budget for a model, which he built with the help of a mechanic in Kiel. Its approximate dimensions were 70cm x 18cm x 29cm, and Bauer demonstrated it to naval representatives in Kiel harbour. Driven by clockwork, it dived and travelled horizontally under the water for five minutes. Its cross-section was similar to that of a seal, and it had an outer hull of copper. Two ballast cylinders were fitted inside the hull, but their pistons could be operated from the outside to make the model surface or dive. Careful adjustment of a weight caused the model to remain motionless under the surface, or move forward propelled by a clockwork-driven, three-bladed screw. An adjustable lead weight was also used to trim the longitudinal angle of the model. Steering was effected by a movable rudder at the stern. In the forward part of the model was a superstructure with a window in the front and an entry hatch at the rear — a forerunner of the future conning tower. On the sides, hand grapnels were provided for use when attaching a mine (carried on the stem of the boat) to the keel of a ship. An upper deck of cork improved the stability and flotation properties of the model.

Although the model had all the essential features of later submarines (and Bauer's colossal ingenuity can not be over-estimated), the naval budget was insufficient to allow production of a full-sized submarine. In his memoirs, Bauer says that he was requested to deliver his model to the authorities, but, as he considered the model to have been his own brainchild and feared that others might steal his ideas, he destroyed it with an axe. Later, however, his hopes were revived by the commander of the Schleswig-Holstein Army, General von Willisen, who set up a commission charged with the construction of a full-sized boat. Initially, construction took place at Rendsburg, in Karl Holler's iron foundry (later known as 'Karlshütte'), but the state of war in the summer of 1850 and the problems of transporting the finished boat to Kiel prompted Bauer to continue work in the iron foundry of Schweffel and Howaldt in Kiel itself. Funds had been raised by voluntary contributions from the Army and the civilian population, but only a part of the necessary sum was realized, and this forced Bauer to eliminate the diving cylinders and reduce the thickness of the hull from 12mm to 6mm. The strength of the frames was reduced by 50 per

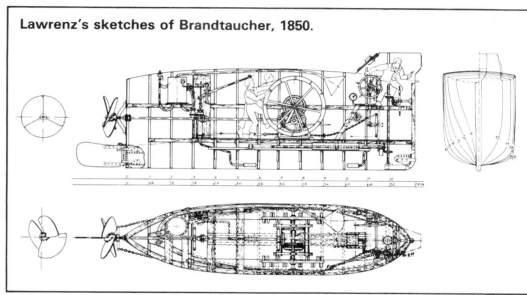

Lawrenz's sketches of Brandtaucher, 1850.

Above: Wilhelm Bauer, the first German submarine engineer. **Below:** A model of *Brandtaucher* by H. J. Lawrenz.

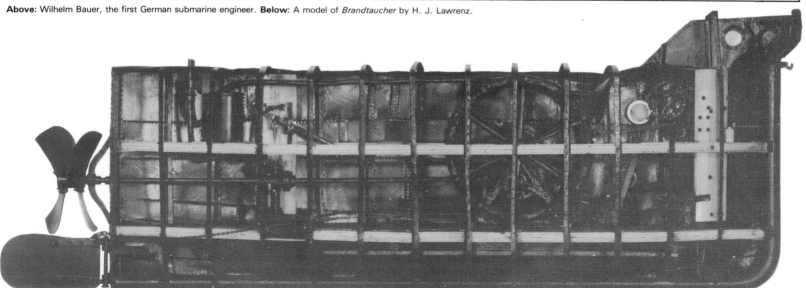

cent, and the distance between them was increased. Bauer gave warning that these changes would reduce the maximum diving depth from 30m to 9.15m, but no-one would listen to him. Iron ballast compensated for the weight lost by these changes. Construction was completed on 18 December 1850. *Brandtaucher* was brought out of the factory on rails and, in front of an amazed crowd, was towed into the water by the paddle-steamer *Bonin*. In the evening, Bauer carried out the first surface trial in the Kiel Estuary — after which, according to his memoirs, the Danish blockade ships left Friedrichsort and anchored outside the estuary.

Brandtaucher's specifications were as follows.

Length overall:	8.07m.
Maximum beam:	2.012m.
Draught (including 20 tons of ballast):	2.63m.
Displacement surfaced (with 20 tons of ballast):	27.5 tons.
Displacement submerged:	30.5 tons.
Crew:	3.

The boat could travel ahead and astern. A man-powered treadwheel with two gears allowed the three-bladed propeller to revolve at 60—115rpm, according to the gear selected. Maximum output of the treadwheel was approximately 20rpm, which gave the boat a speed of 3 knots, albeit for a short time only. The diameter of the propeller was 1.2m, and the pitch of the blades was 0.373m. The steel hull consisted of a keel (U-shaped plates, 6mm thick), vertical stem and stern supports, and twelve frames of 5—6mm angle-iron. The outer skin consisted of 6mm iron plates, overlapped and riveted. A variation from Bauer's original design was that the space between the keel and the inner deck was used as a diving and compensating compartment. To bring the boat to the surface, two bilge pumps expelled ballast water. These were hand-operated piston pumps with a capacity of 1.31m³/hr and 1.69m³/hr respectively; their suction heads were in the approximate centre of the forward section of the keel chamber. The heavier-duty, forward pump ceased to function if the boat became excessively stern-heavy (i.e., if the boat were too much down at the stern). A large valve, opening to the exterior, served as a diving valve, while a second, small valve provided fine adjustment. Water pressure, and consequently diving depth, was measured with a spring pressure gauge. A 500kg cast-iron weight was used to alter the trim; a handwheel in the steering compartment enabled this weight to be moved on rails under the deck planking over a distance of 3.74m. Hydroplanes were not fitted. The vertical rudder consisted of an elongated plate, with an area of 0.766m², controlled from its steering platform by a handwheel through an arrangement of levers, rods and chains. When the boat was on the surface, with its hatch closed, air could be renewed by operating a push-pull piston in a cylinder.

During her first trial, an operational fault caused *Brandtaucher* to sink at her berth near the steamship *Bonin*. She was raised, cleaned and repaired, and was ready for further trials, sixteen days later. On 1 February 1851 at 9am, Bauer and two volunteers, a blacksmith named Thomsen and a carpenter named Witt, entered the boat and closed the conning tower. They hoped to demonstrate to the Naval Committee the boat's ability to submerge to a depth of 1 atmosphere and surface at will. Although they had no experience of the apparatus, no safety precautions were taken.

According to Bauer, at a depth of 9.4m, first the port side, and then the starboard side began to distort, accompanied by groaning and cracking noises. The large treadwheel came adrift, and the strong iron shafts and oak beams gave way. The boat reached the bottom in 54 seconds, and was then at a depth of 16.3m, at an angle of 34°. The crew tried unsuccessfully to operate the bilge pumps and rearrange its iron ballast. Later analysis by Hans-Georg Bethge, a qualified engineer, has indicated that ballast water entering the keel compartment had so weighed down the stern that the boat had listed at an angle of 28°, which was beyond the corrective powers of its trimming weights. Additionally, the boat had taken in too much ballast water, presumably through leaking valves, and so had sunk deeper and deeper. Because she was stern-down at such an angle, the bilge pumps did not work well, and eventually failed. Bethge's investigations showed that the boat must have become unmanageable at a depth of 5.6m. The considerable hull deformation had caused rivets to spring out, and water had entered through these holes. But the plates of the outer skin had not given way; they would have withstood pressure to a depth of 11m if the other components had been made to their correct specifications.

Only Bauer's presence of mind saved his crew. After the mishap, he waited six and a half hours until the internal and external pressures had become even, then opened the conning tower and the three men floated to the surface in a bubble of air. (In the meantime, attempts by the Naval Committee to raise the boat by means of an anchor and chains had been ineffectual and had almost prevented Bauer's escape.)

The sunken vessel was formally taken over by the Naval Committee on 15 February 1851, and unsuccessful attempts were made to raise her. The Danes were likewise unsuccessful in 1855 and 1856. There she remained until 1887, when dredging operations began for the construction of the torpedo-boat base. She was raised on 5 July 1887, and shown first in Kiel shipyard and later in the garden of the Naval Academy. In 1906, she was taken to Berlin and put on show at the Nautical Museum near the Friedrichstrasse Station. In 1950, on the initiative of Professor Macklin, the considerably weather-beaten structure was taken from the ruined museum and brought to Rostock. Between 1963 and 1965, the wreck was restored at the Rostock Neptun Shipyard under the supervision of Hans-Georg Bethge, and accurate measurements were made. On 21 August 1965, the historic submarine became accessible to the public in the War Museum in Potsdam. In 1972—73, part of this museum was moved to Dresden and here, for the time being, *Brandtaucher* has her resting place.

Despite the mishap, Bauer was more than ever convinced that, theoretically, his calculations and constructions had been correct. According to Professor G. Karsten, Professor of Physics at Kiel, the loss of *Brandtaucher* was a result of the weakening of the boat's hull. Bethge calculates that Bauer's original construction would have allowed a diving depth of 25—27m. If Bauer's original plan had been adhered to, that of installing two ballast (diving) tanks together with a compensating cylinder for fine adjustment, the admission of water to the body of the boat would have been prevented. Although Bauer had not planned to use hydroplanes, propulsion at a controlled depth would have been possible, by using a small amount of bow heaviness, controlled by careful adjustment of the trimming weight, with a small amount of reserve buoyancy.

Bauer's activities in Kiel came to an end when Schleswig-Holstein was restored to the Danes and the army was demobilized. These changed circumstances prevented the construction of further submarines. In April 1851, Bauer returned to Munich, via Hamburg, where he began to build a model of a further version of his diving-boat, demonstrating it to all who showed interest, including King Ludwig I and King Maximilian II, technical committees and scientifically-minded colleagues. In March 1852, he showed his model to Emperor Franz Josef of Austria in Vienna, but, although its merits were recognized, no finance or commissions were offered. He lost the model during a demonstration to Queen Victoria and Prince Albert in the Isle of Wight, but built another in Munich, with financial aid from Prince Albert. At this time, he was also working on a gas-engine as a propulsion unit for submarines, and was severely injured during an explosion.

In November 1853, Prince Albert suggested to Bauer that he have the boat built in Britain, and Bauer chose the yard of the celebrated naval architect, John Scott Russell, at Millwall, in London. The contract stipulated that the boat be completed in March 1854, but the work progressed very slowly. Too late, Bauer discovered that the contract was financially disadvantageous to him, and he could do nothing about the slow building. Disappointed, he threatened to offer the invention to Russia, which was soon to be at war with Britain, but here he had gone too far, and he had to leave England in a hurry. The yard finished the boat without his assistance, but she sank with her crew during the first trials.

By now, the Crimean War had begun, and Grand Admiral Grand Prince Konstantin invited Bauer to St. Petersburg, as his ideas had aroused interest at the Tsar's court. In May 1855, the Imperial Russian Navy commissioned Bauer to build his third submarine at the Duke of Leuchtenberg's machine factory in St. Petersburg. *Seeteufel* or *Le Diable Marin* ('Sea Devil') was completed on 1 November 1855, and this time was exactly to Bauer's specifications. She was twice the size of *Brandtaucher* (length, 16.32m; beam, 3.45m; draught, 3.92m; thickness of outer skin, 13mm; distance between frames, 31cm; designed diving depth 47m). As in her predecessors, propulsion was to be provided by man-power.

It took the Russian Navy from 2 November 1855 until 20 May 1856 to transport her from St.

Petersburg to Kronstadt, and the journey would not have been completed had Bauer, himself, not intervened. In the fortified port, Bauer now carried out 134 trials. During the last of these, on 2 October 1856, it was intended to attach a mine to a ship, and explode it. The ship was moored in rather shallow water, and the submarine grounded with her propeller stuck on the bottom. Ballast was jettisoned and water was pumped out of the ballast tanks, and this brought the bows of the boat to the surface. But the clumsiness of a Russian lieutenant caused water to enter the boat through the conning tower and the vessel sank. The crew managed to escape, and the boat was subsequently raised, but was not put back into working order. There followed a disagreement between the Naval Technical Committee and Bauer, concerning fulfilment of the building contract dated 20 June 1855 and the payment of money as set out in that

following year, although obsessed as ever with the construction of a submarine, he turned his attention to the building of a diving-bell, a method of raising sunken ships, a gas-engine as the propulsion unit of submarines, and underwater guns. In 1860, he offered his diving-boat and other inventions to the Prussian War and Naval Ministry in Berlin, but this was of no avail and he returned once again to England. There he took out British patents for the diving-bell and for a new method of underwater cable laying. He worked for a time in the London office of the construction firm of Siemens & Halske, but soon left England for Trieste, where he demonstrated his diving-chambers and his method of raising sunken ships by using 'camels'.

Here at last he found success. His camels were put to practical use in March 1861 when the mail steamer *Ludwig*, which had sunk in Lake

the event of an accident the State may well lose millions.

'It is immaterial whether the enemy hides his guns behind iron plates, ramparts or beneath columns of water; his destruction is what determines who is the victor and, if victory is to be measured by the physical and moral impacts upon the enemy and not on the expenditure of millions in the fight against him, then I submit wholeheartedly my plans for an underwater fighting ship to the German State of Prussia without reserve, because I am convinced that in them are the best means for war and peace without a heavy expenditure in men and money.'

There is absolutely no doubt that Bauer's ideas were far in advance of his time. His new design was for a vessel 37.3m long, 6.2m wide and 3.1m high, with a displacement of approximately 412 tons and with a single-drive internal-combustion engine for surface and submerged propulsion. This engine was to have a capacity of 100hp on the surface and 230hp when submerged, giving a speed of 8–9 knots. For optimum propulsion, it was planned to use a controllable-pitch propeller. Large hydroplanes were to be fitted aft for rapid diving. A transverse propeller forward of the bow planes would assist tight manoeuvring, and ballast that could be jettisoned would ensure fast surfacing.

On the surface, the boat was to be controlled from a retractable observation tower, 2.8m high. This would also provide ventilation for the crew and for the propulsion unit. Underwater observation would be from ports in the hull, which was to have an elliptical cross-section. The hull frames were to be spaced 38cm apart, and the thickness of the plates above the waterline was to be approximately 25mm reducing to 12.7mm below the waterline. The boat would be safe to a depth of 30m. She was to have been armed with five underwater guns, whose recoil was to have been so designed as to have no detrimental effect on the boat's stability. It was estimated that the ten-man crew could survive for 24 hours before it would become necessary to renew the air, but, with an air purification system, using oxygen and caustic potash, a further 24 hours would be gained. Each man would have a life-jacket, and an inflatable boat would be carried aboard.

Well in advance of Otto, Benz, Daimler, and Diesel, Wilhelm Bauer was proposing to use an internal-combustion engine for both surface and submerged propulsion. Submerged, the engine would burn paraffin with oxygen produced from manganese dioxide (MnO_2); on the surface, compressed air was to be substituted for the pure oxygen. The engine was to be two-stroke, with two groups of three cylinders filled with water. Whichever means of combustion was used, whether paraffin with oxygen or with compressed air, the mixture could be fed into one group and ignited with an electric spark, creating a mixture of gas and steam in the cylinders of that group to force the remaining water through a turbine to activate the boat's propeller. This water would then also expel exhaust gases from the cylinders of the second group. The process would then begin in reverse order from the second group of cylinders. A special turbine was envisaged for reverse astern. The

Bauer's working model (length 112cm) of a diving-boat, February 1853.

contract. The money was initially withheld from Bauer because, it was alleged, not all the points set forth in the agreement had been fulfilled. But, on 20 November 1857, he received word from the Shipbuilding Department of the Russian Naval Ministry (letter No. 12,480) '. . . however, your boat has shown that your ideas on underwater travel are basically correct and that if your boat is perfected more satisfactory results can be achieved'.

In the same letter, it was suggested that he remain in Russian service, with the same financial arrangements, and continue his trials in the spring of 1858, with expenses to be met by the Naval Ministry. Bauer now busied himself with a model of a 24-gun submarine corvette. The boat was to be propelled by a high-pressure steam-engine, and carry a crew of 80. Her planned dimensions were: length, 44m; beam, 6.3m; draught, 3.76m. It was intended that the boat should approach an enemy ship underwater, surface and fire her guns, then quickly submerge to reload. Meanwhile, the Russian Navy had lost several ships in the ice so Bauer also worked on the construction of an ice-breaker.

The spring of 1858 saw renewed problems with the Russian authorities, however, and in July Bauer left by sea for Stettin, travelling thence to Munich by way of Leipzig. Here, he tried in vain to obtain a post, appropriate to his knowledge and technical experience, in the Bavarian civil service. During the

Constance, was raised. This earned much esteem for Bauer, and several honours were awarded him. Much of the credit for this publicity must go to Dr. Friedrich Hofmann, who was a whole-hearted supporter of Bauer's ideas and inventions. Hofmann was the editor of *Gartenlaube*, the most widely-read family journal of its time, with a circulation of more than 200,000; its apparently sentimental format concealed a great deal of liberal thought and progressive ideas. In 1864, Hofmann founded in Leipzig a committee for the propagation of Bauer's underwater warships.

The German-Danish war of 1864 seemed to promise favourable conditions for Bauer to realize his submarine projects and other inventions. He entered Prussian service and began preliminary work on what was to be his last important submarine project, the building of *Küstenbrander* (literally 'Coastal Incendiary') at Arthusberg near Stettin. On 18 December 1864, he wrote to the Royal Prussian War and Naval Ministry:

'The most recent extraordinary developments of artillery, machinery and ships are such that, in battle, distance needs to be kept; only the ironclads, which would suffer lesser damage, will manage to shorten this distance.

'It seems to me that the future for these ironclads as weapons of war is limited because their seaworthiness is questionable, they are unlikely to keep pace with the developments of artillery and in

technology of the time could not cope with the problem of driving a steam-turbine direct from a mixture of gas and steam. Nevertheless, in this very detailed concept can be seen the first step on the road to a turbine system independent of outside air, which would one day come to fruition in the Walter system. (See Hans-Joachim Lawrenz, *Die Entstehungsgeschichte der U-Boote*, pp. 43—46.)

Bauer's design was inspected and approved by the Royal Prussian Commission in Danzig, but, after a short time, Bauer gave up working in Prussia because he feared that his invention of an underwater gun would be exploited to his detriment. (His mistrustful nature and choleric temperament probably alienated sympathy and support, which he needed to carry out his submarine projects and other inventions. No doubt, with greater support and assistance, many of his ideas could have been realized.) In 1866 he was able to put his ideas of an underwater gun to the test. In an underwater shooting experiment in the Starnberger See, near Munich, two metal plates were pierced, but the weapon was found to have a rather limited range. During the next two years he worked again on a propulsion method for submarines, a paraffin-engine, and on steerable airships. This work was carried out in the Dingler Machine Factory in Zweibrücken. By now, the health of this restless inventor, ever careless of his own well-being, had been undermined: a nervous condition and arthritis confined him to bed or to a wheelchair. Although a very sick man, he continued to think up new ideas, but time was running out. On 20 June 1875, Bauer, the first German builder of submarines, died in Munich. Now, more than a century after his death, the following story of German submarine construction is dedicated to him.

The Howaldt diving-boat

The development of practical submarines, which Wilhelm Bauer had started in Germany in 1850, meanwhile continued in other countries. The first military success occurred during the American Civil War, when on 6 October 1863, a *David* class submarine (designed by McClintock and Howgate) captained by Lieutenant W. T. Glassell, severely damaged the 3,486-ton ship of the line, *New Ironsides*. On 17 February 1864, the Confederate designer H. L. Hunley's submarine sank the Union sloop *Housatonic* (approximately 1,400 tons); the submarine's commander, Lieutenant G. E. Dixon and his crew of eight died when the spar-torpedo exploded. These boats, which looked like cauldrons bolted together, were 10—15m long, and the crew of 8—10 men operated the propeller by hand-cranks. The trials and use of these 'floating coffins' were blighted by several tragic accidents.

Until the end of the nineteenth century, the most significant personalities in submarine development were the Spaniards, Narciso Monturiol (*Ictineo*, 1866) and Isaac Peral (*Peral*, 1887); the Russian, Drzewiecki (at least seven completed submarine projects from 1879); the British inventors, Andrew Campbell and J. Ash (*Nautilus*, 1884) and Waddington (*Porpoise*, 1885); the Swede, Torsten Nordenfelt (*Abd-Ul-Hamid*, 1886 and *Nordenfelt*

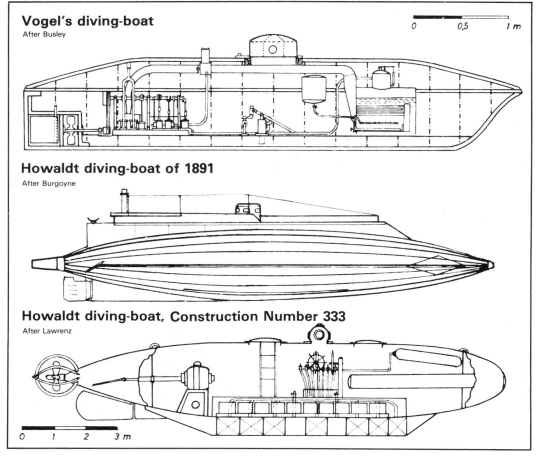

Vogel's diving-boat
After Busley

Howaldt diving-boat of 1891
After Burgoyne

Howaldt diving-boat, Construction Number 333
After Lawrenz

IV, 1887); the Americans, Josiah H. L. Tuck (*Peacemaker*, 1886), John Philip Holland (*Plunger* and *Holland*, 1897) and Simon Lake (*Argonaut*, 1897); and the Frenchmen, Claude Goubet (*Goubet I* and *Goubet II*, 1885—89), Gustave Zédé and Romanzotti (*Gymnote*, 1888, *Gustave Zédé*, 1892) and M. Laubeuf (*Narval*, 1899).

In Germany, there was no lack of interest in diving-boats and no lack of suggestions for underwater travel. According to Busley, 181 submarine projects were offered to the various German navies between 1861 and 1900, but most came from unskilled non-specialists. From the building of Bauer's *Brandtaucher* until 1900, there is evidence of only two practical submarines having been built in Germany — one by Vogel, and the Howaldt Yard's Construction No. 333.

Friedrich Otto Vogel built his small vessel at the Schlick Yard in Dresden between 1867 and 1870. Only 5.3m long, she was equipped with a steam engine specially adapted for use when submerged. It is thought that she did not survive her first trials in the River Elbe.

The German Navy is said to have acquired licences for the building of submarines from Nordenfelt in 1885 and, in 1890, two submarines are reported to have been built in Kiel and Danzig. Of

approximately 35m in length, they were equipped with steam-electric propulsion, but it has not been possible to obtain any reliable information about them. Evidence exists of one 'German' submarine in a photograph said to have been taken by Howaldt at Kiel in 1891 and published by Alan H. Burgoyne in 1903. This shows a spindle-shaped boat, 16m long, with prominent external longitudinal supports, a superstructure similar to that of the later *Forelle*, and a rudder arrangement and diving planes having much in common with those of the later Leps boat, with which it was subsequently repeatedly confused.

Apart from Bauer's *Brandtaucher*, we have knowledge and exact details of only one German submarine before 1900 — Construction Number 333, built by the Howaldt Yard in Kiel in 1897, and referred to by Techel as the 'Leps diving-boat'. This experimental craft is said to have been the brainchild of the German torpedo-engineer, Karl Leps. The main body was cylindrical in shape, rounded off at the bow and tapering to the four-bladed propeller aft. The length of the boat is given as 14m, the maximum beam as 2.4m. It was propelled by a non-reversible 120hp electric motor, which received its current from accumulators built into the bottom of the hull. Diving tanks and trim

Above: Burgoyne's photograph of the Howaldt diving-boat of 1891. **Below and right:** Construction Number 333 (below, in 1899, right, in Kiel harbour).

tanks were situated in a box keel under the hull; these could be flooded individually, and pumped out with compressed air from a connected chamber. Additionally, several iron ballast weights were carried, and these could be detached from inside the hull. Watertight collision bulkheads were fitted forward and aft, the forward bulkhead serving to strengthen a torpedo tube, the orifice of which could be opened from within the hull.

Steering was effected by two horizontal rudders at the ends of metal stabilizers approximately 400mm wide, which ran all the way round the boat and up to half its height. A vertical rudder, protected by a guard, was situated in front of the screw. Control operations were carried out from the centre of the boat. An observation dome, consisting of a diver's helmet with four portholes, was riveted to the top of the hull, but visibility was restricted by the effect of water washing over it on the surface. The boat could reach a surface speed of 6—7 knots. The 2- or 3-man crew was under the command of Captain Arp.

It is doubtful if any diving trials were made with this very primitive craft, which had no air renewal or ventilation system, and whose interior would have been very wet (which probably contributed to the many electrical failures). To replenish its supply

of compressed air, the boat had to make frequent crossing of the deep wide bay at Düsternbrock, to reach the torpedo range of the firm of Schwartzkopf. On one occasion, in order to test her watertight qualities, the boat was lowered to the bottom of the floating dock, but the crew remained connected to the outside by gas piping. There was clearly little future for a craft with such limited capabilities; she was laid up under a wooden cover, and is thought to have been scrapped in 1902.

Krupp, d'Equevilley and Forelle

In 1902, the Spanish engineer Raymondo Lorenzo d'Equevilley-Montjustin approached the firm of Krupp in Essen with plans purporting to be a development in the construction of the French submarine *Narval*. D'Equevilley had been associated in Paris with Maxime Laubeuf, the most famous of French submarine designers. With his two-hulled *Narval* of 1899, Laubeuf had not only won a French government competition, but also ushered in a new era in submarine building — a switch from defensive submarines to offensive long range boats. In 1901, Laubeuf intended that his improved submarine *Aigrette* be powered on the surface by a diesel engine. The main specifications of *Aigrette* were as follows.

Length overall:	35.85m.
Maximum beam:	4.05m.
Draught:	2.63m.
Displacement surfaced:	178 tons.
Displacement submerged:	253 tons.
Propulsion surfaced:	one 150hp diesel engine.
Propulsion submerged:	one 130hp electric motor.
Speed surfaced:	9.25 knots.
Speed submerged:	6.20 knots.
Range surfaced:	1,300 nautical miles at 8 knots.
Range submerged:	65 nautical miles at 3.8 knots.
Armament:	4 torpedoes.
Crew:	14.

D'Equevilley would certainly have been familiar with Laubeuf's designs and had probably used them as a basis for his own submarine concepts, which he had offered to the French Naval Ministry in 1901. Following a rejection, he made his overture to Krupps, and this step gave rise to a host of speculations and suspicions raised in foreign publications. In 1937, in the journal *Verein Deutscher Ingenieure*, Techel commented: 'it is high time that we rejected with vigour the French claim that has repeatedly been made that Germany acquired knowledge of French submarine plans, in particular the plans of the *Aigrette*, in unethical ways.'

On the advice of Germaniawerft (GW), which had recently been taken over by Krupps, F. A. Krupp authorized the construction of an experimental craft in accordance with d'Equevilley's design, and concluded a long-term contract with him. Preliminary work began as early as February 1902. The design called for a spindle-shaped boat of 13m length and 15.5 tons displacement, powered by a 65hp shunt motor with fixed revolutions. A controllable-pitch propeller enabled different speeds to be obtained.

At first, it had been intended to use peat storage batteries (initially 108-, subsequently 94-cell) supplied by the Watt Storage Battery Factory in Zehdenick near Berlin. GW had already used Watt storage batteries in picket boats, and it was thought that the sandwich of peat between the battery plates would be more suitable for sea-going use, especially since this would prevent leakage of acid from the batteries. But the decision to use them came to nothing, because peat storage batteries did not allow for maintenance, had no appreciable length of life, and were impossible to develop further.

Diving and compensating tanks were fitted to the small, single-hulled boat. Control was effected from a platform placed centrally beneath the hatch, through which ran a small, adjustable Zeiss periscope. Hydroplanes were fitted forward; aft, there was only a stabilizing plate, sloping forward at an angle of 1.5°, the operation of which was adjusted by rudder planes attached to it.

Tubes for two 45cm torpedoes were fitted at the sides; the muzzle doors for these were controlled by two small electric motors. Torpedoes were fired by compressed air, but the firing of a torpedo would permit sea water to enter the tube, causing the craft to list by as much as 20°. The boat was designed to be carried by larger warships, and was fitted with lifting padeyes.

On 28 July 1902, she was given the code designation 'Leuchtboje' ('lightbuoy') and construction was handed over to GW. The keel was laid on 19 February 1903, and the boat was completed on 8 June 1903. From 23 June to 6 December of that year, yard trials were conducted by d'Equevilley and Marine Chief Engineer Kritzler, at that time Chief Engineer of GW. After initial steering difficulties, the boat was found to handle well, had an underwater speed of 5½ knots and a range of 25 nautical miles at 4 knots. She was named *Forelle*.

In the autumn of 1903, Kaiser Wilhelm II inspected her and, on 23 September, Prince Heinrich of Prussia took part in a diving trial and steered the boat. She was then demonstrated to the German Navy and also to representatives of foreign countries. GW also hoped to obtain building contracts for larger submarines and, to this end, during the construction of *Forelle*, ideas from foreign countries and ideas of their own were being worked out. In view of the possibility of explosions from petrol and gasoline engines, GW decided in

favour of a paraffin- or oil-burning engine, with fuel containers positioned on the outside of the hull. At the end of 1903, GW projected a 200-ton submarine for the Royal Netherlands Navy, but nothing came of this.

In 1904, however, Russia became engaged in a war against Japan and was interested in building up a modern fleet. GW invited a Russian technical committee to inspect *Forelle* and on 25 March 1904, two Russian naval officers with submarine experience examined her in Eckernförde, where her diving capabilities were demonstrated, despite a rather rough sea (waves 1½m high). As a result, on 20 April, Russia ordered three submarines of

205-ton displacement with 400hp engines from GW. An official contract was placed in June, but before this, on 6 May, six 200hp paraffin engines were ordered from the firm of Körting Brothers of Hannover, who were able to offer engines burning either lamp paraffin or heavy oil at competitive prices. There was still a safety problem — hitherto, Körting had built only 8hp engines of this kind. Acquisition of *Forelle* had been included in the provisions of the Russian contract, and she left Kiel on 20 June by rail for St. Petersburg, where she carried out diving and firing trials in July and August of 1904 before being sent by rail to Vladivostok.

Above: *Forelle* after her arrival at Vladivostock.

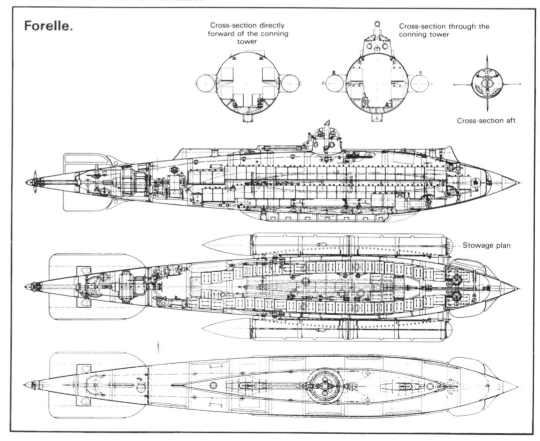

Forelle.

Cross-section directly forward of the conning tower

Cross-section through the conning tower

Cross-section aft

Stowage plan

THE IMPERIAL NAVY AND U-BOAT CONSTRUCTION TO THE FIRST WORLD WAR

The decision to build

During the years 1898 and 1899, the French Navy had built several successful submarines, and this development led the German Torpedo Inspectorate (TI) to suggest the construction of an experimental submarine for defensive operations, or for use as an auxiliary, carried aboard a large ship. The naval authorities, however, thought that the time was not yet ripe for this. At the inauguration of the STG (Schiffbautechnische Gesellschaft, the Technical Shipbuilding Society) in 1899, the Chairman, Councillor Busley, at the request of the Kaiser gave a speech on the development of submarines to that date. After covering the various attempts that had been made to build underwater vessels, he concluded with the negative pronouncement that, despite all efforts, these experiments had confirmed nothing save that the present state of the art was sadly inadequate. 'The present technical unreliability of the underwater vessels, especially the factor of lack of longitudinal stability, was such that one can see very little future for them . . . The German naval authorities are right when they refuse to indulge in expensive and long-drawn-out experiments with submarines, but confine themselves to the construction of battleships, cruisers and sea-going torpedo-boats.' (Busley was later said to have written to Berling that he had made this speech at the request of Admiral von Tirpitz, Secretary of State of the Imperial Naval Office, in order to support him in his battle against the submarine lobby.)

The TI, however, was strongly in favour of submarine development, and its Chief of Staff, Konteradmiral Zeye, and Councillor Veith were present at several trials in *Forelle*. GW kept them informed of its designs and ideas, but actual contracts were vetoed by von Tirpitz. His attitude changed somewhat after the Russians had ordered the three boats from GW. On 11 May 1904, in reply to a question from Deputy von Kardorff as to why no German submarines were being built, von Tirpitz had stated that until then they had been considered of little value; on 22 July, however, he wrote: 'I intend to have a submarine built by the Naval Ministry and authorize 'B' (the Technical Department) to carry out the construction. I request 'B' to find an enterprising construction official of the younger school who is prepared to dedicate himself to submarine construction. This person is to be placed at the disposal of the Naval Ministry. It is hoped to make available several naval construction officials (ship and machine builders) to study competitive plans.'

In the autumn of 1904, a naval engineer, Gustav Berling (b. 6 November 1869), was seconded to the TI and commissioned to build a submarine, while, the following year, several similar projects were planned — initially two smaller, single-hulled boats, and subsequently six double-hulled U-boats (Projects 1–8). The chief items of machinery were built in order to verify that they would fit the space allotted to them, and a number of towing trials were carried out to check hull strength and displacement. Additionally, on 3 December 1904, a submarine similar in design to the three Russian boats was ordered from GW.

The Russian boats (Construction Numbers 109, 110 and 111, later named *Karp* class) were double-hulled, with ballast and fuel tanks on the outside of the hull, and ballast and compensating tanks inside. Measurements and installations were significantly affected by the Russian insistence on the boats being manufactured in sections, to facilitate railway transportation. Their specifications were as follows.

Length overall:	39.9m.
Maximum beam:	3.1m.
Pressure-hull diameter:	2.7m.
Displacement surfaced:	205 tons.

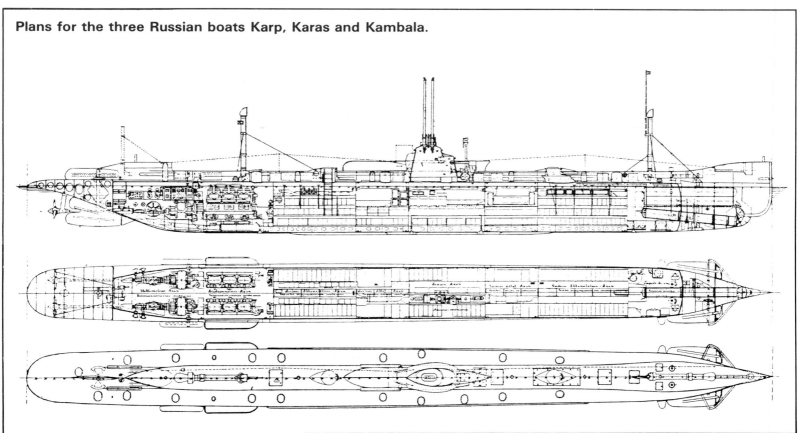

Plans for the three Russian boats Karp, Karas and Kambala.

Displacement submerged:	236 tons.
Propulsion:	two 200hp engines.
Fuel supply:	16.9 tons.
Speed surfaced:	10.8 knots.
Speed submerged:	8.8 knots.
Range surfaced:	1,100 nautical miles at 10.8 knots.
Maximum diving depth:	30m.
Armament:	1 bow torpedo tube, angled downwards 5°; three C/03 torpedoes.

Originally, d'Equevilley had thought that the speeds would be higher — 12 knots on the surface, 10.5 knots submerged — but GW had doubted this from the start. While under way, the trim could be altered by weights moved manually. Two hydroplanes, the aftermost sited forward of the propeller, could be regulated by handwheels, but electrical steering had been provided for the rudder.

The individual sections of the pressure hull were of 12mm sheet steel, of circular cross-section, welded in the Laura Foundry. Cast iron rings, serving as vertical supports, were riveted to them and bolted together. Originally, d'Equevilley had

Above: Karp under Russian flag. **Below:** *Kambala* (in pieces) and *U1* under construction, 1906.

planned a construction without frames (which he thought unnecessary), but he had seriously miscalculated the compression strength of the hull — only the fact that cast-iron rings riveted to the section ends worked like strong frames prevented the boats from being crushed in only a few metres depth.

The conning tower was manufactured of 40mm cast nickel steel, and had two periscopes. The fact that nickel steel is non-magnetic made possible the use of a magnetic compass (which, of course, could function only when electrical power had been switched off).

As with *Forelle*, it had been decided to fit peat batteries, one above another: 396 cells were used and, because of their small capacity, they had to be connected 6 in parallel and 66 in series. As the intended oil engines could not be regulated or reversed, controllable-pitch propellers were provided, but these had an unfortunate effect: even when the boat was motionless, the still rotating propeller absorbed 65hp from the engines (approximately 40 per cent of the total capacity).

The initial submarine for the German Navy (Construction Number 119) was to have been ready

in August 1905, but, shortly after the contract had been placed, important variations from the design for the Russian boats were requested: a horizontal layout for the torpedo tube; an increase in the diameter of the pressure hull; a larger conning tower; an improvement to the frontal profile; a stronger ballast keel; a concentration of the interior ballast in the centre of the boat; special fuel tanks on the outside — for it was feared that the pressure hull rivets would not be absolutely oil-tight — and so many other alterations that no pressure hull was ordered from the Laura Foundry until the middle of April 1905. There were also delays in the development and completion of the engines. As petrol was not to be used for starting these, Chief Engineer Kritzler suggested that heated air be sucked in through the cylinders; after three to five minutes, the cylinders would be so hot that if vaporized paraffin were admitted ignition would be immediate. It is greatly to the credit of Kritzler (who later was to be employed by the firm of Körting) that the many difficulties, which at times must have seemed almost insuperable, were overcome. Nevertheless, it was unavoidable that the first submarine for the Russians was almost

ready before the engines could be delivered, and she was launched without surface engines, undergoing trials in 1906 with electric motors only.

On 4 August 1906, twelve months later than the expected delivery date, the German submarine was lowered into the water by crane. As a safety precaution, the lifting vessel *Oberelbe* had been hired from the salvage company, Nordischer Bergungsverein. Under the direction of the Master of Marine Construction, Berling, the boat was lowered from *Oberelbe* to a depth of 30m, first without, and then with a crew. Finally, at a depth of 30m, water was taken into the boat and then expelled from it. In September 1906, the boat left GW under her own power for her first sea trial. In November she was designated *U1* and, on 14 December 1906, was handed over by GW for service in the German Navy. On 16 December 1906, the RMA (Reichs-Marine-Amt, the Imperial Naval Office) announced:

'*U1* meets German requirements:

1. It is a diving-boat of reasonably large displacement. Its capabilities on the surface are such as to meet the difficult water and weather conditions of the German Bight.

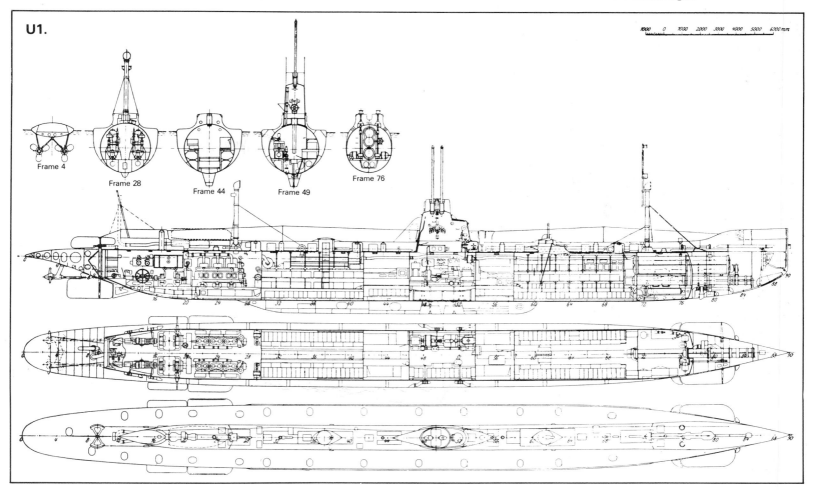

U1.

Frame 4 Frame 28 Frame 44 Frame 49 Frame 76

U1, above, with U2; left, at full speed; and, below, in the Kiel Estuary.

2. It has paraffin-burning engines. Our defence policy lays the greatest emphasis on operational safety. Petrol engines cause a very large number of accidents and these are caused by explosions which have occurred especially often in England. Prior to 1904 it would have been impossible to have built such a boat.'

During the period that followed, both these arguments were used to justify the slow and much-delayed acceptance of the German U-boat. It is a fact that von Tirpitz commissioned a submarine only after strong public pressure, and after the Russians had ordered one from GW — he expected very little of it, seeing it as a weakening of his policy of building up the German Fleet. The naval estimates of 1907—9 were to include only four submarines, and not until 1910 was there to be any notable increase in numbers of this type of craft.

U-boat development and construction, 1906—10

On 4 March 1906, the first U-boat to be built by the TI in collaboration with Berling was ordered from the Kaiserliche Werft in Danzig (KWD) and was known as 'Project 7', subsequently, U2. Great stress was laid on achieving the highest possible surface speed and, although the boat had a 50 per cent greater displacement than U1, her improved hull form gave her a surface speed of 10.5 knots with the same 400hp engines. It was expected that a surface speed of 12.5 knots could be achieved if the engine capacity were increased to 600hp.

The necessary paraffin-burning engines were ordered from Daimler-Benz because Körting engine production was running behind schedule, and Daimler were more successful in solving problems of warm-up times and performance/weight values. The technique of regulating speed by controllable-

Above: *U1, U2, U3* and *U4* at Kiel.

GW boats Ub3 and Ub4 as built for Austria-Hungary.

Key: a, paraffin container; b, pressure-tight paraffin compensation container; c, diving tanks; d, lubricating oil tanks; e, reserve torpedo chamber; f, torpedo firing tube; g, high-pressure compressor; h, low-pressure compressor; i, leak pump; k, telephone buoy; l, retractable ventilation mast; m, silencer; n, ship's boat; o, assembly hatch; p, lifting eye; q, trimming tanks; r, deck porthole; s, driving rods for flooding valves; t, capstan engine; u, safety keel.

Aft living-quarters   Engine room   Control-room   Officers' living-quarters   Forward living-quarters   Torpedo room

pitch propellers was abandoned and replaced by a system of three electric motors. (Significantly, the latter made for more weight and demanded more space.) When manoeuvring, the boat was propelled by electric motors only. In this case, the electric motors, positioned abaft the paraffin-burning engines, served as generators for the paraffin-burning/electric cruising mode.

Further improvements over the design of *U1* were the torpedo armament (two 45cm tubes fitted both forward and aft) and the use of large surface-plate batteries from the firm of AFA, which meant that 130 cells in two parallel batteries sufficed. This type of battery had proved superior to the peat cell during systematic tests carried out in 1905 in a specially established department of the TI. Another innovation was the siting of the control room beneath the conning tower. A third periscope was provided for use in the control room, in addition to the two in the conning tower. As in *U1*, it was planned to use a method, patented secretly by Berling, for automatic trimming during the loading and firing of torpedoes. Finally, it was intended to use an air-renewal device that had been developed by Dräger of Lübeck.

The building of this first U-boat at KWD was considerably handicapped by the fact that, while many new constructional features were demanded, experience of production was lacking. Furthermore, Daimler-Benz did not succeed in producing the improved paraffin-burning engines in the requisite time. (They were ready in 1909; but, after four-and-a-half days of trials, they suffered a crankshaft breakage, and the Navy finally took delivery of them in June 1910. They were not used because by

then a decision had been taken to use diesel engines in future U-boats.)

U2 left the slipway on 18 June 1908, fitted with Körting engines, which gave a lesser performance. She carried out trials until the end of 1908 and, early in 1909, her engine room was altered to accommodate the new Daimler engines. However,

the delivery of these was delayed still further and the boat remained at the shipyard. Even after they had been installed, *U2* suffered dynamo difficulties and was not used. The next two boats (which KWD had been asked to build on 13 August 1907), *U3* and *U4*, were considerably more reliable: with more powerful Körting engines.

In September 1907, *U1* had carried out an endurance trial of some note — in bad weather, she completed a passage of 587 nautical miles from Wilhelmshaven around Skagen to Kiel without breaking down. This was encouraging, and GW now offered an enlarged version with a surface displacement of 325 tons, armed with underwater bow torpedo tubes and an above-water, stern torpedo tube. It was thought that two 225hp Körting engines on each shaft would give an impressive speed of 15 knots. Submerged speed was to be 8.5 knots; surface range would be 1,800 nautical miles at 15 knots.

But the Navy refused it, with the excuse that they did not want more boats of this type from GW. In fact, the TI did not want to hand over their designs for the development of boats that would be more suitable for the German Navy to GW because the latter was considerably involved in building for foreign countries. In March 1907, GW had received contracts from Austria-Hungary, for two smaller, 237-ton submarines (*Ub3* and *Ub4*), and in October 1907 from Norway, for a similar boat (*Kobben*). Improvements over the *U1* design for both these projects were: greater diving depth (50m); a new conning tower, able to withstand greater pressure (three-circle cross-section, *Ub3* and *Ub4*; oval cross-section, *Kobben*) with a pressure-tight hatch at the bottom; trim tanks operated by compressed air and pumps; pressure-tight fuel tanks on the outside of the pressure hull; hydroplanes operated from the central control room; and, in the case of *Kobben*, a stern torpedo tube above the waterline in addition to the two bow tubes.

Underlying the reluctance of the TI to make its designs available to GW was its concern that a foreigner, d'Equevilley, held a prominent position in GW's submarine development department, and d'Equevilley was eventually removed from this post because GW wanted further orders from the German Navy. On 1 July 1907, at the suggestion of Berling, Hans Techel was appointed departmental head of submarine development at GW.

Hans Techel, certainly the best-known German submarine engineer, was born on 12 February 1870, and began his career with GW on 1 May 1895, leaving them on 1 July 1901 to take over a job as head of the newly-established office for warship construction in the Howaldt Yard at Kiel.

The way was now open for GW to take part once again in U-boat building for the German Navy. Drawings were received from the TI and, under Techel's direction, *U5* to *U8* were projected with the following specifications: surface speed 15 knots; submerged speed 10.5 knots; surface range 2,000 nautical miles at 15 knots; two submerged bow torpedo tubes and two submerged stern tubes with a total of six Type C/06 torpedoes; fixed propellers; storage batteries with large surface-area plates; and the same air-purification system as in *U2*.

GW's design for a 500-ton boat with a surface speed of 14.5 knots was presented in February 1908. The pressure hull differed from their earlier boats in that it was riveted with double-lapped longitudinal seams and joints (but, despite the streamlined form, the anticipated speeds and range were not to be achieved). For the first time, a

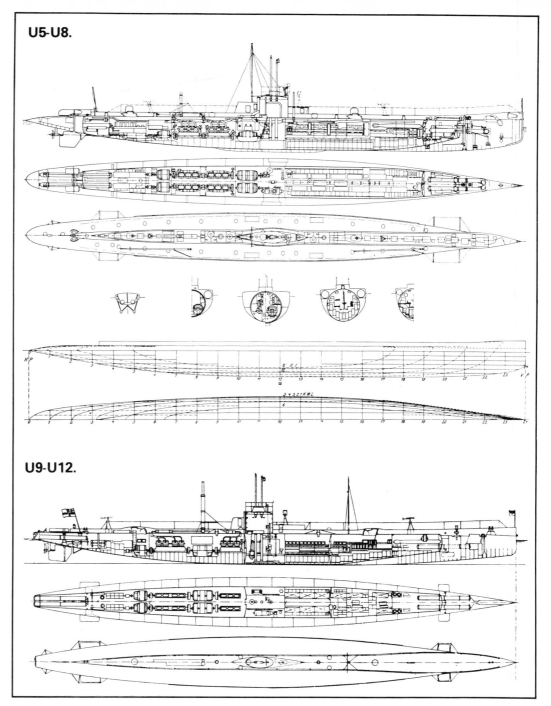

U5-U8.

U9-U12.

gyroscopic compass, made by Anschütz-Kaempfe, was fitted in the control room. Confirmation of contract for *U5–U8* followed on 8 April 1908 and, on 15 July, four 500-ton boats on similar lines were ordered from KWD. These eight U-boats, *U5–U12*, from the 1907/8 naval estimates would form the first real German U-boat force to be superior both

in fighting ability and seaworthiness to all foreign competition.

In 1909, a change took place in the top management of the Torpedo Inspectorate: Vizeadmiral Zeye died and was replaced by Konteradmiral Lans. In October 1906 meanwhile, Privy Councillor Veith had been transferred to the RMA. He was

Above: *U5* and *U6* being fitted-out at GW, 29 June 1910. **Inset:** Hans Techel.

succeeded by Privy Councillor Uthemann. A further change was that Naval Construction Master Schulz was appointed to the U-Boat Department of the TI from the beginning of 1907 until 1911.

In 1909, it was intended to place the construction of a further four 500-ton boats with KWD, because the Navy considered GW's price rather high, but, after delicate negotiations, GW succeeded in obtaining the contract for one of them (*U16*). The first three, *U13–U15*, were formally ordered on 23 February 1909, and *U16* was ordered from GW on 23 August 1909.

Meanwhile, the first tactical trials of *U1*, *U3* and *U4* were being carried out. With regard to the use in action of several U-boats together, the TI reported on 27 November 1910:

'In considering the use of and the carrying out of tests of a tactical nature of several U-boats or groups of U-boats, there exists the real difficulty that, in using these boats to the full, collision danger is a very real one, since it is obvious that once submerged U-boats cannot see each other. As long as there remains no feasible way of boats signalling to each other underwater, it will be necessary for the boats to keep to certain

U13-U16.

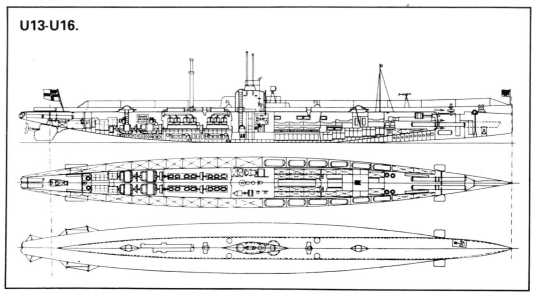

established formations or to operate through certain stated commands when attacking.'

A consequence of this was the suggestion that boats should only operate in certain arcs or sectors, with clear zones left between them.

Setbacks about 1911

After a prolonged fitting-out period at KW (Kaiserliche Werft), Kiel, *U3* embarked on her maiden voyage on 17 January 1911 in stormy conditions. Combined with this voyage was an instructional course for new recruits, which had started in that month. Before leaving harbour, the boat's commander was instructed to carry out a meticulous diving trial in order to establish whether the yard had completed their work satisfactorily. When the upper deck reached the surface of the water, a considerable quantity of water rushed into the engine room through the ventilation outlet, although the indicator showed the valve to be closed. Before anyone realized what had happened (no one having dared touch the apparently closed valve), the boat had taken in so much water that she became stern heavy and sank to the bottom. At this juncture, the commander, who was in the conning tower with the officer of the watch and the helmsman ordered the entire crew to make their way to the bow compartment, in the interest of safety. There were now 29 men gathered in the unlit bow compartment, sharing approximately 8m³ of air, and three men trapped in the conning tower, while the remainder of the boat had filled with water. The men in the conning tower survived for only 10–12 hours, as chlorine gas from the batteries gradually seeped through the speaking tubes and carbon dioxide also began to concentrate in this small area. The men in the bow compartment were able to breathe because of the caustic potash filters of the Dräger system, but the air became more and more stale. Some chlorine gas did make its way into the bow compartment, but was dealt with by the air purifiers.

The accident was reported some two hours later, and immediately two floating cranes, each with a lifting capacity of 150 tons, were sent by KW to the scene of the sinking (two nautical miles from the yard).

The salvage ship *Vulkan* was out of commission in dry dock, but was ordered to be made ready. Some eleven hours later, divers had placed cables round the fore part of *U3*, and the cranes began lifting, the intention being to raise the torpedo tubes out of the water so that the crew could make their way to safety through them. But the upper deck had hardly begun to break surface when the boat began to slip back: the cables parted and the boat sank once more. A further fourteen hours elapsed before a second attempt succeeded; the torpedo tubes were opened and the 29 men, by now in an extremely exhausted condition, made their way out. They had been trapped for 27 hours in the small, dark bow compartment.

Meanwhile, *Vulkan* had been towed to the scene and had anchored above the boat. After a further five hours (i.e. thirty hours after the accident had occurred), *U3* was completely raised and the conning tower was opened. It was almost dry within, but the three men inside it were dead. At the inquiry into the cause of the accident, it was established that during fitting out the closure to the ventilation system had been installed in such a way that, when open, the indicator showed closed. The TI consequently issued the following directions:

'1. When a U-boat begins to dive, it must first of all carry out an airtightness test — of 20 millibar overpressure. Pressure must be maintained for one minute.
2. It is most essential that a second salvage ship be built immediately.
3. Escape apparatus that meets the requirements of war operations must be developed as soon as possible. An appropriate sum of money for this purpose is to be proposed in the Naval Estimates.
4. Underwater signalling equipment is also to be developed as soon as possible.
5. Emergency electrical hand-lamps are to be provided in all watertight compartments.
6. Each watertight compartment in a U-boat must have its own hatch.
7. All ventilation valves leading to the outside must have a double method of closure.'

Between 1910 and 1912, KWD encountered several setbacks in their U-boat construction because of weight problems. Almost all firms exceeded prescribed weights, especially in the manufacture of main engines and switch gear and, as a result, *U9–U15* were heavier than planned. In *U9*, the excess weight was compensated by removing eight battery cells. More serious was the position in *U13*; her excess weight of 4.8 tons could not be compensated by removing ballast, so 14 battery cells had to be removed. On 22 January 1912, the Chief of Staff of the TI, Konteradmiral Lans stated: 'There is no doubt that the blame for these regrettable occurrences is to be laid at the door of either the Technical Bureau (TB), the TI or KWD.' Subsequently, a greater weight margin was allowed for in submarine designs, and this was later to prove a wise precaution.

The adoption of diesel engines

GW had already considered the use of diesel engines for the Russian submarines *Karp*, *Karas* and *Kambala*. Even before the Körting paraffin engines had been ordered, Müller, the Construction Director of GW, had visited Maschinenfabrik Augsburg–Nürnberg AG (MAN) at Augsburg, to inquire about the possibilities of a lightweight diesel engine suitable for U-boats. At that time, MAN engines had a performance/weight ratio of 35–48kg per hp and were considered to be too heavy and too bulky. GW then considered ordering its own design, a 200hp four-stroke diesel engine; by the beginning of March 1904, the drawings had been completed and sent to Augsburg. On 6 April 1904, MAN made an offer which was declined because of the lengthy delivery time. For the time being, therefore, GW stayed with the Körting paraffin engines.

In 1905, renewed inquiries to MAN from GW and the TI elicited designs that required more weight and space than were deemed practical for U-boat construction. Techel, in his book on U-boat construction at GW, was later to express regret that no attempts had been made to build such engines and to try them out in U-boats. Had such experimentation taken place, they would almost certainly have obviated delays at a much later date in the introduction of diesel engines into U-boat technology.

MAN were now working on a four-cylinder four-stroke engine that would develop 300hp at 500rpm, and this was ready for demonstration to the TI in continuous operation in 1907. The TI then requested MAN to formulate a proposal for a six-cylinder engine, which was to be developed to its

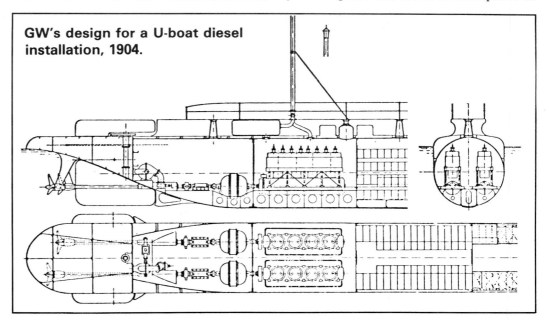

GW's design for a U-boat diesel installation, 1904.

utmost limit. After a design had been submitted, a test engine was ordered from MAN in the middle of 1908.

At the beginning of 1906 meanwhile, GW had begun to build its own four-cylinder, 300hp four-stroke diesel engine. It employed a special crank gearing for starting and for reversing into the two-stroke operation and was demonstrated to the TI in March 1908. This led to GW being requested to formulate a design for a four-stroke and a two-stroke engine with a performance of 850hp at 450rpm. Requests for proposals of two-stroke marine engines were also made to FIAT of Turin, Körting and MAN of Nuremberg, the German Navy being inclined towards the two-stroke process because of its lighter construction and absence of problems with exhaust valves. In November 1908, GW, who were beginning manufacture of a 300hp two-stroke diesel engine for a picket boat, received an order from the TI for an 850hp two-stroke test engine. Simultaneously, FIAT, MAN (Nuremberg) and Körting were requested to build a diesel submarine engine in competition with the Augsburg project.

U1-U16 compared

According to the Imperial Navy's official publication No. LXIII *Stand des Unterseebootwesens*, Berlin 1911.

1. PRESSURE HULL. In *U3–U8*, collision bulkheads, 16–21mm thick, and calculated to withstand pressure at 50m, were fitted in the forward section of the pressure hull. In *U9–U12*, two central water-tight bulkheads were fitted. These were designed to withstand pressure at 20–50m and divided the emergency control room from the remainder of the boat. *U2* and subsequent boats had a conning tower of 30mm nickel steel riveted to the pressure hull.
2. EXTERIOR HULL. The outer skin consisted of 3.5–4mm sheet metal (as used in torpedo-boats) zinc-coated on both sides. The frames were spaced 500mm apart. From *U2* onwards, 8–13 diving tanks and 6 bunkers were distributed along each side of the boat. In *U1–U4*, the tank top was horizontal; in *U5–U12*, it was inclined towards the sides at an angle of 6°. The upper deck was covered with linoleum. Tank testing of model hull shapes was carried out with regard to both surface and submerged propulsion. Table 2 shows the speeds estimated, with the speeds achieved during trials shown in brackets.
3. DIVING AND COMPENSATING TANKS. In *U1*, the tanks fitted to the exterior did not give sufficient negative buoyancy when diving, so four larger tanks were fitted additionally to the floor of the pressure hull and these served also as compensating and fuel-trimming tanks. The exterior diving tanks fitted to *U2* were sufficient to enable the boat to dive. Six internal tanks in the floor of the pressure hull sufficed as trim tanks only. Two more interior tanks, sited under the boat's centre of gravity, were used as compensating tanks. These flat-shaped interior tanks were difficult to construct and to maintain, so from *U3* onwards the compensating and balancing tanks were situated on the outside. In *U3* and *U4*, the compensating tanks were water-tight cylinders situated to port and starboard in the middle diving tanks; from *U5* onwards they were water-tight pockets secured to the pressure hull; in *U5–U8*, the pockets were indented towards the inside of the pressure hull. From *U3* onwards, the fuel-balancing tanks consisted of water-tight cylindrical tubes, which had been moved to the centre of gravity of the fuel bunker and filled with paraffin.
4. STEERING GEAR. In all boats, the rudder was placed forward of the propellers. Its upper and lower halves were separate, in order to minimize heeling when submerged. From *U9* onwards, the rudder was electrically-operated from the control centre. In *U1–U8*, the forward hydroplane was positioned on a common rudder spindle running through the pressure hull in a collar. From *U5* onwards, the forward planes were electrically operated. In *U9–U12*, as an experimental measure to lighten steering, both the forward hydroplanes were made in the form of a shutter, with two rudder blades on each side of the boat coupled by a linkage.
5. PROPULSION. Until 1910, there were only two German power plants available for surface propulsion: a 6-cylinder Körting engine of 220–260hp and an 8-cylinder Körting engine of 310–345hp at 550rpm with a consumption of 400g

Table 1. Pressure hulls, U1–U12

	U1	U2	U3–U4	U5–U8	U9–U12
Maximum diameter (mm)	2,800	3,400	3,400	3,750	3,650
Maximum thickness of metal (mm)	12	12	12	11–12	12
Maximum distance between frames (mm)	1,600	1,000	500	700	500
Frame profile (mm)	140×65×9	120×75×9	130×65×8	110×75×12	130×65×8
Constructional diving depth (m) with safety factor of 2.5	30	30	50	50	50

Table 2. Estimated and actual speeds, U1–U12
Estimated speed shown first; speed achieved during trials shown in parentheses.

	U1	U2	U3–U4	U5–U8	U9–U12
Surfaced (knots)	10.6 (10.6)	12.6	13 (13.3)	14.5 (13.7)	15 (14.5)
Submerged (knots)	—(8.67)	10.5 (8.8)	12 (9.5)	12.5 (10.3)	12.5 (8.1)

Table 3. Comparison of batteries in U1–U16

	U1	U2	U3–U4	U5–U8, U10–U12	U9, U13–U16
Height of element (mm)	370	715	715	715	715
Weight of element (kg)	124	405	372	372	350
Number of cells	396	130	210	220	220
Total weight (tons)	49	65	78	82	77
Total capacity with 3½ hours discharge (ampere-hours)	3,660	6,300	6,300	6,300	8,000
Voltage of battery	130	150	210	210	210

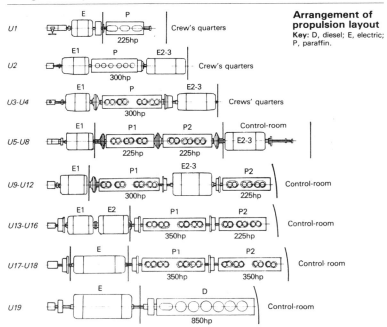

Arrangement of propulsion layout
Key: D, diesel; E, electric; P, paraffin.

In 1908, the TI were contemplating the construction of a diesel-engined boat that would feature a significant number of improvements over existing submarines and would be a great deal larger. The placing of the contract for such a boat, however, was postponed until at least one test engine could be shown to run for six days continuously. Delays occurred in the manufacture of the diesel engines,

and in the spring of 1910 two new U-boats were ordered from KWD. *U17* and *U18*, as they were designated, were to follow the new design, but Korting paraffin-burning engines were substituted for diesel engines.

All firms experienced great difficulty in manufacturing lightweight diesel engines. MAN of Augsburg were the first to produce a test engine, in

August 1910, after a two-year building time. The tests went well and, after slight improvements had been made to the engine and clutches had been fitted, it ran for a further trial period of 24 hours in August 1911. At GW, certain technological difficulties and problems with personnel meant that the preliminary plan for the 850hp two-stroke trial engine had been very considerably delayed. There

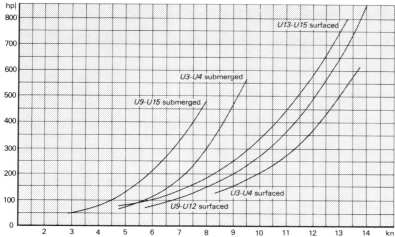

Propulsion curves from test data for KWD boats

onwards, all boats had two submerged bow torpedo tubes and two submerged stern tubes. *U1* carried three C/03 torpedoes, and the others each carried six: C/03 torpedoes in *U2*, C/06 from *U3* onwards. The C/06 torpedoes were somewhat larger than the C/03, had a more powerful propulsion unit (four- instead of three-cylinder) and could be fired at an angle: initially, ±45°; later, ±90°.

8. LIVING QUARTERS. In the first boats, *U1–U4*, the quarters were not suitable for a week's habitation. From *U2* onwards, the crew's quarters were above the batteries. From *U5* onwards, officers occupied compartments separated from the rest of the boat by bulkheads and curtains. Initially, only electrical heating was available. Subsequently, a steam heating arrangement was built in, and this could be connected to the sleeping quarters to reduce the damp that tended to persist there.

The 2-stroke engines required air in the ratio of 20m³ of air for each kilogramme of paraffin burned, and this was sucked from the boat, providing adequate ventilation when surfaced. The TI and the Dräger Works had collaborated to provide an air-purification system for use when submerged, in which air was sucked by fans through caustic potash filters and enriched with oxygen. This would last a 24-man crew for 72 hours, and was fitted from *U2* onwards.

9. RESCUE INSTALLATIONS. External rescue fittings were designed for rapid lifting of the boat in case of an accident. They consisted of a telephone buoy with 80m of cable and two lifting padeyes with lifting hooks spaced 12m apart on the deck, corresponding exactly with similar fittings in *Vulkan*, a ship being built by the Howaldt Yard and intended as an escort, accommodation and salvage vessel. If an accident occurred, two wire-attached buoys could be released from within the submarine. The wires ran through the lifting hooks and could be taken up by *Vulkan*. Hence, it was possible to connect lifting hawsers to the

U-boat without employing divers. Additionally, all boats were fitted with connection points on the outside for air and telephone leads. The main ballast pumps of *U1–U4* could manage 60 tons per hour against water pressure at 60m. This was doubled from *U5* onwards.

10. NAVIGATIONAL AND SIGNALLING AIDS. The periscopes fitted in early U-boats were rather short (those in *U5–U12* being 4.5m long), and it was barely possible to maintain a course beneath the surface at periscope depth. Navigational safety of a U-boat, even when cruising alone, left much to be desired. It was very difficult to estimate surface speed when the boat was being propelled by its oil-burning engine. The magnetic compass was of somewhat limited use. The gyroscopic compasses used in *U5* onwards were more reliable, but were more complicated and expensive. Soundings could only be taken by a hand lead. Chronometers were considerably impaired by the electrical and magnetic effects of the boat and were, therefore, correspondingly unreliable. Radio telegraphy (RT) and underwater telegraphy (UT) were the most important methods of signalling, and all boats from *U5* onwards were fitted with RT. Two aerial masts were necessary, and these could be lowered from inside the boat. Ship to U-boat range was 50–62 nautical miles; that between U-boats was approximately 30 nautical miles. UT installations, initially with a bell, the clanger of which was activated by compressed air, were likewise fitted from *U5* onwards, but were not particularly satisfactory.

11. DIVING TIME. In the normal state (bridge rigged; oil-burning engines running), the time needed to dive to a depth of 9m was seven to eight minutes. In a state of readiness — i.e., with bridge unrigged, electric motors ready for submerged propulsion and conning-tower hatch open — the time was reduced to 2.5–4.5 minutes; 30 seconds could be cut from this time if some of the diving tanks had already been flooded.

of oil per hp per hour and a performance/weight ratio of 24kg per hp. For higher performances, two engines were used in tandem. As the paraffin engines could not be reversed, were incapable of much in the way of speed regulation and (as has already been mentioned) controllable-pitch propellers had disadvantages, a new system was chosen for boats from *U2* onwards. *U2–U12* were to have a complicated paraffin/electric 3-motor system, and *U16*, a 2-motor system. In *U13–U15*, which did not have this system, manoeuvring was carried out by battery current only. Both electric motors drove fixed shafts and, if a battery needed charging while under way, one side of the propulsion plant was used as a generator while the other was used to drive the boat.

6. BATTERIES. *U1* had lead cells with mass plates (grid plates with built-in mass) with peat insulation between the plates, the whole contained in hard rubber housings. As these housings were stacked in layers one above the other, a rather high centre of gravity resulted, which had to be counteracted by a lead keel of 23 tons. *U2–U8* and *U10–U12* used large surface area plates, which AFA had used in 1904 for the Swedish submarine *Hajen*, and

which had a noticeably higher cell capacity. As an experiment, *U9* had mass cells, but peat insulation was not used and the cells could be made, therefore, rather bigger. From *U13* onwards, all U-boats had mass plates possessing a greater specific capacity than large surface area plates. From *U2* onwards, U-boat batteries consisted of two sections: the individual elements in hard rubber containers were grouped together in a lead housing with a rubber surround. Numerous problems soon led to an open ventilated layout of cells on a foundation of angle irons, with hard rubber insulators in the battery chambers. The danger of a build-up of explosive gases from the cells was kept to a minimum by sucking out gas from the cells with a strong concentration of air through hard rubber pipes and soft rubber tubes. By using a block and tackle and trolleys, batteries could be removed in a week and re-installed in a fortnight. Battery life was approximately four years. At an approximate cost of 220,000 marks per battery set, they represented a considerable part of the cost of a U-boat.

7. TORPEDO ARMAMENT. *U1* had only one bow torpedo tube; from *U2*

were special problems, with too high a temperature in the cylinders and pistons, and with the expulsion of exhaust gases which had to be overcome by compressed air, involving special scavenging pumps. The GW engine carried out its six-day endurance trial from 10 to 16 June 1911. (The acceptance test of the 300hp engine for the picket boat *Mentor* had already taken place in March of that year: this non-reversible type of engine was then installed, for the first time in Germany, in the diesel submarine *Atropo*, built for the Italian Navy.) At the acceptance trial of the large GW engine, it was impossible to demonstrate its reversing properties and manoeuvrability because the braking system failed to function. GW were therefore instructed to rectify this as soon as possible, then combine it with a 24-hour endurance test, and this took place in October 1912.

Meanwhile, delays and design alterations to the three other test engines ordered from FIAT, MAN (Nuremberg) and Körting were of such magnitude that they did not come into consideration for U-boat development. Only the four-stroke MAN and the two-stroke GW diesel engines remained as possible contenders. The four-stroke engine used less fuel (190g per hp per hour) and made less noise than the two-stroke, but it had an arrangement of six fittings on the crankshaft, which was not at all well balanced when rotating, and caused starting difficulties when the crankshaft was in certain positions. Starting and reversing were only readily achieved when all the valves worked perfectly. There was also a phenomenon much feared in this era, the danger of torsion resonance in the shafts, which could be corrected only by using a thick, heavy shaft system. The two-stroke diesel engine had a fuel consumption of 220g per hp per hour and was noisier because of a faster revolving drive shaft and the aspiration of scavenging air. However, the horizontal movements were less uneven, and the engine started more readily. In addition, better-balanced torque lessened the problem of torsion resonance. So it was considered that, given an improved performance, the two-stroke engine would be superior to the four-stroke, and would furnish more scope for development.

After the acceptance trial of the MAN test engine had demonstrated the feasibility of using diesel engines, the TI reconsidered its programme for diesel-engined U-boats. It was similar, in form and arrangement, to the design for *U17* and *U18*, but was to have 50cm torpedo tubes for G6 torpedoes. Consideration was also given to fitting an 8.8cm L/30 gun. On 25 November 1910, a contract for the first four of these MAN-engined diesel boats, *U19–U22*, was awarded to KWD. Simultaneously, GW received the type requirements for the new diesel boats, and was able to present a plan for a 650-ton boat by 21 November 1910. Following further negotiations with the TI, the dimensions were somewhat enlarged. In comparison with the last GW boat, *U16*, the following modernizations were evident.

1. Reduced number of fuel containers, and omission of trim tanks.
2. Four water-tight bulkheads.
3. 50cm torpedo tubes for G6 torpedoes.

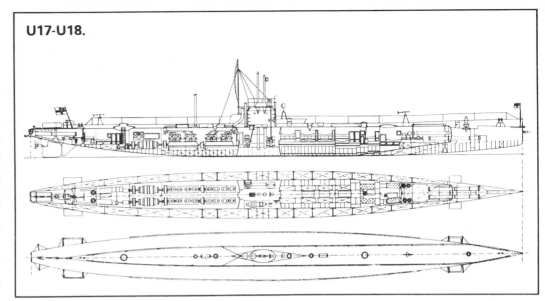

U17-U18.

4. Main rudder abaft the propellers.
5. Guaranteed maximum surface speed of 16.5 knots.

On 18 March 1911, GW was awarded the contract for four diesel U-boats of this type, designated *U23–U26*, even though the necessary engines were not yet ready for testing, and had not been accepted. Berling, the Naval Construction Adviser, ordered them from GW immediately after acceptance of the 850hp trial engine. Although the reversing problem had not been resolved, and despite the long development time of the test engines at GW, eleven diesel U-boats (*U31–U41*) were scheduled for building in 1912 at GW, using the two-stroke diesel engines. By using cylinders bored out to an additional 10mm, they were to develop 925hp at 430rpm. The fear of torsion resonance in the four-stroke engines may well have influenced this decision. Only the four boats, *U27–U30*, the contract for which was given to KWD on 19 February 1912, were equipped with four-stroke MAN diesel engines, each developing 1,000hp. From *U27* onwards, all U-boats had a longer periscope (6.2m) and were able to maintain periscope depth more easily than earlier boats.

In the matter of the ordering of diesel engines, the preferential treatment which GW received as compared to MAN had its sequel at the end of 1912, when it became evident that the delays in providing the GW diesel engines were growing and that the reliability of the engines already produced left much to be desired. GW excused themselves on the grounds that the TI, after acceptance of a successful engine, had requested too many improvements and changes.

The Shipyard Administration laid the blame at Berling's door. It had been his decision to place orders for GW engines for the GW boats, *U31–U41*, and there were also other problems with propulsion units for which Berling in the TI was held responsible, as well as the difficulties with *U2*. Also

held against him were the many failures before and during the autumn manoeuvres of 1912. (From 2 to 23 September, of an average of 13 U-boats, 69.5 per cent were in efficient daily use, 27.2 per cent were partially usable and 3.3 per cent were out of action; in a seven-day period, only 60 per cent were completely operational.) In a communication to von Tirpitz dated 15 December 1912, the Shipyard Administration demanded Berling's immediate dismissal.

On 1 April 1913, Berling was appointed Works Director of new construction at KWK, Kiel: with hindsight, it can be said that he had been hasty in ordering the GW engines, but it cannot be disputed that he had done much to build up the German submarine arm. His successor in the U-Boat Department of the TI was Naval Construction Adviser Reitz, with Construction Official Werner succeeding Schulz in the shipbuilding section. After these appointments had been made, the position regarding delays in the delivery of the GW diesel U-boats hardly changed at all.

Table 4. Delivery schedule for U23–U41, April 1913

Boats	Proposed delivery	Actual delivery	Approx. delay (months)
U23	20 May 1913	11 Sept 1913	3⅔
U24	31 July 1913	6 Dec 1913	4¼
U25	31 Aug 1913	9 May 1914	8⅓
U26	30 Sept 1913	20 June 1914	8⅔
U31	1 Oct 1913	18 Sept 1914	11⅔
U32	1 Dec 1913	3 Sept 1914	9
U33	1 Jan 1914	27 Sept 1914	9
U34	1 Feb 1914	5 Oct 1914	8
U35	1 March 1914	3 Nov 1914	8
U36	1 April 1914	14 Nov 1914	7½
U37	1 June 1914	9 Dec 1914	6⅓
U38	1 June 1914	11 Dec 1914	6⅓
U39	1 July 1914	18 Jan 1915	6½
U40	1 July 1914	29 Feb 1915	8
U41	1 Aug 1914	1 Feb 1915	6

On 30 July 1914, a statement from the newly-formed U-Boat Inspectorate (page 33) on the diesel-engine question established that:

'The 850hp engines of *U19–U22* have been working well and efficiently. To be sure, in some cases, they are not ideal for U-boats in that their construction and accessibility leaves something to be desired, but in detail they exhibit a satisfactory design from which future reliability can be expected. Voyages made up to now by *U27* and *U28* have shown that the 1,000hp engines are reliable and ready for operational use. Report has already been made of the disappointing experiences with the 850hp GW diesel engines. The design of these is unsatisfactory, they have not been constructed with sufficient care, and they still can not be considered as satisfactory operational U-boat engines. Their efficiency does not match that of the MAN engines.'

In time, however, GW succeeded in bringing their diesels up to the standard of the MAN engines. Despite all these difficulties, the German yards succeeded in producing operationally-ready diesel boats in a much shorter time than, for example, France, who had initiated similar trials as early as

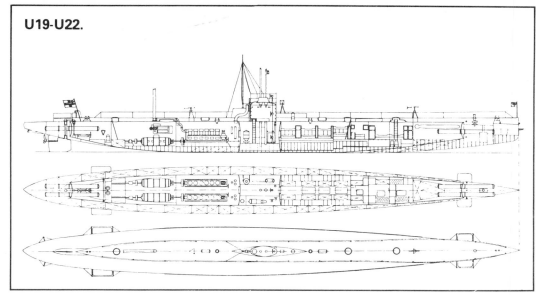

U19-U22.

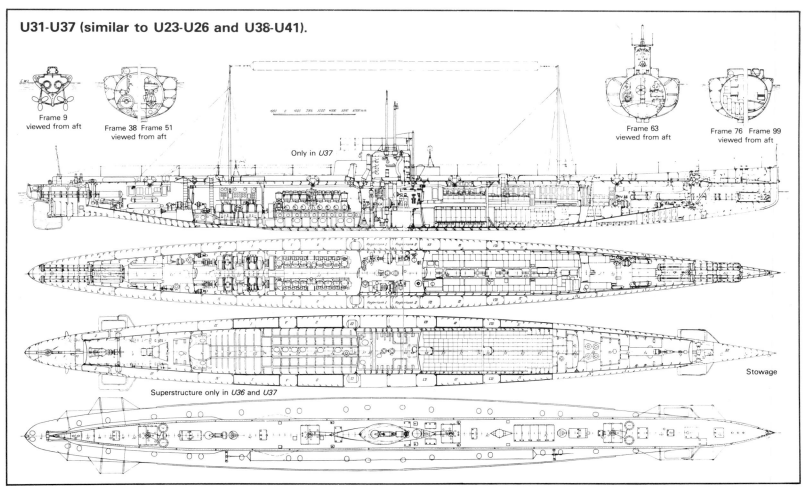

U31-U37 (similar to U23-U26 and U38-U41).

Frame 9 viewed from aft

Frame 38 Frame 51 viewed from aft

Only in *U37*

Frame 63 viewed from aft

Frame 76 Frame 99 viewed from aft

Superstructure only in *U36* and *U37*

Stowage

1903, only to return to steam propulsion after many failures and accidents. It was the diesel engine that changed the rôle of the German U-boat from a defensive to an offensive one and made possible its successful application in a war of blockade.

Single-system propulsion

Early submarines had a single system for both surface and submerged propulsion — initially muscle power, then steam and, finally, electricity. Not until the end of the nineteenth century was surface propulsion separated from, and different from, submerged propulsion. Advantage was taken of two available systems: combustion engines for high speed and range on the surface, with the simplicity and safety of electric motors when submerged. However, the idea ever present was to utilize a single reliable propulsion unit giving a greater range, and this was only to be achieved by the use of combustion machinery. At about the beginning of the century, when the diesel engine was being further refined, designs were being prepared for a propulsion unit that would use an internal-combustion engine whose exhaust gases would be mixed with oxygen in a closed circuit (patented by Jaubert in 1901, Sabathe in 1904 and Winand in 1906).

In Patent Classification 65a No. 188825, Dr George François Jaubert of Paris described this process in the following terms:

'The essential point of the new drive is that explosion engines with a closed circuit are used; they use exhaust gases enriched with oxygen or with oxygen containing gas, to produce an explosive mixture which can be fed into the combustion chamber. Washing devices would be necessary for the cleansing of the exhaust gases, and in them the surface of the free liquid will be kept as small as possible so that stability is affected as little as possible. In order to maintain a constant pressure in the closed circuit, it is essential to expel excess exhaust gases out of the boat by means of a pump or similar system, and this should be an automatic system that would start to operate when the pressure reaches a certain point.'

In his Patent Classification 46a No. 196266, Paul Winand of Cologne suggested the use of cooled exhaust gases to dilute the mixture of oxygen and fuel in two-stroke engines and, in 1907, practical tests following this principle were tried out by GW, with a 30hp diesel engine. Long running times were in fact achieved, but the system was not yet ready for operational use, because regulating equipment for the supply of oxygen was not available, and diesel engines had still not been developed to the right degree. There were also considerable doubts about the use of pure oxygen in a drive unit.

In the Deutz Gas Engine Factory, work now began on another system. In this, a mixture of disintegrated nitrogen dioxide and the gas from the burned paraffin was used. The Navy supported this research from 1906 to 1907, hoping that it would lead to the following performance aspects in a

Left: U-boat construction at GW, Kiel, in the summer of 1913. *U37* is on the left with *U38* (right) on Slip 5. *U25* and *U26* are behind her on Slip 4.

U-boat of approximately 700 tons when submerged: 225 nautical miles at 15 knots, or 360 nautical miles at 12 knots or 800 nautical miles at 8 knots (as against a battery-powered range of only 85 nautical miles at 5 knots in a boat of similar size). In the summer of 1913, an explosion occurred which resulted in some deaths and completely destroyed the test equipment. The research came to a halt.

At about this time, greater safety and a quicker result seemed likely by using a method proposed by engineer Moritz Honigmann of Grevenberg near Aachen. He suggested that, when submerged, exhaust steam be led into concentrated caustic soda. Diluted in this way, the caustic solution would be raised to such a temperature that water, in a surrounding boiler, would be converted to steam. The charging of this steam accumulator would be carried out on the surface by evaporating the caustic solution, using steam from an ordinary steam installation. As long ago as 1886, a submarine using such a steam installation had been built by the American Josiah H. L. Tuck. A 14hp steam engine had served as the propulsion unit; underwater, it had received steam at 6.7 atmospheres overload from a caustic boiler of the type proposed by Honigmann. However, only short dives (of seven-minute duration) for this small, 9.5m-long submarine were recorded. The severe problem of cooling, which arose in the narrow

confines of a submarine using steam for surface propulsion, and the increasing efficiency of the internal combustion engines combined to render steam propulsion obsolete. Nevertheless, attempts to utilize steam continued to be made. These stemmed from the desire for high speeds, the danger of the petrol engines of the time (up to the First World War), and the unreliability of the first diesel engines. Even the initiator of GW's first U-boats, d'Equevilley, had proposed a steam-driven boat in 1908; in several patents, he improved upon the Honigmann steam/caustic-soda drive.

In 1912, in collaboration with the firm of AG Weser, d'Equevilley designed a steam-propelled submarine of approximately 700 tons, which was intended to achieve a surface speed of 20 knots at 4,000shp and a submerged speed of 12.5 knots at 2,000shp. Surface range would be 1,600 nautical miles at 13 knots; submerged range, 18.8 nautical miles at 12.5 knots. These speeds would certainly have been faster than that achieved by other submarines of the period.

In a lecture delivered to a conference of the STG in 1913, Berling examined the steam/caustic-soda boat in a very detailed manner. He drew attention to the prevailing battery-charging time of six to ten hours in the case of boats with oil/electric drive, compared with the relatively short steam-raising time of the caustic solution — three or four hours

when on the move, an hour and a half or two hours when motionless. He also pointed out the superior surface and submerged speeds of craft driven by steam. A further advantage of this system as opposed to a combined oil/electric system was that it was much lighter. Adverse features were having to conduct away heat, erosion caused by the caustic compound, a large space requirement and a lesser surface range resulting from the generally inferior performance of steam engines compared to oil engines. It would take some time to solve these various problems, and the outbreak of the First World War brought an end to these developments at AG Weser.

The U-boat's rôle and construction plans, 1912
On 3 January 1912, the TI submitted a draft plan for the future U-boat programme. The main emphasis was on defence; boats would form a so-called submerged defensive line, each with its own particular zone of activity. A small number were to be considered for offensive purposes in the North Sea or off the coast of Britain. It was not considered that they would play a strongly offensive rôle in a possible war against Britain, even though Vizeadmiral Freiherr von Schleinitz had called for this in the *Deutsche Revue* of August 1908. Von Schleinitz had demanded the building of large boats with a range of at least 5–6,000 nautical

Engine layout of the d'Equevilley system.

(from G. Berling, *Die Entwicklung der Unterseeboote und ihrer Hauptmaschinenlagen*, pp. 131–138):
'(1) The evaporation of the water from the diluted caustic solution is achieved by introducing some of the steam from the surface steam engine through water-pipe boiler 'D'. The steam driven off is then precipitated in the condenser of the steam-engine.
'(2) Before submerging, the fire is extinguished and all surplus steam is led into both caustic soda boilers 'C'. The caustic solution is greatly heated by this and gives off heat to the surrounding water pipe boiler 'D'. In turn, the steam from this is fed to a steam engine. Water-pipe boiler 'D' receives its water from the warm water container 'B'.
'(3) With increasing dilution of the caustic solution, the counter-pressure will build up and, after a certain time, the exhaust steam that has already collected behind the medium pressure cylinder must be led away.
'(4) If the caustic solution reaches such a diluted state that the introduced exhaust steam does not bring about a significant heating, it is condensed and used to refill the warm water container 'B'. The caustic boiler now becomes merely a heat container.'

Raising steam in the caustic solution during surface travel.

Submerged travel 2

Submerged travel 1

Submerged travel 3

D'Equevilley-type steam-sodium diving boat built by A G Weser, 1913

miles, and capable of sinking merchant ships. 'To sink a large number of English merchant ships', he stated, 'would be much more significant than defeating the opponent in a naval battle. Submarines with a greatly enlarged range should be able to leave the River Elbe or River Jade, be capable of making their way round the whole of Great Britain and creating havoc in the Channel and inland waters.' But the TI's plan modestly confined itself within the possibilities suggested by the Naval Estimates and only considered the following:

1. 36 U-boats for protection of the German Bight, 12 being necessary to make up the force needed for a radius of 30 nautical miles around Heligoland, with an interval of 5 nautical miles between each boat. To relieve them daily, 12 boats, based in Heligoland, would be needed. (These twenty-four boats to be allocated to two U-boat flotillas in Wilhelmshaven.) A single flotilla of 12 boats to be held as war reserve at Kiel.
2. 12 boats to patrol the approaches to Kiel, distributed as follows: 1 boat in the Little Belt; 3 boats in the Great Belt and the Fehmarn Belt, with 4 relief boats kept at Kiel; 4 boats kept in reserve. These 12 boats to form a single U-boat flotilla at Kiel.
3. 12 boats for offensive purposes in the North Sea blockade, to be kept as a U-flotilla at Emden.
4. As experiences to date suggested that something like 1 in 6 of all U-boats would be out of action at any one time, a further 10 U-boats to be kept as an essential reserve.

A total of 70 U-boats were necessary for this war commitment, apart from the training boats *U1–U4*. From 1 April 1912, two boats, ready for sea at all times, would be stationed in Heligoland, and the First North Sea U-Flotilla (*U19–U30*) was to be established in Wilhelmshaven in 1914.

An operational problem with the paraffin-burning boats *U5–U18* was the fact that their white exhaust smoke could be clearly seen from a great distance. A system of discharging exhaust gas below the surface was tried, but was not particularly successful. OLEX, a new type of paraffin giving very little visible smoke, was tried successfully, and 3,000 tons of it were prepared; however, as it exceeded the cost of conventional paraffin in the ratio of 13:9, it was to be used only in the event of war.

On 17 June 1912, further TI plans for U-boat building were announced. All but 7.2 million marks of the 1914 estimates had already been used for boats up to *U41*. It was desired to build a further 33 boats after these at a unit cost of 3 million marks. To realize this sum, the estimates for 1915 allocated 19 million marks; for 1916 and 1917, 15 million marks each year; for 1918 and 1919, 18 million marks each year; and for 1920, 96 million marks. Orders would be placed in the following sequence: 3 boats in 1913; 3 in 1914; 4 in 1915; 5 in 1916; and 6 in each year from 1917 to 1919. In 1920, special resources would finance 2 experimental boats (1 from FIAT, and the steam/caustic-soda boat).

In 1912, it had been decided to have a boat built for the German Navy by the well-known Italian submarine builder, Laurenti, at the FIAT-Laurenti

Yard at La Spezia. Before this, Laurenti had sent tenders to the German Navy, and these had been examined by the TI. After the Italian Navy had ordered the diesel submarine *Atropo* from GW (page 28), the German Navy thought it important to get some idea of diesel boat development in other countries, and the purchase of the Laurenti boat would enable the Navy to test it thoroughly and determine its essential qualities.

Laurenti's design had an inner hull of elliptical cross-section, as he considered this to be a better basic shape, and to provide more space. Frames and beams between this inner hull and an outer hull gave rigidity, and the space between them housed the various tanks. When submerged, the strains imposed by water pressure were taken by both hulls and, because they strengthened each other, the sheet-metal construction of the inner hull could be lighter than that in German submarines (despite the fact that the cross-section had departed from the circular) in which only the inner hull took the pressure. In this way, the FIAT boat, officially known as 'UF', gained in terms of space and weight saving. The superstructure was watertight and could be flooded, which gave considerable reserves of buoyancy and stability. Control of the boat was from a central position — the conning tower was merely a shaft equipped with an observation dome. The storage battery was housed in a special

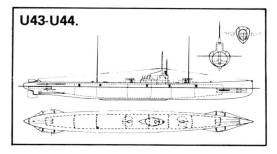

U43-U44.

watertight, pressure-tight compartment. For propulsion, Laurenti equipped the boat with two 1,250hp FIAT diesel engines, which enabled the boat to achieve a surface speed of 19 knots. However, following the rather discouraging experience with the GW diesel engines, the German Navy had inserted a clause in the contract stipulating that, in the event of the FIAT engines not giving the required performance or not being ready in time, MAN engines should be used instead. The order for the 728-ton FIAT boat, designated *U42*, was placed in the summer of 1913, and construction began on 18 August. Delivery was promised for 1 January 1915, and the price was to be 3,658,000 marks.

In the summer of 1912, the Vulcan Yard at Hamburg indicated that they would like to receive U-boat contracts from the German Navy, and offered to try their hand at building a submarine. The TI established that the only design in hand was for *U23*, and it seemed pointless to have boats of the same type built by two different private firms. It would be more appropriate to choose a new design for test building. Such a design would be

ready by October 1912, and would include several innovations, some of which related to the FIAT-Laurenti type. On 25 April 1913, however, Vulcan's request was turned down by the RMA, on the grounds that it would not be in the interests of efficiency to have the planned 6 boats per year built by more than two private yards, in addition to KWD. As AG Weser were now seriously involved with their steam/caustic-soda boat, Vulcan could no longer be considered.

The new U-boat type, for which Vulcan might have been considered, was given instead to KWD on 10 July 1913, the contract being for two boats, *U43* and *U44*. (The third boat, intended for 1913, *U45*, was not ordered until 22 June 1914, but was finished in a considerably shorter time than her predecessors.) *U43* differed in certain essential respects from previous boats up to *U41*. She had external pressure hull framing; a different compartment layout (living quarters sited between the diesel compartments and the control room, moving the control room and conning tower forward); an increase in the armament to six torpedo tubes (four submerged bow, two submerged stern) for 50cm G6 torpedoes; the incorporation of the upper deck in the outer skin; elimination of the so-called tank deck; and longer periscopes (7.5m) to give a periscope depth of 12m.

It was estimated that this new type would have a diving time of 60–90 seconds when in a state of preparedness. It was not planned to change to the G7 torpedo (50cm diameter, 7m in length), as the boat would have to made larger to accommodate them and the increase in range of these torpedoes was not seen as a particular advantage. Opinion at that time was that a U-boat should approach a target to within 800–900m and fire her torpedoes from that close range.

The U-Boat Inspectorate
The years 1910 to 1913 saw a grave increase in the burden borne by the TI. The problems posed by the excessive weights of KWD's boats, diesel engine trouble in GW's boats, the increasing number of tasks envisaged for U-boats, the commissioning of further U-boats — all resulted in a need for more and more staff and material at the TI. In the autumn of 1913, it was requested that an independent inspectorate be instituted, with the following responsibilities.

1. Control of training programmes in all submarine departments and all U-boat flotillas.
2. Maintenance of U-boats on a war footing.
3. Development of the U-boat arm and preparations for its use, especially establishing and improving operational regulations.
4. Control of operations at the Submarine School.

Under the control of this U-boat Inspectorate (UI) were to be:
(a) Submarine Departments.
(b) Existing U-boat units and individual U-boats.
(c) The Submarine School.
(d) Technical experiments and trials of U-boats already built.

By an Imperial Decree of 13 December 1913, the U-boat arm was separated from the TI. The new UI would be based at Kiel and, controlled by a Chief of

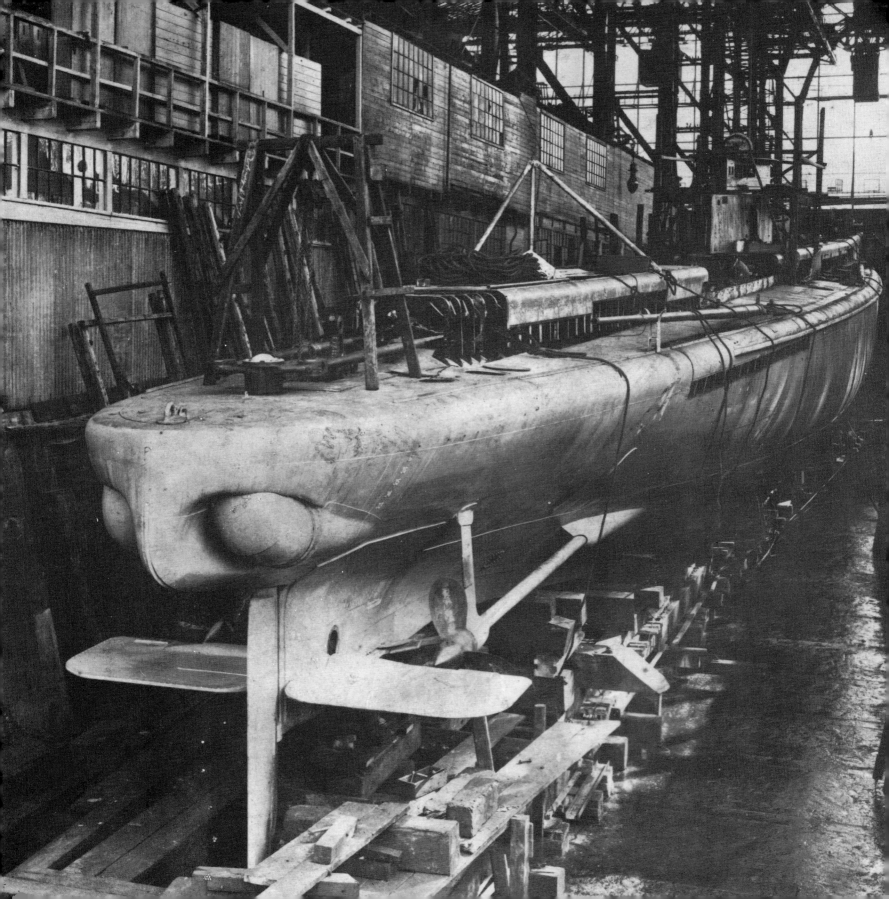

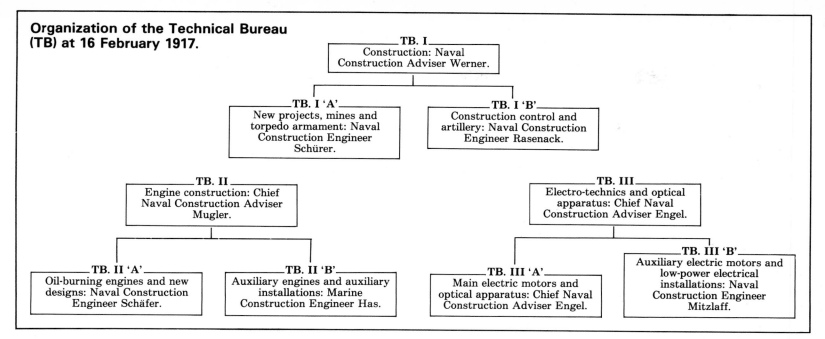

Organization of the Technical Bureau (TB) at 16 February 1917.

TB. I
Construction: Naval Construction Adviser Werner.

TB. I 'A'
New projects, mines and torpedo armament: Naval Construction Engineer Schürer.

TB. I 'B'
Construction control and artillery: Naval Construction Engineer Rasenack.

TB. II
Engine construction: Chief Naval Construction Adviser Mugler.

TB. II 'A'
Oil-burning engines and new designs: Naval Construction Engineer Schäfer.

TB. II 'B'
Auxiliary engines and auxiliary installations: Marine Construction Engineer Has.

TB. III
Electro-technics and optical apparatus: Chief Naval Construction Adviser Engel.

TB. III 'A'
Main electric motors and optical apparatus: Chief Naval Construction Adviser Engel.

TB. III 'B'
Auxiliary electric motors and low-power electrical installations: Naval Construction Engineer Mitzlaff.

Staff of U-boat Affairs, was charged with the execution of the tasks outlined above. The date for setting-up the UI was left to the Secretary of State in the RMA. In fact, it happened on 15 March 1914, after all preliminary organizational details had been settled. The appointed Chief of Staff was Kapitän zur See Nordmann, with Kapitän zur See Siemens as adjutant and Kapitänleutnant Blum as Military Liaison Officer. The Technical Bureau (TB) remained under the control of Naval Construction Adviser Reitz until 1917. As at 16 February 1917, it had the operational structure as shown in the diagram. From August 1917, the TB came under the direction of Construction Adviser Müller, but the individual departments remained unaltered. In the autumn of 1918, an attempt was made to separate the TB from the UI and control it directly from the RMA in Berlin, but the Armistice intervened, and nothing came of this. Further U-boat developments during the years 1913 and 1914 were heavily dependent on the development of propulsion units — diesel engines and the steam/caustic-soda installation. The tendency was clearly towards the development of larger U-boats, better adapted for combat, having faster surface speeds and a greater range, able to carry out operations west of the British Isles and, therefore, to be considered as offensive boats. Following good results from the MAN 1,000hp six-cylinder diesel engine, the UI considered that it would be perfectly feasible to enlarge the engine by 500hp (by boring out the cylinders!) without going to the trouble of building a test version.

Despite past experience, it was decided not only to involve GW largely in the building of these new

U-boats, but to employ them for engine construction. An enlarged diesel building programme for the Russian Navy led to this decision. Based on GW designs, eight 1,500hp engines were to be built, two at GW itself, and six more in Russia. The first engine would not be ready for test until the spring of 1915; on the other hand, the new boat design had been promised for 1914. It was not considered feasible to wait for the trial results of these new engines.

In order to expedite at all costs the production of operationally sound engines and to avoid construction delays similar to those already experienced, the UI suggested that GW separate the main propulsion from the ancillary — the main engines would propel the boat, and a secondary diesel system would drive compressors, bilge pumps, etc. In this way it should be possible for GW to supply 1,500hp engines with much the same cylinder dimensions as the 950hp two-stroke engines that had already been delivered. The advantages were the short, main engine, with its considerable reserve for operational safety, and the facility for boosting the main compressor with the auxiliary system. The disadvantage of requiring more space and weight was not considered too serious in this larger U-boat type, which received the project numbers 31 and 31a. (See also page 54.) GW agreed to build propulsion units of this type and received a contract to design the new 1914 U-boats in accordance with the stated requirements; but the outbreak of war put a stop to these plans, in favour of designs that had been tried and tested.

Germaniawerft export submarines
Up to the outbreak of war, GW made strenuous endeavours to export their successful submarine

technology. Following the contracts for the three Russian and two Austrian boats, and the Norwegian *Kobben*, discussions were held with the Italians concerning the building of a submarine for them. Originally, a boat had been envisaged having a surface displacement of 255 tons, armed with three torpedo tubes, as in *Kobben*, and having a diesel installation that would give 14.5 knots on the surface. However, economic requirements dictated that the boat be made smaller and that the stern torpedo tube be dispensed with. Only 12 knots were now required as a surface speed, this reduction having no essential significance because GW, when making their earlier bid, could only offer the 350hp diesel engine. The order was not finally placed until the autumn of 1910.

The Italians stipulated that control of the boat when submerged must be from the central control room, so a periscope was provided in the control room, in addition to the one in the conning tower. For the first time in German submarine construction, both periscopes were given tapered ends. The conning tower was manufactured from non-magnetic metal, and had a magnetic compass which could be read from the central control room. The diesel engines could not run in reverse so controllable-pitch propellers were used. The time allotted for the diesel engines to reach trial state was exceeded, and delays therefore occurred in the building of the boat. As compensation, the Italians were given a top surface speed of 14.75 knots, which far exceeded the required performance. The boat was named *Atropo*.

Kobben (A1) having been a success, meanwhile, the Norwegian Navy decided to acquire more submarines and, in November 1910, asked various yards, including GW, for tenders. GW's design was based on the second version of *Atropo*, but with a

The centre section of *Kobben*, exposed to show the engine-room.

greater displacement and two submerged bow torpedo tubes and two surface tubes at the stern for 45cm torpedoes. In May 1911, the Norwegians ordered three submarines (*A2–A4*) from GW, and a fourth boat (*A5*) was ordered in 1912. The design of *A2–A5* differed from the previous boats in that the rear hydroplanes were placed abaft the propellers. These were the first small submarines to have a gyroscopic compass, an RT installation with only one mast, and a transverse propeller in the bows to give manoeuvrability when stationary for torpedo firing. The main specifications of *A2–A4* were as follows.

Length overall:	46.5m.
Beam:	4.8m.
Pressure hull diameter:	3.18m.
Displacement surfaced:	268 tons.
Displacement submerged:	353 tons.
Propulsion surfaced:	two 350–375hp non-reversing diesel engines.
Fuel supply:	12.8 tons.
Maximum diving depth:	50m.
Armament:	3 torpedo tubes, five 45cm torpedoes.

Early in 1914, *A2*, *A3* and *A4* were handed over to the Norwegian Navy and proceeded under their own power from Kiel to Horten.

In December 1910, an inquiry came from the Turks, who were interested in a larger submarine. On 12 December 1910, GW asked the RMA if there were any reason why one of the larger submarines then being built should not be sold to Turkey. Permission was given to GW 'so that the German U-boat industry can get a foot into the Turkish camp and because it is very likely that, in replacing the boat that will be sold to them, we shall acquire an improved design at the same price'. *U7*, *U8* or *U16* were suggested for the sale, but nothing further transpired, supposedly because the price was too high. Five 635-ton submarines were ordered in 1913 from GW for the Austro-Hungarian Navy, and these were to have high surface and submerged speeds. (See also page 39.) GW gave them the construction numbers 203–207.

Further considerable submarine business with Greece seemed imminent in June 1914 and, by the beginning of July, negotiations had so far advanced between GW and the Greek Navy that the sale of *U33–U37* seemed a foregone conclusion. The GW had promised the RMA that the sale of these boats to Greece would not bring about any delay in promised building construction of German boats. It was not possible to equip the boats for the Greek Navy with G6 torpedoes, and the arrangement by which hydroplanes were fitted abaft the propellers in boats from *U38* onwards was not employed in exported submarines. However, the outbreak of war effectively put a stop to this proposed sale. These negotiations show clearly how little, in the summer of 1914, the German Navy was thinking in terms of a major war and how little importance was attached to submarine resources by the RMA. Not until after the sensational success of Otto Weddigen in *U9* against three British cruisers on 22 September 1914 did a reappraisal of the rôle of the submarine take place.

Atropo.

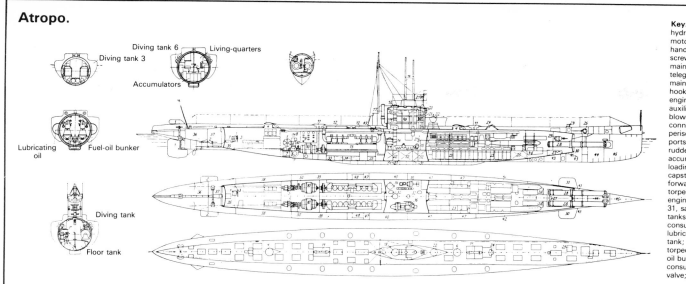

Diving tank 3

Diving tank 6   Living-quarters

Accumulators

Lubricating oil   Fuel-oil bunker

Diving tank

Floor tank

Key: 1, vertical rudder; 2, after hydroplane; 3, vertical rudder motor; 4, companion hatch; 5, hand-wheel for activating wing screw; 6, starter; 7, coolers for main electric motors; 8, engine telegraph; 9, switch panel; 10, main electric motor; 11, lifting hooks; 12, silencers; 13, diesel engine; 14, main bilge pump; 15, auxiliary bilge pump; 16, turbo-blower; 17, auxiliary air mast; 18, conning-tower hatch; 19, periscopes; 20, conning-tower ports; 21, helm for vertical rudder; 22, telephone buoy; 23, accumulators; 24, torpedo loading hatch; 25, warping capstan; 26, anchor capstan; 27, forward trimming tank; 28, torpedo tube; 29, anchor-raising engine; 30, forward hydroplane; 31, safety weights; 32, regulating tanks; 33, lubricating-oil consumption tank; 34, lubricating-oil tank; 35, trimming tank; 36-45, diving tanks; 46, torpedo-firing cartridge; 47, fuel-oil bunker; 48, fuel-oil consumption tank; 49, main air valve; 50, extra compressor.

Below: *Atropo* undergoing trials.

2 U-BOAT CONSTRUCTION DURING THE FIRST WORLD WAR

CONSTRUCTION AT THE BEGINNING OF THE WAR

At the outbreak of hostilities, 45 U-boats were either ready for service or in the course of construction. Of these, *U1–U28* (with the exception of *U2* which was in need of a fairly lengthy period of overhaul) were in service, and *U29–U41* would have been if the promised delivery dates had been met. The boat ordered from FIAT had not been handed over to Germany.

The mobilization plan provided for the immediate placing of contracts for 17 boats of the most recently built *U41* type (four torpedo tubes) and *U45* type (six torpedo tubes), 12 to be built by GW and 5 by KWD. On 7 August 1914, KWD received their order for *U46–U50*, but, because of the

troubles that GW had been having with the 16 two-stroke diesel engines for *U31–U41*, only 6 (*U51–U56*) of the intended 12 Mobilization (Ms) boats were ordered from them on 23 August 1914. The remaining 6 boats were to be given to AG Weser, who had been active for two and a half years in the building of boats in the steam/caustic-soda category. AG Weser's boats were to be built to the design of KWD's *U27* (four torpedo tubes), but the UI was not prepared to give them the contract unless they could be built more quickly than at KWD. After protracted negotiations, the contract for *U57–U62* was awarded to AG Weser on 14 November 1914.

It was intended that the MAN four-stroke diesel engines be used for all these boats, as the two-stroke engines which GW had used in *U23–U26* and *U31–U41* had not proved sufficiently reliable. A

building time of eighteen months was allowed for the first production boat of each order. The contract provided for these 17 Ms boats to be handed over between December 1915 and December 1916, but because it was considered most unlikely that the war would last until then, all U-boats that could possibly be made ready within the next three months were given priority over all other building projects.

Meanwhile, a number of submarines were in various stages of construction for foreign navies. At the beginning of the war, the building capacity of GW was taken up by the building of a small submarine for the Norwegian Navy, and the completion of five large submarines for the Austro-Hungarian Navy.

In May 1911, the Norwegian Navy had ordered three (and subsequently a fourth) submarines of

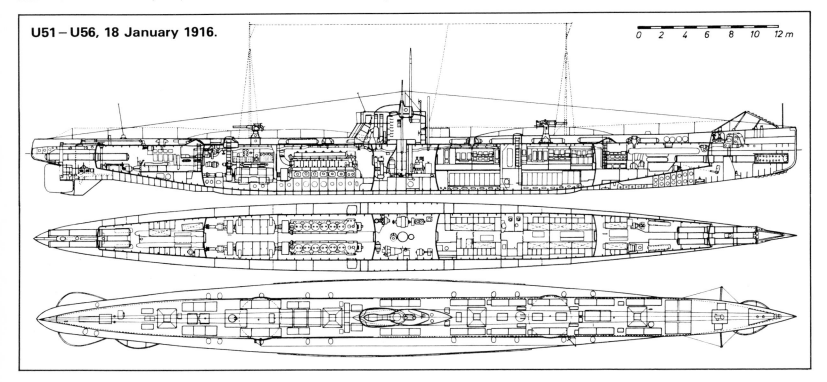

U51 – U56, 18 January 1916.

0 2 4 6 8 10 12 m

approximately 270 tons displacement, equipped with three 45cm torpedo tubes (two submerged bow tubes and one surface stern tube). Surface propulsion was by 2 non-reversing 350hp GW diesel engines. (Details of the essential innovations, stern hydroplanes abaft the propellers and a transverse propeller forward, have been given on page 36.) While the first three boats were delivered to the Norwegians early in 1914, the fourth was taken over by the German Navy on 14 August 1914 and designated *UA*. After undergoing numerous small alterations to make her suitable for German requirements, *UA* was used initially for coastal protection and, later, for training purposes.

The submarines (Construction Nos. 203–207) that had been ordered for the Austro-Hungarian Navy in 1913 had a relatively large surface displacement of 635 tons. They were designed to

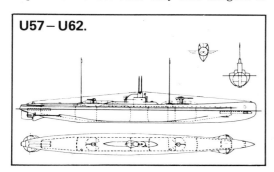

U57 – U62.

achieve the high speeds of almost 17 knots on the surface and 11 knots submerged, which necessitated the employment of batteries with a large surface area. In order to maintain a low bridge profile, no conning tower was provided, which considerably reduced submerged resistance, and the periscope was manned from the central control room. For the first time in a GW U-boat, four bow torpedo tubes were provided, and two submerged stern torpedo tubes were added, but all torpedo tubes were still of 45cm calibre.

On 7 August 1914, the RMA ordered that work on these five Austrian submarines be accelerated. After discussions with the Austrian authorities, the German Navy took them over on 10 November 1914, as *U66–U70* of Type UD. In the course of completion, torpedo calibre apart, these were

brought into line with the other Ms U-boats by the addition of a conning tower, which had the effect of reducing one of their special properties — high speed. Despite the reduction in number of torpedo tubes to five, the surface displacement rose to 791m^3.

Coastal U-boats: Types UB and UC

After Belgium had been invaded, the Belgian coastline afforded bases for operations in the English Channel. With this in mind, on 18 August 1914, the RMA asked the UI to investigate the possibility of producing a large number of small U-boats that could be operational before the short war envisaged came to an end. They were to have a range of approximately 500 nautical miles and to be armed with two torpedo tubes. The UI considered that such boats, of a type displacing 150–200 tons,

could be completed in 14 months, but only if the building of the large U-boats already ordered were delayed. They felt this would not be sensible, and said as much on 25 August 1914.

However, on 11 September, Dr. Werner (head of TB.I) went over the heads of the Admiralty Staff at the RMA and suggested that small minelaying boats be built for use off the French coast. The UI was subsequently asked to look into the question of building a purely electric-drive U-boat, intended solely for minelaying. On 13 September, they reported that, under the most favourable circumstances, the building time for a wholly electric-drive boat of approximately 80 tons, and armed with a single torpedo tube (Project 32) would be about four months. No information was available about the mines, — the military value of which, in any case, the UI considered to be very slight.

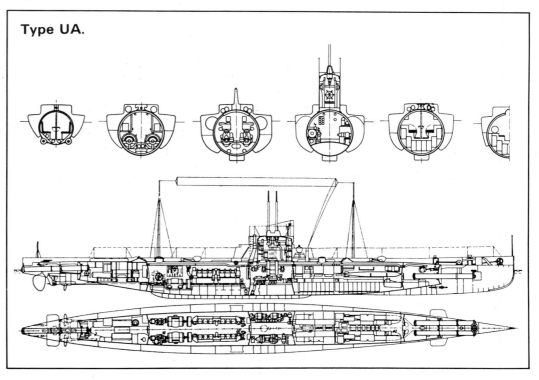

Type UA.

U66–U70 (Type UD), 17 July 1915.

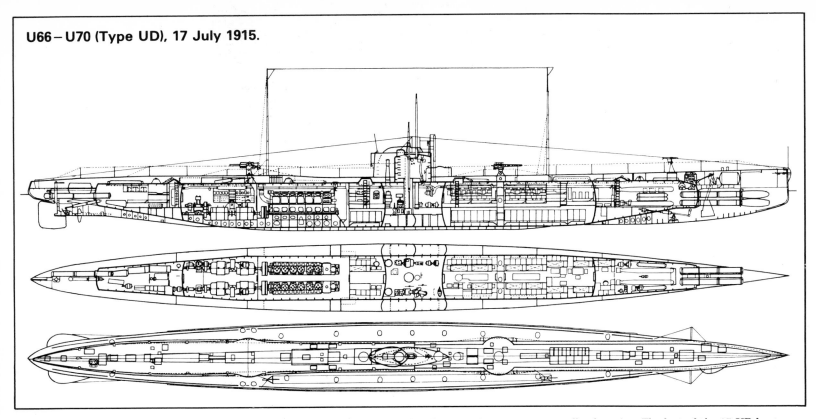

The advances made by the German Army in Belgium increased the demand for coastal U-boats to be made available as soon as possible and, on 14 September, the UI were asked to look into the question of building small U-boats that could be transported by rail. Having received several designs that met this requirement, the RMA accepted Project 34, which envisaged a torpedo-armed boat of approximately 125 tons. An adequate range was achieved by the fitting of a small 60hp diesel engine, made by Körting for use in launches and readily available. It was suggested that the boats be built at GW and AG Weser and, on 15 October, the building of 15 of this new Type UB was authorized.

Because of their limited size, only single-hull construction and single-propeller propulsion would be used. Diving and compensating tanks and bunkers accounted for only 23m³, and were easily accommodated within the pressure hull, the diameter of which was restricted to 3.15m by the gauge of the railways. The lines of these boats, although single-hulled, were considerably different from the similar-sized Holland boats produced in other countries. This was because the Type UB was considered to be a seaworthy diving-boat rather than a true submarine. The pressure hull was formed from conical sections riveted together, which gave a somewhat angular shape at the waterline. The cross-section of the pressure hull was almost circular throughout its length, but flattened slightly to an ellipse in order to accommodate two

side-by-side bow torpedo tubes. A short superstructure was sited forward, and along the top of the boat ran a narrow, floodable upper deck on which a relatively large bridge was placed.

The 60hp diesel engine provided surface propulsion, with a 120hp electric motor, from Siemens Schuckertwerke, for use when submerged. The diving tanks were situated amidships, with the batteries foward and aft. These consisted of 112 13 MAS 505/5 cells, which gave ten hours of submerged cruising at 4 knots. Maximum submerged speed was 5.5 knots. This was lower than had been envisaged, but operational modifications demanded a heavier structure, and this in turn, led to greater water resistance. The surface range of 1,600 nautical miles at 5 knots, however, seemed satisfactory for the planned rôle. Because the diving tanks had many inlet valves, the new UB boat could submerge in the unbelievably short time of 22 seconds. Armament consisted of two 45cm bow torpedo tubes for C/03 torpedoes, plus an 8mm machine-gun.

UB1–UB8 were ordered from GW on 15 October 1914, and *UB9–UB15* from AG Weser. On 25 November, two extra boats, *UB16* and *UB17*, were ordered from AG Weser, because it had been decided that *UB1* and *UB15* would be handed over to the Austro-Hungarian Navy after they had been completed.

The contracted building time was four months, but the first of the series was completed by GW in only 75 days — a sensational time for building a

small submarine. The last of the 17 UB boats was completed in May 1915. *UB1* and *UB2* were tested underwater to 5 atmospheres for 1–2 hours without ill effect. At their yards, the pressure hulls were tested with water pressure of up to 3 atmospheres, to try thoroughly the tightness of the rivets.

Most of these boats were sent to their destinations by rail, each boat requiring three wagons — one for each of the three main hull compartments — and further wagons for the conning tower, parts of the upper deck engines and batteries. Assembly, at Hoboken and Antwerp — and later at Pola — took approximately fourteen days. At these assembly points, the only test for watertightness that could be made was by compressed air at 50mm of mercury over pressure. From Antwerp, the boats had to be towed through the Scheldt, and through the Ghent-Bruges Canal, to their operational base at Bruges; this operation, using caissons and two tugs, took five-and-a-half days. It had been thought that *UB16* and *UB17* could be assembled at the Stenia Yard in Constantinople, for use off the Dardenelles, but transportation would have been impossible, and the idea was abandoned. However, two of the boats made the journey by sea from Pola, and showed themselves well able to undertake long voyages, so six boats were eventually sent from there.

On 17 October 1914, despite the UI's disapproval, the RMA ordered two experimental (Project 35a), 150-ton minelaying U-boats. One was to be built by GW and the other by AG Weser, and

Type UBI.

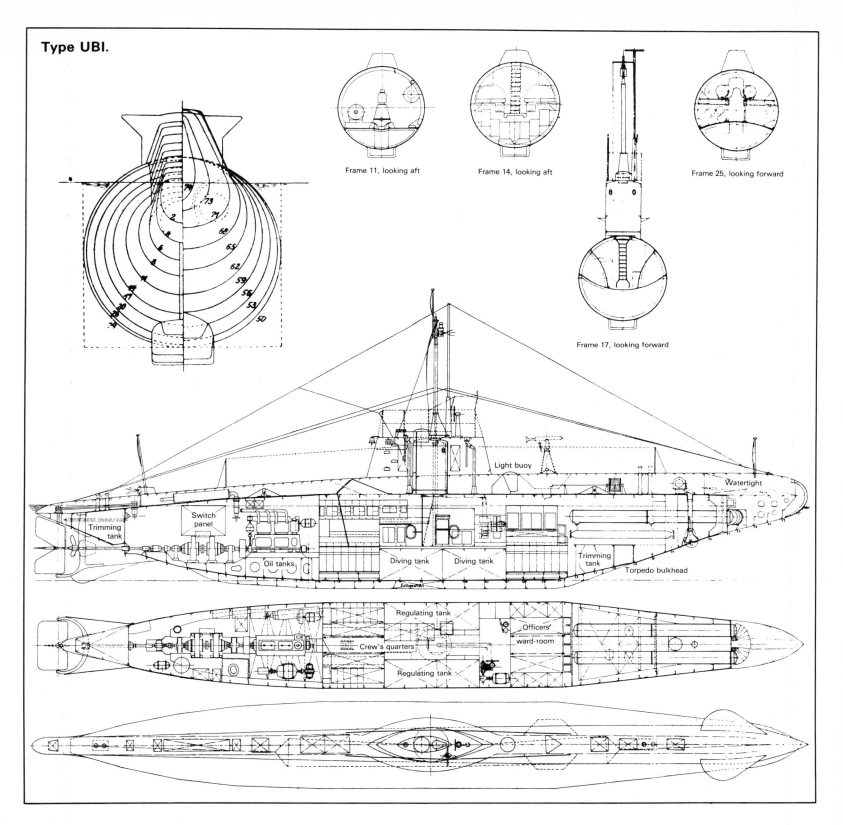

Frame 11, looking aft

Frame 14, looking aft

Frame 25, looking forward

Frame 17, looking forward

Light buoy

Watertight

Trimming tank

Switch panel

Oil tanks

Diving tank

Diving tank

Trimming tank

Torpedo bulkhead

Regulating tank

Officers' ward-room

Crew's quarters

Regulating tank

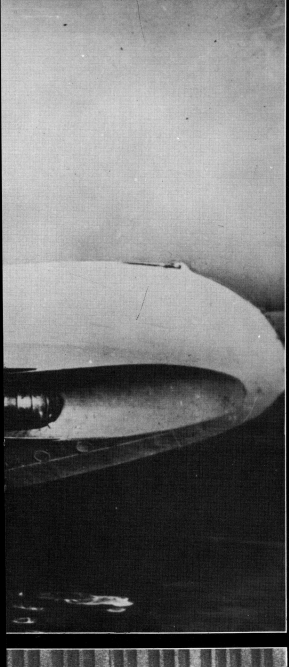

Left, top: *UB1* being lowered into the water by crane. Left, below: *UB13* en route to Antwerp by rail. Above: Transportation of a UBI boat by floating pontoons from Hoboken to Bruges. Right and below: Assembly of *UB7* at Pola, (both photographs show the stern section).

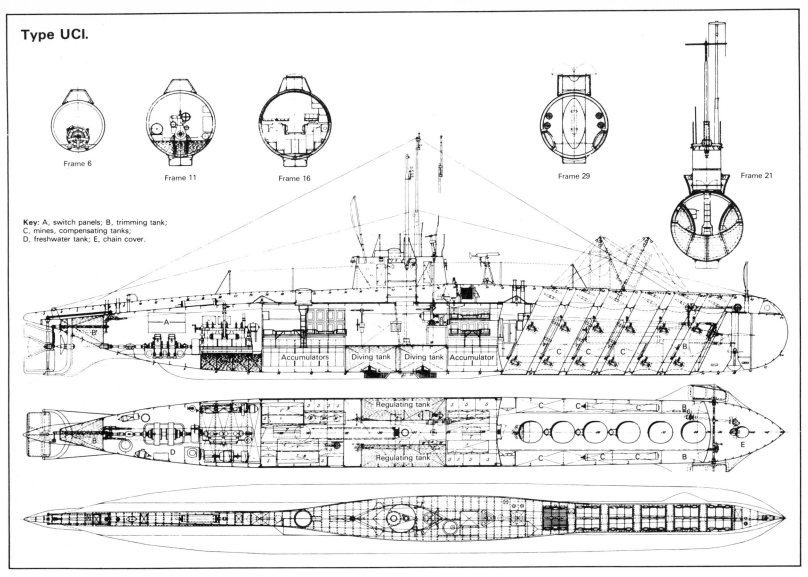

Type UCl.

Frame 6

Frame 11

Frame 16

Frame 29

Frame 21

Key: A, switch panels; B, trimming tank;
C, mines, compensating tanks;
D, freshwater tank; E, chain cover.

Accumulators   Diving tank   Diving tank   Accumulator

Regulating tank

Regulating tank

a building time of only four months was requested. The design and manufacture of a suitable mine (UC/120) and minelaying equipment was a new venture for the UI, and took some time. Type UB was taken as a starting point: the torpedo hatch aft of the conning tower was replaced by a normal entry hatch and the forward section of the boat was redesigned to accommodate mine tubes and 12 mines. The modifications to the boat would increase her resistance and the engine was uprated to compensate for this. The mine tubes were built-in at a sloping angle, so that minelaying could be undertaken while the boat was moving; this, however, caused problems with the pressure-tightness of the area adjacent to the tubes.

The UI completed their work so quickly that by 21 November 1914 they were in a position to award contracts. GW and the KWD were so overloaded

that it was necessary to find a new yard, in addition to AG Weser. AG Vulcan of Hamburg, who had previously applied unsuccessfully for U-boat work, were chosen and, on 23 November 1914, orders for 15 of the new Type UC were placed: *UC1–UC10* from Vulcan, and *UC11–UC15* from AG Weser. Both yards calculated a building time of 5–6 months for the first boat. As Vulcan were new to the business of U-boat building, they were requested on 14 December 1914 to expedite the work and to give it precedence over the building of torpedo-boats already in hand. In fact, the first UC boat, *UC1* left the yard on 26 April 1915. *UC1–UC11*, broken down into components, were sent by rail to Flanders, and *UC12–UC15* were sent to Pola. At the time, it was difficult to predict the rôle that Types UB and UC would play, for there was no previous experience on which to draw; but

U-boat personnel themselves were very sceptical of their possibilities.

Dry-storage minelayers: Type UE
The considerable emphasis placed by the RMA on the building of minelaying U-boats caused the UI to involve itself to a considerable extent in the construction of improved, larger boats of this type. The small UC boats, because of certain constructional limitations (short building time, necessity to transport them by rail, use of ready-made launch engines) were very restricted in their deployment: their storage tubes were underwater, and depth settings for the mines could not be reached for adjustment while at sea. It became imperative to produce a truly ocean-going minelaying U-boat.

As early as 5 January 1915, the UI completed

Above: The completed *UC2* on a crane at AG Vulcan, Hamburg. **Below, left and right:** Minelaying boat *U73* in dock at KWD.

designs for Project 38 — Type UE — a minelaying type of 600–700 tons, with dry storage for 34 mines. Additionally, a small torpedo armament was to be provided. To achieve a short building time, a simple, single hull form was adopted, and a 450hp diesel engine was selected. Construction was to be entrusted to Vulcan and KWD, and the first boat was to be ready in September 1915. Diesel engines were to be prepared so that 10 boats could be completed by the end of 1915. KWD could undertake this new contract only if they could be allowed to suspend work on *U47–U50* until the autumn of 1915, and take auxiliary engines and batteries from submarines just being built by KWD for the first four minelaying boats. GW and AG Weser were so overloaded that they could not contemplate further building.

On 6 January 1915, the RMA suggested that Vulcan and KWD build only 2 boats each — it was not thought necessary to place a large order because it was assumed that the war would not last beyond the autumn of 1915. On the same day, *U71* was ordered from Vulcan, and *U73* from KWD. The other 2 boats, *U72* and *U74*, were ordered on 9 January.

The final concept of the UE type was Dr. Werner's. In his article *Das Hochsee Minenunterseeboot*, Schiffbau vol. XXI/3, 12 November 1919, he describes fully the evolution of this new U-boat type, and only the most important points are given here. Mines were of the new UE/150 type, and were stored astern. They were expelled by cog drive through two tubes of 100cm diameter, each tube being able to carry three mines at a time. The large space devoted to mine storage, weight compensating tank and trim tank meant that the

engine room had to be moved forward into the centre of the boat; the central control room, conning tower and storage batteries were moved even farther foward. As there was now insufficient space for the low torpedo tubes, the two 50cm tubes were sited on the upper deck, a bow tube to port and a stern tube to starboard. The 8.8cm U-boat gun was fitted abaft the conning tower. Trimming now became difficult, and the requisite submerged stability was achieved by fitting a 50-ton box keel beneath the pressure hull. In order to achieve the desired range of 8,000 nautical miles at 7 knots, saddle tanks with fuel bunkers were fitted on both sides. There can be no doubt that the diesel plant was not powerful enough for these large boats, the displacement of which during successive planning stages had risen to 750 tons. In rough seas, they dipped deeply into the waves, which slowed them

Type UE (U71—U80).

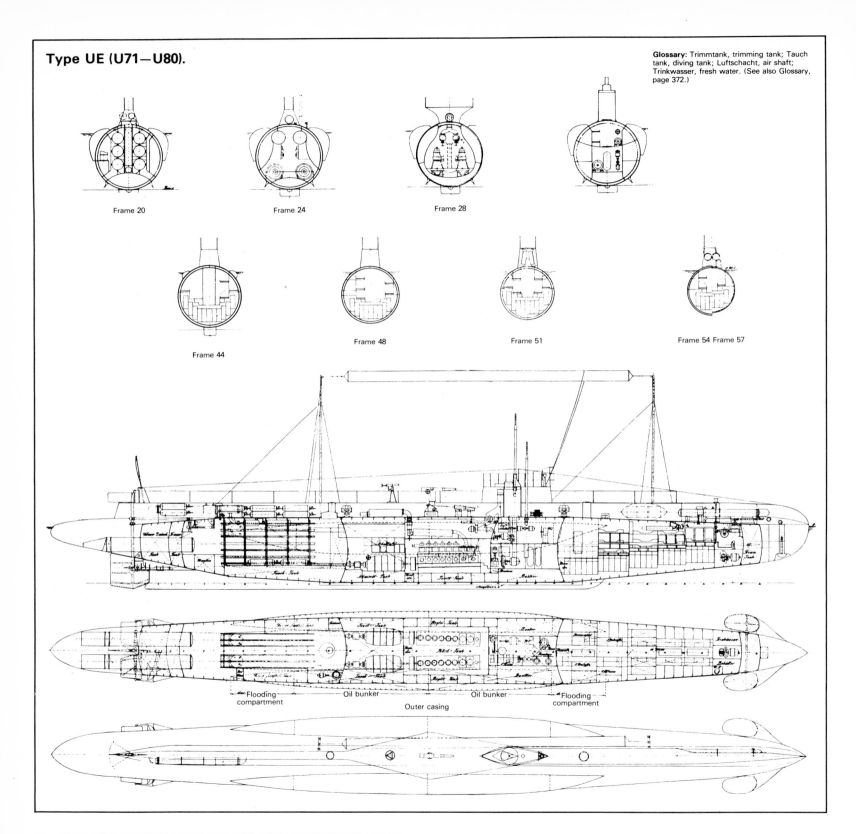

Frame 20

Frame 24

Frame 28

Frame 44

Frame 48

Frame 51

Frame 54 Frame 57

Flooding compartment

Oil bunker

Oil bunker

Flooding compartment

Outer casing

Type UE frame lines.

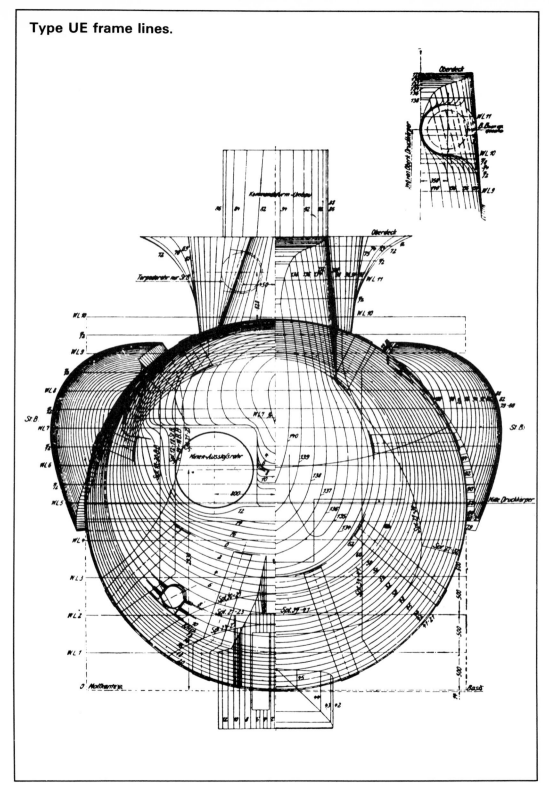

down even more. The designers were well aware of this disadvantage, but there was nothing they could do about it — all German submarine construction was governed by the availability of diesel engines and the boats were wanted in only six months' time.

On 20 February 1915, the UI suggested that more U-boats be built by GW, AG Weser and Vulcan. On the 27th, the RMA (having accepted that the war might continue beyond the autumn of 1915) authorized the building of 6 more Type UE boats by Vulcan and 6 Type UF boats by GW and AG Weser. Type UF, a variant of Type UE, was developed because of the need to have a larger boat armed with torpedoes, to be produced in a relatively short time. On 9 March 1915, the 6 Type UE boats, *U75–U80*, were officially ordered from Vulcan, the contract stipulating that they be completed between 20 November 1915 and 20 February 1916.

The 6 Type UF boats, however, were not to be built. Instead, the RMA informed the Admiralty staff on 2 March 1915, that 3 Ms U-boats of *U51* type, *U63–U65*, should be ordered from GW. The building of the further 3 torpedo-armed U-boats could be discontinued because AG Weser would deliver *U57–U59* five months earlier than had been anticipated. All 6 Ms U-boats would have the 1,150hp two-stroke engines originally ordered by the Russians and now almost complete, which meant that a quick delivery could be guaranteed. In the case of GW's 3 boats, *U63–U65*, a further saving of time was achieved by simplifying construction (including a reduction in the number of diving tanks). By these means, the 3 Ms U-boats were built in the incredibly short time of eleven months, an achievement that was to remain unsurpassed.

PLANNING AND CONSTRUCTION, 1915–16

On 4 February 1915, the German Government declared the waters around the British Isles to be a 'War Zone' in which, from 18 February, commercial traffic to and from Britain would be attacked without warning or discrimination. (This declaration was in reply to the British blockade of Germany.) However, it would be impossible to enforce this unless sufficient boats were made available and this was impossible in the early part of 1915.

The following figures provided by the UI in April 1915, indicate progressive monthly totals of available U-boats (excluding the ten Type UE minelaying boats) against an estimated monthly U-boat loss.

1 April 1915:	27	1 January 1916:	30
1 July 1915:	27	1 April 1916:	36
1 October 1915:	28	1 July 1916:	40

Hence, on 1 July 1916, the establishment stood at 40 U-boats, 32 short of the number allowed for in pre-war estimates.

The construction plan for the building of larger U-boats was greatly hindered by the fact that some yards were relatively new to this work. Foundries, firms supplying engines, etc., all had to contend with severe technical problems. The yards, too, had been deprived of trained workers by the mobilization of the Army, and these vacancies could not be filled adequately by personnel fit only for garrison duties, or by women. Delivery dates, therefore, suffered considerably: delivery times for *U57–U62* (AG Weser) were exceeded by two to four months, and those for *U71* and *U75–U80* (Vulcan), by two-and-a-half to five months. Throughout the war, U-boats delivered on time were the exception rather than the rule. It is odd, therefore, that the UI did not urge an acceleration of the U-boat construction programme, but contented itself (in a memorandum published in April 1915) with formulating a programme spread over a very long period (up to 1924!), an attitude of mind more suggestive of peace than of war. This programme laid down the following requirements. To carry on the blockade of Britain, excluding the most northerly part, 48 boats with a performance equalling that of the Ms U-boats were seen as necessary. Attempts would have to be made, however, to simplify this type and, if possible, reduce the displacement (600–650 tons) somewhat to keep down the replacement cost of these boats, which were the ones most frequently sunk by enemy action. A further 12 U-boats were

required in the Baltic, with a further 12 at the disposal of the Flag Officer, U-Boats (FdU).

According to the UI, to provide these 72 boats, 32 extra boats would have to be laid down. In the first batch of these, it would be impossible to contemplate any alteration to the Ms type already in use, because of the lengthy delivery time for new engines.

MAN could produce only a pair of diesel engines per month, and it was therefore necessary to call upon other firms such as GW and Sulzer for engine production. GW and AG Weser would each be commissioned to build 3 more U-boats of the Ms type, equipped with MAN engines, to be delivered between July 1916 and January 1917. The UI would be requested to look further into the possibilities of a simplified 650-ton type, and investigate delivery times. For this, Vulcan, Hamburg, AG Weser, GW and Blohm & Voss were considered; appropriate diesel engines would come from MAN, Sulzer and GW. The contracts were to be distributed in such a way that all 26 U-boats of this new type could be ready by the early part of 1919, which meant, roughly, a delivery of 1 boat per month.

To wage an effective blockade in the Atlantic and in the northerly approaches to the War Zone, greater performance was required from U-boats — particularly high surface speed, adequate surface

cruising speed, long range, adequate engine power, and an ability to stay longer at sea, which meant better living conditions on board. The UI, thereupon, delivered its Project 31, a plan based on operational experience of the war up to that time. A total of 46 boats with these characteristics would be required, and would have next priority.

Initial planning would be carried out by KWD and GW in the shortest possible time, so that orders for more boats of this type could be contracted out. Delivery dates were to be determined by the availability of the new 1,500hp diesel engines, three sets of which were to be ordered as quickly as possible from GW and MAN. Thus, shortly after completion of the initial work by GW and KWD, 3 boats of Project 31 would be ordered from each yard for delivery in 1917–1918. Construction of the remaining 40 boats would then be so organized that, after delivery of the new 650-ton boats had been completed, 1 large boat would be delivered monthly. In this way, all the large boats would be delivered by the end of 1922.

Finally, in the light of experience gained from the UA boat and the UB boats, a special U-boat of 200–300 tons was to be developed for coastal operations. Compared with 'offensive' boats, this new type would have a lesser surface speed and surface range, torpedo and artillery armament,

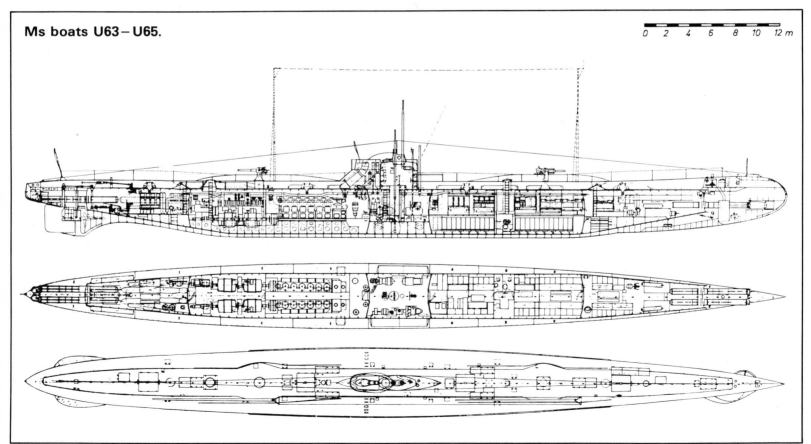

Ms boats U63–U65.

0 2 4 6 8 10 12 m

duration and complement. A total of 18 of these coastal U-boats was thought to be necessary for the North Sea and Baltic. Orders were to be so placed as to achieve delivery of all of them by 1923–24. The U-Boat Programme thus envisaged construction of 154 boats, excluding very small UB and UC boats, minelayers and experimental boats. Further development was seen in terms of steam propulsion for higher surface speeds. The following was noted in the memorandum of the plan.

'Despite the main disadvantages for submarines — heat, very large seals in the pressure hull, and high fuel consumption — the construction of steam-driven boats must be seriously investigated and, ideally, in two versions:

(a) Steam/electric drive.

(b) Steam/caustic-soda drive (single unit drive).

It is suggested that (b) be pursued by AG Weser immediately after the conclusion of the war. But research must be carried out not only on the steam/caustic-soda project: there is also the need to investigate the steam/electric method of propulsion, because, if high surface speeds are demanded, it seems unlikely that a diesel engine, in the present state of the art developing at best 2,000hp, will give a U-boat a surface speed in excess of 20 knots.'

This long-term programme could have no effect on the conflict at that time, early 1915, when it was

generally assumed that the war could not last long. It was intended principally as a political weapon for the post-war period. Nevertheless, some of the ideas expressed were to have an important effect on U-boat development. In an introductory argument to the memorandum, the UI stated:

'Just as the U-boat is proving itself to be a main weapon in the war against England, so will it play a vital rôle in the future if it forms the basis for a U-boat fleet designed for blockade against England as, being a positive deterrent that cannot be overcome by threats, it will be a positive force for peace. Although this point does not invalidate the need for battlecruisers and battleships, no matter how the war ends, the building up of U-boat fleets is even more urgent than the building of these other fleets; beside the direct threat to English and Irish trade routes posed by our U-boats besieging all their harbours and trade routes — with later U-boat development permitting offensive operations against England to be taken even further afield — a war against Germany will be very uninviting for England, and we, behind our bulwark of a strong U-boat fleet, will be able to build our surface fleets up in comparative security to take our place as a world power.'

On 15 May 1915, the UI requested the immediate building of 11 Ms U-boats, with no gaps permitted

in the delivery of them from the autumn of 1916. Following this, on 17 May, GW were commissioned to build U63–U65, which had already been decided upon. On 16 June 1915, the building of these 11 additional boats was authorized by the RMA. No decision was made, however, concerning the long-term building programme corresponding to suggestions in the UI memorandum. GW and AG Weser competed for the new contract. GW stated on 23 June 1915 that MAN engines could be delivered for 6 Ms U-boats, but the remainder would have to have GW engines. On 24 June, GW received an order for 6 Ms boats, U81–U86. The remaining 5 boats, U87–U91 were awarded to KWD on 1 July 1915, because prices and delivery times from AG Weser were excessive and they wanted 400–500 more workers with the cost to be borne by the Navy, who regarded these conditions as unacceptable.

On 13 August 1915, KWD's contract was increased to 6 boats, as diesels for an extra boat (U92) were available from Vulcan, who had been building them on an experimental basis. As there would be capacity for more Mobilization boats at AG Weser and GW from the autumn of 1916, the UI ordered 6 Ms boats from each of these yards on 1 September 1915. This meant that on 15 September 1915, U93–U98 had been authorized

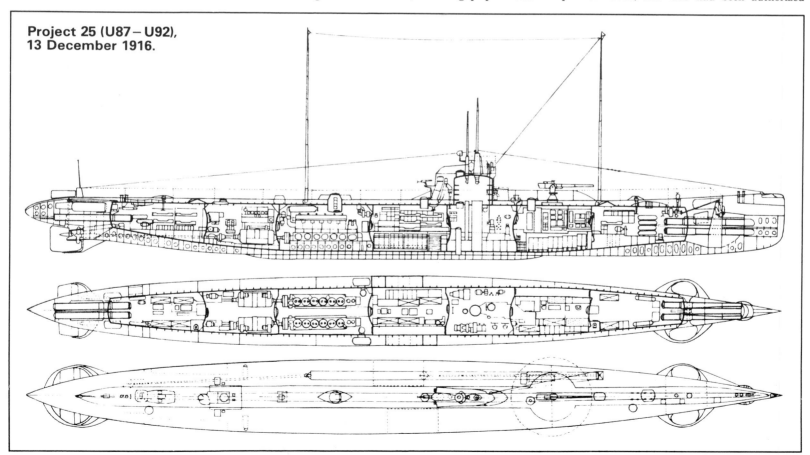

**Project 25 (U87–U92),
13 December 1916.**

from GW, and *U99–U104* from AG Weser. Clearly, AG Weser's demands had been settled.

After a lengthy period, *U96–U98* received newly-built two-stroke diesel engines from GW; the other boats received four-stroke diesels from MAN.

The development of the Ms U-boats was characterized by the adoption of six 50cm torpedo tubes, four submerged bow, two submerged stern (fitted by GW, from *U93* onwards); the fitting of one 10.5cm U-boat gun instead of two 8.8cm guns (fitted by KWD from *U87* onwards, and by GW from *U93* onwards); and the altering of the rounded bow profile to a sharp, clipper-like bow (fitted by GW, from *U81* onwards), with which it was hoped to break through submarine nets more easily. The step in the cross-section of the upper deck was eliminated, and the bulwarks were drawn upwards with a rounded fairing into the deck (fitted by KWD from *U43*, by GW from *U63*, but not in UD boats *U66–U70*). With regard to diesel engines, it had been hoped to go over to the MAN six-cylinder, 1,200hp four-stroke engine, or the GW two-stroke, but the general shortage meant that whatever was available had to be used.

In June 1915, KWD had been instructed to expedite Project 31, for which the UI was responsible; it was hoped to be able to start building U-boats of this new type as soon as possible. In the meantime, following the sinking of the Cunard liner *Lusitania* on 7 May 1915, which brought sharp reaction from neutral countries, particularly the United States, attacks on large passenger liners were prohibited, and U-boat blockade activities were considerably restricted. A new crisis with the United States occurred after the sinking of the liner *Arabic* in August 1915 and, on 18 September, U-boat operations in the English Channel and Western Approaches were suspended. The High Seas Fleet and the Naval Corps in Flanders also suspended aggressive activities against merchant shipping in the North Sea. The U-boat menace was now notably reduced. It was thought that the U-boat campaign could still have considerable success in minelaying and against merchant ships if the U-boats were armoured and mounted sufficiently heavy artillery. By the end of 1915, it was thought that unconditional U-boat warfare could re-commence during the spring of 1916.

Enlarged coastal U-boats: Types UBII and UCII
Although the small UB type of boats had fulfilled the rôle for which they were designed, their duration and armament were not equal to the increasing demands made on U-boats as the war progressed. A particular disadvantage was the single-shaft propulsion unit; in the event of an engine breakdown, the boat was completely helpless. It became obvious that, when new contracts for small U-boats were being considered, this type would not be retained. In April 1915, therefore, the UI announced its Project 39, for an enlarged coastal U-boat with a two-shaft drive, greater surface speed and greatly increased surface range: later it was designated Type UBII.

The submerged range was enlarged and the resistance caused by the greater profile of the outer hull necessitated a considerable enlargement of battery

capacity, which was achieved by using Type 20 MAS 820/5. All the storage batteries were placed forward of the central diving tanks so that the engine installation, which was now much heavier, would stay in equilibrium.

The armament was increased by using 50cm G torpedoes, with twice as many reloads as hitherto, and by the fitting of a 5cm gun for surface use. Unlike the UB type (later called Type UBI), the torpedo tubes were fitted one above the other in order to provide better bow lines for surface travel. A second periscope, manned from the central control room, a two-masted wireless aerial and forward hydroplanes corrected other weaknesses in Type UBI.

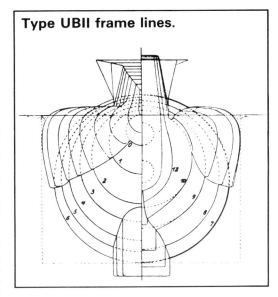

Type UBII frame lines.

These improvements could only be achieved by significantly increasing the weight of the boats (270 tons surface displacement), so it was no longer demanded that they be transportable by rail. This, in turn, meant that restrictions on the diameter of the pressure hull were no longer necessary, so saddle tanks were fitted to the pressure hull to house the greatly-increased fuel-oil supply, and these brought the overall beam to 4.36m. (Subsequently, with the U-boat playing a greater rôle in the Mediterranean, it was demanded that the boats be transportable by rail in separate components. Too wide for the gauge of the railways, they had to be broken down into longitudinal sections of appropriate size.)

On 20 April 1915, the UI announced its plans for the commissioning of these Type UBII boats, all of which were to be completed by the end of 1915. KWD, GW and Vulcan were not considered because of lack of skilled staff or delays in the building of Ms and UE boats. AG Weser could handle a maximum of 6 Type UBII only, so that the use of a new yard seemed unavoidable. Blohm & Voss, who until now had taken care not to involve themselves in U-boat construction, agreed to undertake the building of boats of this type 'in the present urgent

circumstances'. Daimler, Korting and Benz agreed to manufacture the 140hp diesel engines for 17 boats in the specified time. Initially, 6 boats were to be ordered from B&V, and 6 from AG Weser, who demanded an additional 200 workers. The RMA gave its assent, but it was decided that only as many boats should be ordered as could be completed by the end of 1915, as no future was seen for this type of submarine in peacetime.

Meanwhile, Schichau of Elbing had asked to be considered for U-boat building, but had been rejected because they were already building a large number of torpedo boats, in addition to the battle-cruiser *Lützow*, and would not be able to meet delivery dates of their important existing war programme. To give Schichau a new type of U-boat to build would overload them completely, and to provide them with a larger work force would be less productive than supplying the workers to yards that were accustomed to U-boat constructions. So, on 30 April 1915, 6 Type UBII boats, *UB18–UB23*, were ordered from B&V and, on 1 May 1915, 6 boats, *UB24–UB29*, were ordered from AG Weser.

In the summer of 1915, it became evident that the war would last into 1916, and the question of follow-up contracts for small U-boats became acute. On 1 June, the Reiherstieg Yard at Hamburg let it be known that they would like to undertake U-boat work and, on 22 June, the UI decided to use them for the building of more Type UBII, possibly as a subcontractor to B&V.

The Shipyard Department of the Navy had doubts about the technical ability of Reiherstieg to build complete U-boats: they had no first-class construction staff, and the number and quality of their skilled workers were insufficient for U-boat construction. A further problem, which was only gradually resolved during the course of the war, was the lack of senior naval officials for supervising and overseeing building construcion in private yards. But the UI's proviso that Reiherstieg be subcontractor to B&V was approved. On 7 July 1915, the building by B&V of 6 more Type UBII boats, *UB30–UB41*, was authorized, and the contract was placed on 22 July. A further 6 boats, *UB42–UB47*, were awarded to AG Weser as a follow-up contract for 1916.

With the restriction imposed on offensive U-boat warfare in the summer of 1915, and its virtual cessation in the autumn, the significance of the minelaying U-boat became more prominent. The small UC type, later Type UCI, could not be considered for future construction, for the same reasons that Type UBI was unsuitable.

In the summer of 1915, the UI published its Project 41 for a larger minelaying U-boat of 400 tons, with wet storage facilities for 18 UC/200 mines, in 6 shafts situated in the forward part of the boat. In addition, three torpedo tubes for 50cm torpedoes (two surface bow and one submerged stern) and an 8.8cm U-boat gun were carried. In the interests of better aiming, neither angled tubes nor torpedo tube cowlings were fitted. Instead, pressure-tight, above-water torpedo tubes were fitted alongside the mine shafts, which projected from the pressure hull. The platform for the 8.8cm U-boat gun was positioned in a well between the

Type UBII.

Glossary: Trimmtank, trimming tank; Treibölbunker, fuel-oil bunker; Tauchtank, diving tank; Akkumulatoren, batteries or accumulators; Munition, ammunition; Vorderer, forward; Trinkwasser, fresh water; reglertank, regulating tank; Kleider u Wasche, wardrobe and wash-room; Kojen, berths; Proviant spinde, store cupboards; Luftpatronen, air cartridges; Mannschaft spinde, crew's cupboards. (See also Glossary, page 372.)

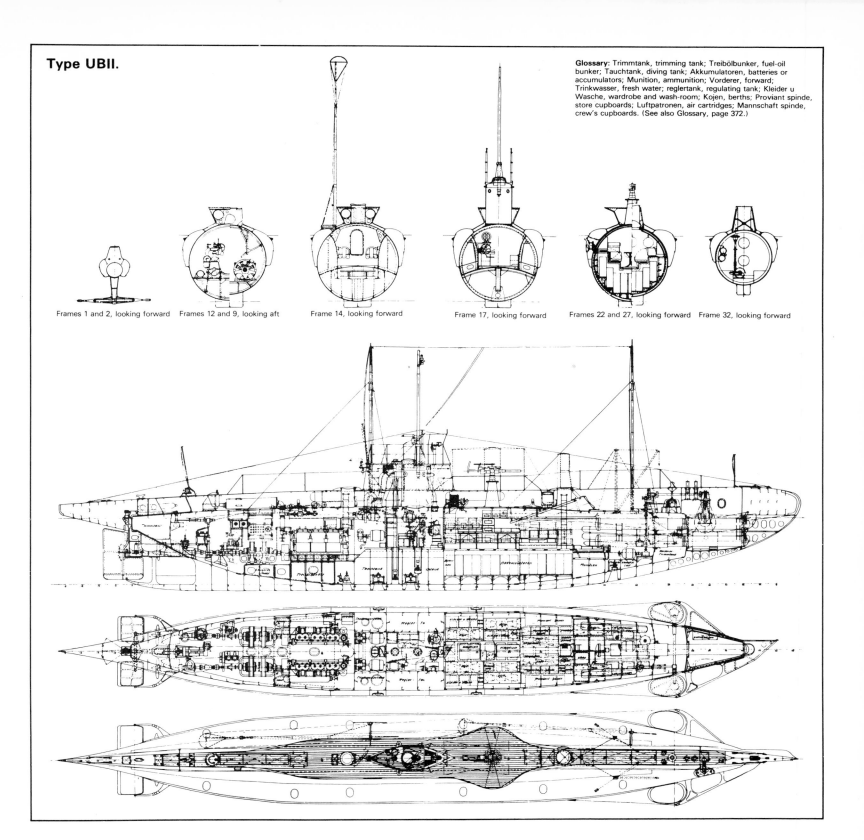

Frames 1 and 2, looking forward   Frames 12 and 9, looking aft   Frame 14, looking forward   Frame 17, looking forward   Frames 22 and 27, looking forward   Frame 32, looking forward

Type UCII.

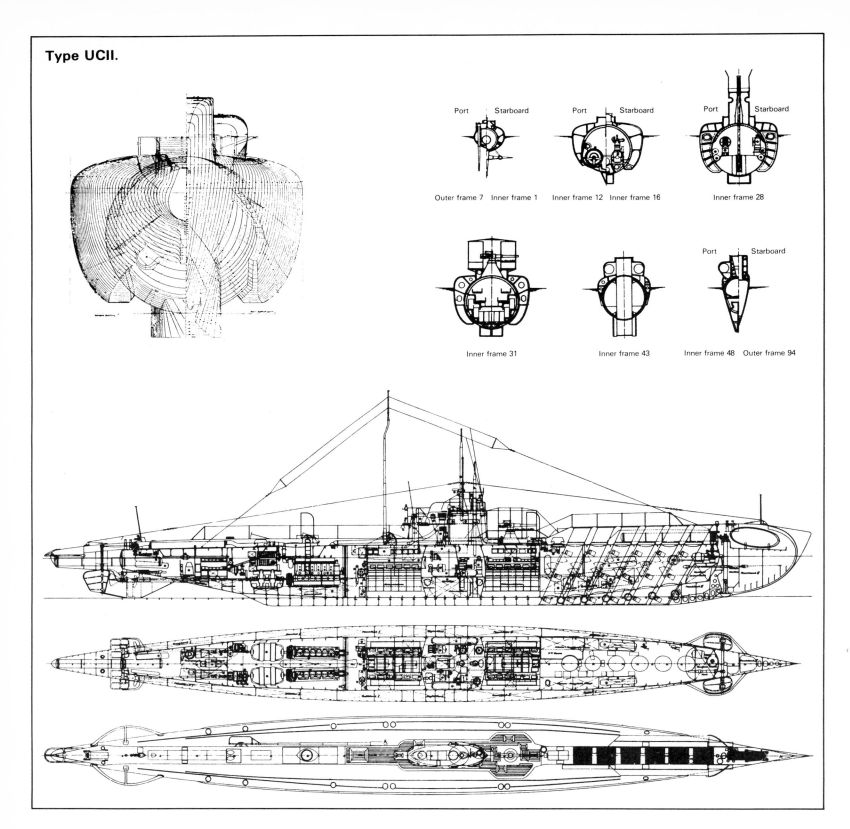

Outer frame 7 Inner frame 1   Inner frame 12 Inner frame 16   Inner frame 28

Inner frame 31   Inner frame 43   Inner frame 48 Outer frame 94

raised fore section and the conning tower, and tended to be awash in rough seas. To improve surface handling, a return had been made to the double hull principle, but the outer skin did not completely surround the pressure hull, being attached to it from below. A relatively wide, 100cm-diameter ballast keel was necessary because of the mine shafts projecting below. Two 250hp diesel engines from MAN (later also from Körting and Daimler) and two 230hp electric motors were provided. The storage battery, consisting of two 62-cell 26 MAS units, was sited under the living quarters forward and aft of the control room.

A strong influence on the decision to increase the displacement, was the requirement that these minelaying U-boats be able to reach the Austro-Hungarian U-boat bases in the Mediterranean by sea, thereby obviating the vexatious problem of transportation by rail. A building time of eight months for the first boat was assumed: if a start were made immediately, the first boat of this new Type UCII could be ready early in 1916.

On 15 July 1915, the UI authorized contracts for 8 of these improved UC boats, in addition to a considerable number (20) of the UBII boats.

However, on 20 August, the Shipyard Department suggested that only 24 UCII boats be built, by B&V and Vulcan. GW and AG Weser would have to delay current building (*U81–U86* and 4 torpedo-boats plus a light cruiser) to cope with an additional contract. On 29 August 1915, the Secretary of State in the RMA decided that B&V should be required to build 9 minelaying U-boats (*UC16–UC24*), that Vulcan should build a similar number (*UC25–UC33*), and that these should be delivered between March and June 1916. Following the cessation of the U-boat blockade, the UI recommended further building of the new Type UCII minelaying U-boats, over and above the numbers already ordered. Additionally, consideration was given to converting UBI boats to UCI boats, but it was evident that the considerable number of necessary changes would so delay this project that not a lot of use would come of it. On 9 November 1915, the RMA gave its approval to the continued construction of the Type UCII, 'as many as can be built by the end of September 1916'. On 20 November, the UI ordered 21 boats of this type: 6 from B&V (*UC34–UC39*); 9 from Vulcan (*UC40–UC45*) and 6 from AG Weser (*UC46–UC48*).

At the beginning of 1916, the increasing significance of minelaying U-boats led to the personal intervention of the Secretary of State in the RMA, Grand Admiral von Tirpitz. He ordered that a careful check be made to determine how many UCII boats could be made ready by the end of 1916, if all new shipbuilding and torpedo-boat projects scheduled for completion after 1 October 1916, and all new U-boat building projects scheduled for completion after 1 January 1917 were put back. The answer from the UI, on 8 January 1916, was 31 boats. These additional UCII boats were therefore ordered on 11 January 1916 and were allocated thus: *UC49–UC54* to GW; *UC55–UC60* to KWD; *UC61–UC64* to AG Weser; *UC65–UC73* to B&V; and *UC74–UC79* to Vulcan. This represented the first large order, which brought with it, especially at B&V, the advantages of mass production. Originally, von Tirpitz had placed little trust in U-boats, but as the war progressed he had become strongly convinced of their indispensable rôle and, with this large order, made his feelings known. (His successor, Admiral von Capelle, was not initially inclined to agree with him.)

A Type UCII minelaying boat in dock at KWD.

Larger U-boats and Type UBIII

For the UI, 1915 was a year of tremendous planning activity, engendered partly by changing war tactics and partly by their efforts to improve Types UB, UC and UE, the designs of which had been worked out in the shortest possible time at the beginning of hostilities. In a memorandum dated April 1915, the UI emphasized the importance it attached to the U-boat blockade of Britain by announcing an enlarged U-boat, Project 31. The former TI had originally formulated this design in the autumn of 1913, to some extent as an alternative to the steam/caustic-soda project of AG Weser, but it was to usher in the next generation of U-boats for the Imperial Navy.

The most significant departure from current boats, which hitherto had been built to the design of Type *U43* (Project 25), was the shape of the pressure hull, the cross-section of which was altered to horizontal twin-circles, with a pressure-tight passageway between. This extended from the control room to the forward and after sections of the boat. It was, in fact, an extension of the control room, and housed the most important valves and controls. As in *U43*, the frames were exterior, but were spaced farther apart. The constructional strength of the pressure hull was examined mathematically, and was thought sufficient to merit the new demands. A diving depth of 75m was estimated. The new pressure hull form rendered it perfectly feasible to increase the battery capacity (in three components) by 50 per cent over those in existing U-boats, which, although the boat was larger, would give a submerged range of 120 nautical miles at 5 knots, as against the 90 nautical miles at 5 knots of *U43*, and would increase the submerged top speed from 10 to 11 knots. The use of new 1,500hp diesel engines would also improve the surface performance considerably. A maximum surface speed of 18.5 knots was calculated, while the surface range was slightly greater than in the case of *U43*. The torpedo armament consisted of four bow and two stern tubes of 50cm diameter, as in *U43*. Additionally, a twin torpedo tube, with swivel mounting, was fitted on the upper deck. The artillery armament was similarly improved over that of *U43*, by fitting a second 8.8cm U-boat gun abaft the conning tower. These very comprehensive features meant that the new boat was 165 tons heavier than *U43* (875 tons instead of 710 tons); 5–7m longer (70–72m instead of 65m.) and 1m wider (7.2m instead of 6.2m); and cost 3.75 million marks (instead of 3 million marks). A further slight lengthening of the boat to approximately 75m would improve the lines of this new type, and give a surface speed of 19 knots.

The Shipyard Department gave its support to Project 31, but were not sure about the proposed G/7 torpedoes, as the question of appropriate U-boat torpedoes was still under discussion. The necessity for a second 8.8cm U-boat gun was not thought to have been proved. It was decided, however, that a thorough look at the whole project from a building point of view should be made by KWD. The governing factor in U-boat building was

the engine, and it was essential to wait and see how the diesel engines faired in *U19* and *U26*, the first boats to have had them installed. As an alternative, KWD would determine the feasibility of a project based on *U43*, but with additional upper-deck torpedo tubes. However, it was mid-May before all the dates for Project 31 had been sent to KWD, for their evaluation by 1 August 1914. At about the same time, GW received a similar task (Project 31a), to investigate a special 1,500hp diesel combination (see page 35). The outbreak of war delayed further evaluation of this project.

On 9 September 1914, the UI had authorized KWD to build, in addition to the 5 Ms U-boats *U46–U50*, two U-boats of Project 31. The RMA announced on 14 September that it was proposed that KWD should build two of these U-boats, but that Danzig should accelerate the preparation of the necessary plans, and produce them. However, the performance of diesel U-boats to date, and the initial general operational experience, indicated that a comprehensive examination of this particular project was necessary on the part of the UI. On 16 June 1915, the RMA requested the UI to carry out a comprehensive investigation of Project 31, with the other departments in the light of wartime operations. A boat could then be built in

accordance with this project: KWD was apparently destined for the construction task.

The result was a new plan for a large Ms U-boat (Project 42). Certain details of the former (Project 31) boat (new pressure-hull shape and surface torpedo tubes) were omitted, which meant that, with the enlarging of bunker capacity, the surface range was increased from 8,000 to 10,000 nautical miles at 8 knots. In the course of the project, surface displacement increased to 1,200 tons, length to 82m and beam to 7.5m. In order to give such a large boat the hoped-for surface speed of 18.5 knots, it was necessary to provide, in addition to diesel engines with an optimum performance of 1,650–1,750hp, two 450hp diesel dynamos. The freqently suggested arrangement of two diesel engines in tandem acting on the same shaft had been rejected by the UI designers for technical reasons, and because such an arrangement was considered unreliable. Commensurate with the rôle envisaged for this boat, i.e., as en offensive U-cruiser against merchant shipping, the armament was strengthened to two 10.5cm guns.

On 9 December 1915, the UI was able to present the new Project 42, on 22 December it was discussed at the RMA, and on 3 January 1916 the UI was requested to obtain prices and delivery

Right: *U135* (Project 42) running trials.

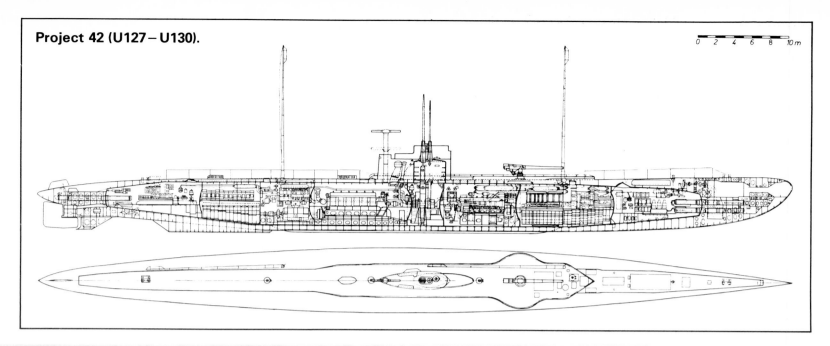

Project 42 (U127 – U130).

0 2 4 6 8 10 m

times for 12 boats of this type. On 11 January 1916, however, following the restoration of the long-delayed scheme for building 31 UCII boats, the possibilities of building Project 42 seemed bleak. Subsequently, on 14 January, the RMA requested the UI to determine afresh how many Project 42 boats might be constructed by the various yards. On 26 March, approval was given for a contract to be placed with KWD for 2 boats of the new type. The request from the Howaldt Yard in Kiel to participate was refused on the grounds of their lack of experience in building such a new, large U-boat. On 25 May 1916, the UI was in possession of tenders for 12 U-boats of Project 42 type, from GW, AG Weser and Vulcan. The UI recommended that the RMA use only KWD and GW, and suggested that orders be placed at fixed prices. However, the RMA decided to make use of AG Weser also. On 27 May 1916, 4 U-boats of the new type (*U127–U130*) were ordered from GW, 4 (*U131–U134*) from AG Weser, and 4 (*U135–U138*) from KWD.

By the autumn of 1915, a new design for an improved Ms U-boat had been completed, under the designation 'Project 43'. Its external lines were similar to GW's *U93* type (raked bow, set-back conning tower, rounded cross-section), but had external pressure hull frames like the KWD's other Ms U-boats and was, therefore, approximately 40 tons lighter. Project 43 also envisaged increased bunkerage to provide a 27 per cent greater surface range of 11,470 nautical miles at 8 knots, as against the 9,020 nautical miles at 8 knots of *U93*. In some respects, this type may be seen as a smaller version of Project 42: the internal fittings corresponded to those of *U87–U92*, except for a change of position between the after batteries and the control room (analogous to the development of Type IX from Type IA). The drawings for *U87–U92* could, for the most part, be used.

KWD was heavily committed with existing contracts and with Project 42, and there seemed little likelihood of their building this new type. On 6 October 1915, Schichau of Elbing offered to build 2 U-boats at their own expense, because of the official refusal to permit them to participate in U-boat construction. This was very much to the liking of the UI, as it presented the possibility of having the new type built without interrupting current building, and might stimulate other private yards to take on Ms boats of Project 43, which would introduce them to the construction principles of the large Project 42 boats. The two boats were ordered from Schichau, but the firm was so heavily engaged in torpedo-boat construction, and lacking experience and materials that building was very much delayed. So on 22 September 1916, the boats were designated 'war' boats *U115* and *U116*, orders for them were placed officially with Schichau and delivery was scheduled for the beginning of 1918.

In their memorandum of April 1915, the UI had called for a simplified U-boat of approximately 600 tons, for deployment in the blockade against Britain. The shortage of Ms U-boats was occasioned by their relatively long building time and the use of the 1,200hp engines, delivery times of which inevitably determined orders for U-boats. The renewal of unrestricted submarine warfare

early in 1916 made imperative the development of a medium-sized, torpedo-armed U-boat that could be built quickly. The Type UBII coastal boat was too lightly armed for this purpose, and its range confined it to the North Sea and the English Channel. The new torpedo U-boats would need to be capable of operating around the British Isles, and in the Mediterranean.

Type UCII (Project 41) served as a prototype. A new profile was given to the forward section of the boat, the minelaying shafts were replaced by a torpedo compartment with four 50cm submerged torpedo tubes and six G/6 torpedoes. Apart from this, the successful UCII construction was hardly changed, but as an improvement a larger conning tower with two periscopes was fitted, as in the Ms U-boats, and a pressure-tight bulkhead separated the control room from the conning tower. This was Project 44, later to be designated Type UBIII.

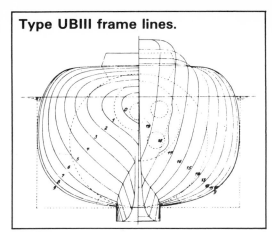

Type UBIII frame lines.

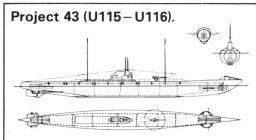

Project 43 (U115 – U116).

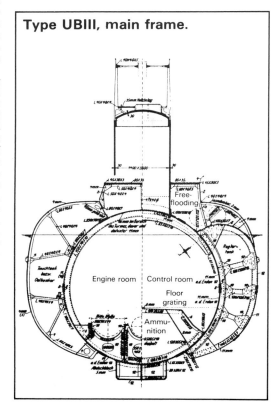

Type UBIII, main frame.

Free-flooding

Engine room · Control room

Floor grating

Ammu-nition

Type UBIII.

Glossary: Unteroffizier-Raum, NCOs' quarters; Akkumulatoren-Raum, battery room; Trinkwasser-Tank, fresh water tank; Munition, ammunition; Offizier-Raum, officers' quarters; Mannschafts-Raum, crew's quarters; Tauchtank, diving tank; Zusatzbunker, auxiliary bunker; Trimmtank, trimming tank; Reglertank, regulating tank; Torpedo Zwischen-Tank, torpedo intermediate tank; Kettenkasten, chain cover. (See also Glossary, page 372.)

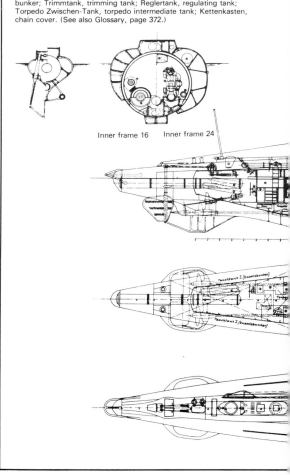

Inner frame 16   Inner frame 24

During the design stage, in order to improve a rather poor surface speed while increasing the surface displacement by only a modest 20 tons, the UI decided to install 450–550hp engines instead of the 300hp diesels as fitted in Type UCII. Range was to be increased by greater bunkerage, which meant that the length and beam needed to be increased until the boat finally displaced 500 tons, like the *U16*. The increase in offensive power (larger calibre torpedoes, two more torpedoes carried plus an 8.8cm U-boat gun), was achieved at the expense of a considerable loss in submerged speed and submerged range; this was caused by the battery being 40 per cent smaller and yielding an output of only 72 per cent of that in *U16*. There were, however, certain improvements brought about by more modern building methods and, in any case, it should be remembered that the submerged resistance of this boat was significantly greater than

that of the older U-boats. In the light of operational experience, hitherto, this was held to be quite acceptable.

The RMA had intended to award contracts for the new type in March 1916, but preparation of the final construction drawings took the UI longer than had been envisaged. So, on 19 April 1916, the UI was requested to secure delivery of the more important components (chiefly engines) for 24 boats, well in advance of the actual ordering of the boats. Negotiations with the yards began in May 1916, and the UI received tenders from GW, B&V, AG Weser and Vulcan. On 2 May, 6 UBIII boats were ordered from B&V (*UB48–UB53*); 6 from AG Weser (*UB54–UB59*); 6 from Vulcan (*UB60–UB65*) and 6 from GW (*UB66–UB71*). Building was to commence after the UBII and UCII contracts had been concluded, with delivery of the last of the order scheduled for April 1917. However, the

customary building delays occurred, and the last of the boats did not leave the first three yards until August 1917, those from GW in November 1917. Time and time again, the yards — knowingly, or with false optimism in their own production capabilities — made delivery promises they were unable to keep, and no steps were taken to prevent this until the beginning of 1918.

The construction programme for the 800-ton minelaying boats *U71–U80* had been rushed through in a short time, and this factor manifested itself in the numerous defects and unreliability of the boats, and led, quite early on, to the desire for an improvement of this type. Following the successful UCII construction, there was not the same degree of urgency for a large minelaying boat, and, initially, it was considered part of the long-term plan. The urgent need for a boat equipped with dry storage for mines did not crop up until the

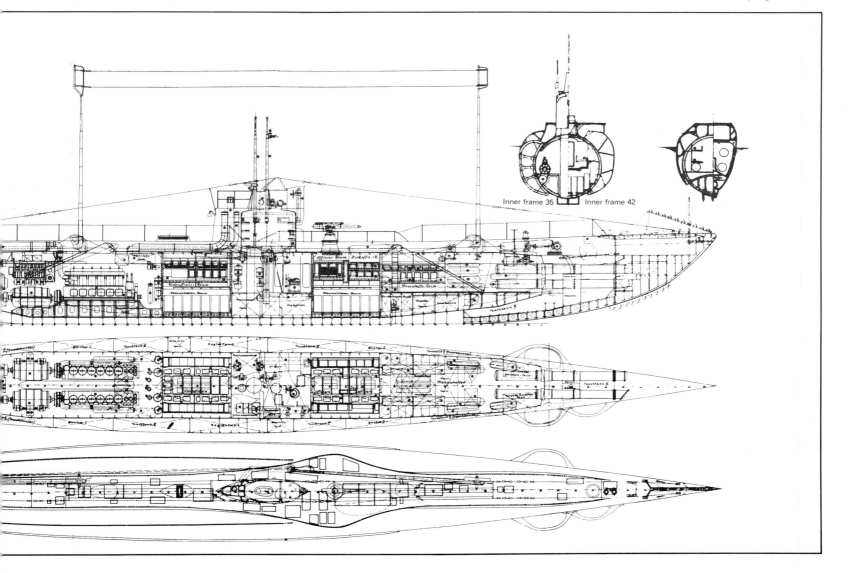

Inner frame 35   Inner frame 42

beginning of 1916, when it was planned to resume the campaign against merchant shipping. This UI Project 45 depended, in its principal features (internal fittings, and all structural members, especially external frames), on Project 43. The stern compartment, however, requiring space for mine storage, was changed and was based upon that in *U71–U80*. Armament consisted of two 10.5cm U-boat guns and four submerged bow torpedo tubes (six G/6 torpedoes) and a minimum of 32 and a maximum of 40 UC/200 mines. Surface speed was 14 knots, and surface range was 5–6,000 nautical miles at 9 knots. The submerged range was less than that of the Ms U-boats because mine storage had increased the displacement to approximately 1,000 tons, but battery capacity had remained the same. The length was increased to 77m.

The UI assumed that, bearing in mind the quantity of engines available, 9 boats of this type could be built by Vulcan and B&V during the summer of 1917, as Vulcan was experienced in the construction of mine installations of an appropriate type. However, during verification of the plan, it became clear that the pressure hull shape of Project 43 was inadequate for the exceptional space requirement in the after part of the boat. The profile and cross-section measurements of the pressure hull had to be changed several times. In fact, the mine compartment had to be made elliptical, but, because of the double-hull form, the outer lines of the boat were not changed. On the surface, total propulsion efficiency was 50 per cent, which was reckoned to be good. But, as a result of the numerous projections and additions, including the two 10.5cm guns and a large navigating bridge, the submerged propulsion efficiency was naturally inferior, amounting, after towing trials had been made, to 32 per cent. A peculiarity of this design was the storage of a further ten torpedoes in pressure-tight containers, positioned in special troughs on the port and starboard sides of the upper deck. In place of these torpedoes, 30 additional mines could be carried in deck storage boxes and could be slid along rails to the after launching position.

On 13 May 1916, the UI suggested building 10 of these Project 45 boats, and tenders were received from Vulcan and B&V on 25 May. On the 27th, contracts for 5 boats from each yard were awarded: *U117–U121* to Vulcan, *U122–U126* to B&V.

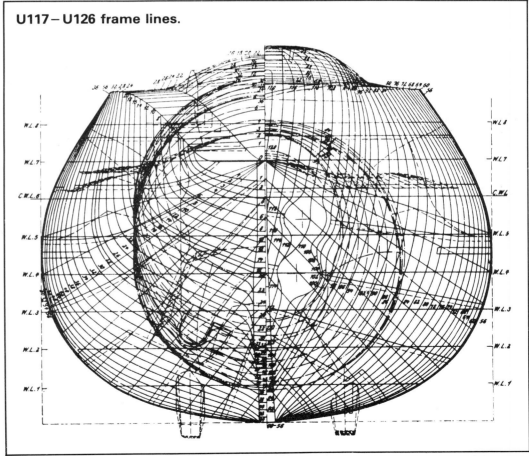

U117 – U126 frame lines.

Left: Slipway launch of an UBIII boat at B&V. These series boats were not built entirely on the building-slips; the fittings were added only after the incomplete boats had been transferred to a floating dock.

Project 45 (U117 – U126).

Glossary: Minen-Raum, mine compartment; Trimmtank, trimming tank; Schaltafel, switch panel; E-Maschinen, electric motors; Öl-Maschinen, engine; Munition, ammunition; Kommando-turm, conning tower; Hilfmaschinen, auxiliary engines; Brunnen, well; Zentrale, control room; Akkumulatoren, batteries; Mannschafts-Raum, crew's quarters; Hinterer Oberdeckstank, stern upper deck tank; Tauchtank, diving tank. Reglertank, regulating tank; Minen Ausgleichtank, mine compensation tank; Proviant, stores. (See also Glossary, page 372.)

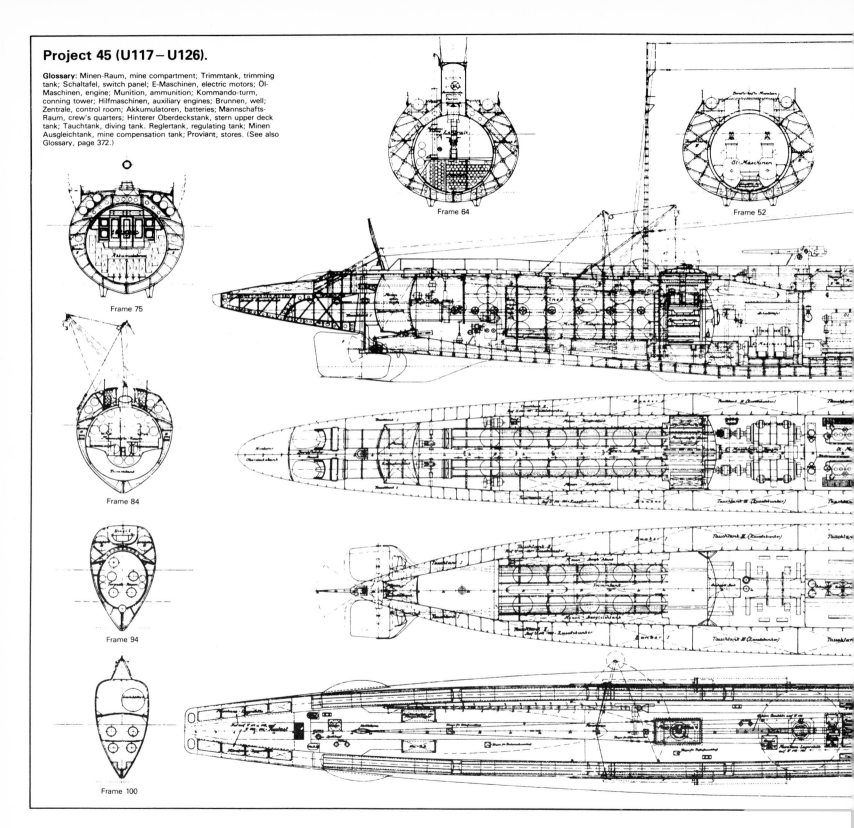

Frame 75

Frame 84

Frame 94

Frame 100

Frame 64

Frame 52

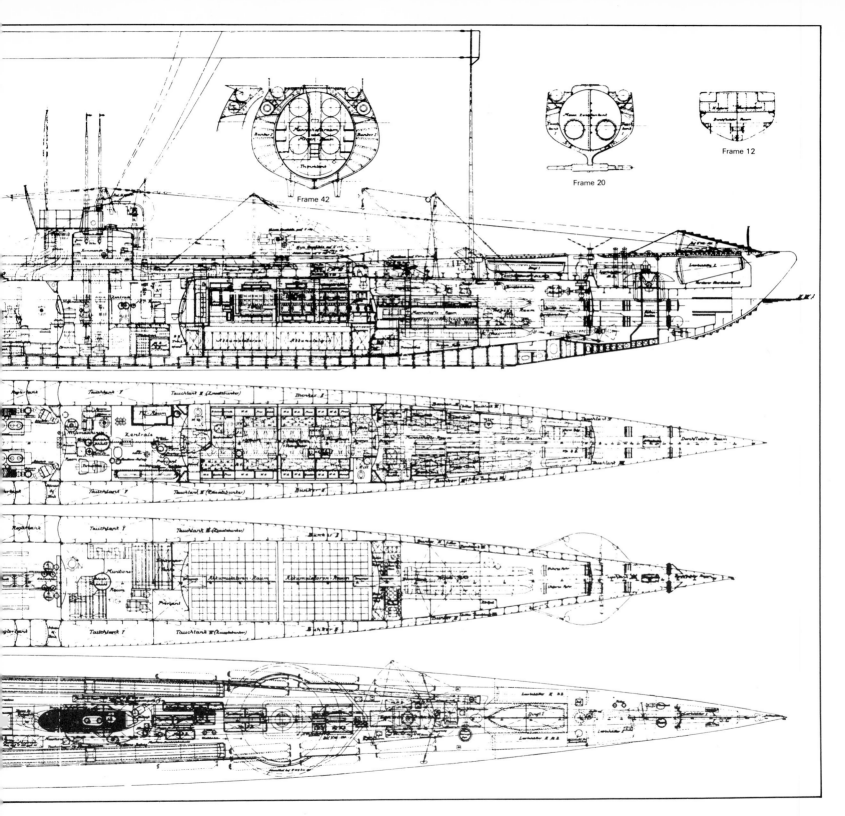

Frame 42

Frame 20

Frame 12

U-boat planning, January 1916

On 6 January 1916, in a memorandum from Department BIII of the Naval Staff to the Kaiser 'Concerning means for prosecuting an economic war of destruction against England', a comprehensive U-boat programme to ensure the successful blockade of Britain was demanded for the first time. More importantly, the planning revealed in this memorandum looked beyond the Continental conflict to a future, final confrontation with Britain, with political and military aims being complementary. It may be of interest to quote extracts from this memorandum.

'1. Our war aim, apart from destroying the English Fleet as the principal means by which Britain controls its Empire, is to reduce its total economy in the quickest possible time, bringing Great Britain to sue for unconditional peace. To achieve this it will be necessary:

(a). To cut off all trade routes to and from the British Isles.

(b). To cripple in all the seven seas, all ships flying under the British flag and all ships under neutral flag plying to and from Great Britain.

(c). To destroy military and economic resources and by means of air attack disrupt the trade and commerce in the British Isles, showing its population quite mercilessly the stark realities of war.

'2. The shutting-off of the British Isles from all incoming and outgoing passenger and mail supplies in such a way that the British Isles are encircled by blockade and forbidden to neutral shipping; any ship attempting to breach the blockade will be destroyed. This blockade will be enforced in the inner waters, as far as our resources allow by minelaying from mine-carrying U-boats and in the more distant approaches by U-boat operation. It is anticipated that defensive operations on the part of our opponents will compel our U-boats frequently to avoid the immediate vicinity of the coast and to move from place to place, and all this will mean that a very extended territory will need to be patrolled. It is not advised that surface ships be used for this blockade on account of danger from English submarines and other warships.

'3. The German Bight is the main starting-point for U-boat operations. The coast of Flanders is the natural support-point for operations against the mouth of the Thames and the English Channel. Most important for the carrying on of the U-boat campaign in the North Atlantic would be bases in the Faeroes and in the Azores and also on the Spanish coast. Bases in these places would reduce considerably the lines of approach for U-boats and facilitate greatly the task of blockading the British Isles. One cannot tell at this point in time whether, when peace is declared, the Faeroes and the Azores may be acquired and whether in the next war it will be possible to obtain the use of Spanish ports for our purposes: all this will depend completely on future political alignments. But for the present, none of these bases can be counted upon at all for the present conflict.

Left: *U117-U120* (Project 45) on the slips at AG Vulcan, Hamburg.

63

'4. To designate the whole of the Mediterranean as a Zone of War and a blockaded territory and to deny it to all shipping, out of consideration for our allies and for neutral countries, is not possible. However, all traffic through the Suez Canal and traffic bound for Egyptian harbours will be forbidden and any ship infringing this will be treated as an enemy unconditionally. In the remaining Mediterranean areas a blockade against merchant shipping will be enforced. As surface maintain in being our threat to the main artery of our chief opponent and not be dependent politically and in the military sense on other powers. However, in measuring the Mediterranean forces available to us we can, to some extent, reckon on the submarines of our allies, taking into account also that their bases and yards are available to us and form a useful supplement.

'6. The use of U-boats and surface cruisers in the blockade of distant countries depends upon the that our opponent has no time to work out countermeasures, and it will shorten the war. At the same time we must consider neutral intervention against us in the event of England collapsing at our onslaught. Reorganization of U-boat fleets must take place in the shortest time so that we have an effective weapon to back up our policies. This building-up must be done in at most five years. The possible disadvantage in the building of a large number of similar U-boats, the

Above: *U122* (Project 45) running trials.

ships are not ideal for mercantile warfare, the whole campaign rests on our U-boats. Alongside torpedo U-boats, minelaying U-boats play a most significant rôle in ensuring the constant closure of the Suez Canal and the large harbours.

'5. Whether and to what degree we should allow our allies to undertake sea operations in the Mediterranean is, both politically and from a military point of view, a rather open question. Our experience of our allies in the war to date is not such as to incline us to allow them to look after the Mediterranean aspect of hostilities on their own. And this point apart, it behoves us not to look at the war situation in that sphere from a short-term point of view only. We need to think ahead and in particular to the acquisition of bases in the Adriatic and on the coast of Asia Minor so that we can maintain our position in the Mediterranean and

future development of U-boats and on our possessing suitable bases. There is no doubt that the appearance of German submarines around North American harbours, in the approaches to the Panama Canal, at Cape Verde, or in the Indian Ocean would be very effective. However, with the increase in operational distances, and the duration of journeys, ships to keep U-boats in supplies will be needed and bases will be absolutely essential for all operations in distant waters. The number of U-boats that would be needed to maintain an economic blockade from such bases and the number of U-boats needed to defend these bases depends solely on strategic considerations and local conditions and they are not to be evaluated here. The use then of U-boats in remote parts of the world must remain a question for the future. . . .

'7. Number of U-boats: Our U-boat fleets must be so numerous that a decisive victory is not only certain, but can be achieved quickly. This will mean

attendant feature that developing technology may overtake them, is outweighed by the need in which we find ourselves; we have to put up with this. As a corollary, the demands for U-boats, especially large ones, should be restricted to the number required for realizing our war aims.

'8. The requirements that are set out below seek to strike a balance between the foregoing points. They take account of a similar grouping of opposing forces as in this war, that is to say that England, France, Russia and Italy are our opponents and Austria-Hungary, Turkey and Bulgaria fight on our side. . . .

'9. For Western operations the requirements are as follows.
From the German Bight Base:
(a). For sealing-off the British Isles by the constant occupation of 27 positions, 170 ocean-going U-boats.
(b). For military operations in the North Sea, for

patrolling the Eastern Territory and for offensive operations against the enemy fleet, 20 ocean-going U-boats.

(c). For keeping open the German Bight from minelaying operations and from enemy submarines, 30 small U-boats (improved type). Among these, small UB boats can be included.

From Flanders:

(d). Westwards, Dover-Calais in four positions, 13 small U-boats (improved type).

(e). At the eastern approach to the English Channel in two positions, 6 small U-boats (improved type).

(f). For coastal protection, 6 small U-boats (improved type). Among these, small UB boats may be included.

Total requirement:

Ocean-going U-boats 190+10% reserve=209.

Small U-boats 55+10% reserve=60.

'10. Approach routes to the important ports used by the English battle fleet and English merchantmen must be kept mined at all times. Therefore, each fortnight, new mines must be sown at the approach to each port. These mines are to be fitted with a time-unpriming device so that, after they have been in position for a particular length of time, they are unprimed or desensitized and sink, so that our U-boats are not endangered on subsequent occasions.

(a). The east coast of Great Britain in six positions, 11 ocean-going minelaying U-boats.

(b). The west coast of Great Britain in nine positions, 29 ocean-going minelaying U-boats.

(c). For occasional mining of six positions, 8 ocean-going minelaying U-boats.

(d). Operating from Flanders and for mining the Thames approaches and Channel ports, 15 small minelaying U-boats.

Total requirement:

Ocean-going minelaying U-boats 49+10% reserve=54.

Small minelaying U-boats 15+10% reserve=17.

'11. Baltic (including the Kattegat) requirements:

(a). To repel any Russian offensive by guarding and threatening the approaches of the enemy from his main bases and to cut off his economic supply routes in six positions, 23 ocean-going U-boats.

(b). For constant patrols in the Kattegat and in the Danish sea routes in three positions, 7 small U-boats of the improved type.

(c). For coastal protection and for setting-up observation points in the Baltic, 15 small U-boats of the improved type.

Total requirement:

Ocean-going U-boats 23+10% reserve=26.

Small U-boats 22+10% reserve=25.

'12. The following minelaying U-boats are required:

(a). For mining the Russian and Finnish ports approximately at fortnightly intervals in four positions, 9 ocean-going minelaying U-boats.

(b). For mining the inner waters and the Gulf of Riga in eight positions, 18 small minelaying U-boats.

Total requirement:

Ocean-going minelaying U-boats 9+10% reserve =10.

Small minelaying U-boats (improved type) 18+10%

reserve=20. (Among the small minelaying U-boats the UC boats may be included.)

'13. Mediterranean requirements are:

(a). For preventing enemy commerce and sealing off the Suez Canal from six positions in the eastern and western Mediterranean, 20 ocean-going U-boats.

(b). For maintaining two further positions in the central Mediterranean, 7 small U-boats (improved type).

(c). For operations against enemy warships and against French lines of communication in the western Mediterranean, 12 ocean-going U-boats.

(d). For protection of necessary bases in the Adriatic and along the coast of Asia Minor, 6 small U-boats (improved type).

'14. Minelaying U-boats required in the Mediterranean:

(a). For mining on a fortnightly basis from four positions in the eastern and western Mediterranean, 12 ocean-going minelaying U-boats.

(b). For mining at approximately ten-day intervals, from three positions in the central Mediterranean, 7 small minelaying U-boats (improved type).

'15. If we assume that the Austro-Hungarian Navy can provide 10 ocean-going U-boats, 3 small U-boats and 3 ocean-going minelaying U-boats, we arrive at what is required from us in the Mediterranean, and this is as follows:

Ocean-going U-boats 32+10% reserve=35.

Small U-boats (improved type) 10+10% reserve =11.

Ocean-going minelaying U-boats 9+10% reserve =10.

Small minelaying U-boats (improved type) 5+10% reserve=6.

'16. This leads us to the following grand totals for all three spheres of operation:

	Ocean-going U-Boats	Small U-Boats	Ocean going minelaying U-Boats	Small minelaying U-Boats	Total
Western	209	60	54	17	340
Baltic	26	25	10	20	81
Mediterranean	35	11	10	6	62
Total	270	96	74	43	483

If we now take into account the figures as at 1 January 1916, of U-boats completed and under-construction, and ignoring the expected sinkings which will be made good by the replacement building, the number required comes down to:

	Ocean-going U-Boats	Small U-Boats	Ocean going minelaying U-Boats	Small minelaying U-Boats	Total
	75	44	10	4	133
Which leaves to be built:	195	52	64	39	350'

With the resumption of unrestricted U-boat warfare, the UI reconsidered its U-boat requirements. The figure of 154 large, torpedo-armed boats (or 200 if one includes minelaying and coastal boats) had been calculated in April 1915, without including the Mediterranean requirements. Now, at least 300 U-boats were required and, of these, 191 would be needed by the end of 1916. Presuming the loss of 20 boats by the end of 1916,

at the beginning of 1917 some 170 boats of diverse types would be at the Navy's disposal. Thus, the total necessary to reach the strength of 300 U-boats would be 130, and these would be required in the shortest possible time. Additionally, future losses would have to be made good, and it was assumed that 4 boats might be lost monthly from 1917 onwards. This quantity seemed so high that the UI thought it unattainable even if all yards pushed their building to the limit and produced in 1917 as many U-boats as were projected for 1916, i.e., an average of 12 U-boats each month. (The actual monthly average for 1916 turned out to be 9, and for 1917 was 7.25.) In reality, however, the awarding of new U-boat contracts was governed less by planning and strategy than by the delivery capabilities of the various engine-producing firms and yards.

Building contracts for 1917

On 12 February 1916, the UI emphasized in a report to the RMA that the engine contracts given to MAN would expire at the end of 1916, and that to avoid production gaps it would be necessary for a further U-boat contract to be negotiated. Projects 41, 43, 44 and 45 were suggested, as many as possible of these types to be produced by the autumn of 1917. All the private yards that had been used for U-boat building hitherto would be considered for this except KWD which would be totally occupied with Project 42. The RMA deleted Project 41 (UCII) from the list because contracts for sufficient boats of this type had already been placed. On 1 April 1916, the Shipyard Department and the UI discussed the 1917 contracts. The RMA expressed the opinion that U-boat construction should be governed by the capacities of the yards and the availability of spare parts, without any consideration of the fact that the war might end before the contracts had been completed. But the yards were only to be engaged with the short-term Project 44 (UBIII) during the first quarter of 1917, because it was not possible to issue contracts for the second quarter of 1917 until July 1916. Additional costs for this double allocation had to be taken into consideration.

With regard to the larger U-boats, the UI suggested that no more Ms U-boats be built. Instead, Project 42 boats should be built, following on immediately after the last Ms boats had been completed in the summer of 1917. A preliminary inquiry by the UI revealed that it would be possible to build 24 of these 1,200-ton boats during the last six months of 1917, but it was decided that only 12 should be built in the stated time, plus 10 of the enlarged minelaying Project 45 type. Meanwhile, further investigation by yard managements had shown that, with regard to the possibilities for Project 42, the problems inherent in the building of large boats of this type had led to considerable underestimation of delivery expectations, and it seemed likely that no Project 42 boats could be ready before 1 October 1917. This meant that there would be a three-month gap in the delivery of the larger U-boats. This was a disaster in the eyes of the UI who regarded the large boats as indispensable for blockade purposes in the Western

Approaches and on the North Atlantic trade routes. Worse, 2 or 3 large boats were being lost each month; to replace these losses adequately, GW would have to be given an immediate contract for 12 more Mobilization boats of the *U96* type, equipped with GW engines, to follow after *U98* from the end of March 1917. Delivery would be one boat each in March and September and two boats monthly from April up to and including August. However, GW could only commit itself to the delivery of 10 Ms U-boats in the prescribed time. By mid-April 1916, the programme for 1917 was as follows:

10 enlarged minelaying boats (Project 45) with Vulcan, subsequently also with B&V.

12 large Ms U-boats (Project 42) with various yards other than Vulcan.

10 Ms U-boats of the *U96* type with GW.

24 UBIII boats (Project 44) in the first quarter of 1917. From then on, a quarterly estimate of requisite boats of this type would be made.

On 24 March, the cross-Channel steamer *Sussex* had been torpedoed, and American nationals were among the 50 passengers killed in the explosion. This event caused tensions with the United States, and led the German Chancellor to order a restriction of U-boat activity on 24 April 1916. The Navy could see little future in carrying out U-boat operations according to the Prize Regulations laid down in the Hague Convention, and they feared increased losses if they were obliged to carry out surface attacks against merchant ships that were heavily armed and escorted by warships. After all, they emphasized, submarines were designed primarily for submerged attacks. So they ceased the patrols around the British Isles and confined U-boat activity to supporting the Fleet. The protagonist of the 'all or nothing' attitude to U-boat activity was the Fleet Commander, Admiral Scheer. He was in direct opposition to the Naval Staff, who were of the opinion that for political reasons restricted U-boat warfare was better than none at all. Future events would show that their attitude was correct when, in the winter of 1916/17, with relatively small losses, substantial — if not decisive — successes were achieved by operating according to Prize Regulations. On the other hand, U-boats carrying out Fleet work were only successful in the sphere of reconnaissance, and they were certainly not successful during the Battle of Jutland on 31 May 1916. This vacillation on the part of those responsible for U-boat deployment was clearly to influence the awarding of further U-boat contracts during the course of 1916.

To be sure, certain contracts for which decisions had already been made were confirmed in May 1916: on 5 May, 10 Ms U-boats, *U105–U114*, to GW; on 20 May, the 24 UBIII boats, *UB48–UB71*, to GW, B&V, AG Weser and Vulcan; and, on 27 May, the 12 large Ms U-boats of Project 42, *U127–U138* to GW, AG Weser and KWD, plus 10 large minelaying boats, *U117–U126*, to B&V and Vulcan. But following this there was a gap in ordering for this type, which lasted until early 1917. The only contracts to be excluded from this gap were those of UBIII, which had been reduced to 16 for the second quarter of 1917 from: Vulcan, *UB72–UB74*; B&V, *UB75–UB79*; AG Weser, *UB80–UB87*; and all orders being placed on 23 September 1916.

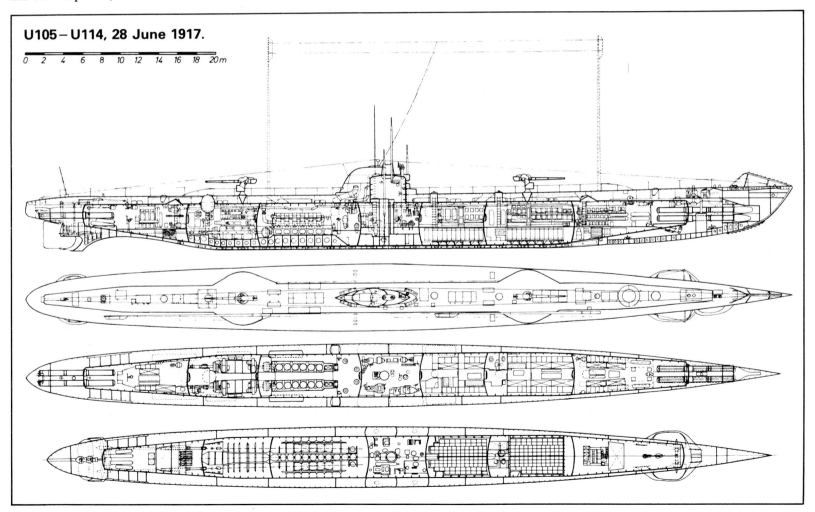

U105–U114, 28 June 1917.

0 2 4 6 8 10 12 14 16 18 20m

On the other hand, great efforts were now made to develop a U-cruiser for operations against merchantmen, and its development was undertaken at the expense of conventional U-boats of other types already in the course of construction. The altered concept manifested itself in different conversion plans. Hence, certain of the large minelaying Project 45 boats were fitted-out for the U-cruiser campaign with the mine storage equipment replaced by extra fuel and extra accommodation for a prize crew. For the resumption of U-boat activities according to Prize Regulations, the Flag Officer, U-Boats (FdU) decreed on 30 August 1916 that all large U-boats be immediately fitted-out for an eventful resumption of commerce raiding in the Western Approaches. In particular, U63–U65 were to be given an increased range; U71–U80 were to undergo a provisional conversion from mines to torpedo tubes; and all ocean-going U-boats were to be armed with a 10.5cm U-boat gun. In the large minelaying U-boats of Project 45, a 15cm gun would replace the two 10.5cm guns that had been planned.

CARGO U-BOATS AND U-CRUISERS

By 1915, the British blockade of Germany had brought about a distinct shortage of raw materials, especially nickel and rubber, and several attempts to deliver essential commodities to Germany had failed, to the detriment of the economic situation. The State Secretary of the Treasury hit on the idea of using U-boats to bring in supplies. A suggestion that rubber could be transferred, at sea, from neutral cargo ships to U-boats was dismissed as impracticable; and the loading of operational submarines in neutral ports was not permitted by international law. The only solution seemed to be the building of unarmed cargo U-boats.

Deutschland Class
A similar idea had occurred to Alfred Lohmann, a wholesale merchant of Bremen. Early in 1915, he discussed his plan with the State Secretary for the Treasury. He would form, with Norddeutsche Lloyd and the German Bank, a limited liability company with a capital of 2,000,000 marks to build and operate a cargo-carrying U-boat. The State would guarantee the associates their capital investment plus 5 per cent interest, and keep any ensuing profits. By 8 November 1915, his terms had been accepted and 'Deutsche Ozean-Reederei GmbH' was established, with Carl Stapelfeld of Norddeutsche Lloyd as honorary commercial head. The purchase of cargoes was to be undertaken, free of charge, by the firm of Lohmann & Co. Originally, it had been planned to design and build the boat at AG Weser, who suggested in October 1915 that the RMA be brought into the affair. At about this time, the firm of Krupp, which had large quantities of nickel stored in the United States, announced that they were interested in having a cargo U-boat. Krupp had arrived at the idea independently of Lohmann, and had asked GW to work out a suitable

design. They intended to present the boat to the nation, provided it was used to transport their nickel.

On 18 September 1915, Vulcan, having heard of the project, suggested to the RMA that the minelaying U-boats, U79 and U80 be converted to cargo U-boats. The suggestion was rejected on 2 October, whereupon Vulcan submitted a tender three days later for 4 cargo U-boats, to be built along the lines of the minelaying U-boats, U71–U80. GW offered to deliver 2 cargo U-boats, with a cargo capacity of 600 tons (according to the plans) in a shorter time than AG Weser or Vulcan, and they were awarded a contract for 2 boats (one to be charged to Deutsche Ozean-Reederei GmbH, the other to Krupp; both to be controlled by the former). Building costs were calculated at approximately 2.75 million marks for each boat. In the Navy, these submarine freighters were known by the code designation 'U200'.

The design of these, the largest German U-boats to date, presented problems. Certainly, the absence of armament simplified internal installations, but no data existed to show how a hull of such large cross-section would behave at depth. The strong degree of urgency attending the project meant that it was essential to use engines and fittings that had been tested and were available. Surface propulsion was provided by two GW diesel-generator engines, each of 400hp at 360rpm, which had been intended for the new capital ships Sachsen and Ersatz Gneisenau. For submerged steering the corresponding unit from Ms U-boats was chosen. Available electric motors were used, arranged in tandem with open air cooling. The large diameter of the pressure hull (5.8m) permitted the installation of a fixed deck above the battery compartment so that, for the first time in a German U-boat, trolleys could be used for maintenance and to stow and unship the batteries. It was intended that rubber be stored in the floodable compartments outside the pressure hull. The designer of the boat was the engineer, Rudolf Erbach. The main specifications of U200 as at 24 April 1916 were:

Length (waterline):	65m.
Maximum beam:	8.9m.
Draught (outward journey):	4.25m.
Draught (return journey):	4.8m.
Displacement surfaced:	1,440 tons.
Displacement submerged:	1,820 tons.
Propulsion surfaced:	two 380hp.
Propulsion submerged:	two 400hp.
Speed surfaced:	9.5 knots.
Speed submerged:	7.5 knots (2 hours duration).
Surface range with 215 tons of fuel oil:	14,000 nautical miles at 9.5 knots.
Load (return voyage):	170 tons rubber stowed internally, 230 tons rubber stowed externally, and deadweight cargo 340 tons. Total: 740 tons.

The pressure hulls for both boats were ordered from Flensburger Schiffbau AG; GW were responsible for machinery and construction. On 28 March 1916,

only five months after the contract had been placed, the first boat, Deutschland, left the slipway and was ready for trials six weeks later. The second boat, Bremen, followed shortly afterwards. Both boats were designed and built entirely as commercial vessels, with registered tonnages of 791 gross, 414 net.

From January 1916, Ozean-Reederei had been purchasing rubber in various parts of the United States, and a total of 1,800 tons, sufficient for three voyages, was gathered together at Baltimore for loading into the U-boats. Deutschland made two voyages. On her first trip, she carried 163 tons of concentrated dye worth approximately 1.4 million dollars. On the return jouney, she carried 348 tons of rubber (257 tons externally), 341 tons of nickel and 93 tons of tin. The rubber alone was worth 17.5 million dollars — which was several times more than the building cost of both boats. Bremen sailed on her maiden voyage at the end of 1916, but was lost at sea, cause unknown.

After Deutschland's successful trials, 6 more cargo U-boats to this tested pattern were ordered from GW in the summer of 1916. GW, however, were fully committed, and no slipways were available, so the hulls for 3 boats were ordered from Reiherstieg of Hamburg, and hulls for the other 3 from Flensburger Schiffbau AG, the Stülcken Yard in Hamburg, and the Atlas Yard in Bremen. GW built the diesel engines and were responsible for the final fitting-out. It was hoped to build these 6 cargo U-boats in the short time of approximately seven months: in fact, launching at the various yards followed from April to May 1917.

Meanwhile, the proposed rôle of these boats had been changed. As early as 2 September 1916, the UI had suggested that two of them be used for war purposes. Of three possible conversion options — fuel-transporting U-boat, minelaying U-boat or U-cruiser with heavy artillery — the last seemed the most appropriate. A U-boat armed with 15cm guns, with a long range and good submerged qualities would, despite her slow speed, have good chances of success when operating on distant trade routes. On 16 December 1916, 4 cargo U-boats being built by Reiherstieg and Flensburger were changed to a war rôle and designated U151–U154. Following the decision to restrict submarine warfare from 1 February 1917, it was also decided to convert the remaining 3 cargo U-boats (Deutschland and the boats being built by Atlas and Stülcken) and designate them U155–U157. These boats were taken over by the Navy on 18 February 1917. The conversion of the seven boats was carried out by KW Wilhelmshaven, who received the necessary drawings from GW. In addition to two 15cm guns, the boats, with the exception of U155 (the former Deutschland), were fitted with two bow torpedo tubes (eighteen torpedoes). U155 had 6 lattice torpedo tubes in a double arrangement under the upper deck, angled at 15° away from the boat's sides. A somewhat higher top speed of approximately 11 knots was achieved by using new propellers that allowed the use of electric and diesel engines simultaneously on the same shaft. From the summer of 1917, these first U-cruisers came into service at monthly intervals.

Deutschland.

Glossary: Hilfsmaschinenraum, auxiliary engine room; Maschinisten, engineers; Kojen, berths; Klapptisch, folding table; Trimmtank, trimming tank; Stützschott, support bulkhead; E-Masch.-R, electric motor room; Oelmaschinenraum, engine room; Laderaum, cargo compartment; Gang, passageway; Zentrale, control room; Kapitän, captain; F.T. Raum, W/T room; Obermaschinist, Chief Engineer; W.C. f. Offiz., officers' W.C.; Messe, wardroom; Vorrate, provisions; Küche, galley; Heizer, stoker; Koch, cook; F.T. Gast, W/T operator; Matrosen, ratings; Assistenten, clerks; Arzneischrank, medicine chest; Ladeluke, cargo hatch; Hilfsmasch., auxiliary engine; Akkumulatorzellen, battery cells; Lenzbrunnen, bilge well; Reglertank, regulating tank.
(See also Glossary, page 372.)

Key: *After auxiliary engine room.* 1, motor for horizontal rudder propulsion; 2, motor for hydroplane propulsion; 3, auxiliary bilge pump; 4, motor for hydroplane propulsion; 3, auxiliary bilge pump; 5, emergency steering station; 6, oxygen bottles. *Control-room.* 1, high-pressure compressor; 2, main bilge pump; 3, auxiliary bilge – and trimming pump; 4, turbo-blower; 5, compressed air distributor; 6, main bilge valve casing; 7, auxiliary bilge valve casing 8, propulsion for flooding-doors; 9, handwheel for after hydroplane;

10, handwheel for forward hydroplane; 11, handwheel for horizontal rudder; 12, periscope winch; 13, gyro-compass; 14, repeater compass; 15, periscope hoist. *Forward auxiliary engine room.* 1, motor for hydroplane propulsion; 2, anchor-motor; 3, auxiliary bilge pump, 4, auxiliary bilge valve casing; 5, oxygen bottles; 6, propulsion for flooding-doors.

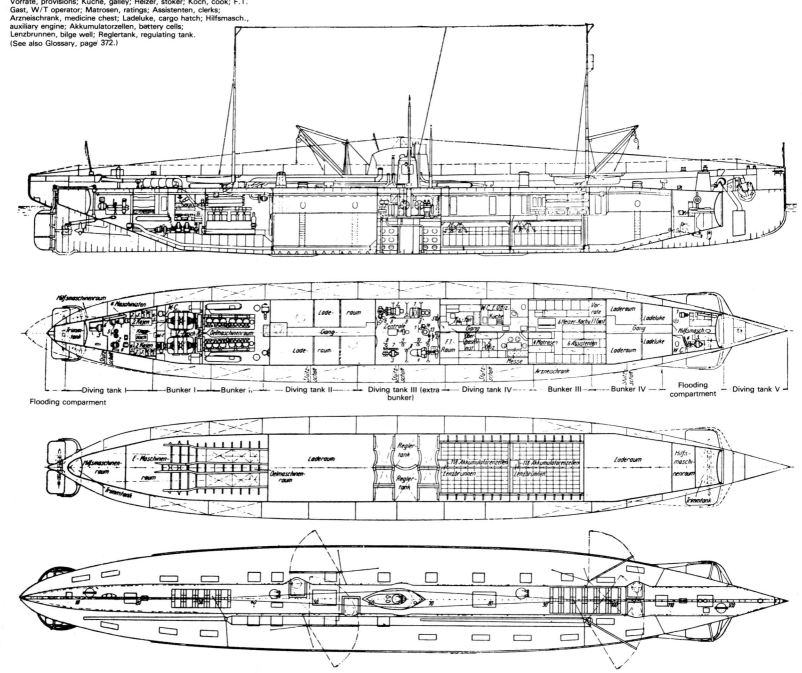

Diving tank I — Bunker I — Bunker II — Diving tank II — Diving tank III (extra bunker) — Diving tank IV — Bunker III — Bunker IV — Flooding compartment — Diving tank V

Flooding comparment

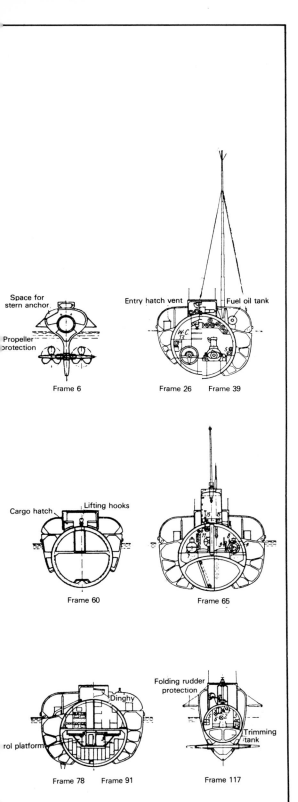

Space for stern anchor

Propeller protection

Frame 6

Entry hatch vent Fuel oil tank

W.C

Frame 26 **Frame 39**

Cargo hatch Lifting hooks

Frame 60

Frame 65

Dinghy

Folding rudder protection

rol platform

Trimming tank

Frame 78 **Frame 91**

Frame 117

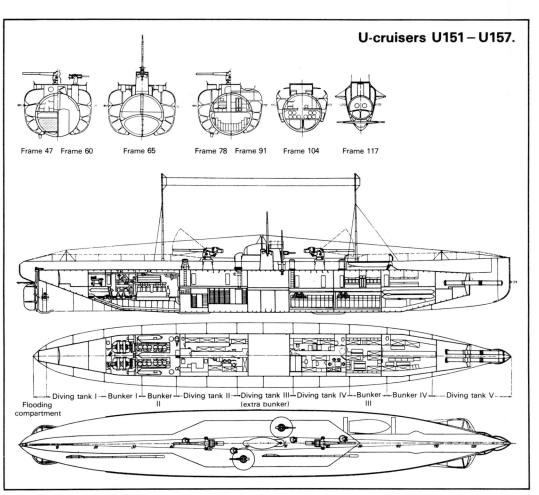

U-cruisers U151 – U157.

Frame 47 Frame 60 Frame 65 Frame 78 Frame 91 Frame 104 Frame 117

Flooding compartment

Diving tank I – Bunker I – Bunker II – Diving tank II – Diving tank III (extra bunker) – Diving tank IV – Bunker III – Bunker IV – Diving tank V

Above: Cargo U-boat *Deutschland* prior to her launch from Slip 8 at GW.

Project 46 U139 – U141.

Key: Forward torpedo room – 1, torpedo tubes; 2, reserve torpedoes; 3, warhead; 4, motor for forward hydroplane; 5, anchor motor; 6, auxiliary bilge pump; 7, propulsion for flooding-doors; 8, air purifier; 9, cold cartridges; 10, handwheel for forward hydroplane. Control room – 1, gyro-compass; 2, propulsion for ammunition hoist; 3, periscope shaft; 4, periscope winch; 5, air purifier; 6, helm for after hydroplane; 7, helm for forward hydroplane; 8, helm for main rudder; 9, exhaust cases for diving tanks. Auxiliary engine room – 1, cargo and extra engine; 2, main bilge pump; 3, main ventilator; 4, cold air engine; 5, turbo-blower; 6, battery ventilator; 7, auxiliary bilge pump; 8, shunt switch panel; 9, auxiliary switch panel; 10, oil cooler; 11, ammunition hoist. Oil engine room – 1, fuel-oil consumption tank; 2, lubricating-oil pump; 3, cool water pump; 4, fuel-oil loading pump; 5, main bilge pump; 6, oil cooler; 7, friction clutch. Electric-engine room – 1, main electric engine; 2, cool air; 3, main switch panel; 4, auxiliary switch panel; 5, thrust bearing; 6, air cooler; 7, motor for main rudder; 8, extra compressor; 9, transformer for control installation. After torpedo room – 1, torpedo tubes; 2, auxiliary bilge pump; 3, motor for warping capstan; 4, Main rudder propulsion; 5, trimming pump; 6, propulsion for after hydroplane; 7, handwheel for main rudder; 8, handwheel for after hydroplane; 9, air purifier; 10, bilge valve casing.

Glossary: Vorrate, stores; Küche, galley; Kühlraum, cold-storage; Navigation, chart room; F.T. Raum, W/T room; Kommandant, commander; Messe, wardroom; Hilfsmaschinenraum, auxiliary engine room.

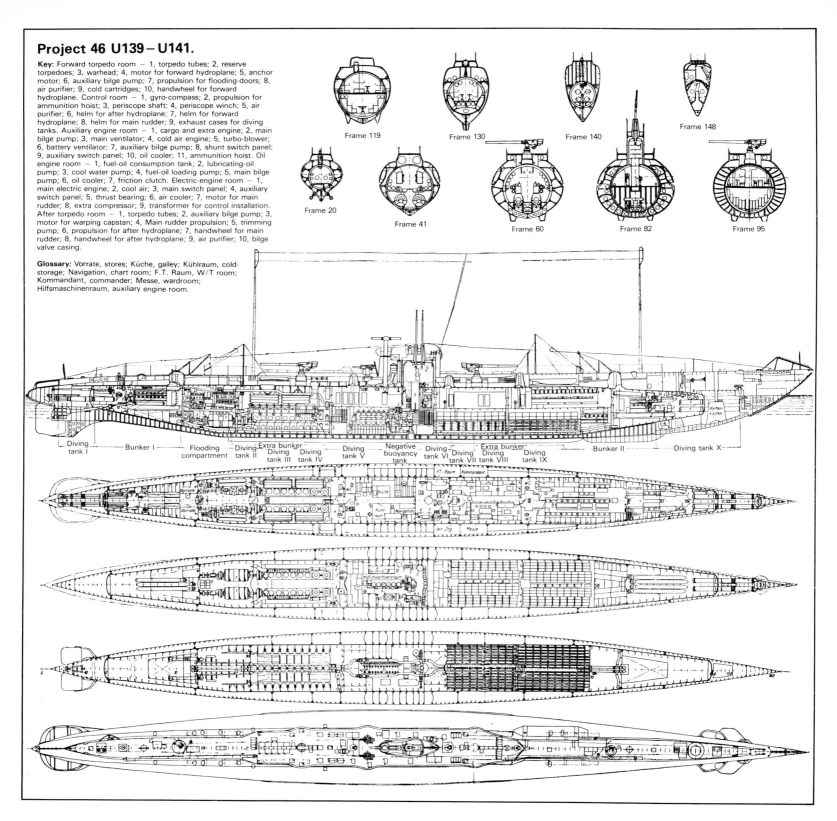

U-cruisers: Projects 46 and 46a

By the end of April 1916, as a result of the German Admiralty's decree regarding Prize Regulations, the U-boat blockade of Britain had ceased because the Fleet Command and the Marinekorps had withdrawn their U-boats. The Naval Staff now requested large, powerful U-cruisers which could serve as commerce raiders, and they ordered the UI, on 27 May 1916, to design and build a U-boat of this kind as soon as possible. At the RMA, representatives of the UI discussed this problem of providing larger U-boats with an increased surface performance, which could successfully take on armed merchant ships. In the opinions of those involved, the U-cruisers would need to have powerful guns and be well armoured.

The construction of the first cargo U-boats had provided valuable experience in diving techniques as applied to larger U-boats, but for these U-cruisers a higher surface speed was desirable. The problem, then, was clearly one of engine power. Although MAN were thinking in terms of a 3,000hp engine, there was no fast-running diesel available with a power greater than 1,700hp, nor could such an engine be expected in the near future. The use of steam turbines in submarines had, until now, been rejected because of the difficulty of getting rid of the boiler heat and the difficulty of constructing the large exhaust valves. The UI were, therefore, faced with the task of designing a U-cruiser of medium speed, using the available 1,650–1,750hp diesel engines. This was designated Project 46.

On 29 July 1916, the placing of contracts for three U-cruisers of this type was discussed at the RMA. The UI had its plans worked out to the extent where contracts could be awarded immediately if the yards could realize them. GW were chosen because they had shown in their designing and building of cargo U-boats that they could construct large U-boats in a relatively short time. GW declared themselves ready, provided they were allowed to put back the work in hand on the large Ms U-boats U127–U130, and transfer to the Bremer Vulkan Yard in Vegesack, the complete building programme for Ms U-boats U111–U114. Permission was granted on 1 August 1916, and the order for three U-cruisers, U139–U141 of Project 46 was awarded to GW.

Kapitänleutnant Otto Weddigen's boat *U140* (Project 46).

Project 46a (U142–U150), 1918.

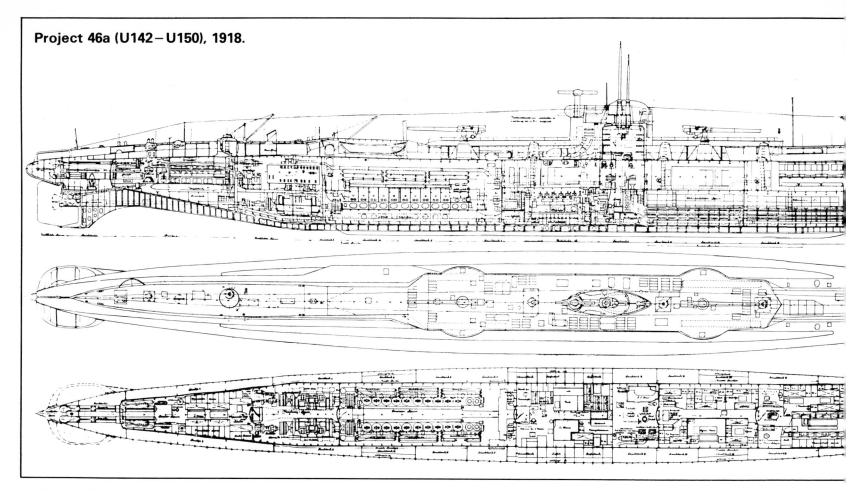

Although this programme was given priority over almost all other contracts, the agreed building time was exceeded by eight months because of various difficulties; compared with the cargo U-boats, these were more complicated craft, and no account had been taken of this. There were problems of supplies (shortage of coal) and there was an acute deterioration of work performance. In fitting-out, especially with regard to engine installation, GW could fall back on the design it had worked out for the large Ms U-boats of Project 42. However, in contrast to those boats, Project 46 called for only one battery-charging generator of 450hp. As in Project 42, the forward hydroplanes could be retracted into the upper deck for surface travel. For the first time in German U-boats, periscopes with fixed eye-pieces at the end were used. The control room was separated from the auxiliary engine room, and the command centre was given a protection layer of 60mm metal — a total of 90mm! Thicker metal was also used for the pressure hull (maximum 25mm) as a diving depth of 75m was considered desirable. The deck was of 8mm sheet steel, and the outer hull bulwarks were of 10mm sheet steel. Two 15cm U-boat guns were provided, with mechanical means for supplying ammunition,

Gun arrangement of U142–U144 and U173–U176, 7 February 1918.

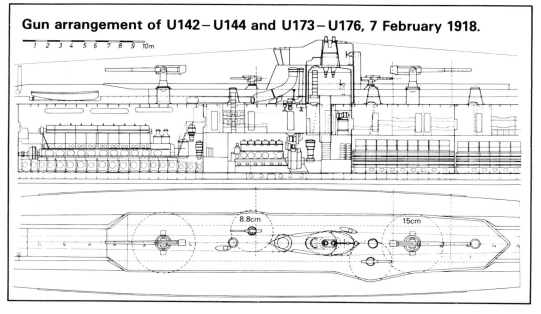

1 2 3 4 5 6 7 8 9 10m

8.8cm   15cm

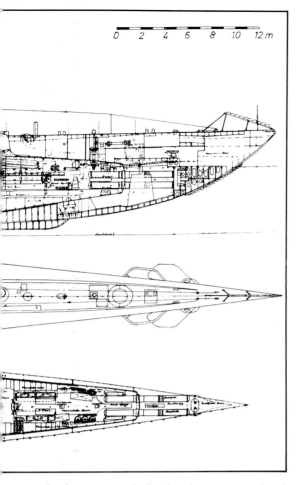

670,000 marks was for the gun armament and 55,000 marks for the compass installation).

In October 1916, five months had elapsed since the placing of the previous contract for larger U-boats (apart from the three U-cruisers *U139–U141)*. To make further use of the capacities of the yards and engine builders, it was necessary to decide which types should be built in the future.

The RMA decided, once again, in favour of Project 46, for the same reasons that had led to the ordering of the first three U-cruisers on 1 August 1916. They asked the UI, on 14 October 1916, to establish how many boats of this type could be completed by the summer of 1918. On 23 October 1916, the UI decided to place contracts for a further 9 boats of the improved type, Project 46a, with GW, AG Weser and Vulcan. They were to have the new MAN ten-cylinder, four-stroke, 3,000hp engines, delivery of which MAN had guaranteed. These would give a speed of 18 knots, as against the 15 knots of the Project 46 boats. The main specifications of Project 46a were:

Length overall:	97.5m.
Displacement surfaced:	2,000 tons.
Range surfaced:	22,000 nautical miles at 8 knots.
Armament:	two 15cm U-boat guns, two 8.8cm AA guns. Torpedo armament as in Project 46, but with an additional twelve torpedoes in pressure-tight containers on the upper deck.
Crew:	57, with 20 men for prize crews.

Remaining specifications were as in Project 46.

It was hoped that all the U-cruisers would be ready by the spring of 1918, but the Secretary of State in the RMA considered the promised short building time to be optimistic in view of worsening labour and material shortages. He was concerned with the possibility that the war might end sooner than was expected, with the need to build more battleships and with questions concerning the post-war development of the Navy. So, on 8 November 1916, he asked the Head of the Naval Staff to reduce the 9 U-cruisers to 3. On 12 November, the Admiralty Staff replied, saying that the 9 U-cruisers should be built 'without consideration of any other questions'. A further statement from the Secretary of State to the effect that he would not take responsibility for the building of more than 3 new U-cruisers did not change the opinion of the Admiralty Staff. Consequently, on 28 and 29 November 1916, contracts for the 9 U-cruisers of Project 46a were given to GW (*U142–U144*), Vulcan (*U145–U147*) and AG Weser (*U148–U150*). The yards suggested a delivery time between the end of 1917 and early 1918, if Vulcan were allowed to delay completion of the large minelaying U-boats, *U119–U121*, and AG Weser to delay completion of the large Ms U-boats, *U131–U134*.

Armoured U-cruisers: Projects 47 and 50 (K44)

As early as the summer of 1916, the UI had considered the possibility of a fast, powerfully-armed and armoured U-cruiser that could operate as a commerce raider in distant waters. The first sketch for an armoured cruiser, Project 'P' (Panzerkreuzer: armoured cruiser) dated 18 June 1916, envisaged a 2,500-ton boat approximately 110m long, equipped with two 3,000hp diesel engines and two 1,750hp diesel generators, giving a maximum of 21 knots. The boat was planned as a three-shaft type. The two outer shafts were to be driven by a 3,000hp diesel engine and a 500hp electric motor; the middle shaft was to be driven by a 2,000hp electric motor receiving current from the diesel generators when the boat was travelling on

and a larger range-finder for the guns was fitted on the conning tower. Torpedo armament corresponded to that of the normal Ms U-boat — four submerged bow torpedo tubes and two submerged stern torpedo tubes; twelve torpedoes G/6 were carried. Further specifications of Project 46 were:

Length overall:	90.5m.
Displacement surfaced:	1,950 tons.
Propulsion surfaced:	
U139	two 1,650hp GW two-stroke diesel engines.
U140–U141	two 1,750hp MAN four-stroke diesel engines.
Speed surfaced:	14–15 knots.
Speed submerged:	8 knots.
Range surfaced:	12,000 nautical miles at 10 knots.
Range submerged:	90 nautical miles at 4.5 knots.
Crew:	55, with 20 men for prize crews.

As voyages would now be of longer duration, an apparatus for producing fresh water was fitted, and this could be heated by the exhaust gases. Building costs amounted to 8.7 million marks (of which

U-cruiser *U145* on the slips at AG Vulcan, Hamburg.

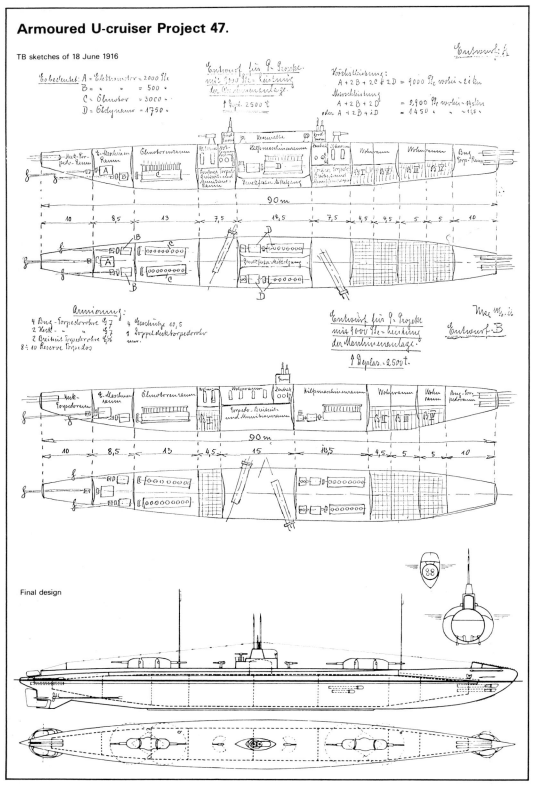

Armoured U-cruiser Project 47.

TB sketches of 18 June 1916

Final design

the surface. Armament would consist of four 10.5cm guns, six 50cm torpedo tubes (four submerged bow, two submerged stern), two 45cm side torpedo tubes and twin surface torpedo tubes fitted on deck. Further design work established that the estimated displacement was very much too low, which meant that the estimated surface speed had been optimistic. The gun armament was too weak for the proposed operations, and the placing of guns between the two conning towers was impracticable. A developed plan designated 'Project 47' was ready at the beginning of 1916, and its main specifications were as follows.

Length overall:	110m.
Maximum beam:	11m.
Draught:	6.5m.
Displacement surfaced:	3,800 tons.
Performance surfaced:	9,500hp.
Speed surfaced:	18 knots.
Speed submerged:	8 knots.
Range surfaced:	13,200 nautical miles at 10 knots, or 16,200 nautical miles at 8 knots.
Range submerged:	80 nautical miles at 4 knots.
Armament:	four 15cm U-boat guns (300 shells each).*
	two 8.8cm AA guns (200 shells each).
	six 50cm torpedo tubes (four submerged bow and two submerged stern).
	two 45cm side torpedo tubes (total of sixteen torpedoes).
Armour:	bulwarks 40–60mm, deck 20mm, conning tower 60mm, outside (+45mm inside).
Crew:	100, with 20 men for prize crews.
Cost:	16.6 million marks (without armament and compass installation) i.e., approximately twice the cost of a small cruiser.
Building time:	20 months.

*This particular arrangement of the 15cm guns (see sketch) was chosen in the interest of an acceptable submerged resistance, and as protection against wash.

The enormous building cost and long building time provoked fierce controversy as to the practicality of this design. On 1 May 1917, an official pronouncement from the Admiralty established that, compared with Project 46, the UI's Project 47 called for a doubling of displacement, crew and building costs without achieving any notable increase in endurance, submerged speed and radius, or accommodation for a prize crew. On the positive side, there was a significant increase in the surface top speed, doubling of the gun armament, a strengthening of the torpedo armament and a considerable increase in armoured protection. But the design fell short of what was expected from a U-cruiser, in that speed was lacking and potential for good observation was less than could be desired. Nor did the Navy Staff consider Project 47 as cost-effective in her proposed rôle of commerce raider. In unrestricted submarine warfare, the smaller, cheaper and more quickly-built Ms U-boats (e.g., *U35*) were much more useful than very large U-boats. For operations in more distant waters, the auxiliary cruiser of the *Möwe* type (approximate building cost, 5 million marks) had proved herself suitable.

Finally, it was essential to wait for the results obtained from Project 46 before initiating the building of very large U-boats. The most important questions were: 'What is the least depth of water in which such a large U-boat can safely dive and travel? How will she behave on touching the bottom?' The Admiralty concluded: 'At the present time, the completion of U-boats under construction that could still be used during this war is suffering considerably through delays and through all kinds of procrastinations, which stem from the attitudes of those employed in their construction, in the production of raw materials and their handling for war purposes and in transport problems. It is not in our best interests to increase the difficulties by giving out contracts for a large constructional undertaking such as this one.' To this, the Shipyard Department replied on 30 May 1917:

'1. The range of Project 47 can, without any change of construction plan, be increased from 16,200 nautical miles at 8 knots (14.5 per cent reserve displacement) to 19,300 nautical miles (11 per cent reserve displacement) by using two diving tanks as fuel bunkers, or to 22,000 nautical miles (8.5 per cent reserve displacement) by using four diving tanks as fuel bunkers. Through a suggested alteration made by the UI concerning the machinery installation, but without any other constructional change, a further increase to 26,400 nautical miles at 8 knots (8.5 per cent reserve displacement) could be attained.

'2. Auxiliary cruisers could only put to sea in winter, given certain favourable weather conditions. The use of U-cruisers, on the other hand, is not restricted in the same way. The argument that auxiliary cruisers have the advantage of taking prisoner the crew of a sunken ship, thus concealing their presence, is irrelevant, as a U-cruiser, with its ability to dive, does not require to take in enemy crews in order to remain concealed.

'3. As a safe diving depth for submerged travel for the 4,000-ton U-cruisers, the UI suggested 40 metres, which would be adequate for an outward journey through the German Bight. BV is of the opinion that one must not retard the development of ever more powerful underwater vehicles, the performances of which can be obtained only by an increase in displacement. If we are to keep our advantage in this submarine arm over all other navies, we must make a positive step forward, such as Project 47 will provide, without any delay. The Shipyard Department "B" therefore suggests putting in hand the building of Project 47

immediately, by ordering two such vessels, as the availability of two such experimental craft would allow a quicker and more certain evaluation of the type's possibilities.'

The TI had intended to use a new, twin-shaft MAN engine, with two opposed pistons in each cylinder, for the diesel installation. It would take but six or seven months to manufacture a 4,000hp test engine, and a further seven months to achieve delivery of two six-cylinder engines, which might provide some increase in the surface speed. But the Navy remained adamant. High construction costs and, especially, the long construction time for a U-boat that in essence was hardly better than the existing smaller types such as Project 46a led to the end of Project 47.

The UI now began to think in terms of a smaller U-cruiser with a higher speed, for which only a steam turbine could provide the desired performance. Hitherto, the problem of boiler heat disposal while submerged and the technological difficulties of designing the necessarily large, pressure-tight closures had ruled out this method of propulsion. A 'diving' boiler, patented by Naval Construction Master Schäfer and Engineer H. Wölke of the Technical Bureau, provided a really efficient solution to the first problem. Their invention stemmed from the discovery that the water-pipe boiler of a steam launch that sank accidentally in Kiel Harbour, had not exploded as had previously been assumed. Wölke's patents provided four diving boilers housed in cylindrical recesses outside the pressure hull, and these would be flooded when the boat submerged. Between them was situated the propulsion unit, consisting of four steam turbines, two electric motors and two 450hp diesel generators.

The U-cruiser plan, using a steam-electric drive of this kind, was designated 'Project 50' (or K̄44). The hull was developed in accordance with Project 46a, but a greater length (approximately 125m) was envisaged, to give an increased surface speed of 22—25 knots. In order to facilitate safe diving for such a long boat in the shallow North Sea, additional retractable hydroplanes were fitted amidships. The torpedo armament corresponded to that of Project 46a. Guns consisted of three 15cm quick-firing guns, two forward and one abaft the conning tower, and two 8.8cm AA guns. On 24 November 1917, the Weapons Department ('W') demanded four 15cm quick-firing guns, which the UI rejected as impossible due to weight problems, and suggested instead four guns in twin mountings. 'W' refused to consider twin mountings for U-boats, and insisted on four QF guns — if need be, at the expense of the AA guns. After further work on the project, it was decided that the firm of Erhardt should provide the new, hydraulically-operated 15cm L/45 U-boat gun in a special submarine mounting. The question as to whether three or four 15cm guns would be used was not resolved.

In February 1918, 'War Contract AA' was awarded to KW Kiel for a U-cruiser of this type, K44 (Kreuzer 44), to be known as *UD1*. In May, work started in the mould-loft and workshops in conditions of great secrecy, but the keel was not

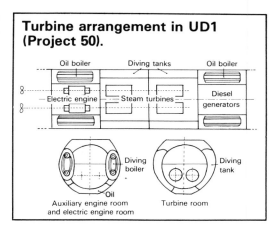

Turbine arrangement in UD1 (Project 50).

laid down and, at the end of the war, all drawings and incomplete components were destroyed. Erich Gröner's *Die deutschen Kriegsschiffe 1815–1945*, Vol 1, p. 376, shows the main specifications as follows.

Length overall:	approx. 125m.
Maximum beam:	approx. 10.5m.
Draught:	approx. 6m.
Displacement surfaced:	approx. 3,800 tons.
Propulsion surfaced:	four 6,000hp steam turbines; two 450 diesel generators.
Propulsion submerged:	two 1,900hp SSW electric motors.
Speed surfaced:	25 knots.
Speed submerged:	9.5 knots.
Armament:	six torpedo tubes (four submerged bow, two submerged stern); three or four 15cm U-boat guns.
Crew:	approx. 104.

CONSTRUCTION AFTER THE DECLARATION OF UNRESTRICTED WARFARE

In 1916, the tug-of-war between Navy and Government on the question of stepping up the U-boat campaign was resolved. Above all, Chancellor von Bethmann Hollweg wished to avoid anything that might bring America into the war, but the Naval powers demanded unconditional and unrestricted submarine warfare, and the Supreme Army Command (OHL) hoped for a decisive and successful U-boat campaign against the Allies — for success on land now seemed beyond their grasp. After a German peace initiative had foundered, a memorandum from the Navy Staff (BI) dated 22 December 1916 forecast that, if unrestricted U-boat warfare recommenced, Britain would be brought to her knees within six months. Bethmann Hollweg consented to a resumption from 1 February 1917 and, on 9 January, the Kaiser signed the Declaration, which was to present the U-boat arm with an impossible task, and which was to bring the United States into the war.

Pressure was now on to get the maximum number of U-boats into action in the shortest possible time, but the severe winter of 1916/17, with its attendant transport problems, shortage of coal and the poor morale of the workers, delayed the building programme to such an extent that, on 15 January 1917, Field Marshal von Hindenburg sent Lieutenant-Colonel Bauer, from the OHL, to the UI at Kiel to discover exactly what the problems were and how to solve them. In particular, it was agreed that miscellaneous raw materials and U-boat components would be given priority of transport, and the OHL would be furnished with the names of soldiers who were skilled in U-boat building, with a view to obtaining their release from the Army. Furthermore, unofficial liaison was set up between the UI and the OHL. On 19 January 1917, the UI used this liaison to complain that if a successful unrestricted campaign were waged for six months, it would mean that no new U-boats would be ordered. They maintained that it was essential for immediate contracts to be placed for 25 UBIII boats for the end of 1917, 10 further UBIII, and 28 Ms U-boats by the middle of 1918, plus a further 70 U-boats of various types by the end of 1918. The RMA however, was not prepared to order boats unless they could be delivered by the beginning of 1918. To do otherwise, they felt, would merely place an unnecessary burden on the already overloaded armaments programme and on the post-war budget.

Emphasis was now laid on the ordering of the UBIII boats — their relatively short building time and comparatively great offensive power meant that they were ideal for an overall blockade around the British Isles, and in the Mediterranean. Their handy, medium size and their expected performance above and below water made them ideal torpedo weapons for use in unrestricted submarine warfare. On 6 and 8 February, 15 boats of this type (War Contract Q) were ordered from Vulcan (*UB88–UB102*), 15 from B&V (*UB103–UB117*) and 15 from AG Weser (*UB118–UB132*). KWD were not acquainted with UB construction and they were given only two new Ms U-boats, *U158* and *U159*, with an increased range (War Contract R). No more boats would be ordered from KWD until early 1918 because of their existing contracts and the shortage of diesel engines. GW were so overloaded with cargo U-boats and U-cruisers that they could take no further contracts. Instead, the Bremer Vulkan Yard in Vegesack, having already carried out subcontract work successfully for GW in the building of the Ms U-boats, were given a contract on 6 February 1917, for 4 Ms U-boats (*U160–U163*).

However, even the placing of these contracts did little to bring about a noteworthy increase to the U-boat fleet, and the UI remained concerned that construction would break down. On 15 May 1917, the RMA and the Navy decided not to look at further U-boat construction for the time being. The UI, in a letter to Lieutenant-Colonel Bauer on 28 May 1917, noted:

'Small yards could build by the end of 1917/ beginning of 1918 approximately 20 smaller boats, given the use of 12,000 to 15,000 skilled workers. What are the prospects? Some large yards have still not received (by January 1917) their necessary labour. RMA is not inclined to place orders: end of the war is in sight, there is concern for peacetime estimates, weakening of the Fleet plan [Flottengesetz], difficulties with providing materials, etc.

One therefore expects that in the coming year the same gaps in production will exist as now: 6–8 instead of 12–18 as in the winter. Improvement only in July: 130 operational boats and, with 3 per cent monthly losses, never over 220. Losses may well be greater however.'

At the same time, MAN wrote to the OHL, pointing out the severe consequences for the U-boat programme posed by the non-fulfillment of orders for engine parts. These letters led the Chief of the General Staff of the Army, on 9 June 1917, to urgently request the Navy Staff to prevent a decrease in U-boat production at all costs: 'If the ordering of new U-boats and U-boat engines is not made a matter of urgency, serious disruption of the U-boat construction programme cannot be avoided.'

In the meantime, a new project was being discussed. This stemmed from Navy Staff discussions, on 15 May, as to whether the surface range of the large minelaying U-boats, *U117–U126*, could not be increased to at least 12,000 nautical miles; and whether, in view of the importance of minelaying and the heavy losses of UC boats, some of the newly-ordered UB boats could not be built as UC boats. Of 17 boats sunk since 1 February 1917, 12 had been minelaying U-boats. On 18 May, the RMA replied as follows:

'1. The range of U-boats *U117–U126* can be increased to 12,000 nautical miles at 8 knots by using some of the diving and compensating tanks as fuel-oil bunkers. A further increase is hopefully possible by filling the mine compensating tanks with fuel-oil. This, however, is only feasible when no mines are on board.

'2. To rebuild the UB boats as UC boats would involve such a quantity of alterations that one would be almost starting from scratch and would lose the work done to date on the Type UBIII. We strongly advise against this.'

This was accepted by the Navy, but a request was made that 15 new UC minelaying U-boats be built as replacements for losses.

In a letter dated 25 May 1917, improvements in these new UC boats were requested to rectify various faults found in the UCII boats:

1. Diving qualities were not up to expectations; in winds greater than Force 5, it was exceedingly difficult to submerge.

2. Very wet bridge condition because of deck tubes was noticeably unpleasant during the winter months.

3. Very draughty in the boat. (Cause of much sickness among personnel!)

Furthermore, the Admiralty desired a strengthening of the gun armament by one 10.5cm quick-firing gun, the surface speed to be increased to 14 knots and the submerged range to approximately 90 nautical miles at 3 knots.

This U-boat, designated UCIII (Project 41a), which had been projected by the UI and its details developed by B&V and KWD, differed only in externals from the UCII type. In an attempt to solve some of the above-mentioned faults, a new hull shape was designed, which sloped gently downwards from the conning tower; the new 10.5cm quick-firing gun was raised higher than the gun in

U-boat deliveries, 1916—17.

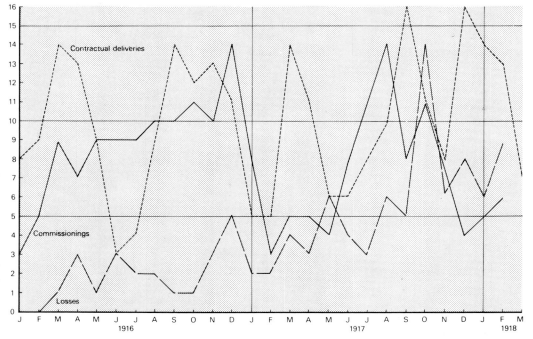

Type UCIII.

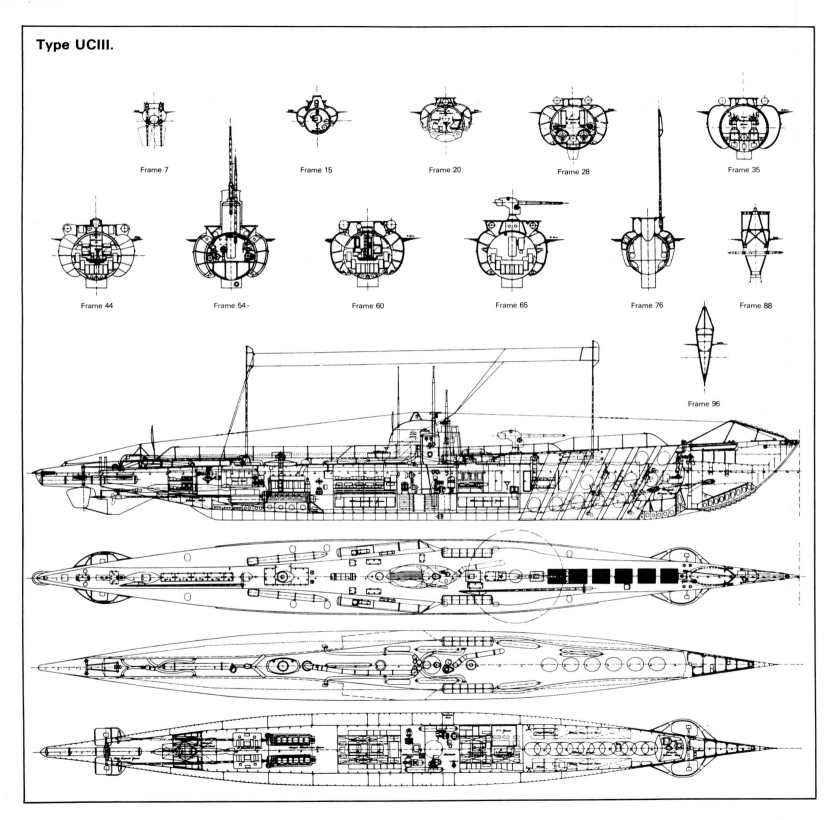

Frame 7

Frame 15

Frame 20

Frame 28

Frame 35

Frame 44

Frame 54

Frame 60

Frame 65

Frame 76

Frame 88

Frame 96

the Type UCII; and the external torpedo tubes were brought aft abreast the bridge. This certainly solved the problems of water spraying over the gun platform and bridge, but it did cause a stream of foam to form at the torpedo-tube hatches, which was clearly visible from some distance away. By altering the flooding and ballast tubes, the flooding time of the diving tanks was reduced from 30 seconds in the UCII boats to 20, as compared, but the diving time of the boat remained unchanged at 45–50 seconds because of the numerous upper works, which were freely floodable. The increase in overall displacement meant a lesser submerged stability and lesser submerged speed, but in view of the purpose for which the design was intended these still seemed adequate. Further departures from the UCII boats were stronger construction for oil bunkers and an increase in the size of the storage batteries (plates being increased from 26 to 32).

On 2 June 1917, a discussion took place between the U-Boat Department, the Marinekorps, the RMA, the UI and the Navy to try and establish requirements for the construction of further U-boats in the light of war experience and operational losses: 'It was adjudged essential for the prosecution of the war that everything that could be built in any possible way by 1 January 1919 be put in hand right away, as the general outlook of the war gave no justification for any reduction in the most-committed work on, improvements to, and increase in numbers of U-boats.'

For ocean-going operations and for the Mediterranean, large U-boats were required. The 2,000-ton U-cruiser of Project 46a seemed to be the requisite type for tasks in the Atlantic, to the west of Ireland and France, and in the Mediterranean. (On the other hand, the continued building of the relatively old Ms type could only be recommended if they were built by yards that specialized in this type, and could not switch quickly to building other types. Nor was there much in favour of continuing to build the large Ms U-boats of Project 42, as these had no real advantages over the 800-ton Ms type and the 2,000-ton U-boats, building time of which was no longer, and which were far better equipped for operating at greater distances from the coast.) Apart from these large boats, it was necessary to order the quickly-built, medium size UBIII and UCIII types for torpedo and minelaying tasks in the War Zone. Consequently, at the end of June 1917, a total of 95 U-boats were ordered for construction:

39 UCIII boats (War Contract S): *UC80–UC86* from KWD, *UC87–UC89* from AG Weser, *UC90–UC118* from B&V; for completion between 1918 and early 1919.

37 UBIII (War Contract T): *UB133–UB141* from GW, *UB142–UB153* from AG Weser, *UB154–UB169* from Vulcan; for completion between the summer of 1918 and early 1919.

9 Ms U-boats (800-ton): *U164–U172* from Bremer-Vulkan, Vegesack; ready between the summer of 1918 and January 1919.

10 U-cruisers, Project 46a (War Contract U): *U173–U176* from GW, *U177–U178* from Vulcan, *U179–U180* from AG Weser, *U181–U1812* from B&V; ready between the summer of 1918 and January 1919.

The relatively large spread of orders for UCIII and UBIII types gave the various yards the advantage of building entire series of boats. The main reasons for the niggardly doling-out of many small orders during the years 1915–16 — the constantly changing view of the U-boat's rôle and ever-variable operational requirements of individual types — were no longer valid now that unrestricted U-boat warfare had been resumed. The main problems now were the crippling shortage of materials and the lack of skilled labour. On 23 July 1917, the Secretary of State in the RMA made a request to the War Office that production of the U-boat series that had been initiated at the beginning of 1917 and given the classification of 'Most Urgent (Class I, Group A)' now be given even higher priority, over all other forms of production. The War Office agreed only to make the comment in its 'Notes of Authority' that delivery of them should be considered to be of the utmost importance. (Such 'Notes of Authority' were given preferential treatment.) The lack of skilled workers was to be minimized by a rigorous curtailment of certain aspects of surface-ship production. On 11 August 1917, the RMA gave the order that, at all private yards, new U-boat and torpedo-boat construction should take preference over new capital-ship construction, and new U-boat construction should take preference over all new torpedo-boat construction, with the exception of the light cruiser *Cöln* at B&V, and the torpedo-boats at Schichau. On 27 September 1917, the Production Control Department of Vulcan, Hamburg, reported to the RMA that U-cruisers *U145–U147* could be ready by the middle of 1918 only if the authorized number of workers were provided, and if all work on surface ships except one torpedo-boat could be suspended. Of the 655 workers allotted to Vulcan, only 133 had been provided.

The Fleet Commander, Admiral Scheer, was of the opinion that only an authoritative body, under the control of the Naval War Staff, could deal with such difficulties. After some preliminary moves concerning this, he wrote on 8 November 1917 to

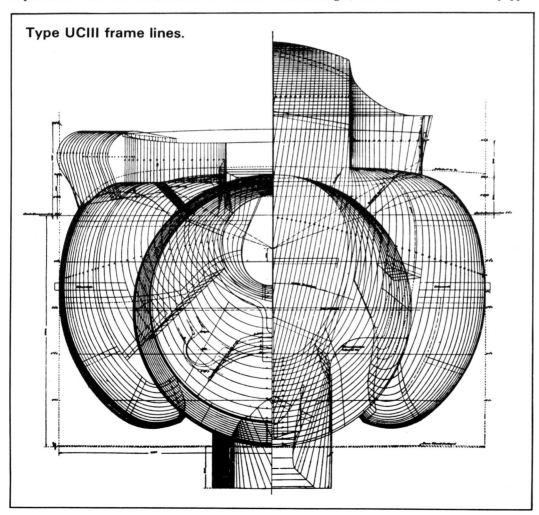

Type UCIII frame lines.

the Secretary of State in the RMA:

'The U-boat enters a critical stage; the enemy is growing in strength and the convoy system concentrates our opportunities for attack to ever-decreasing locations and fewer sea routes, and the changing situations are not known by us. Experienced commanders are being lost, and new ones cannot initially replace them adequately. Various measures have been tried, including removal of the specialization factor among personnel (artillery, torpedo, electrical training) and through re-grouping in military fashion (several boats working together as a group, etc.) in an attempt to improve the effectiveness of various boats. The reduction in overall effectiveness can only be arrested by our increasing the number of U-boats available for the U-boat campaign. In actual figures, during recent months U-boat losses have exceeded new deliveries.

'We cannot anticipate what future losses will be. Developments in U-boat construction and the repairs being made on boats at maintenance yards during recent months remain less than our expectations. Relief in the form of quicker new U-boat production and repair must be attained. Problems and hindrances that exist are known to me. As I have told Your Excellency on several occasions and have recently emphasised verbally through my Chief of Staff, these problems must be overcome. The course of events in the last few months has brought me to the conviction that normal channels of organization are not sufficient. Effective action will only be achieved by unremitting support from the Naval War Staff, but this essential and positive co-operation can only be supplied by the Naval War Directorate if a special Central Authority is immediately set up, directly under its command. Its mandate should be: to demand the production of U-boat materials. Its authorities: direct links with all bodies involved in production, especially with the UI, the U-Boat Department in the RMA, which should be separated from the Shipyard Department and placed under your immediate control, together with the Imperial and Private Yards and with the operational bases.

'The urgency of this question has led me to draw the matter to the attention of the Chief of the Navy Staff on his visit to Wilhelmshaven on 7 November, and to recommend him to authorize the formation of a 'U-Boat Office' directly under control of the Directorate for the war at sea. I have made it plain to him that it is not a question of increasing the Navy Staff in a sub-section or a department, but that this 'U-Boat Office' demands complete autonomy and must have its own Head to control matters.'

Scheer was especially critical of the Director of the Estimates Department, Vizeadmiral Krafft, whom he regarded as the principal cause for the faltering aspects of U-boat ordering. At a meeting of the RMA at the end of November 1917 held to make decisions concerning new U-boat construction for the year 1919, Krafft had stated that, according to an agreement between the Head of the Navy and the RMA, 18 U-cruisers and 60 U-boats of different types were envisaged for 1919. This was 'adequate' and there was 'no point in further discussion' — a pronouncement that aroused the disagreement of

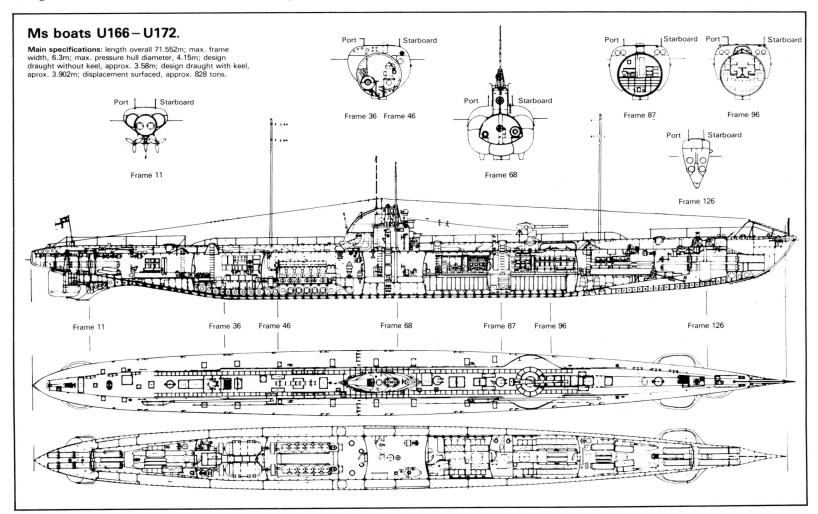

Ms boats U166 – U172.

Main specifications: length overall 71.552m; max. frame width, 6.3m; max. pressure hull diameter, 4.15m; design draught without keel, approx. 3.58m; design draught with keel, approx. 3.902m; displacement surfaced, approx. 828 tons.

Frame 11

Frame 36 Frame 46

Frame 68

Frame 87

Frame 96

Frame 126

Frame 11   Frame 36   Frame 46   Frame 68   Frame 87   Frame 96   Frame 126

almost all those taking part in the discussion. The representative of the Navy Staff made it plain that this number of U-boats would not even suffice to cover the losses (102 U-boats per year) that could be expected in the light of sinkings to date (losses in 1917, 63 boats).

The UI stated that 118 U-boats, including 22 U-cruisers, could be accepted provisionally from the yards. It was thought advisable, however, to reduce the number of U-cruisers to 14, because 3 UBIII, or 4 UCIII, or 5 new single-hull boats could be constructed in place of a single U-cruiser. The UI thought it completely feasible to build, additional to the 78 mentioned by Krafft, an extra 24 single-hulled boats. At this, Krafft made the rejoinder that, of the number of U-boats mentioned by him, there would be an overlap into 1919 of 38 U-boats, and that only 10 single-hulled boats could be built at most.

The new single-hulled boat, with the designation UF (Project 48a), had been planned by the UI in the autumn of 1917, at the instigation of Kapitän zur See Bartenbach of the Marinekorps. It was designed chiefly for use in the English Channel and North Sea, in operations based on Flanders. Its principal virtue was that it did not have oil bunkers outside the pressure hull, which reduced the possibility of tell-tale oil leakages if the boat were attacked by depth-charges, which the enemy had developed to a dangerous pitch. The UF boats had a comparatively short diving time and a relatively powerful torpedo armament. Their construction was much simplified, giving a short building time, and it was thought the boats could be built by yards that were new to U-boat building. The main specifications of Project 48a were as follows.

Length overall:	44.6m.
Maximum beam:	4.4m.
Draught:	3.95m.
Displacement surfaced:	364 tons.
Displacement submerged:	381 tons.
Propulsion surfaced:	two 300hp.
Propulsion submerged:	two 310hp.
Range surfaced:	3,500 nautical miles at 7 knots.
Range submerged:	64 nautical miles at 4 knots.
Speed surfaced:	11 knots.
Speed submerged:	7 knots.
Armament:	five 50cm torpedo tubes (four submerged bow, one surface stern); one 8.8cm U-boat gun, two MG.
Crew:	30.

The vehement criticism that the Fleet levelled at what was, in their opinion, inept political handling of the U-boat programme led to a discussion on 4 December 1917 between the RMA, the Navy Staff and the OHL. Agreement was sought as to exactly what the significance of the U-boat campaign was, as seen against the overall war pattern; the possibility of supporting the U-boat construction programme, chiefly by the Army supplying further skilled labour, was also discussed. Ludendorff, the Principal Quartermaster General, stated that he would like to give every kind of support to the overriding importance of the U-boat campaign, but, as to providing a labour force, the Army itself was finding it difficult to replace losses, and he could go no further than in what had been promised hitherto. Nor should the armaments programme for the Army be reduced. The tempo of delivery of those boats that were under construction, and the general implementation of the U-boat programme, however, were directly geared to the numbers of skilled workers available. Although it was now possible, following the cessation of hostilities with Russia, to use new yards, which hitherto had built such vessels as minesweepers, in order to bring about a definite increase in production, a yard experienced in U-boat construction, Schichau of Elbing, were chosen to build the first UF boats. (Schichau was already in the process of building two Project 43 boats, *U115* and *U116*.)

On 17 December 1917, the U-boat programme for 1919 was finally decided. Despite the inability of the OHL to provide further skilled workers for U-boat construction, the number of boats was substantially above that suggested by Krafft, and comprised:

36 UBIII boats (War Contract W): *UB170–UB177* from GW, *UB178–UB187* from AG Weser, *UB188–UB205* from Vulcan, Hamburg.

34 UCIII boats (War Contract V): *UC119–UC133* from B&V, *UC134–UC152* from KWD.

20 UF boats (War Contract X): *UF1–UF20* from Schichau, Elbing.

12 Ms U-boats (800-ton) (War Contract Y): *U201–U212* from Bremer Vulkan, Vegesack.

18 U-cruisers (Project 46a, War Contract Z): *U183–U190* from GW, *U191–U194* from B&V, *U195–U200* from AG Weser.

PRODUCTION PROBLEMS AND THE SCHEER PROGRAMME

The U-Boat Office that Scheer had suggested started life on 5 December 1917 as a sub-department of the RMA. Under the leadership of Vizeadmiral Ritter von Mann, it was to liaise with all RMA sections connected with U-boats, and was directly responsible to the Secretary of State. Its main tasks were to accelerate delivery of U-boats, construction of which had been severely delayed, and to make use of new yards.

On 28 January 1918, an order for 12 UF boats, *UF21–UF32*, was awarded to the Tecklenborg Yard at Geestemünde (Bremerhaven). Three new yards had been selected in December 1917 and, as their building of minesweepers was now discontinued, Atlas of Bremen was given *UF33–UF38*; Neptun of Rostock *UF39–UF44*, and Seebeck of Geestemünde *UF45–UF48*. This meant that 11 yards were now engaged in U-boat construction. With the help of five 'new' yards, an additional 5 U-boats could be delivered each month from the beginning of 1919. The remaining yards were pushed to the limit of their capabilities as far as the end of 1919: only by using night shifts and additional personnel and workshop space could any increase be achieved. First, however, the long-standing problem of constructional delays had to be solved. It seemed necessary to make an exact analysis of the causes of these and, in a lengthy report from the UI to the U-Boat Office on 1 March 1918, it was established that, with regard to GW:

'In 1917, as a result of sub-contracting some constructional items, the delivery tempo of new U-boat construction at GW was determined chiefly by the work performance of two trades, that of coppersmiths and locksmiths. Both of these have increased in numbers, as compared to December 1916, by 30 per cent and 45 per cent respectively, through the provision of additional skilled workers. However, with the delivery of *U151–U157*, the position altered, in that, since the end of the preceding year, certain shipbuilding trades such as riveters and caulkers were well under strength, as were, to some extent, shipwrights, and this determined the maintaining of momentum, and will continue to do so in the future. In short, there is no hope of increasing the trades that, in the light of experience, require strengthening and for which additional numbers have been requested previously in July and November 1917.'

'According to the calculations of the UI, in order to bring about a planned delivery of all new U-boat construction in accordance with the dates set out on 20 February 1918, 185,000 riveters' day-work would be required during the current year. But the statistics for the second half of 1917 show that work will have to remain in full production with a work force of only 145,000 riveters' day-work plus those drawn from torpedo-boat construction. One is talking, therefore, of a shortfall of 22 per cent from this particular trade against the optimum number. In the case of caulkers, the shortfall is up to as much as 32 per cent; however, in our experience it is easier to train caulkers than riveters. . . .'

Further reasons for delays were given as strikes, delivery difficulties and absenteeism during the bad weather at the beginning of January 1918. On 23 March 1918, KWD reported that workers were refusing to work overtime. This could not really be held against them, because their diet was very inadequate. In the summer of 1918, an epidemic of influenza led to further absenteeism. Inquiries at the yards elicited the information that their capacity would be considerably increased by going over to full day and night shifts and by restricting production to one or two U-boat and engine types. Indeed, B&V reported that their U-boat production could be increased by a third if only one type were built at a time, in full day and night shifts. However, this would require an additional 3,000–4,000 workers, and engine delivery times would have to be exactly as scheduled.

KWD suggested that, instead of allocating ship-building work to subcontractors, who invariably fell short of their delivery promises, their skilled workers be taken into the yards, where they could be employed on a more rational basis. In order to set up a night shift at KWD, 317 additional engine fitters and 130 additional shipwrights were required. To attract these additional workers, it was suggested that they be given an extra allowance of 1,400g of bread per week, and 1 litre of soup free for each night worked. Obviously, the key to any increase in U-boat production lay in the employment of additional skilled personnel and, in general, these could only come from the Army front-lines. However, prior to and during the big offensive in the west early in 1918, there was no chance that the OHL would release any men.

To clarify the question of which U-boat types could be delivered for 1920, a discussion took place in the RMA on 8 May 1918, between the U-Boat Office, the UI and the heads of individual operational bases. The starting-point of the discussions was the Navy Staff's opinion that:

'(a). The further building of U-boat types suitable for war purposes is of prime importance.

'(b). U-boat orders must be placed with various yards according to their full capacities without any thought of a possible ending to the war.

'(c). As each new type will mean a heavier burden being placed upon the personnel of the UI, delays in construction and problems in the yards, new types or major changes to present types are to be avoided as far as possible.

Following this, the Navy Staff recommended the further building of 800-ton Ms U-boats, and UBIII, UCIII and UF boats. The Commander-in-Chief of U-Boats and the head of U-boats in Flanders emphasized that 'through the increased surveillance by the enemy of the operational territories, the increase in protection given to convoys and the improved weapons carried by merchant ships, the use of U-boat artillery was becoming less and less effective, and that U-boats should mainly employ submerged torpedo attack by day, and surface torpedo attack at night.' Mediterranean conditions, however, were much more suitable for the use of artillery, and so it was not required that U-boats cease to use their guns.

The 2,000-ton U-cruiser (Project 46a) had been calculated to have a range of only 16,000 nautical miles at 7.5 knots; while adequate for operations off the North American coasts and the blockade areas between the Azores and Dakar, this was insufficient for the Gulf of Mexico and Brazil. An enlarged version of this type was therefore required, of approximately 3,000 tons with a range of 20,000 nautical miles at 8 knots. But the considerable strain on the industry that the building of a U-cruiser imposed meant that only two were ever built. Additionally, there were strong pleas for the construction of large Ms U-boats of the improved Project 42a: with its higher speed of 17–18 knots and greater range of 10,000 nautical miles at 8 knots, it was better than the 800-ton Ms type, and its better specifications allowed it to get within firing range much more frequently when manoeuvring against convoys in the open seas. On the other hand, large minelaying U-boats were no longer of prime importance. In the course of these discussions, the following requirements were mentioned:

2 3,000-ton U-cruisers.
6 1,200-ton Ms U-boats on the lines of Project 42a.
36 800-ton Ms U-boats.
50 UBIII boats.
35 UCIII boats.
30 UF boats.

As the boats built hitherto as large Ms U-boats of Project 42 had given a good account of themselves, especially with regard to their submerged qualities, further Project 42a boats were to be built at the expense of the UBIII boats.

For the coming year then, and taking losses into account, the increase in operational U-boats was calculated as shown in Table 5.

Table 5. Planned U-boats operational, May 1918 to January 1921

Position on	1 May 1918	1 Jan 1919	1 Jan 1920	1 Jan 1921*
U-cruisers	—	6	20	25+ 2
Large U-boats	40	33	21	9+42
UB boats	42	53	48	20+50
UC boats	31	31	33	15+35
UF boats	—	—	27	11+30
Total	113	123	149	184

*Minus 55 boats lost.

The actual requirements for U-boats made in June 1918 by the U-Boat Office was dictated by operational demands and consisted of:
44 UBIII boats (War Contract AB): *UB206–UB219* from AG Weser, *UB220–UB249* from Vulcan, Hamburg.
40 UCIII boats (War Contract AC): *UC153–UC192* from B&V.
48 Ms U-boats (800-ton) (War Contract AD): *U229–U246* from GW, *U247–U262* from Bremer Vulkan, Vegesack, *U263–U276* from Schichau, Elbing.
16 large Ms U-boats (Project 42a, War Contract AE): *U213–U218* from KWD, *U219–U224* from AG Weser, *U225–U228* from B&V.
44 UF boats (War Contract AF): *UF46–UF48* from Seebeck, *UF49–UF60* from Tecklenborg, *UF61–UF72* from Seebeck, *UF73–UF76* from Atlas, *UF77–UF80* from Neptun, *UF81–UF92* from Schichau, Elbing.

As War Contract AA, the steam-turbine U-cruiser *UD1* had meanwhile been ordered in February 1918 from KW in Kiel. (See page 75.)

After the German spring offensive in August 1918 had finally failed, and the German Army had gone over to a completely defensive rôle, the decisive nature of the U-boat became more and more evident. Now, in the opinion of the U-Boat Office, the Army would have to provide the necessary labour for U-boat construction.

In a U-Boat Office treatise on the theme of 'Extensive U-Boat Construction Programme' prepared for a meeting of the Naval War Staff (SKL) on 15 August 1918, the following recommendations were made:
1. Immediate drafting of 15,000 workers for a 25 per cent increase in production from U-boat yards used hitherto. (Accelerated construction of U-boats already ordered=Small Programme.)
2. Enlargement of the constructional facilities of the yards by the drafting of an additional 50,000 workers for an additional increase in U-boat production of approximately 70 per cent in eighteen months. (Enlargement of building capacity=Large Programme.)
3. Transferring of building contracts for torpedo-boats, minesweepers and steam trawlers to yards in occupied Baltic territories. Yards thus freed of this work in the Reich could be used for U-boat construction.
4. The use of Austrian yards in Trieste, Fiume and Monfalcone for U-boat construction. By drafting 10,400 workers from Austria, it should be possible to place orders there for 37 UBIII boats. In order to acquaint Austrian yards with German U-boat practice, the following cartel relationships were projected: Cantiere Navale Monfalcone with AG Weser; Danubius Fiume with GW; Austria Yard, Trieste with B&V.

All these measures should enable the production of a maximum of 12.7 U-boats monthly in 1918 to be doubled by the end of 1919.

In a communication to the Chief of the General Staff of the Army, on 30 August 1918, even greater demands were made:
1. 20,000 specialist workers required by 1 October 1918, and a further 30,000 to follow them in order to accelerate the current U-boat building programme (a 25 per cent increase).
2. 70,000 men for the enlargement of the U-boat programme from 1919.

Instead of the present calculation of 54 large and 133 smaller U-boats from October 1918 to the end of 1919, the U-Boat Office calculated that the labour force required under (1) would allow 74 large and 188 smaller U-boats to be built. If the labour force enumerated in (2) could be used, an additional increase in output of 70 per cent would be attained in eighteen months. In 1920, therefore, 102 large and 136 smaller boats (monthly average 28 U-boats) could be delivered.

On 11 August 1918, Admiral Scheer became Head of the Naval Staff in succession to Admiral von Holtzendorff. To 'tighten up' the German naval effort, he had founded (with reference to the OHL) the Naval War Staff (SKL) which was to work in close harmony with the Grand Strategic Headquarters, with the OHL and with the Kaiser. Scheer saw his most important task as that of strengthening the U-boat arm. At the OHL on 12 August 1918, four days after the British success at Amiens, he met Hindenburg and Ludendorff; both acknowledged to him that 'the hope for a favourable end of the war remains now chiefly in a successful U-boat offensive'. Ludendorff promised to do his best to strengthen the U-boat arm, despite the acute shortage of manpower that was affecting the Army, but maintained that the Army must first find replacements for its considerable losses of the summer of 1918.

On 5 September 1918, discussions took place at the War Office between various procurement bodies under the control of the OHL, in which consideration was given to the OHL's demand for immediate Army replacements of 80,000 men of Category A2. The railways and mines would have to supply some of these, and much serious criticism was levelled at the idea. Furthermore, under the catch-phrase 'Bring down the age of the Army', younger men were to be taken from industry and replaced by

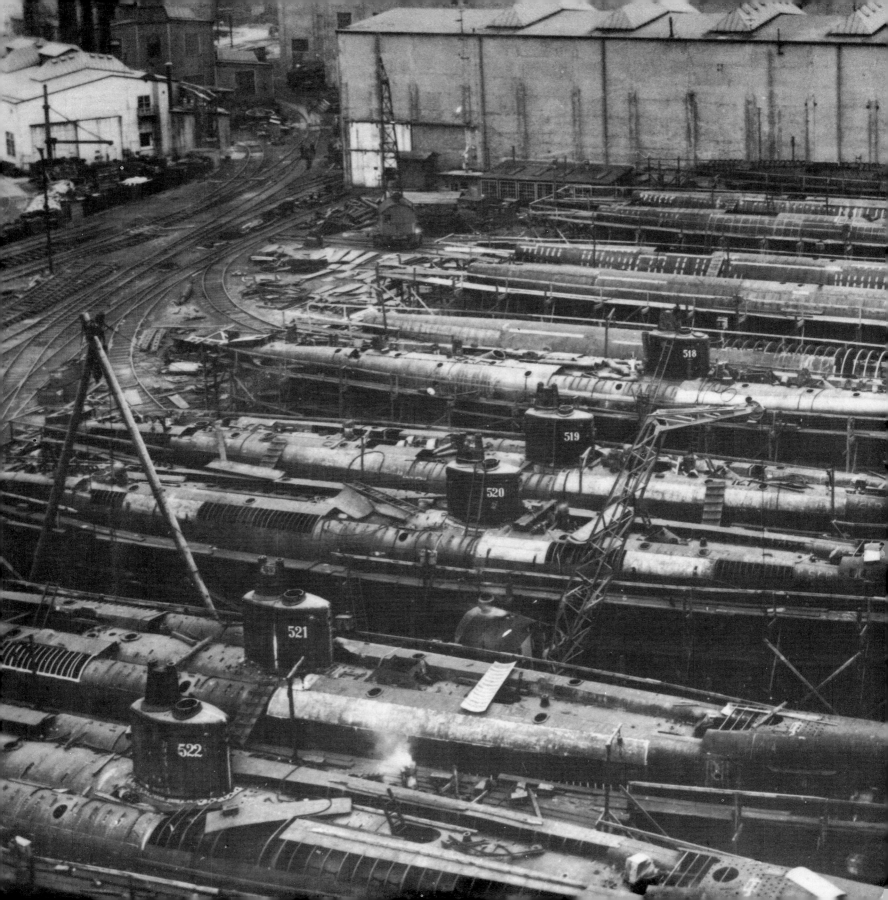

older men: by 1 December 1918, 30 per cent and, by February 1919 40 per cent of men born between 1898 and 1900; and, by 1 April 1919, 25 per cent of men born between 1894 and 1897. At this, the naval representative stated: 'The Navy will also be obliged to make worker claims on the OHL. A reduction of U-boat production is not to be contemplated. The Navy really needs to urge as firmly as possible that, in the affiliated naval industries, as well as in the extraction of 10 per cent of A2 men, that the most thorough and careful consideration be given to naval requirements. The supplying of the A2 personnel as demanded by the OHL can really only be achieved at the expense of other industries.' A Memorandum from Korvetten-kapitän Scheibe (BI) concerning the provisional development of merchant ship tonnage on the Allied side from August 1918, estimated an increase in its cargo capacity for 1919 by 8.28 million gross registered tons and, to compensate for U-boat losses, he demanded the building of 257 new U-boats by the end of 1919. This number represented an increase of only 19 on the 238 that had been agreed in the U-Boat Office's most recent production programme, and was considerably less than the number called for, on 15 August, by the U-Boat Office's demand for a 'Large Building Programme'.

Scheer was palpably distrustful of Navy Staff memoranda following their inaccurate forecasts on the consequences of unrestricted U-boat warfare. He calculated that increased defensive measures on the part of the Allies would lead to a less favourable ratio of sinkings per U-boat and judged that a successful outcome of the U-boat campaign could only be achieved by a steep increase in the number of deliveries, far and away above the number called for in the 'Large Building Programme'. He hoped that this could be attained by pushing the entire industry to even greater efforts and by giving U-boat construction absolute top priority. On 16 August 1918, he stated:

'It is most essential to limit U-boat construction to a very small number of types; specialization and the desire to work out improvements must be subordinated to the more important aspect of speeding up the construction programme. We must also apply the American building methods of factory, mass-produced ships, of which we are not completely ignorant in Germany, to the extent that the whole German iron industry and engine industry play their part in this operation for the production of necessary parts. The assembly of boats will be made in 'collecting' yards; and a big advantage will be that the question of skilled labour will be eased, as this system demands a smaller number of really skilled workers in one place. It would be essential to have a meeting between a number of leading personalities from German yards and from iron industries and engine industries and the Navy Staff and the Imperial Naval Office, to work out a programme as to the nature, scope and

Left: *UB155-UB159* (Project 44) series production at Vulcan, Hamburg. Launching was achieved through a gantry erected on the quay walls.

83

division of responsibilities of this work. One must set a distant goal in order to realize the greatest possible end results. Next, would be the setting up of a small committee of dedicated industrialists, whose careers to date would have shown them capable of extraordinary achievement in industry . . . Under the control of the Secretary of State of the Imperial Naval Office, the committee would be responsible for carrying out the programme with a sweeping authority similar to that of the War Office, as regards the awarding of contracts to industry and overall control of work in progress.'

Following the removal of the SKL to the Grand Headquarters in Spa on 10 September 1918, Scheer began immediately to put theory into practice. On the 12th, he met Hugo Stinnes, a major industrialist. He summarized the result of their discussions in a memorandum as follows:

'In the light of the present military situation, the U-boat arm is the only offensive means open to us. If we go over to the defensive we shall not achieve a worthwhile peace settlement. It is therefore absolutely necessary, and there must be no delay, that we develop our sole offensive means with all the capacity that Germany possesses, so that the goal of achieving a worth-while peace is attainable. . . . To make sure that in the future we continue to sink more ships than our enemies can build, we demand the essential monthly totals of new building:
Fourth quarter 1918: 16 U-boats (instead of 12.7)
First quarter 1919: 20 U-boats (instead of 12.7)
Second quarter 1919: 25 U-boats (instead of 17.3)
Third quarter 1919: 30 U-boats (instead of 16.0)
Fourth quarter 1919: 36 U-boats (instead of 22.3)
First quarter 1920: 36 U-boats (instead of 16.0)
Second quarter 1920: 36 U-boats (instead of 15.3)
It is essential that the whole industry be subordinated to this task. To achieve this it is again essential that certain leading personalities in industry have discussions together. The personalities chosen must work out the requirements and make known how many workers they require for realization of their own tasks in the overall U-boat programme. When this number is established, the SKL must approach the OHL. When the latter body understands the basis on which this number has been calculated and why it is essential to carry out the Large Building Programme, then there is every hope that the OHL will release the workers . . . The State Secretary of the RMA must grant extraordinary powers to the Head of the U-Boat Office so that the latter can dedicate himself completely and utterly to a realization of the U-boat undertaking.'
Discussion was held concerning several further points:
'1. Account must be taken of the need of further workshops in the yards and supply organizations when U-boat building contracts are given out.
'2. A solution to the fuel-oil supply problem will have to be found if the Large Building Programme is to be carried through.
'3. Austro-Hungarian industry must be made to play its part in U-boat affairs.'
On 14 September, in the Grand Headquarters, Scheer discussed these requirements and problems with representatives of the RMA and of the U-Boat Office. The RMA mentioned certain difficulties that stood in the way of the Large Building Programme: that of providing crews for the additional U-boats, the question of recruitment (in 1918, the Navy was

Table 6. Delivery timetable for 1919

	1918 Oct.	Nov.	Dec.	1919: Jan.	Feb.	March	April	May	June	July	Aug.	Sept.	Oct.	Nov.	Dec.	1919: Total	1920: Monthly
GW																	
U-cruisers	1		1					1	1	1	1	1	1	1	1	8	
Ms boats																	3.5
Large Ms boats				1	1	1	1									4	
Type UB		1	1	1	1	1	1	1	1	2	2	2	2	3	3	20	
B&V																	
U-cruisers							1		1	2/3	2/3	2/3	2/3	2/3	2/3	6	
Large Ms boats																	1
Type UC	6	6	6	3	4	4	5	6	6	6	6.5	6.5	6.5	6.5	6	66	6.5
Weser																	
U-cruisers		1				1		1				1		1		4	
Large Ms boats									1	1	1	1				4	1
Type UB	2	2	2	3	1		2	2	3	3	3	3	3	3	3	29	2.5
Type UC				1		2										3	
Vulcan																	
U-cruisers		1 [1]					1		1		1			1		4	[2]
Type UB	2	2	3	3	3		3	3	4	4	4	5	4	6	7	46	7
KWD																	
Large Ms boats	1		1														1
Ms boats		1	1													1	
Type UC			1	1	2	2	2	3	3	3	3	3	3	3	3	29	
Schichau																	
Ms boats							1	1				1	2	2	2	9	3
Type UF				1	2	3	3	3	4	4	4	3	3	1	1	32	
Bremer Vulkan																	
Ms boats	1	1	1	1	1.5	1.5	2	2	2	2	2	2	2.5	2.5	2.5	23.5	2.5
Tecklenborg																	
Type UF					1	1.5	1.5	1.5	1.5	1.5	1.5	1.5	2	2	2	17.5	2
Neptun																	
Type UF									1	1	1	1	2	2	2	10	1
Seebeck																	
Type UF									1	1	2	2	2	2	2	12	1
Atlas																	
Type UF										1	1		1	1	1	5	0.5
Total	13	12	18	15	16.5	18	22.5	23.5	30.5	31 1/6	33 2/3	33 2/3	34 2/3	37 2/3	36 1/6	333	32.5 [3]
Existing delivery timetable	12	10	14	11	13	13	13	15	17	16	15	14	14	15	16	172	
U-Boat Office's Large Programme	12	13	15	15	16	17	17	18	19	21	22	21	22	21	23	232	
Scheer's demands of 12 Sept. 1918	16	16	16	20	20	20	25	25	25	30	30	30	36	36	36	333	

[1]Large minelaying U-boat. [2]An additional U-cruiser in Jan. 1920. [3]Plus 5 Ms boats per month at new yards.

10,600 men short; in 1919, this would become 40,000!) and the shortage of raw materials. The Minutes of this meeting concluded with the comments: 'After much shilly-shallying, with the SKL repeating its conviction that the only means that promised success were those which closely involved industry, the RMA gave its agreement to have discussions with certain named individuals from industry. It was resolved to wait and see what came of these discussions.'

Discussions then took place on 19 September 1918 at the RMA. Industry was represented by Hugo Stinnes, Director General Vögler and Dr. Petersen (from the Association of German Iron Foundries), Reichs Councillor von Rieppel, Director Karstagne (from MAN) and Hermann Blohm (as spokesman for the yards). It was established that in the interior of the country industry was well able to accomplish its part in the Large Building Programme without much redirection of labour, if only it could be relieved of certain other war production tasks. MAN could then bring about 70 per cent increase in production with only 1,000 additional workers. The steel industry required approximately 2,000–2,500 more men, and requested that more rational and co-ordinated orders be placed with the rolling-mills than had hitherto been the case. The main problem was the considerable shortage of labour at the yards themselves. It was obvious that no more than 40,000 men could be extracted from the OHL. The riveters and caulkers required, over and above this number, were to be provided by the bridge-building and metal-container industries. A compulsory transferring of personnel was rejected by Blohm and by von Rieppel. Von Rieppel suggested that voluntary transferring of labour be achieved by better pay and conditions at the yards. Blohm thought that it was unfeasible to award contracts for pressure hulls to steel plants in the interior; they should be considered for production of components only. He would like to discuss this question further with the yards involved. He maintained that an increase in U-boat production was absolutely practicable if only work on U-cruisers could be suspended.

On 20 September 1918, Ludendorff telegraphed a letter setting out his attitude to the labour demands made by the Navy. Once again, he acknowledged emphatically the importance of the Large Building Programme, but, faced with the critical situation on the Western Front, did not feel himself to be in a position to release labour forces to the extent demanded. Colonel Bauer of the OHL acted more obligingly, if with the same effect, when one day later he approved the application for the use of 40,000 men for November 1918, if the situation at the Front permitted.

On 24 September, the Head of the U-Boat Office telegraphed Scheer that, following consultation with the yards, the Large Building Programme could be carried out in its entirety. At the same time, he presented a detailed delivery scheme for 1919, which the yards had approved as being within their capacity if only they could be given 48,000 fully-trained workers for new U-boat construction, and a further 16,000 fully-trained workers for

U-boat repairs. A further 5,000 fully-trained workers were necessary for subcontract work in the interior of Germany. Of the total number of workers required, 17,000 would be needed by 1 November 1918, the remainder during the course of 1919. The requirement for the yards could be reduced by 8,000 if certain aspects of ship fitting could be transferred to steel construction plants in the interior. Following this, on 26 September, Scheer invited representatives from industry to meet representatives from the Naval Directorate and the OHL at the Hotel Excelsior in Cologne on 1 October 1918 to thrash out labour problems once and for all.

Meanwhile Germany's war was going from bad to worse. The collapse of the Bulgarian Front prompted the OHL to report to the Kaiser on 29 September that the situation required inevitably that overtures be made for a cessation of hostilities and for peace negotiations. The OHL's opinion strengthened the already widely-held view that any conditions imposed by the enemy should be accepted — an attitude in no way changed by Ludendorff's opinion that the Western Front could, if necessary, be held throughout the winter. Although there was now very little chance of a realization of the Large Building Programme, which by now had been designated the "Scheer Programme", the measures thought necessary to bring it about were continued for the time being.

On 1 October 1918, nine representatives from industry met under the Chairmanship of Admiral Scheer. In addition to those participants of the conversations of 19 September, these were Director Flohr (Vulcan, Hamburg), Director Zetzmann (GW) and Director General Nawatzki (Bremer Vulkan), as well as the responsible Staff officers of the SKL and of the RMA under their new Head, Ritter von Mann, plus Colonel Bauer as representative of the OHL. It was now generally agreed that the Scheer Programme could be carried out if the OHL agreed to the provision of 69,000 additional workers. Of these, 15,000–20,000 would be needed for 1918 and the remainder for 1919.

Colonel Bauer was of the opinion that the OHL, following a running-down of war operations (which was expected for the middle of November 1918), would release the 15,000–20,000 men. The workers could then be requested by name. Additionally, a new inquiry could be initiated for technicians and engineers from the Army. He also wished to get in touch with the War Office in Berlin, in order to make known the wishes of the Navy. (A lesser requirement of munitions for the Army was not brought to the fore.)

During the discussions, the yard representatives emphasized that the question of extra rations for workers in order to maintain their morale was especially important, and it was agreed that the yards should take all possible steps to supply their workers with extra food, the expenses of this being set against the total calculations. The RMA was to negotiate with the Ministry of Food over the provision of extra rations. To secure supplies of coal and electricity for the yards, Colonel Bauer proposed to get in touch with the Reichs Coal Commission. Blohm's fears that the future might

see the yards suffering air attack were set aside by Admiral Scheer.

In order to work out a new delivery plan for 1920, the questions now were: which U-boat types would best meet the changing circumstances? More importantly, in addition to the 92 UF boats already on order, would more of this relatively small type be needed? In fact, at the beginning of August 1918, the UI had been considering further development of Type UF. They felt that the 92 UF boats ordered by June 1918 would be sufficient, and it was not intended that a considerable number of UF boats be built just so that the four new, smaller yards, and perhaps some other yards, could be kept on U-boat construction. The UI felt that the complicated UBIII boats, in which weight problems had called for more than normal accuracy of construction, were unsuitable for the smaller, less-experienced yards. They suggested that, as an extension of the UF building programme, an enlarged UF type be built, which in displacement and in essential operational features would approximate to the UBIII type. If it were designed as a single-hulled boat (possibly with diving tanks on the outside), it would be simpler to build, possess greater submerged stability and, on account of its interior fuel tanks, would be less inclined to leave traces of oil if attacked by depth-charges. This new type was given the designation 'Type UG'. Initially, a boat of about 600 tons was considered, but with the only available UBIII diesel installation this would have given a surface speed of only 12 knots. As 13 knots was held to be the lowest desirable surface speed, the boat had to be made smaller in size. The main specifications were as follows.

Displacement surfaced:	530–550 tons.
Speed surfaced:	13 knots.
Range surfaced:	7,000 nautical miles at 6 knots.
Fuel-oil:	60 tons.
Engine and battery capacity:	as in UBIII
Armament:	four 50cm torpedo tubes (two submerged bow, two surface stern); eight to ten G/6 torpedoes; one 8.8cm U-boat gun, 300 rounds.
Diving depth:	75m.

It was considered that the stronger and simpler method of construction, greater stability and greater reserve weight of this design, as opposed to that of UBIII, was sufficient compensation for the reduced surface properties of the single-hulled boat. Not too much concern was shown at the surface speed of 13 knots, and if this were reduced by 1 knot, a somewhat larger boat could be given a larger battery and, therefore, have a better submerged performance than UBIII. The U-boat Office decided, on 5 August 1918, that this Type UG (Project 51) was worthy of development and that later, if the Type UF proved its worth, would be built along with UF boats. By 26 August 1918, the design for the new Type UG had advanced to the stage where official discussions could be held.

In addition to the UI and the U-Boat Office, the Commander-in-Chief, U-Boats, and the Flag Officer for U-Boats, Flanders, took part. The Technical Bureau of the UI suggested the alternatives shown in Table 7.

Depth-keeping and turning qualities were thought to be better than in the UBIII type, but the diving time was rather inferior to that of the UF type. During the discussions, the UI and the Commander-in-Chief, U-Boats, commended UGI because of its advantageous performance in depth of diving, stability, range and armament. The Commander of U-Boats, Flanders, preferred the smaller UGII, however, seeing advantages in a manoeuvrable and speedy boat; but, because he held that four bow torpedo tubes were essential, he too finally came down in favour of the UGI type.

It was then decided that the shape of the bridge should be that of GW's Type UCIII. The boat was also to be given a negative buoyancy tank, which would be situated considerably farther from the centre of the boat. Four of the six reserve torpedoes would be carried in the bows and two on the upper deck; and, for the latter, attempts were to be made to render the torpedo containers pressure-tight. Finally, the U-Boat Office stated (contrary to its pronouncement on 5 August 1918) that the various yards building UF boats would be switched to Type UG as soon as possible.

The U-Boat Office suggested further, in a letter to the SKL dated 11 September 1918, that with regard to the Large U-Boat Programme, the various types of boats to be built should be ordered from those yards that could guarantee favourable constructional conditions. In particular, the following five yards were mentioned: GW, Bremer Vulkan and Schichau, but only for the Ms U-boats; and AG Weser and KWD only for the large 1,200-ton Ms U-boats. After completing its series of UCIII boats, B&V should build only large Ms U-boats, and building of the UBIII should only be carried out by Vulcan, Hamburg. As it appeared likely that the Type UG could well replace the Type UF and Type UBIII, both types built by Vulcan and the smaller yards could later be replaced by the UG boat. U-cruisers, of which, at this point, 37 were being built, would no longer be requested.

In their reply, dated 15 September 1918, the SKL asked for the following points to be discussed:
1. The building of U-cruisers should continue, at a rate of approximately 12 per year.
2. Types UBIII and the large minelaying U-boat (Project 45) should be discontinued.
3. The remaining types should be built according to the following ratios: large Ms U-boats: Ms U-boats: UG: UCIII=1:2:3:3.

As early as 19 September, the Commander-in-Chief, U-Boats, expressed his reaction to these suggestions in a lengthy telegram. The construction of further U-cruisers was not seen to be of any urgency. Instead, further building of the large minelaying type should continue, as the range of the small UCIII boats would be insufficient to enable mines to be laid in the western approaches to the French coast after the expected closure of the Dover Straits had been completed. (No German U-boats had passed through the straits since 14

August 1918!). As a result of this, the UI conceived a design for a new minelaying U-boat (Type I) of 800 tons, which would have a building time shorter than that of Project 45 and would, supposedly, carry mines in wet storage in shafts, alongside the pressure hull.

The Commander-in-Chief, U-Boats, did not agree with the suggested type ratios. He was of the opinion that, with the expected strengthening of the enemy's defence systems and his blockade operations in coastal waters, the main sphere of activity for U-boats would be farther out in the Atlantic, which gave greater significance to the larger U-boat. With this in mind the following ratios were suggested: large Ms U-boats: Ms U-boats: UG: UCIII:= 1:2:3½:1½. The Flag Officer for U-boats, Flanders, however, wanted the medium Type UG to be the most numerous, suggesting the ratios: large Ms U-boats: Ms U-boats: UG:UCIII:= 1:4:12:4.

The Flag Officer for U-Boats, Mediterranean, who had not been present at the discussions concerning Type UG in August 1918, and who had been kept in the picture only by letter, declared that he disagreed with the cessation of building of UBIII, as it was just this particular type that had proved itself in the Mediterranean, and he did not expect similar results from the single-hulled design UG, with its inferior surface performance. For the Mediterranean, therefore, he saw the following proportions as desirable: 50 per cent UBIII; 25 per cent UCIII; 25 per cent Ms type. However, as the displacement of the UBIII boats built hitherto did not really allow of improvements in this type, the Flag Officer for U-Boats, Mediterranean, thought that efforts should be made to prepare an improved version of the UBIII instead of building the Type UG — a double-hulled boat of 600 tons with a surface speed of 13.5 knots that could be maintained without a supercharger, and of 15 knots with a supercharger. Other aspects of performance and armament would correspond with those of the UGI type.

The final determination of the type ratios followed on 2 October 1918, in a discussion between the SKL Operations II, the Commander-in-Chief, U-Boats, the High Seas Fleet Command, the Flag Officer for U-Boats, Flanders, and the Navy Staff. After weighing all stated wishes, the following ratios were decided: large Ms U-boats: Ms U-boats:

Table 7. Alternative designs for Type UG

	UGI	UGII
Surface displacement	640 tons	570 tons
Engine installation	As in BIII, but with supercharger. This would increase output from 2 × 550hp to 2 × 950hp	
Surface speed at 2 × 550hp	12.6 knots	13 knots
Surface speed at 2 × 950hp	Approx. 14.5 knots	Approx. 14.5 knots
Fuel-oil supply	75 tons	60 tons
Surface range	8,000 nautical miles at 6 knots	6,500 nautical miles at 6 knots
Battery weight	67 tons	57.5 tons (as in BIII)
Armament	6 torpedo tubes (4 submerged bow, 2 surface stern) 12 torpedoes. 1 × 10.5cm U-boat gun	4 torpedo tubes (2 submerged bow, 2 surface stern) 10 torpedoes. 1 × 8.8cm U-boat gun
Diving depth	100m	75m

Table 8. The Scheer Programme and additional orders

	Project 42a	Ms type	Large minelaying boats	UCIII	UBIII	UG	Total
GW	—	26	—	—	—	—	26
B&V	13	—	—	69*	—	—	82*
AG Weser	6	—	—	—	31**	—	37**
Vulcan, Hamburg	—	—	15	—	12	14	41
KWD	8	—	—	—	—	—	8
Schichau, Elbing	—	29	—	—	—	—	29
Bremer Vulkan	—	20	—	—	—	—	20
Tecklenborg	—	—	—	—	—	18	18
Neptun	—	—	—	—	—	12	12
Atlas-Werke	—	—	—	—	—	4	4
Seebeck	—	—	—	—	—	8	8
Nordseewerke	—	—	—	—	—	24	24
Flensburger SBG	—	—	—	—	—	19	19
Scheer's new construction programme	27	75	15	69*	43**	101	330
Addn. to orders for 1920	16	35	—	—	13	UF 15	79
Total ready in 1920	43	110	15	66	55 / UF 15	G 101	405
Type ratio	1 :	2.5	:	1.6	:	4	

*3 UCIII boats already marked down for delivery in 1919.   **1 UBIII boat already marked down for delivery in 1919.

Various Ms boats in front of the shelter 'Emden' (the forerunner of the Second World War bunkers) in January 1918.

UG: UCIII=1:2½:4:1½; with, additionally, 15 large minelaying U-boats. For the time being, UF boats and U-cruisers were no longer to be ordered. It was not intended to build a boat specially for the Mediterranean as, in view of the Large Building Programme, it had been decided to build as few types as possible. These proceedings meant that, over and above the Scheer Programme, the U-Boat Office had made the additional orderings shown in Table 8, which were to be delivered by 1920.

Although organizational preliminary work for the Large U-Boat Programme was continuing, German diplomacy was all in favour of the quickest possible ending of the war, as can be seen from the peace overture made by the new Chancellor, Max von Baden, to President Wilson on 5 October 1918. Flanders had been evacuated by the middle of October 1918 and, on the 21st, in accordance with Wilson's demand, the U-boat war against passenger shipping was suspended. Admiral Scheer recalled all U-boats from commerce raiding, but stuck to his U-boat programme so that, if the proceedings for the suspension of hostilities broke down, he might have the means to pursue an increased U-boat campaign, perhaps gaining more favourable peace conditions thereby.

At the end of the month, a further meeting concerning the Scheer Programme took place in the RMA, when the question of crews for the new U-boats was discussed. The building of extensions at the yards had already begun, but the additional workers agreed to by the OHL had not yet arrived. Long-term planning, however, had now become completely unrealistic and, on 29 October 1918, the Admiralty Staff pronounced: 'The construction of all new surface vessels and U-boats that cannot be completed by the beginning of July 1919 is to be suspended in the interests of completing as many U-boats as possible by the beginning of 1919.' What might possibly affect adversely the delivery of U-boats in the early part of 1919, was a plan projected by the OHL for a tank-building programme to commence in November 1918 (with a planned increase from 150 to 1,000 tanks by 1 April 1919). If this programme came about, it would mean a reduction by 30 per cent in the number of U-boats by the middle of January 1919, but the OHL admitted that, as fuel for these tanks was in very inadequate supply, a realization of the scheme was rather doubtful.

The cessation of hostilities on 11 November 1918 put an end to all plans and preparations for the Scheer Programme. Even if the war had continued, it is doubtful if it would have been fulfilled as planned. In his book, *Die Deutsche Marinepolitik 1916–1918*, p. 138, Dr. Stegemann states:

'At the psychological moment, the exigencies of the situation called strongly for a programme such as was projected, and we have to assume that, while the SKL was not convinced that the programme in its entirety could be carried out, it was necessary to commence preparations in order to impress the enemy and our own population.'

3 FOUNDATIONS OF THE NEW U-BOAT ARM, 1925–1935

EXPERIMENTAL PROJECTS ABROAD, 1925–32

Avoiding the submarine ban: IvS

One of the essential conditions of the cessation of hostilities was the delivery of the German U-boat fleet to Britain. A further condition went beyond this in stating that, from 16 January 1919, U-boats that had not been delivered or were in the course of being built should either be destroyed or dismantled. Concerning this, the State Secretary of the RMA wrote on 7 February 1919 to People's Delegate Noske in the Reichs Government:

'. . . As we cannot think about laying down new U-boats after the peace treaty has been concluded, this means just this: Germany will have not a single U-boat at its disposal in the foreseeable future. This is unbearable. Even the smallest countries with a coastline have some submarines for their defence. The complete lack of this method of defence would be an invitation for other countries to take possession of important islands, of fishing bases, and of ports on our coasts, in just the same way that the lack of an organized defensive army has encouraged the Poles to take possession of parts of our border territory. The outside world will therefore be led to carry out deeds, the reversing of which will be infinitely harder than their prevention. . . . A complete ban on any kind of U-boat defence — to the extent that we shall not even be able to train personnel in U-boat ways and means — signifies an immense and far-reaching danger to our country against enemy sea attacks. I stress therefore as a matter of urgency and make full representations that, while we may perhaps not be able to make it a condition of the cessation of hostilities, we must at least try to press in most definite terms the peace negotiations for the return of some of our U-boats.'

The Peace Treaty of Versailles, signed by Germany on 28 June 1919, nevertheless confirmed the conditions of 16 January for the cessation of hostilities, and called for an absolute and complete ban on the production of U-boats:

'Article 188: Within one month of the implementation of the present Treaty, all German submarines, submarine-lifting ships, submarine docks — including tubular docks — must be delivered up to the principal Allied and associated forces. Those submarines, vessels and docks which, in the view of the appropriate authority, can proceed under their own power or by being towed, shall be delivered up by the German Government to those Allied ports as are designated. The other submarines, and that includes those under construction, will be completely dismantled by the German Government under supervision of the appropriate authority. This must be completed in not more than three months after the implementation of the present Treaty.

'Article 189: All parts, engines and material items of any kind that derive from the dismantling of any kind of German warship — service ship and submarine — may only be used exclusively for industrial or trade purposes. They may not be sold nor be transferred to foreign countries.

'Article 191: The construction and acquisition of any kind of submarine, even for trade purposes, is forbidden to Germany.'

Furthermore, Article 181 stated categorically, regarding the forces allowed to the German Navy that 'submarines are not permitted'.

At the dictates of the cessation of hostilities and of these articles of the Treaty, a total of 176 boats (8 U-cruisers, 62 U-boats, 64 UB and 42 UC boats) were delivered to Britain and finally divided up between Britain, the United States, France, Italy and Japan — they were to have considerable influence on submarine construction in all these countries. However, it was not decreed that all constructional details be handed over, so the direct copying of these models was not an easy matter. Those U-boats that remained in Germany, in an unseaworthy or unready state, were broken up under the control of the Allied Commission.

The U-Boat Inspectorate and the U-Boat Office were dissolved, after dismantling had been completed. Subsequently, in 1920, a U-Boat Section was created within the new Inspectorate for Torpedoes and Mines (TMI) in Kiel. This section dealt chiefly with the war diaries, test records and other documentation relating to U-boat development and U-boat warfare, the main objects being to collect material for a history of the German U-boat campaign and to study the development of submarine defence methods. In 1922, this office was similarly dissolved, and the complete documentation was handed over to the Reichs Archives.

Part of the German U-boat fleet was duly handed over to the Allies and the remainder was destroyed. Nevertheless, the yards and the new Naval Directorate were anxious that submarine development work should continue, and so, with a view to turning their considerable skill and experience to financial account, they sought to supply constructional drawings, workers and advisers to neutral or friendly countries. By 1920, the GW and Vulcan designs for the U-cruiser, *U142*, and for the large minelaying U-boat, *U117*, had been sold to Japan: construction drawings for boats designated *I1–I3* and *I21–I24* by the Japanese, were produced at the Kawasaki Yard in Kobe under the supervision of German designers from GW and Vulcan, and partly under the personal direction of Dr. Techel. By permission of the German Naval Directorate, Kapitänleutnant Robert Bräutigam (Retd.) acted as adviser during the trials of these boats. As a member of the former UAK (U-Boat Acceptance Commission), he possessed considerable knowledge in this sphere.

In 1921, the Argentinian Navy invited the former Head of the U-Boat Flotilla in Flanders, Korvettenkapitän Karl Bartenbach, and two former naval architects, Friedrich Schürer and Wilhelm Krankenhagen, to act as civilian consultants for the creation of an Argentinian submarine arm. At the beginning of 1922, Bartenbach informed the German Naval Directorate that the Argentinians intended to build 10 submarines in their own yards. The Navy, therefore, asked Vulcan to form, with the two Krupp yards, GW and AG Weser, a consortium to carry out the project, and work together on future undertakings of this kind. The Krupp yards replied that they were quite willing to do this.

On 12 April 1922, GW announced that a plan had been outlined by the three yards for a combined undertaking. Apart from work on the Argentinian project, there were also plans for participation in submarine construction at an Italian yard (by Vulcan) and in an undertaking with Sweden which had already begun (Weser). Essential requirements for this combined work were the application of German U-boat experience and capacity to develop ideas in the planning of designs for projects, the preparation of construction drawings, consultancy, and assistance in submarine building and testing. However, the conditions imposed by the peace treaty made these activities impossible for a German firm, and it was necessary to set up such a venture in a foreign country: for geographic and political reasons, Holland was chosen and, in July 1922, N.V. Ingenieurskaantor voor Scheepsbouw (telegraphic abbreviation 'Inkavos'), commonly referred to as IvS, was formed. The new firm was headed by Doctor of Engineering Hans Techel as Technical Director, and Korvettenkapitän Ulrich Blum (Retd.) as Commercial Director. A board of directors for overall control of the firm was chosen from the three yards, and all profits and losses were to be shared. The start was quite modest: the founding capital was only 12,000 Dutch guilders, each yard contributing a third. The opening of the office in The Hague was delayed because the Dutch Government rejected the application for registration, so IvS was run initially from an office at GW in Kiel. A team was gradually built up, consisting of Hugo Seligmann, Georg Behrmann, Hugo Peine, Karl Knorre and Richard Wagner. All were formerly on the staff of GW, and were skilled in U-boat construction.

A start was made by sifting background material and plans, and by working out tenders that bore close resemblance to German Navy U-boat constructional practice — for Argentina, a design for a 570-ton boat, Pu7, was similar to Type UBIII; and, for Italy, the design for an 850-ton boat Pu4, was similar to the Ms type. In the meantime, however, the Argentinians had given up the idea of a submarine project, and the business with Italy came to nothing either. Nor was the attempt successful to conclude a development project with Spain for 6 C class submarines. This work went to the American Electric Boat Company, whose designs had been built from 1924 by the Spanish state yard, Constructura Navale, Cartagena, a firm strongly connected with Vickers-Armstrong.

At this time, the German Navy was greatly interested in a close working collaboration with Spain, and had sent Kapitänleutnant Wilhelm Canaris several times as an intermediary in armament deals between German firms and the Spanish Government. In 1924, Spain had in hand an ambitious building programme of 40 submarines. Of these, the previously mentioned construction company, Constructura Navale, had an option for 28 boats, which they proposed to build according to Vickers designs (D class). The remaining 12 boats of the programme were to be put out to tender. The requirement was for a 1,000-ton boat, with high surface speed (approximately 20 knots) and an extensive range.

IvS offered an appropriate design, Pu53, through the medium of a Spanish contracting group closely associated with Krupp, UNL (Socieda Anonima Espaniola Union de Levante). The main specifications of Pu53D were as follows:

Length overall:	78.5m.
Maximum beam:	7.2m.
Draught:	4m.
Displacement surfaced:	990 tons approx.
Displacement submerged:	1,300 tons.
Speed surfaced:	20 knots.
Speed submerged:	8.5 knots.
Propulsion surfaced:	two 2,440hp diesel engines.
Propulsion submerged:	two 700hp electric motors.
Armament:	six torpedo tubes (four bow submerged, two stern submerged; fourteen 53.5cm torpedoes.

(A later version, with MAN diesel engines each developing 1,400hp, with a maximum surface speed of 16.5 knots, was given the designation Pu53E.)

Simultaneously, B&V, a French and an Italian firm were also competing for the tender. The IvS design, on the other hand, was to be built at a yard belonging to UNL.

The Spanish Government decided in favour of a German design but with the new MAN diesel engines, offered only by B&V. This put IvS in a difficult situation because the Spanish Government was unwilling to have its boats built by the Krupp-dependant UNL. Also sympathetically considered by the Spanish Government were designs from Don Horacio Echevarrieta, an industrialist strongly connected with the Spanish throne, who wanted to build up an armament industry completely divorced from foreign influence, and to build submarines at his own shipyard, Larrinaga y Echevarrieta, in Cadiz. He even wished to build accessory items (MAN diesel engines, AEG electrical fittings and torpedoes) entirely in Spain. The German Naval Directorate, fearing that IvS would once again be frustrated in their application, arranged for B&V to withdraw their offer, and transferred the MAN licence to the IvS design. Furthermore, it wanted to bring about the dissolution of the contract between IvS and UNL so that collaborations with Echevarrieta could take place freely. But, in the summer of 1925, a crisis in Morocco plus other political difficulties caused the Spanish Government to shelve their entire submarine programme. For the time being, any further endeavour by IvS in Spain would be pointless.

Thus, by 6 July 1925, the receipts for IvS were very meagre, amounting to only 93,000 marks for the designing of 53 possible projects. The largest single amount in this total was the gift of 39,000 marks from UNL for their participation in negotiations. A further, largish sum of 31,000 marks came from the firm of C. Illies, Hamburg, who represented IvS in Japan.

In the summer of 1925, the eleven-man staff of IvS moved from Kiel to The Hague, occupying business premises on the corner of Wagenstraat and Gedempte Burgwal. IvS was to stay here until its dissolution in 1945. Until May 1937 and August 1938, the firm was controlled by Blum and Techel, respectively.

Clandestine organizations and plans
In view of the existing competition, it seemed that a commercial breakthrough would not be made by IvS without financial guarantees and subsidies. This applied also to the efforts of Ulrich Blum, who was trying to obtain a contract from Turkey for two 500-ton submarines to be built at the Dutch yard of Fijenoord in Rotterdam to IvS designs. The financial risks of the business could not be borne alone by the three yards represented by IvS, and it was necessary for the German Navy, which had a great interest in any submarine built to German designs and under German control, to lend financial support. The means to accomplish this lay in the secret funds of BS (Seetransportabteilung im Allgemeinen Marineamt 'B', or 'Sea Transport Department') headed by Kapitän zur See Walter Lohmann. But, as the Navy was not allowed to have any direct part in IvS, BS set up a dummy firm with the designation 'Mentor Bilanz' (for bookkeeping, financial transactions and consultancy). From 1 July 1925, this firm was to serve as a contact point between the Navy and IvS. It acquired as Director, the former Korvettenkapitän

and U-boat commander, Robert Moraht, and joined the three founding shipyards of IvS. Lohmann was ready to provide a subsidy of 1,000,000 marks for the 500-ton submarines for Turkey, and maintained that, if necessary, he was prepared to subsidise IvS in difficult years to a total of 120,000 marks per year. In this way, the German Navy became the main backer for IvS.

Apart from the financing and contact firm of Mentor Bilanz, Lohmann started another dummy firm with the designation 'Tebeg GmbH' (Technische Beratungs-und Beschaffungs-gesellschaft MbH, or 'Technical Advisory and Procurement Company'), which was to be a kind of armaments and supply office for mobilization preparations, especially those connected with submarine undertakings. The direction of this company was entrusted to Fregattenkapitän Herbert Goehle (Retd.) Both of these dummy firms were situated, together with BS, in the premises of the Weapons Department BW of the General Naval Office ('B') in Berlin, Lützowufer 3.

On the advice of Canaris, a clandestine U-boat department, with the cover designation 'Au' (Anti-U-Boat Defence Questions) was set up in the Naval Command Office ('A'). Control of this department was given to Kapitän zur See Arno Spindler on 1 September 1925. His task was to collaborate with IvS (through Mentor Bilanz), select U-boat types for mobilization plans, and make preparations for U-boat construction. On 5 February 1927, this U-boat department was subordinated to the Fleet Department, and was given the designation 'A II u'. To assist Spindler, and to act as liaison man between A II u, Mentor Bilanz and IvS, Oberleutnant zur See Hans Schottky was appointed (meanwhile being officially placed on the Navy retired list).

Background material and drawings from the former Technical Office of the U-Boat Inspectorate (TB), which were available in the new Construction Office ('K'), made possible the formation of projects for mobilization planning in the U-boat sphere without any recourse to IvS. To this end, in June 1927, under the control of Chief Marine Consultant (Retd.) Friedrich Schürer, a clandestine U-Boat Construction Office of the German Navy was set up as the 'Technical Department of Mentor Bilanz'. When Moraht resigned from Mentor Bilanz, the question arose as to who should replace him as Director of this office. On 15 September 1927, the Naval Directorate made the following suggestions to Offices 'A' and 'B':

'The way that things have developed has led me to the conclusion that 'Mentor' in its present form may be considered either as superfluous, or merely as a negotiating agency for U-boat questions. The present Director Dr. M[oraht] has left. It is essential that Oberleutnant zur See Schottky takes over the direction; U-boat problems and the connection with IvS demand this. 'M' suggests that the new organization be based in such a way that, as in all other arms, things run thus:

'1. A II u (Konteradmiral Spindler) works out all 'A' undertakings.

'2. A new office, called either 'Mentor' or better perhaps, BWu (Oberleutnant zur See (Retd.)

Schottky) takes care of 'B' work on U-boats and is the liaison man with IvS. It is expedient that he should remain unofficial collaborator with A II u for questions of mobilization operations and training problems (A I —, A III — considerations).

'3. 'K' — questions remain, as before, the province of the Schürer Office. Up to now, this office has been financially dependent on 'Mentor'. If 'Mentor' is dissolved, which 'M' thinks should be done, the question arises whether BWu should be affiliated to 'Tebeg' like Schürer or be a direct part of BW.'

Friedrich Schürer.

Mentor Bilanz was consequently placed under BS for organizational purposes, and was designated 'BS I u'. Control of it was given to Schottky ('BS I ua'), and Schürer's office was given the designation 'BS I ub'.

However, as the Lohmann affair began to come to light (his secret financial transactions having been disclosed by the Press and questions asked in the Reichstag), the beginning of the end of Mentor was in sight. Although itself not directly compromised, when BS and Tebeg were liquidated, Mentor was similarly dissolved and replaced, in the autumn of 1928, by the newly founded dummy firm 'Igewit' (Ingenieurbüro für Wirtschaft und Technik GmbH, or 'Engineering Office for Economics and Technics GmbH'). Once again, Schottky (Military Questions) and Schürer ('K' aspects) were placed in control. The Tebeg undertakings were taken over by the new department, BSt, in the General Naval Office.

In the summer of 1929, Spindler left the U-boat department A II u, to devote himself solely to

historical research in the Naval Archives into the rôle of the German U-boat during the First World War. His successor was Schottky, who now not only represented the various U-boat affairs but also those of 'A' and 'B': for a former Oberleutnant zur See, he fulfilled a unique rôle in German U-boat history.

Medium submarines for Turkey and Finland
Discussions as to which type of submarine should be built when Germany would eventually be free from the Versailles ban resulted in the medium U-boat Type UBIII and UCIII from the First World War being chosen (for mobilization purposes). Research was carried out during the winter of 1921/22 by Kapitänleutnant von Mellenthin on the question 'Which of our U-boat types that we used during the war are most appropriate for future development?' and Spindler, Schottky and Schürer and many former U-boat personnel were also concerned with the issue. The Navy, through the medium of IvS, showed a strong interest in the development of testing of these types, and especially in the two submarines being built in 1926 for the Turkish Navy. Designated Pu46, they were based on Type UBIII and had the following specifications.

Length overall:	59m.
Maximum beam:	5.8m.
Draught:	3.5m.
Displacement surfaced:	505 tons.
Displacement submerged:	620 tons.
Power surfaced:	two 550hp diesel engines.
Power submerged:	two 390hp electric motors.
Speed surfaced:	14.5 knots.
Speed submerged:	9.5 knots.
Range surfaced:	7,500 nautical miles at 6 knots.
Range submerged:	80 nautical miles at 4 knots.
Armament:	six torpedo tubes (four bow submerged, two stern surface); ten 45cm torpedoes.

The contract with Turkey stipulated that IvS should have the right to select crews and attend all trials of the boats. As no officers having the appropriate experience were available in Holland, IvS turned to Mentor for help: this gave the German Navy a fine opportunity to acquire precise information as to the qualities of the boats. Out of political consideration for Holland, the Naval Directorate wished only officers no longer on the active list to be used; which meant that Mentor, in collaboration with Spindler, had to either retire existing officers or find people no longer in service.

The first boat, Fij 304 (*Birindci Inönü*), left the slipway on 1 February 1927, and the second, Fij 305 (*Ikindci Inönü*), followed on 12 March. Trials of the first boat started on 30 April and lasted until the end of June. The other boat was tested after this date because only one crew was available. (The commander was Kapitänleutnant Werner Fürbringer (Retd.) and the engineering officer

Kapitänleutnant Walter Hülsmann (Retd.).) Schottky, together with Schürer and Naval Construction Adviser Schotte from the Construction Office, came to Holland towards the end of August 1927 for the final phase of the trials. However, the Turkish Navy was not ready to accept the two boats until the spring of the following year, so it was not until 22 May 1928 that the boats left Rotterdam. They reached Istanbul after an eighteen-day voyage during which much valuable operating data was acquired. Fürbringer and Hülsmann were responsible for taking Fij 304 to Turkey and another crew was made up by Mentor Bilanz for the other boat. This was commanded by Kapitänleutnant Karl Neumann (Retd.) and the engineering officer was Senior Naval Engineer Papenberg (Retd.) The Naval Director authorized Fürbringer and Hülsmann to remain in Turkey to supervise the formation of a submarine school.

Following his rather unsuccessful negotiations with Argentina, Bartenbach had been Naval Adviser to Finland since 1924, and had taken pains to persuade the Finns to have submarines built to IvS designs. His initiative was rewarded in 1926, when the German Navy received a contract for 3 torpedo-armed minelaying submarines, similar to the IvS design for Pu89, to be built by the Crichton-Vulkan Shipyard at Abo (now Turku) in Finland. In contrast with the German UC boats of the war, the mines would be carried in wet storage, in shafts next to the pressure hull; this enabled submerged torpedo tubes to be fitted forward and aft. With this design, IvS achieved an operationally-sound U-boat type, which greatly exceeded UCIII in handling properties without requiring larger surface displacement. The main specifications were as follows.

Length overall:	63m.
Maximum beam:	6.1m.
Draught:	3.2m.
Displacement surfaced:	493 tons.
Displacement submerged:	715 tons.
Propulsion surfaced:	two 580hp Atlas diesel engines.
Propulsion submerged:	two 300hp electric motors.
Speed surfaced:	14 knots.
Speed submerged:	8 knots.
Range surfaced:	4,000 nautical miles at 10 knots.
Range submerged:	75 nautical miles at 3 knots.
Armament:	four torpedo tubes (two submerged bow, two submerged stern); six 53.3cm torpedoes. 20 200kg mines, five shafts on both sides

The first boat, CV702 (*Vetehinen*), was laid down in September 1926. At the beginning of 1927, IvS sent three experienced U-boat builders, Hugo Peine, Wilhelm Etzbach and Edgar Rickmeier, to supervise work at Abo and, at about this time, CV703 (*Vesihiisi*) and CV704 (*Iku-Turso*) were laid down. The building time was very long — almost three-and-a-half-years. The yard's lack of experience, the difficult route for delivering materials, but above all the lengthy breaks during the very cold winter months meant that CV702 did not leave the slipway until 2 June 1930. CV703 followed on 2 August.

As before, IvS organized the trials through the Berlin U-Boat Office. On this occasion, as Abo was geographically very remote, the selection of personnel was not hampered by political considerations. As it seemed likely that this particular submarine type might have considerable significance for the future construction programme of German U-boats, Schottky himself took over direction of the crew, which included Papenberg as engineering officer and the active officers, Kapitänleutnant Karl Topp, Kapitänleutnant (Engineer) Karl Thannemann, and Oberleutnant zur See Hans Rudolf Rösing, and the retired officers, Leutnant zur See Plaas and Leutnant (Engineer) Lorek, plus the young designer, Wätje, from IvS. As Topp and Thannemann had to leave the trials' crew for some time, Oberleutnant (Engineer) Bartel was later included. After a shakedown cruise of fourteen days (the crew, apart from Schottky and Papenberg, having had no experience of submarines), trials of CV702 began on 14 July 1930. In all essentials, they had been completed by 6 September 1930 and, at the conclusion of his report of them, Schottky claimed: 'With regard to the diving qualities, the seaworthiness and the offensive abilities in relation to the displacement, Kapitän Bartenbach and I are of the opinion that these are better than any foreign submarines.'

The Spanish project: E1

Early in 1926, the 1918 Type UG (Project 51a of the Imperial Navy) was chosen instead of the UBIII type by the U-Boat Planning Department in case a mobilization plan became reality. This design had not been fully worked out when the war ended. First, IvS had to make a thorough evaluation of the available data, and the drawings were sent to them in May 1926. Then it was necessary to have a test boat built in a friendly foreign country, with German participation and under German direction. Finally, the German Navy needed an opportunity to thoroughly test the submarine.

For the furtherance of this scheme, Spain seemed especially appropriate. In support of this was the fact that the ambitious Spanish industrialist, Echevarrieta, had stated that, in return for the granting of a sizeable German credit 'immediately the Spanish Navy gave him the contract for the construction of submarines, he would authorize construction of the boats through a German firm with assistance from the Naval Directorate and pay special heed to the wishes of the German Naval Directorate with regard to building instruction and participation in trials'. (Communication from Lohmann to the Reichs Finance Minister dated 31 March 1926)

On 18 August 1926, Lohmann and Canaris travelled to Spain, taking with them designs that IvS had worked out for the Type UG, in order to see what the possibilities were of a test construction to this design. Spain, however, had originally stated that its interest in future submarine building lay in the larger type (1,000 tons) with a higher surface speed, and was not yet ready to sign an appropriate contract. The fact that IvS was still bound by contract to UNL, while the Spanish Government gave preference to Echevarrieta, also militated against the scheme. During further discussions, it appeared that the Spaniards wanted to enlarge the deal and to include the submarine in a 'package' (an oil-tanker, fishing trawlers, torpedo-boats, etc.). On Canaris' initiative, early in 1927, Oberleutnant zur See Eberhard Messerschmidt (Retd.) was sent to Madrid as Naval Adviser to the Spanish Admiralty, where he worked in permanent liaison between the German Naval Directorate, the Spanish Navy and Echevarrieta.

In July 1927, the Spanish Defence Ministry sent Echevarrieta to Berlin to carry out further negotiations, and Canaris informed him that the German Naval Directorate was ready to assist in the construction of Type UG boats in Spain, in terms of both money and labour. In practical terms, this meant that Echevarrieta would place his yard at their disposal, and that all further expenditure on submarine building would be financed in advance by the German Navy. In the meantime, Krupp had intervened to the extent that the contract between the UNL and IvS was dissolved, which meant that this obstacle no longer existed.

On 23 August 1927, a meeting to discuss finance took place, chaired by Konteradmiral Pfeiffer (A), with Fregattenkapitän Assmann (A II), Canaris (A I), Spindler and Schottky (A II u) and the naval architects Ehrenberg, Grauert and Schotte from 'K' Office. It was agreed to support Type UG building programme from the secret re-armament fund to a total of 4 million marks, and it was estimated that the total building costs would amount to 4.6 million marks. To justify this considerable expenditure, A II u explained in a memorandum dated 17 October 1927:

'In evading the Treaty of Versailles by maintaining submarine development and, if possible, training a limited number of personnel, it is essential that the far-from-prosperous IvS be given all possible support. . . . Our contracts in Spain make it possible that, currently, an expenditure of 1.5 million marks immediately, and in toto 3–4 million marks (spread over three years) to be used as directed by the IvS, will enable us to approach the target of building the best and most modern submarines, of acquainting our architects and yard personnel with all that is best in modern thinking, and of achieving the best military crews (both seafaring and technical) in the submarine field.'

By the end of 1927, negotiations between Canaris, Messerschmidt and the Spanish Admiralty had come to a decisive point. In the meantime, Echevarrieta and IvS had agreed on the construction of a test boat based on Type UG, the hull of which would be built in sections by the Dutch Fijenoord yard, and assembled at the small private yard of Echevarrieta in Cadiz. At the end of November 1927, Schotte and Schürer travelled to The Hague and to Cadiz to discuss preliminary

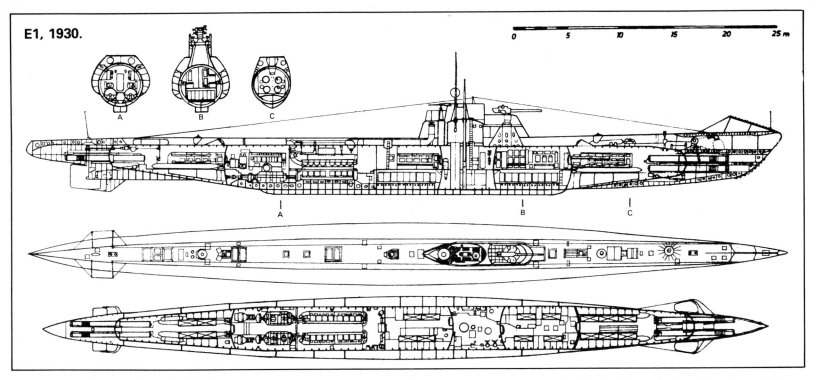

E1, 1930.

constructional details with IvS and Echevarrieta. Various circumstances (including the tardy extension of buildings in the Cadiz yard) delayed commencement of work until 1928, and by then the final design from IvS for the experimental construction, Project Number Pu111, had become a considerably enlarged double-hulled submarine in contrast to the smaller, original Type UG of 640 tons. The reasons for this change were requests from the Spanish Navy for 1,400hp diesel engines and for a greater surface range, which could not be achieved with the predominantly single-hulled forms of Type UG. The new design included an outer casing, which was drawn right down to the lowest part of the pressure hull and contained diving and trimming tanks as well as fuel-oil bunkers. It was planned to change the torpedo armament from 50cm diameter to the international 53.3cm (21-inch) calibre and to include several other modifications, such as using new electric (and thus wakeless) torpedoes. The main specifications of Pu111 were as follows.

Length overall:	72.38m.
Maximum beam:	6.2m.
Draught:	4m.
Displacement surfaced:	745 tons.
Displacement submerged:	965 tons.
Propulsion surfaced:	two 1,400hp MAN diesel engines.
Propulsion submerged:	two 500hp electric motors.
Speed surfaced:	17 knots.
Speed submerged:	8.5 knots.
Range surfaced:	7,000 nautical miles at 10 knots.

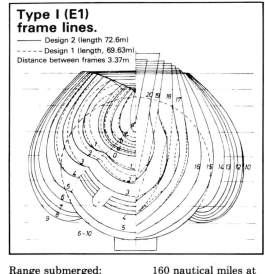

Type I (E1) frame lines.
——— Design 2 (length 72.6m)
- - - - Design 1 (length, 69.63m)
Distance between frames 3.37m

Range submerged:	160 nautical miles at 4 knots.
Armament:	six torpedo tubes (four submerged bow, two submerged stern); ten 53.3cm torpedoes. one 10.5cm L/45 U-boat gun; one 2cm AA gun.
Crew:	32.

The laying-down of this submarine, which was given yard designations Ech21 and E1, followed in February 1929. Although much of the preliminary construction work had been done in Holland, and the delivery of engines and most items of equipment from Germany went well, the assembly work in Cadiz lasted eight months longer than it should have, even though this work was under the supervision of Constructional Advisers (Retd.) Schotte and Hey, and a group of specialists including Ludwig (Engines) and Meesel (Electro-technics) from the Naval Yard at Wilhelmshaven. In the meantime, Echevarrieta had overreached himself by his lofty projects and had become bankrupt. E1 was now to be completed solely by IvS, with 100 per cent financial support from the German Navy. Spain merely had the option to purchase the boat.

On 22 October 1930, E1 was launched, but grounded and stuck fast a short distance from the slipway. There were further difficulties with fitting-out, which meant that the projected trials could not start until the summer of 1931. Early in that year, the following active and retired naval officers had been selected for the trials' crew: Kapitänleutnant Robert Bräutigam (Retd.) (commander), Papenberg (chief engineer), Oberleutnant zur See Rösing, Oberleutnant zur See (engineer) Heerhartz and Leutnant zur See Harald Grosse. Additionally, there were several IvS architects (including Ebschner and Seidel) and a group of ship construction students, together with a detachment from the Torpedo Testing Establishment at Eckernförde, with their chief, Kapitän zur See Hirth, who were to test a new torpedo-firing device designed by Chief Torpedo Engineer (Retd.) Kunze. The trials lasted from May until 4 July 1931. Schürer took part as an observer from 24 June and reported favourably to the Naval Directorate. The subsequent fall of the Spanish Monarchy in 1932 and the unrest in the country prevented the planned Spanish purchase of E1.

The 'Lilliput' project: CV707

Early in 1924, Finland had expressed interest in a small minelaying submarine, for which IvS, via Bartenbach, made a proposal (Pu23). The boat, of only 99 tons, had been designed by Hugo Seligmann, and was intended for special operations on Lake Ladoga. However, the Finnish Navy had been reluctant to give a decision, possibly because the boat was rather too small to serve as the nucleus for a Finnish submarine arm. During the following years, the offer was repeated in the form of Pu78/79, in connection with the larger design Pu89, but it was not until 1929 that Bartenbach succeeded in persuading the Finns to agree to the building of a small boat to an improved design, Pu109/110. She was built at Hietalahden Laivatelakka in Helsingfors, left the slipway on 2 July 1930, and was given her trials by Schottky's crew in the autumn of that year, together with CV702 and CV703. After her acceptance by the Finnish Navy, she was named *Saukko*, and was the smallest submarine in the world at that time. The main specifications of Pu110 were as follows.

Length overall:	32.95m.
Maximum beam:	3.2m.
Draught:	3.22m.
Displacement surfaced:	99 tons.
Propulsion surfaced:	one 200hp diesel engine.
Speed surfaced:	10 knots.
Speed submerged:	6.25 knots.
Range surfaced:	500 nautical miles at 8 knots.
Range submerged:	50 nautical miles at 4 knots.
Armament:	two bow torpedo tubes (45cm, 5.7m in length); two torpedoes in tubes; special reloading device.
	nine 80kg mines in three sets of guide rails.
	one 13mm MG.

With regard to discussions concerning the most suitable U-boat type that would be required in the event of mobilization, Constructional Adviser Erich Hey suggested on 10 January 1926 in a 'Memorandum pertaining to small, rapidly-built U-boats' from the clandestine Armament Office, Tebeg, that the 99-ton submarine planned for Finland could be taken as a basis. Konteradmiral Spindler (A u), however, rejected this small type on strategic and tactical grounds. On 23 April 1926, a meeting took place at A II, consisting of: Kapitän zur See Loewenfeld with his staff officers, Fregattenkapitän Kurt Assmann and Fregattenkapitän Canaris, Kapitän zur See Ernst Bindseil from the Staff of the General Naval Office

(BZ), Fregattenkapitän Goehle (Retd.) from Tebeg, together with his collaborators, Kapitänleutnant Kurt von der Borne (Retd.) and Constructional Adviser Hey, Ministerial Adviser Wilhelm Laudahn (Diesel Engines) and Constructional Adviser Albrecht Ehrenberg (*Möwe* class and *K* cruisers) and, also from A u, Konteradmiral Spindler. At this meeting, Hey's suggestion was finally turned down, and it was stressed that a 250-ton U-boat was the smallest possible unit for mobilization planning. This conference can be seen as the starting-point for the later Type II: a concept was established that, though occasionally departed from, was never really lost sight of during the development of the new German U-boat arm. The essential result of the discussion was as follows.

'The attitude of A u to Hey's Memorandum was that, in view of wartime experiences with UBI boats and backed up by the evidence of War Diaries from the Flanders Flotillas and in the judgement of Kapitän Bartenbach, both types — *Forelle* and the Finland boats — were, from a nautical and military point of view, unsuitable for operations in a future war sphere. Bearing in mind the need for boats with a short building time, and this is backed up by the opinions of Kapitän Bartenbach, it regards a 250-ton U-boat as the smallest type that is of nautical and military worth in war undertakings. The building time of such a boat, if sufficient initial preparations are made and simplified layouts for engines and internal fittings are borne in mind, would be approximately five months for the first boat and, all in all, the building time of this small type of boat would be significantly shorter than those of 550-ton boats envisaged previously. [The construction time for engines had not been verified at this stage.]

'Moreover, A u regards the establishment of the building time of the most useful type of U-boat in case of war as fairly unimportant, and regards the whole question for the time being as more or less a purely academic constructional operation. To this, Herr Laudahn asserts that the fast-revving diesel engine will burn approximately 5 (as opposed to 22) kilogrammes per hp/hour — a very considerable advantage from the point of view of weight and storage space, although this favourable ratio will be reduced somewhat by the need for a gearing mechanism. In the light of wartime experiences, A u suggests therefore that a smallish number of UBIII boats, which alone were under consideration, be built and these would be of about 550 tons, and the main emphasis should be on a substantially smaller boat — a sort of improved UBII — of approximately 250 tons surface displacement.

'A u appends a memorandum; "K" has been given a copy (and "B" should also receive a similar copy). In the light of this memorandum, "K" will prepare some preliminary designs, and these will ultimately be handed over to IvS for thorough constructional working-out. It would be of great advantage if a friendly foreign power would build a boat of this kind according to the IvS plans so that experience could be obtained from it and complete constructional drawings prepared.'

As early as 14 April 1924, under the designations Project Pu22 and Pu26, the IvS had developed a

Saukko (Pu110), shortly before her launch from the slips at Hietalahden Laivatelakka in Helsingfors.

design for a 245-ton submarine for Estonia, and Bartenbach had tried to interest Finland in this also. The Finns, however, wished to await the completion of the three 493-ton boats of the Pu89 design (*Vetehinen* class), before making a decision about a new contract. For the time being, nothing materialized with regard to the 250-ton type in Germany. Shortly after its concept had been formulated, the 'K' Office began to lay greater emphasis on the more offensively-designed Type UF dating back to the Scheer Programme of 1918 (page 85), and this was to be the smallest projected submarine type in mobilization planning until 1929. Not until after 1929 was a small boat, in the 200—250-ton displacement category, considered for a mobilization programme, and only then because of its considerably short building time and the fact that it could be used equally for torpedo and minelaying operations.

In a 'Programme Sketch concerning Chapter 3 of Office "B"'s Economy' dated 20 February 1930, the new Head of A II u, Hans Schottky, made a statement on the expenditure of funds received up to then for submarine projects and added a statement on 'new requirements for the future':

'1. Especially important is the preparation of a small, simple and quickly-built U-boat type. We are thinking of a single-hulled boat of approximately 200-tons displacement with a 12-knots surface speed and a torpedo armament of three 53cm bow tubes. We should try to get a project on these lines built and completed to the trials stage in a foreign country as soon as possible. If the 1.5 million marks

Type II frame lines (IvS Design J7).

Main specifications: Length overall, 35.82m; beam, without saddle-tanks, 4.13m; beam, with saddle-tanks, 4.86m; draught, 3.32m; displacement surfaced, 249.8 tons.

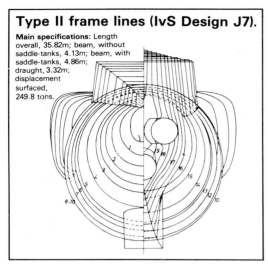

Type II (CV707) frame lines.

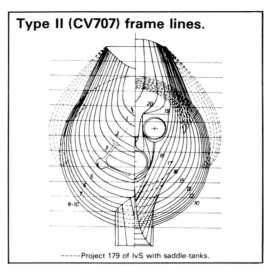

-----Project 179 of IvS with saddle-tanks.

cannot be allocated for this, the construction will have to be postponed until the "B Economy" is in possession of the proceeds resulting from the test construction of the G-type (E1). It is to be assumed that this will take place in the course of 1931. A test construction, on these lines, of a boat of about 200 tons, would provide a valuable task for the architectural staff (IvS). The construction would provide useful training for personnel both on the active list and on the retired list, and would provide us with essential building experience and background (working drawings) and also sea-trial experience and results, which are essential, when we come to build vessels of this type for our own use, in helping us avoid teething troubles, breakdowns and crew mishaps.

'2. Immediately constructional details and trial results are available for a type as outlined in Point 1 (above), ways must be found of preparing all the important components necessary for a number of boats: torpedo tubes, engines, auxiliary equipment, accumulators, periscopes, gyroscopic compasses,

Vesikko (CV707).

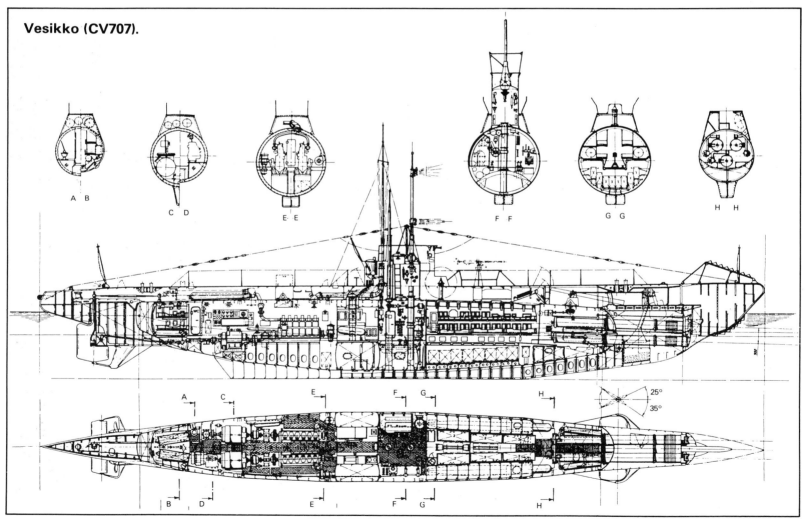

castings, pressure-hull plates, armatures, etc. In this way, one could achieve the assembly of a quantity of these boats, if day and night work were carried out, in a very short time indeed, that is to say in eight weeks at a selected yard. At least 6 such boats are essential, as at any one time only one-third of the complement of vessels is at a state of readiness.

'3. The U-boat training course at the TS, which has been requested and which would supply a certain number of officers trained step-by-step in theoretical and practical matters, could also supply personnel to man these boats. . . .'

That is how Schottky outlined future development policy in 1930. The new Head of the Navy, Admiral Raeder, who was interested in the new type because of its short building time, laid stress on financial backing. Although the construction of E1 in Spain had almost completely exhausted the Special Construction Estimate of 1930, Raeder succeeded in having made available a first instalment of 1 million marks for the new 250-ton project, which was given the cover name of 'Lilliput'. The full building price of 1.5 million marks was included in the 1931 expenditures. By these means, the building of an appropriate submarine was assured, and it was to be built in Finland. In effect, until the boat was purchased by the Finnish Navy, the German Naval Directorate was the real commissioning body (as had been the case with E1 in Spain), organizing and supervising the enterprise through the disguised U-boat office, Igewit, in Berlin.

After the fitting-out and successful trials of the 3 *Vetehinen* class and *Saukko*, Finland was prepared to award a contract for the 250-ton boat. In connection with this, Schürer sent several IvS designs (Projects 170 and 172) together with a design of his own (I5) to Bartenbach on 27 May 1930. The German Navy was especially interested in the Igewit designs I5 and, later, I7 (which was to be the basic concept for the final design of Project 179, and was to be worked out by IvS). On 9 October 1930, after a successful trial of *Vetehinen*, a contract was placed by the Finns for the building of a 250-ton submarine by Crichton-Vulkan at Abo. The fitting-out and constructional supervision were entrusted to IvS.

In effect, Project 179 minus the saddle tanks formed the basis of the design. The single hull was chosen because of a desire for better resistance to depth-charges and a shorter diving time — the same requirements that had led to the building of Type UF for North Sea operations in 1917. A characteristic of the new 250-ton design was the arrangement of three 53.3cm bow torpedo tubes (in place of the four 50cm bow tubes in Type UF). The bow torpedo compartment was fitted-out as conventional living quarters with twelve bunks. Beneath this compartment was the battery installation of 62 cells (32 MAD 580; 6,350 amp.hr with 20 hours discharging) made by the Swedish firm of Tudor. The control room was immediately abaft the bow compartment, above the centre diving tank in the pressure hull.

Two periscopes were fitted, one for the conning tower and one for the control room. Both were raised by the same electrical winch, to which the required periscope had to be connected. The galley was conveniently sited abaft the control room, with its entry hatch and two compensating tanks at the sides. In order to provide a powerful diesel installation in the small boat (as had been requested on 23 April 1926), high-speed diesels had to be fitted. Since it was expedient to use engines that were already at the disposal of the Navy, the MWM (Motoren-Werke Mannheim) type, producing 350hp at 1,000rpm, as used in the new motor minesweepers, were chosen. They took up much the same space as the much less powerful 142hp six-cylinder, four-stroke diesels of the similar sized UBII boats of the First World War. On one shaft and clutch, each diesel was connected to a double electric motor of 180hp. The fuel-oil bunkers were sited in the pressure hull beneath the propulsion unit. As no stern armament was carried, an additional living compartment with four bunks could be installed at the rear of the stern section; in practice, it was never really satisfactory when the

boat was at sea. As with the other boats built in Finland, the building time was very lengthy: CV707, as she was designated until handed over to the Finnish Navy, was not launched until 10 May 1933.

The trials carried out with this boat presented yet another opportunity of instructing young naval officers in submarine crewing and handling. Earlier, on 15 June 1932, the order had been given that, with effect from the Autumn Reorganization of 1932, Oberleutnante zur See Freiwald (Torpedoes), Behr (Torpedoes), Ewerth (Torpedoes) and Grosse (Wireless Telegraphy) and four unnamed Engineer Officers should join a three-month course in theoretical submarine science and tactics, under the direction of Fürbringer, and be trained to take part in the trials of CV707. The course began on 3 January 1933 at the TNS (Torpedo und Nachrichtenschule, the Torpedo and Communications School at Flensburg-Mürwik). The Technical Instructor was the former U-Flotilla Engineer, Korvettenkapitän Rusche (Retd.) In addition to the four deck

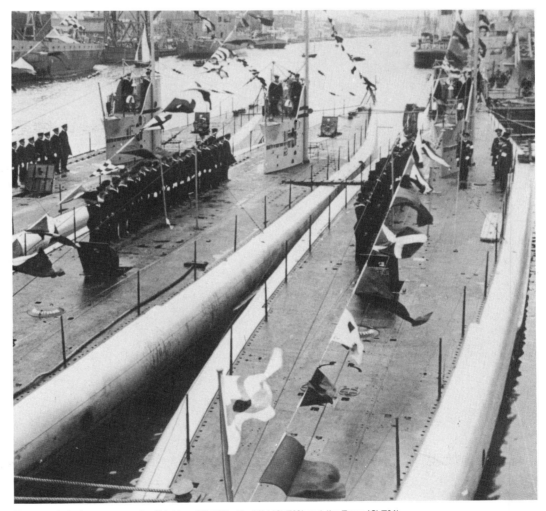

The commissioning ceremony for *Vetehinen* (CV702), *Vesihiisi* (CV703) and *Iku-Turso* (CV704).

officers, the following personnel participated: Oberleutnante (Engineering) Albert Müller, Heinrich Schmidt, Winkler and Droeschel, and two young construction officials, Aschmoneit and Friese.

Trials began at the end of May 1933, with Fürbringer as commander, and Papenberg as chief engineer. (In addition to the 10 named participants from the instruction course, two external and retired officers, Hans Lorek and Johannes Kausch took part.) In August 1933, Bräutigam took over direction of the trials after Fürbringer had suffered a heart attack. The submerged handling qualities of the boat proved first class. It was possible to dive safely and exactly to any desired depth, no matter how the rudder was positioned or how fast the boat was moving. At slow and at half speed, the boat could be kept at periscope depth by changing the position of one man by only half a metre without using the hydroplanes. The boat kept a steady course for five minutes at a speed of 4.7 knots, again without using the hydroplanes. At slow speeds, the boat handled best with the forward hydroplanes; from 6.5 knots to full speed (8 knots), she handled best with the aft hydroplanes alone; and, at intermediate speeds, she handled best with both hydroplanes. When a salvo of three torpedoes was fired, the boat gently inclined 2 metres higher in the water, but stayed safely below the surface. The boat could be put into reverse without any fluctuation of depth. The submerged range proved to be 122.6 nautical miles at 2 knots, 61.1 nautical miles at 4 knots and 15.5 nautical miles at 7 knots. On the surface, she proved very seaworthy. Manoeuvrability was described as 'typical U-boat handling': when going astern only vigorous movement of the helm would cause the boat to change direction, a rolling test produced 10 oscillations in 61 seconds and, over a measured mile on the surface, a speed of 13.002 knots was attained.

On the debit side, the following points were revealed:
1. The diving time was lengthy — 45 seconds to achieve a depth of 9.3m. This resulted from the fact that the central diving tank took 30 seconds to flood instead of the 20 seconds demanded when the contract was placed.
2. Range was restricted (1,960 nautical miles at 8 knots compared with the 3,700 nautical miles at 8 knots in the case of the UBII of the First World War).
3. The unsuppressed noise of the high-speed diesel engines was very loud.
In general, CV707 was criticized more sharply by Fürbringer than by Bräutigam. Originally, it had been arranged that CV707 would now be handed over to the Finnish Navy, but Bartenbach succeeded in extending the trial period into the summer of 1934 so that the boat could be of use to the newly-founded U-boat School, set up in the autumn of 1933 under the cover name 'U-Boat Defence School'. CV707 was eventually commissioned by the Finnish Navy on 13 January 1936,

Left top and below: Two photographs of the preserved *Vesikko* (CV707), taken in August 1965.

and was named *Vesikko*. She survived the Second World War, and was later placed on display as a submarine memorial in Sveaborg.

Mobilization contingency plans to 1932
In a memorandum dated 3 March 1926 'Concerning Military Requirements in Constructional Specifications for Medium and Small U-boats in the light of our Operational Wartime Experiences', Spindler emphasised that, faced with the possibility of mobilization (and assuming the opponents would be France and Poland), the medium U-boat types UBIII and UCIII were ideal for torpedo and minelaying operations, with the UBII type for coastal operations. In this, Spindler was in accord with the trends of thought of many of the younger U-boat commanders who were greatly influenced by the theoretical writings of von Mellenthin and Marschall. Moreover, at that time, the Construction Office also considered that these U-boat types, which were well proved and well tested, were a good basis for further development, having a short building time and the further advantage that, constructional plans being to hand, a series could be built without initial delays.

However, in a very short time, the 'modern' U-boat projects of the Imperial Navy from 1918, namely UF (350 tons) as replacement for UBII and UG (640 tons) as replacement for UBIII, were established as the basis for a new mobilization programme consisting of 36 UF boats, 42 UG boats and 6 UCIII boats. Improvements were to be made to the latter type. IvS was required to work out designs for these, making use of all recent developments. A building time of six months was calculated for Type UF, and twelve months of Type UG. In the event of mobilization, the 42 UG boats should be built by Vulcan, the UF boats by GW, and the UCIII minelaying U-boats by B&V.

The minelaying boats were intended especially for Mediterranean operations, but the Type UCIII was rather small for operations in this theatre. At a meeting of 14 February 1927 between Kapitän zur See von Loewenfeld (A II), Fregattenkapitän Kurt Assmann (A II a), Spindler and Schottky (A II u), Korvettenkapitän Hermann Mootz (A III), Korvettenkapitän Heinrich Schickardt (BW) and Constructional Adviser Friedrich Schotte (K I g), it was agreed to prepare plans for a larger minelaying U-boat type which, in the event of mobilization, would be able to sail from German ports for a '45-day operation in the Mediterranean'. Again, another U-boat project, dating back to 1918, suggested itself: the 800-ton minelaying U-boat Type UI. The constructional data for this was available in the 'K' Office, and was handed over to Tebeg, who could now include this type in their mobilization planning. On 19 March 1927, Tebeg suggested that, in the event of mobilization, 12 of these Type UI boats should be built by B&V. On this occasion, however, the further working-out of this particular project was not passed to IvS; the intention was to have it processed through one of the Navy's own construction offices. To achieve this aim, a 'Technical Department' under the control of Schürer was set up at Mentor Bilanz in June 1927. The mobilization programme for 1928

now consisted of 36 UF boats, 36 UG boats and 12 UI boats.

When the Spanish boat, E1, had been built along the lines of the enlarged IvS design Pu111, this design was used in place of the UG type in mobilization planning, although with its displacement of 745 tons it represented a significant increase on the original idea of a medium boat of 500–600 tons. As a corresponding temporary measure (1930–32) and following the successful trials of the combined torpedo and minelaying type Pu89 of the IvS in Finland, this medium type was especially favoured by Schottky for mobilization planning. With the new development of 250-ton U-boats, and the actual construction of a boat of this type in Finland, Type UF was abandoned. A basic factor was the decision to change to the 53.3cm torpedo. Also, the possibility that torpedo mines of 53.3cm calibre might soon be ready for use meant that the design for the minelaying Type UI was no longer necessary. In effect then, in 1932, the most appropriate prototypes for a U-boat mobilization programme were CV702 (*Vetehinen*), CV707 (*Vesikko*) and E1.

PREPARATIONS FOR NEW CONSTRUCTION, 1932–35

The Reconstruction Programme of 1932
In the autumn of 1932, a so-called Reconstruction Programme was decided on, in order to build up a modern, battleworthy German Navy by 1938 (Decree of the Reichs Minister of Defence dated 15 November 1932). In a memorandum dated 2 November 1932, the Defence Department AI of the Naval Command Office had suggested, in connection with this, the construction of a small U-boat fleet consisting of eight 500-ton (*Vetehinen* class) and eight 800-ton (E1 class) boats. The Head of the Fleet Department A II, Kapitän zur See Guse, was in agreement. The objective now was the completion of 16 U-boats by early 1938, and these would be divided into 3 half-flotillas, each consisting of 4 boats, of which 2 would be for instructional use and 2 for trials purposes. The programme was to be worked out in three stages: the first from 1932 to 1934, the second from 1934 to 1937 and the third from 1937 to 1938. For the first stage, 8.6 million marks were to be made available. Of this sum, the Naval Yard at Wilhelmshaven would receive 4 million marks for work on the proposed U-boat construction programme; 3.8 million marks would be the first instalment for the awarding of contracts for 2 U-boats, and 0.8 million marks, for the outline programme (U-boat instruction, etc.).

On 22 November 1932, the General Naval Office 'B' discussed the measures that would be necessary to establish the 'MVB Branch', as U-boat development would now be designated (Motorenversuchsboot, or 'Experimental Motorboat'); specially discussed were measures needed for a commencement of U-boat construction. The Navy hoped that both the IvS boats E1 and CV707, in which so much had been invested, could be acquired by Germany to provide the basis for the new German U-boat arm. For any manufacturing preparations within Germany itself, only the quickly-built CV707 type was considered. The conference established two alternatives for the first stage: either that materials and engines be prepared for six 250-ton U-boats, or an immediate start be made on the building of four 250-ton U-boats. Either alternative would require approximately 6 million marks. For the building, the Kiel-Gaarden yard of Deutsche Werke Kiel AG (DWK) was exclusively selected. It was also suggested that a U-boat base, with docking facilities for 6 boats, be constructed at Kiel-Wik. Rather than the Navy's own yards in Wilhelmshaven, DWK in Kiel was preferred, for geographic and economic reasons.

On 10 December 1932, Admiral Groos (A) decided that, until further notice, only the E1 type codenamed 'MVBI' and the CV707 type (MVBII) should be considered, and that planning should take account of both types in numbers appropriate to an equal cost outlay, i.e. three 250-ton boats to one 750-ton boat. The development of a useful intermediate type of approximately 500 tons (similar to the earlier UBIII) should be borne in mind for a later date. The establishment of the U-boat base in Kiel-Wik and the personnel requirements for the basic U-boat organization (100 men and officers) were now authorized.

An examination of the IvS designs for E1 and CV707 gave rise to some desire for detail changes: in both types, it was desired to reduce the size of the conning tower in order to diminish the silhouette. In the case of MVBI, it was felt that the sub-structure for the gun, which extended to half the height of the bridge, should be removed. In MVBII, it was thought that the bridge, which had been enlarged in accordance with the wishes of the Finns, should revert to its original size, and the bridge steering position was eliminated. The torpedo installation was to be converted to use G7a and G7e torpedoes, as well as torpedo-mines. Arrangements would be made for MVBI to carry as many as possible of the newest mines in wet housing beneath the upper deck; in MVBII, investigations would be made to determine whether a further one or two reserve torpedoes could possibly be accommodated. From a shipbuilding point of view, it was intended to go over to comprehensive welding of the pressure hull — the scrapping of interior straps, and the weight saved thereby, could only strengthen the skin of the pressure hull.

The building time for the MVBI type was estimated as two years, for the MVBII type approximately one year. The actual building times would be determined by the delivery of new-type torpedo tubes, which meant, effectively, that completion of the first MVBII boat could not be expected before 1 July 1934, and of the first MVBI type before April 1936. To provide personnel for the first two boats, which were to be built in Germany from the autumn of 1933, Reichs Defence Minister von Blomberg authorized, on 2 February 1933, the foundation of a U-boat School in Kiel-Wik, to start

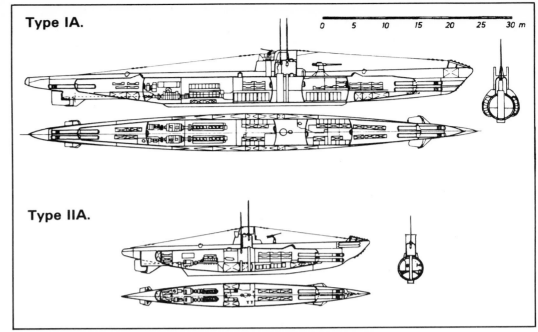

Type IA.

Type IIA.

on 1 October 1933. For undercover reasons, the official designation was 'U-boat Defence School' (Ubootabwehrschule, or UAS), and it came under the control of the Torpedo Inspectorate.

On 17 March 1933, a total of one million marks was put aside for the provision of components for these two small U-boats. To assist in the construction of further boats, three plans were presented on 8 April 1933, each envisaging the building of 32 MVBI boats (800 tons) and 16 MVBII boats (250 tons).

Plan 1 (for quick construction): 16 U-boats, 1934—36; 32 U-boats, 1937—41.
Plan 2 (for construction by 1945): 16 U-boats, 1934—38; 16 U-boats, 1938—43; 16 U-boats, 1943—45.
Plan 3 (replacement plan for existing shipbuilding plans): 16 U-boats, 1934—36; 12 U-boats, 1937—38; 20 U-boats, 1940—42.

These plans however, had no noticeable effect on further developments, and were soon displaced by other considerations. On 31 March 1933, Igewit concluded a 500,000 marks contract with IvS for building preparations for a 250-ton boat. On 26 April 1933, this contract was increased to take in 3 boats of this type. In a discussion at Head Office (Amtschef 'B') on 2 May 1933, it was discovered that negotiations with DWK were planned to commence in June, with a view to begin building the 3 boats on 1 October. An additional 3 large MVBI boats were to be prepared, and the construction of these was to be in the hands of GW. In the interests of concealment, however, negotiations with GW would not begin until 1 October 1933. Building was to start on 1 April 1934, or even earlier if possible. IvS was to act as the authority placing the contracts for all these boats. For building preparations, 1.5 million marks

were now available for the small boats and 4.5 million marks for the large boats.

After a lengthy discussion at 'B' on 3 July 1933, the ratio between small and large boats was once again established as 3:1, and it was agreed to build 6 small and 2 large boats — 3 small boats at DWK and 3 small boats at GW, while B&V, Hamburg, were envisaged for both the large boats. In the event of mobilization, a decision would be made to have six 250-ton boats built at the two yards that could provide the quickest construction. The modified CV707 type was now designated Construction No. 1110 or 'MVBIIA', while the modified E1 type was designated Construction No. 1120 or 'MVBIA'.

As planned, the UAS was opened on 1 October 1933 for training purposes, under the direction of Korvettenkapitän Kurt Slevogt. The instructors were Fürbringer and Hülsmann and two U-boat officers, Rösing and Freiwald, who had received their training in submarines built by the IvS. Eight officers (Looff, Ewerth, Werner von Schmidt, Michahelles, Scheringer, Meckel, Weingärtner and Looschen) attended the first course, plus 70—80 non-commissioned officers and men who had been assembled in Kiel since the summer of that same year. The U-boat building programme, however, did not get under way as quickly as it might have done, and this first course continued until the autumn of 1934. As it turned out, Hitler's foreign policy (especially towards Britain) made a commencement of building during 1933 no longer possible and, on 28 October 1933, Amtschef 'B' discussed financial terms for a new plan. For 1933, the preparation for the building of only 6 small U-boats (3 million marks) and 2 large U-boats (2.3 million marks) were now envisaged. Planning for the following years was now to be as follows.

1934: Completion of preparations for 2 large U-boats (0.7 million marks); completion of 2 small U-boats (2 million marks).

1935: Completion of 4 small U-boats (4 million marks).

1936: Completion of 2 large U-boats (6 million marks); new construction of 6 small U-boats (9 million marks).

1937: New construction of 6 small U-boats (9 million marks); new construction of 2 large U-boats (9 million marks).

This would mean that, together with E1 and CV707, at the beginning of 1938, 5 large and 19 small U-boats would be at the Navy's disposal. On 19 March 1934, this was enlarged to provide a total of 72 U-boats by 1949, of which 24 would be of Type MVBIA, and 48 of Type MVBIIA.

In the summer of 1934, the hoped-for fleet agreement with Britain had an influence on U-boat planning. Because of a British:German tonnage relationship of 100:33⅓ — which meant a submarine tonnage ratio between the two countries of 52,700:17,566 — the planning of 72 U-boats totalling 31,200 tons by 1949 had to be abandoned. On 4 June, therefore, A IV suggested

20 boats of 800 tons (Type IA)	16,000 tons
6 boats of 250 tons (Type IIA)	1,500 tons

which, in fact, represented a distinct preference for the large boat. In the Shipbuilding Replacement Plan of 1934, however, the emphasis was still on a large number of small U-boats to get U-boat construction off to a quick start. It was now intended by 1938 to have ready 10 Type IA and 18 Type IIA boats, totalling 12,500 tons.

Preparations to build Types IA and IIA

On 15 December 1933, a discussion took place at DWK chaired by the Head of (Amtschef) 'B', Konteradmiral Heusinger von Waldegg, with Yard Directors Middendorf, Serno, Löflund, Immich and Drechsler, concerning preparations for the proposed building of the 250-ton U-boats. It was decided that the next step should be the erection of a shed where the two boats could be built secretly. While this could not be completed before the middle of June 1934, the laying-down of both boats could begin in May, in the still incomplete shed. The Navy estimated a building time of five months for the first boat, and five-and-a-half for the second: this meant that delivery dates would be 1 November and 15 November 1934. Components and materials for a total of six 250-ton boats should be prepared and stored at the DWK. Appropriate contracts between Igewit and DWK were concluded in January 1934.

Rolled-steel was shipped from the Ruhr via Holland (IvS) to DWK, and arrived at Kiel in January 1934. (The purpose for which this material was required was a strict secret, and this gave rise to problems in Customs clearance.) The main and auxiliary engines followed in the early part of 1934. The torpedo tubes for the first two Type IIA boats were manufactured and made ready for installation at Pintsch, Fürstenwalde 40km east of Berlin. In view of the limited life of batteries, none was actually supplied, but an agreement was made for their provisional preparation; on the grounds of

keeping the whole business concealed, a similar arrangement was entered into with regard to periscopes. Fitting-out items that had been ordered in 1933 for both the Type IA boats, at a cost of 1.5 million marks, were to be stored for the time being at DWK, Friedrichsort (near Kiel), where the torpedo tubes for this type were being manufactured.

On 17 February 1934, it was decided to enlarge the conning tower of Type IA on account of the change to a periscope with a fixed eyepiece. The erection of two further construction buildings at DWK was authorized on 18 May 1934, following the agreement that a total of six 250-ton U-boats should be constructed there, and this left GW free for the two large boats, for which constructional items were now being prepared and stored.

Although the final assembly of the first two boats had not begun at DWK, Raeder gave orders on 27 June 1934 that building preparations should be initiated for an additional six 250-ton boats. For these, Igewit requested 'B' on 29 June 1934 for an improvement in the diving time to 30 seconds as well as an increase in range to 4,000 nautical miles at 8 knots. Increasing the surface range to double that of IIA would be achieved by including an additional oil bunker beneath the control room, if the boat were enlarged by three frame spacings. This design, enlarged to 275 tons, was designated Construction No. 1110B, or 'MVBIIB' and was also to be built at DWK. Completion of the design of this Type IIB was to be handed over in January 1934 to the fifteen-man construction office in DWK, and personnel from GW would also be taking part in this. Until now, for reasons of concealment, orders had been placed through IvS; but for this series, they would now be placed directly by Igewit or by DWK. In a further discussion at 'B' on 17 July 1934, however, it was decided to have Type IIB built at GW. To this end, GW were to set up their own construction office. GW was not to be considered any longer for the two large boats, but the engines and fitting-out items were to remain at DWK, where they were being stored, and constructional materials at GW. For the manufacture of torpedo tubes for the new Type IIB, Pintsch and DWK, Friedrichsort, were the intended manufacturers.

Now that measures had been taken to make preparations (in Germany) for a rapid building programme of a sizeable number of submarines, and as neither an immediate lifting of the U-boat restrictions imposed by the Treaty of Versailles nor an impending mobilization were to be expected, it was resolved not to take over E1 and CV707, but to sell them. E1 was offered to Turkey at 3 million marks, that is to say, at a considerable loss. Furthermore, the Turks had to be encouraged by a simultaneous gift of six new electrically-propelled torpedoes. (Supplying the new German G7e torpedoes to a foreign power before they had ever been fitted in a German boat was to cause a storm at a later date, but it was too late to withdraw the offer.) Negotiations were started with the Finnish Navy for the sale of CV707.

By the middle of August 1934, all the material necessary for the assembly of the first 6 U-boats

was ready at DWK: the first shed was ready, and the other two were in course of construction. Up to that time, 0.7 million marks had been spent on each boat, and each would cost a futher 0.8 million marks to assemble. For Type IA, procurement of appropriate material and its storage in Kiel was still in progress. As things stood at that time, it was calculated that assembly would take between ten and twelve months. Financial outlay for the preparatory work for each boat amounted to 1.5 million marks, and for assembly 3 million marks per boat were calculated. For the torpedo armament, eleven electrically-propelled torpedoes were ready or being manufactured, although, of these, six had been allocated to Turkey. A further thirty G7e had been ordered. Of conventional compressed-air torpedoes, thirty G7v were ready, with a further 270 in the course of manufacture. The proposed improved G7a and the torpedo-mines were still in the process of development.

The order for the boats to be assembled was not given, however, for the actual commencement of assembly was not so much a problem of organization as politics. Having come to power, Hitler was not willing to risk possible hostility from Britain and France, bound together as they were by treaty; the Saar Plebiscite was pending, and an agreement with Britain concerning relative fleet limitations (The Anglo-German Naval Agreement) was still unresolved — it might yet permit 'legal' U-boat re-armament. During a discussion on 27 June 1934, he instructed Raeder to maintain secrecy about building preparations, and not to authorize the commencement of assembly work before the end of the year. On 6 October of that year, the new delivery date for the first U-boat was scheduled for 1 April 1935, and 11 small U-boats would follow at half-monthly intervals. Assembly of the 2 large U-boats was now scheduled to take place at Deschimag-AG Weser, and they should be ready on 1 February and 1 March 1936. As it was more difficult to conceal the building of large boats, preliminary work would not start at AG Weser before 1 January 1935, with assembly on 1 April 1935.

To cope with the U-boat construction planned for the beginning of 1935, another class was initiated in the U-boat School (UAS). This meant an increase in U-boat personnel to the extent that, by the middle of 1935, there were at the Navy's disposal 15 deck officers, 9 engineering officers and 190 non-commissioned officers and men. On 1 December 1934, it had been agreed to admit a further 580 men to the UAS on 1 October 1935, which meant that crews for 14 large and 12 small boats would be ready by the middle of 1936.

On 12 October 1934, in a discussion at 'B', it was agreed that, to aid construction purposes, a branch office of the IvS would be placed at the disposal of AG Weser, and this would be established in Bremen at the beginning of 1935. As a number of IvS collaborators had come from The Hague to the new U-boat Construction Office at GW (Etzbach, Stötzel, Strehlow, Buhr and Freitag), and others had left or were leaving to join the Construction Control Department of the Navy in Kiel (Jany and Reimer), Techel's construction office, which was now dissolving connections with the German Navy, was very considerably weakened. In order to ensure speedy assembly work and smooth-running commissioning of U-boats as soon as the command was given, Igewit, UAS, the Construction Control and the proposed Acceptance Authority for the new U-boats were amalgamated into a special organizational U-boat Department, under the control of Kapitän zur See Bartenbach (who had returned from Finland), and this body was given very extensive jurisdiction.

By 16 October 1934, it was evident that, as the order to commence assembly could not be expected before 1 February 1935, the corresponding delivery dates must be postponed. The intervening time was to be used for increased preparations for Type IIB. And, if lack of official sanction for commencement led to further postponements, more U-boats were to be prepared. In this connection, 'A' wanted 4 large U-boats to be prepared, and these could eventually be built in the dry dock at DWK.

Between 7 and 9 November 1934, personnel from the U-boat Department of the General Naval Office (Ubootabteilung im Allgemeinen Marineamt, or

BU) visited Kiel to acquaint themselves with the state of preparations and to discuss possibilities of speeding up construction work. Workshop drawings in the new construction office of GW, under the control of Wilhelm Etzbach, and lofting work (Building Section 1) had been partly completed, which meant that the official commencement of workshop work (Section 2) could be established for 1 December. Assembly (Section 3) could then follow at GW on Slipways 1 and 2 of the large construction building. As camouflage, these building sites were fenced-in with corrugated iron. Temporary construction numbers (the numbers of six minesweepers being built at that time) were used, with an additional designation 'Group 950'. When building commenced, 3 boats could be completed at each slipway. A total of 600—900 workers was authorized for boat-building, and the same number for engine construction. The additional two sheds were to be completed at DWK by 20 December 1934, and the keel blocks would immediately be prepared in these buildings (114a—c). It was envisaged that the welding and matching-up of frames for the upper deck, foundations, stringers, outer-hull tanks, central keel, etc., would take place outside. Once prepared, these constructional items

would then be taken into the buildings and stored near the keel blocks. In Building 67, a start would be made with the construction of the engine installation on its original foundations.

On 12 December 1934, discussions took place with Deschimag concerning the preparations for building both the large U-boats. IvS would deliver all workshop drawings to AG Weser. In order to ensure secrecy for these preparations, it was suggested that the lofting be carried out in a special building entirely separate from the yard's shipbuilding operations. Before starting work on the boats, the slipway was to be surrounded by a fence.

On 11 January 1935, GW were requested to deliver Deschimag the constructional material that had been assembled for Type IA boats, so that, with effect from 1 February 1935, all three yards would be in a good position for speedy commencement of their actual constructional work.

Other requirements: Types III — VII
Given that Types IA and IIA had been chosen for the start of a new U-boat re-armament, and that

preparations for building had already begun, the question arose as to what further types would be necessary when Germany had received permission to build her own submarines. A special minelaying U-boat was thought essential. It was a fact that, through the development of special torpedo-mines — anchor mines (Torpedo-Ankertauminen, or TMA) 3.64m long and sea-bed mines (Torpedo-Grundminen, or TMB) 2.3m long — any U-boat could perform basic minelaying; but there was still need for a boat capable of carrying a large supply of mines.

On 13 February 1934, a discussion with Igewit established that the requirements for a minelaying U-boat would be secured in the simplest and quickest way by increasing the length of the available IA by approximately 7.5m. A mine-storage compartment of that length could be built-in, and would contain either 30 TMA or 45 TMB, plus the necessary mine-compensating tanks. If no torpedoes were carried, the total number of mines would be 54 TMA or 75 TMB. The mine-storage compartment could be installed either abaft the bow torpedo tubes, or forward of the stern tubes. Using the fore part of the boat had the advantage that very little conversion work would be required.

The central control room and conning tower, which at the present were forward of the centre of gravity, would automatically be moved back to the centre of gravity. Additionally, there would be four minelaying tubes. If an arrangement in the after part of the boat became necessary, the control room and rear battery compartment would have to swap positions to avoid the conning tower being placed too far forward. The two halves of the battery system would then be joined together in one compartment. The boat would then be approximately 80m long, displace 870 tons, and have a maximum surface speed of 18.5 knots (instead of the estimated 19 knots of Type IA).

Building costs were estimated at approximately 4.8 million marks (i.e., only approximately 300,000 marks more than Type IA), and the building time would be very little longer than that of the Type IA. As an alternative, the possibility of accommodating mines in dry storage containers on the upper deck was also discussed. On 9 April 1934, Schottky presented an outline sketch for this project and, following further work on the constructional details, the main specifications were now as follows.

Length overall: 79.9m.
Maximum beam: 6.2m.
Draught (normal): 4.05m.
Draught (fully laden): 4.35m.
Displacement surfaced
  (normal): 880 tons.
Displacement surfaced
  (fully laden): 970 tons.
Speed surfaced: approx. 18.5 knots.
Range surfaced: 12,000 nautical miles
  at 10 knots (fully
  laden!)
Speed submerged: 9 knots.

Installations were to be as in Type IA except for the mine-storage compartment abaft the bow torpedo tubes, which could also serve as a supply store for twenty-one reserve torpedoes, and for the group of compensating tanks, of necessity placed farther forward. An increase in ballast made for improved stability, and this permitted the installation of a second 10.5cm gun (on the after deck). In addition, Igewit contemplated the building of a housing for small motor torpedoboats. Once again, Type IA was chosen as a starting-point. Two small speedboats could be carried in a pressure-tight hangar abaft the conning tower. This weight would be compensated by a mine compartment forward of the stern tubes. The pressure hull arrangement of Type IA could be used right up to the engine compartment, and only outercasing enlargement would be necessary. After the restoration of this project in the summer of 1945, the main specifications became as follows.

Length overall: 78m.
Maximum beam: 7.4m.
Mean draught: 5m.
Displacement surfaced: 1,500 tons.
Displacement submerged: 2,000 tons.
Speed surfaced: 15.5 knots.
Speed submerged: 7 knots.
Range surfaced: 7,500 nautical miles
  at 10 knots.
Fuel-oil supply: 100 tons.

Type III (conjectural).

Armament was to be as in Type IA, but with eight reserve torpedoes and forty-eight TMA. In pressure-tight housings would be two motor torpedo-boats, each of 10 tons weight and 12.5m length. The cost of each U-boat was estimated at 7 million marks.

On 29 June 1934, Igewit informed the General Naval Office 'B' that the requisite development tasks in suggested sequence were:

1. Reconstruction of Type MVBII to achieve a diving time of 30 seconds.
2. Reconstruction of Type MVBII to achieve a range of 4,000 nautical miles at 8 knots.
3. Improvement to the loading and stowing of conventional torpedoes in Types MVBII and MVBI. (N.B. The above remarks (1—3) were to be applied to the preparation of the second series of six 250-ton boats, with the condition that no delay be caused in the preparation and building dates for that series.)
4. Reconstruction of Type MVBI to achieve a diving time of 30 seconds.
5. Reconstruction of Type MVBI to achieve a diving depth of 100m.

Type VII.

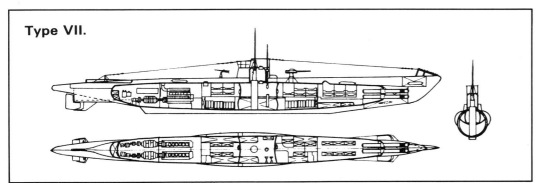

6. Reconstruction of Type MVBI to carry a supply of at least 50 mines (MVBIV).
7. Construction of an MVB to serve as a supply and workshop ship for offensive MVBs (MVBIII).
8. Construction of an MVB according to the suggestions of Engineer Walter (MVBV).
9. Reconstruction of an MVB approximately of the size of MVBI, and to make use of the steam engine as sole propulsion system for surface and submerged cruising, as designed by Schmidt-Hartmann (MVBVI).
10. Construction of an MVB as a motor torpedo-boat carrier (MVBVII).

On 6 August 1934, these tasks were approved by 'B' with a very few changes, such as the re-designation of the minelaying U-boats mentioned in 6 (above) as MVBIII. For the supply and workshop U-boat mentioned in 7, the designation MVBIV was now suggested. This boat was intended to supply operational U-boats with torpedoes, mines, fuel, lubricants, provisions, drinking water and spare parts, and was to be able to carry out the more common repairs at sea. She would be a large boat of approximately 2,500 tons surface displacement, and would have to be able to remain at sea for at least three months.

The idea of building an MVB as a motor torpedo-boat carrier (designation MVBVII) was abandoned, as the expenditure for an item that would not be used very often seemed too high. Furthermore, there seemed to be serious practical difficulties in the way of launching and recovering the small boats. It was argued that with a similar expenditure it would be possible to build an operationally-sound U-cruiser, the value of which would be greater at all times than that of U-boats built for such special purposes.

At the end of 1934, it was decided that Types IV—VI were not to be proceeded with, partly because the state of development of new types of engine installations did not permit further work on them, and partly because tonnage limitations in the impending Anglo-German Naval Agreement would call for a concentration on operationally-sound, medium sized U-boats. This, then, was probably the real reason for the construction of a medium-sized U-boat, that can be seen as an enlarged version of the well-tested CV707. It had a single-hull shape, extending to the forward and after parts of the ship, to the upper deck, with its small bridge, and to

Type VII frame lines.

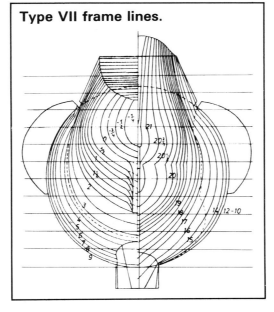

the keel which, however, had bulges at the sides, each of which contained diving and trimming tanks.

Saddle tanks of this kind had already been investigated during the development of CV707 and in towing tests on models. Additional diving tanks were situated outboard in the bow and stern; the large main diving tank was placed in the pressure hull, beneath the central control room. All this made for a short diving time. The fuel-oil containers were situated abaft the control room in the pressure hull, which meant that if damage were caused to the outer hull by depth-charges, oil would be unlikely to leak to the surface. These ideas, like the Type II, date back to the First World War UF concept.

On 10 January 1935, BU discussed this new type and, in view of the abandoning of the MTB carrier project, it now received the designation MVBVII. It was not possible to incorporate all the original requirements, particularly a submerged stern torpedo armament, in a boat displacing 500—550 tons, and certain requirements were dispensed with. The result can be summarized as follows.

Maximum displacement:	550 tons.
Speed surfaced:	16.5—17 knots.
Speed submerged:	8.5—9 knots.
Range surfaced:	6,000 nautical miles at 8 knots.
Range submerged:	75 nautical miles at 4 knots.
Propulsion:	two 1,050hp (corresponding to six-cylinder performance of the E1 diesels).
Battery weight:	provisionally 55 tons.
Diving depth:	100m (i.e., the same diving capacity as MVBIA)
Armament:	four bow torpedo tubes, and one fixed stern tube on the upper deck; nine torpedoes maximum. one 10.5cm U-boat gun; one 2cm MG.

The control room could be sealed by a pressure-tight bulkhead (capable of withstanding pressure at 50m); the remaining compartments were divided by bulkheads of lesser strength.

In further discussions at Offices 'b' and 'c' of Igewit, it was agreed to try for a maximum propulsion installation weight (MI and MII) of 176 tons. If possible, the two diesel engines were not to weigh more than 38 tons, i.e., 15—16kg per hp, but it was thought doubtful that this could be achieved with the available engines. The HSVA then evaluated the proposed specifications by performing towing tests with a model of the new Type VII. They found that, at 11—13 knots, the saddle tanks caused a deterioration in the C_e values of the boat which had no saddle tanks, and at 14—18 knots an improvement in these values. This U-boat Type VII, conceived by Schürer and Bröking, determined German naval strategy during the Second World War, to a greater degree than any other warship.

4 U-BOAT CONSTRUCTION FROM 1935 TO 1939

The Replacement Programme of 1935

Following the agreement on the main specifications of the new U-boat Type VII, it was decided to start building it as soon as possible, in preference to ordering further IA boats, and GW was chosen as the building yard. On 16 January 1935, Igewit wrote to GW to say that 6 boats of Type VII were to be laid down on Building Slips III and IV during 1935. However, it was thought that initial planning would take until 1 June 1935 before workshop drawings could be prepared. Project drawings, adequate for building work, were to be prepared by the Branch Office of IvS at Deschimag. For official correspondence, the new design, MVBVII was designated 'Con. No. 1115'. On the assumption that working drawings would be delivered to GW by 1 June 1935, the following delivery dates were published: first boat 1 June 1936, second 15 July 1936, third 1 September 1936, fourth 15 October 1936, fifth 1 December 1936, sixth 15 January 1937. A final decision about this proposed construction was not taken, but inquiries were made as to the possibilities of building Type VII at DWK. On 21 January 1935, Director Löflund replied:

'1. There is no large enough space free before 1 September 1935.

'2. From 1 April 1937, there will be one construction place free (Building Slip I) and some shipwrights and welders (who would not be free before this date) available for additional work.

'3. No personnel will be available for fitting-out work on additional construction before the beginning of 1938.'

DWK could no longer be considered for construction work on Type MVBVII before 1 April 1937, and was left out of further discussions. On the other hand, AG Weser did have building capacity for an immediate start. On 28 January 1935, Deschimag was informed that it must build 4–6 550-ton MVBs, which meant that the total number of proposed Type VII boats had risen to 10: of these, finally, GW would build 4, and Deschimag, 6. Project drawings suitable for both yards were to be produced by the IvS Branch Office at Deschimag; the workshop drawings would be prepared at GW, with additional help in the form of personnel from Deschimag. The green light for starting the assembly work for the first 6 small Type IIA boats was given to DWK on 8 February 1935. The work

on the 6 IIB boats started at GW a month later. The contract for a further 12 boats, with slight changes in the IIB design (Con. No. 1110C) had been released on 2 February: 8 were to be built at GW and 4 at DWK, these differing from Con. No. 1110B by having a longer conning tower with direct steering facilities on the top. All the 24 250-ton submarines were to be delivered by 15 May 1936.

U-boat construction in the Replacement Programme of 1935, now consisted of 24 boats of 250 tons; 10 of 500 tons and 2 of 750 tons, making a total tonnage of 12,500. According to the proposed 35 per cent clause in the Anglo-German Naval Agreement, there would still be approximately 6,000 tons at the disposal of the German Navy. At Amtschef 'A' on 8 April 1935, a Construction Plan was formulated to make full use of all available submarine tonnage by 1942. Although these boats were said to be of only 600 tons, in view of their cost estimated on 11 April 1935 at 5 million marks per boat, it is highly likely that they would have been Type IA boats, which were some 150 tons larger.

Building commencement 1936: 4 boats of 600 tons, in service by the beginning of 1938.

Building commencement 1937: 4 boats of 600 tons, in service by the summer of 1939.

Building commencement 1938: 2 boats of 600 tons, in service by the beginning of 1941.

Following a vote by the Defence Department AI of the Naval Command Office, large U-boats were no longer to be built. In future, emphasis was to be on 500-ton boats. In the Replacement Programme for 1935, of 11 May, therefore, it was recommended that the building of 500-ton Type VII boats continue. This, from a tonnage point of view, would make possible the building of a further 2 boats, and would give considerably shorter building times. In total, U-boat planning now consisted of 36 MVBs from the 1934—35 Estimates, and these should be ready by the summer of 1936. Additionally:

Estimates for 1936: first series of 4 boats of 500 tons (*U37–U40*), ready by 1 October 1937.

Estimates for 1937: second series of 4 boats of 500 tons (*U41–U44*), ready by 1 October 1938.

Estimates for 1938: third series of 4 boats of 500 tons (*U45–U48*), ready by 1 October 1939.

Following the conclusion of the Anglo-German Naval Agreement on 18 June 1935, to the amaze-

Type IIA (U1-U6).

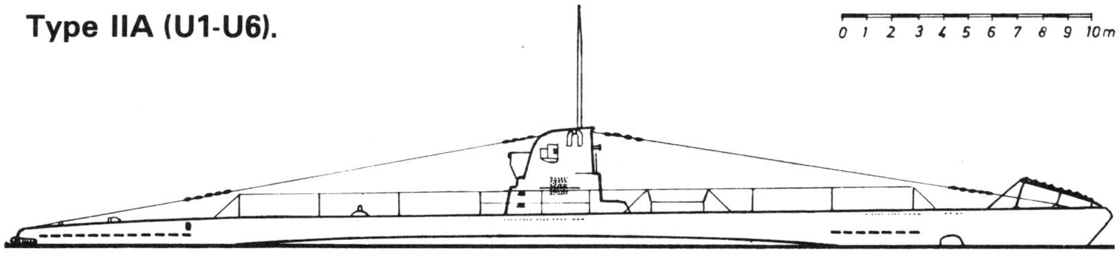

0 1 2 3 4 5 6 7 8 9 10m

Type IIB (U7-U12).

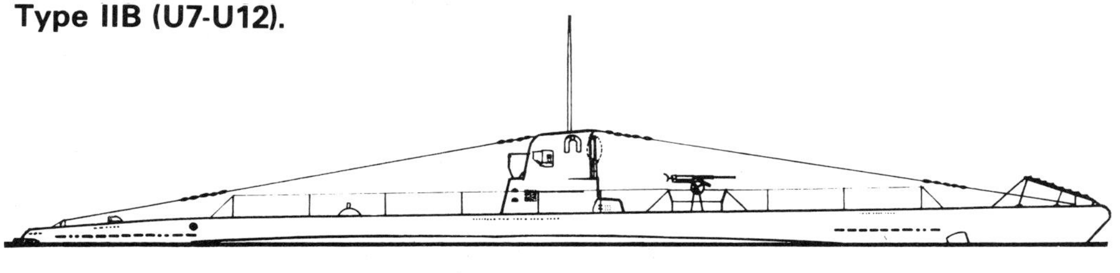

ment of the world, the first small Type IIA U-boats came into service, after an ostensible building time of a mere four months, thanks to the comprehensive preliminary preparation of components. The treaty, while fixing the total German Fleet tonnage at 35 per cent of overall British tonnage, allowed Germany parity in submarine tonnage. The Germans, however, had stated that they would not make full use of this concession initially, but build to only 45 per cent of the British submarine tonnage (i.e., they would not build an amount exceeding 22,050 tons). It is very likely that it was not political consideration that dictated this, but restricted building capacity and a desire to proceed with caution until those U-boats under construction had proved themselves.

The speedy completion and commissioning of *U1–U12* was the result of smooth collaboration between Igewit (Schottky, Schürer and Bröking); good supervision at the shipyards (Papenberg, Jany, Ludwig, Kluge and Reimer), the newly formed U-Boat Trials Commission (EAU, or Erprobungsausschuss für Unterseeboote: Bräutigam, Hülsmann, Aschmoneit and Friese) and the U-boat School (UAS: Slevogt, Fürbringer) in the special U-boat Department (BU) of the Supreme Naval Command under Kapitän zur See Bartenbach. The method of working in the new office was marked by a freedom from bureaucratic restrictions, and was made possible by the fact that, in essential matters, it was directly under the control of the German Naval Directorate, which from 21 May was given the new designation Navy High Command (Oberkommando der Kriegsmarine, or OKM).

On 23 July 1935, U-boat planning in the Replacement Programme was reduced to 10 boats, but the 500-ton type remained.
1st series: 4 boats to be ready 1 January 1938 instead of 1 October 1937;
2nd series: 4 boats to be ready 1 January 1939 instead of 1 October 1938;
3rd series: 2 boats to be ready 1 January 1940 instead of 1 October 1939.

Political considerations (the intended occupation by armed forces of the demilitarized Rhineland) led, in October 1935, to the postponement of the laying down of the remaining Type IIB (*U21–U24*) and of the 4 Type VII boats; following a planning revision of 21 October, this would not commence before 1 April 1936. However, the rebuilding of the U-boat

fleet would then proceed with all speed. For this, the 1936–37 Estimates provided for 8 boats which would likewise be laid down on 1 April 1936, 4 at GW and 4 at AG Weser. This construction plan was to be well advanced by the end of 1935, with ultimate completion of the 8 boats by 1 October 1937. The remaining boats, whose number had been increased to 5, was similarly postponed by a year (i.e., commencement of building 1937, completion at the end of 1938). The following plan was confirmed on 16 November 1935.
U21–U24, *U31*, *U32*, *U35*, *U36*: laying down 1 April 1936, completion from 1 September 1936; the decision to lay down earlier if possible remained open.
U37–U44: laying down 1 April 1936, completion from 1 April 1938.
U45–U49: laying down 1 April 1937, completion from 1 April 1939.
Additionally, two U-boat depot ships were authorized.

However, nothing came of the proposed building programme for these additional 500-ton boats of Type VII (*U37–U44*) for 1936. In October 1935, the U-boat Department (BU) was dissolved and its responsibilities were distributed among departments of the OKM. At the same time, the 'fathers' of the new U-boat arm, Schottky and Bartenbach, who had championed the building of the medium U-boat very strongly, retired from further U-boat development. In June 1935, Raeder had selected Kapitän zur See Dönitz to be in command of operational boats and for U-boat training outside the U-boat School. At first, Dönitz — also a champion of medium U-boats — had little influence on U-boat development, which was now being increasingly influenced by the Naval Command Office. Contrary to the U-boat philosophy that obtained in the First World War, the Naval High Command now tended to regard the U-boat not as *the* weapon of destruction in a war of commerce, but as *one* integral component of the Fleet, to whose strategic aims it must be subordinate. Furthermore, in the eyes of many staff officers, the significance of the U-boat seemed questionable when faced with the detection devices being developed (especially by Britain) and in the light of the restrictions imposed by the London Naval Treaty of 1930, to which Germany was a party.

U-BOAT DESIGN DEVELOPMENTS: TYPES IX, VIIB AND X–XII

The evolution of Type IX
In a statement issued by Naval Command Office on the military, political and strategic situation of Germany at the end of 1935, Paragraph 7, U-boats, declared:
'U-boat tonnage at 45 per cent means 22,050 tons are available, of which 12,500 tons are in use through boats complete and under construction [*U1–U36*] and 9,550 tons are unused. The planning for U-boat construction goes back in time prior to the Naval Agreement. It was formerly a question of evolving types the assembly of which would take only a short time so that, in the event of an outbreak of war and of the abolition of the restrictions of the Treaty of Versailles, boats could be ready as soon as possible. The use of knowledge gained through the building of boats for Finland and Spain gave birth, therefore, to the first types of U-boat fleets. Initially, the Naval Agreement opened up the way to recognize the military requirements for future U-boat construction. It is essential for the continuance of operations that the especially important sea lines of communication in the Mediterranean be cut, and that the U-boat be used in that sphere of operations as a torpedo- and mine-carrier and also for reconnaissance purposes, as the enemy superiority in surface vessels and in air force potential makes the employment of U-boats the only possibility for success. The fulfilment of all these military requirements hangs on the knife-edge of the very small amount of free tonnage still available — 9,550 tons. It is therefore clearly a question, on the one hand, of effecting as large a number as possible of units and, on the other hand, of achieving the most urgent military requirements. Therefore, the following requirements need to be met in the new construction of U-boats:
'A range to be sufficient for a lengthy stay in the Western Mediterranean.
'A sufficiently high cruising speed to keep as short as possible the time spent in getting to and from the zone of operation and to facilitate quick and speedy results when in action.

'The ability to carry a sufficient number of torpedoes or mines, whichever has to be carried, to bring about the maximum effect on all operations undertaken.

'Boats built recently and those under construction of the larger type do not fill these requirements satisfactorily. They can reach the Western Mediterranean at a reduced cruising speed, but after a relatively short time there, need to return on account of insufficient fuel reserves. Also, for the scope of such operations, the supply of ammunition is too small. The application of present U-boats and those planned for the future can be considered for the following undertakings: the small 250-ton boats can be used first in home waters as far as Biscay and the Gulf of Finland, both in a reconnaissance rôle and as torpedo- and mine-carriers. Their use in these areas will be greatly influenced by what the Fleet has to carry out. The larger boats are primarily for operational use along the French coast, in the Atlantic, in the Mediterranean and along the African coast, unless they are required for special purposes to work alongside the Fleet.

'The provision of a special mine U-boat [Type III] is rejected. The present situation is not such that we can afford the building of a special type, but if speed of construction were to become a prime consideration, then such a project might be worthwhile. The current development of U-boat mines permits the equal and interchangeable use of torpedoes and/or mines and this suits the military requirements most fully.'

In the Construction Office, these requirements led to development of a new U-boat type closely connected in size and shape with Type IA, but responding to the desire for an increased surface range and torpedo supply. The resemblance to Type IA guaranteed a short development time and reduced difficulties in building preparations. An initial list of specifications made at the end of 1935, envisaged the following.

Displacement:	730 tons.
Maximum speed surfaced:	20 knots.
Cruising speed surfaced:	14 knots.
Range surfaced:	approximately 10,000 nautical miles at 10 knots.
Armament:	four bow torpedo tubes and two submerged stern tubes, with twelve torpedoes carried. Additionally, an installation for the storage of further torpedoes in pressure-tight containers on the upper deck. If needed, the storage of 22 new TMC, 44 TMA or 60 TMB mines.

The increased surface speed was to be achieved by using nine-cylinder diesels (instead of eight-cylinder, as in Type IA), by installing superchargers and by slightly changing the boat's

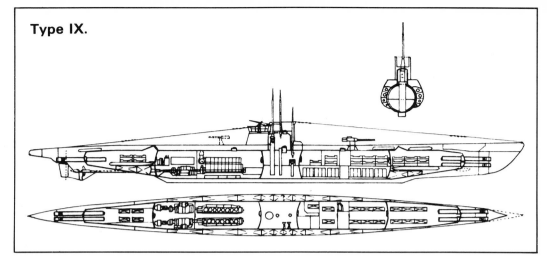

Type IX.

profile. The fore section of the boat was drawn out in a slimmer form and, as value was placed on short torpedo tube shutters (which involved a full bow back to the shutters), the line of this section had a distinct 'S' curve. The more comprehensive and weightier diesel installation required a different division of compartments. The engine rooms adjoined the control room and the battery compartments, and all crew quarters were moved to lie forward of the control room. The conning tower was moved farther aft, in contrast with Type IA, and was now situated in the centre of the boat. The pressure hull diameter increased by 12cm. The upper deck had to be widened in order to accommodate the torpedo containers, which led to some reduction in the maximum submerged speed. Finally, an increase in the AA armament (one 3.7cm gun at the stern and one 2cm gun on the bridge). This new project was designated Type IX.

At the end of 1935, it was decided that the 13 additional boats be of this type, which meant that the 9,950 tons still outstanding from the Anglo-German Naval Agreement were now completely taken up. The following plans had now been made by 'A': 2 boats of Type IA; 24 boats of Type IIA or B; 10 boats of Type VII; 13 boats of Type IX. Of the new Type IX boats, 8 were to be laid down in 1936 and the remaining 5 in 1937. The yards suggested were Deschimag for *U37–U40* and GW for *U41–U44*.

On 31 January 1936, 'A' made its first report on the new Type IX to Admiral Raeder, Supreme Commander-in-Chief of the Navy. On this occasion, Raeder raised the point as to whether 'it is possible to build a commerce submarine for carrying cargo, which could be excluded from the existing U-boat tonnage arrangement. In the event of mobilization, the boat could be used for general supplies or for military supply purposes.' To this, AI replied: 'The project for a U-boat of this kind for use for the last-mentioned purpose has, at the request of AI, been thoroughly evaluated by BU, as a war game at the Naval Command Office, and documentary details should be available.' (It is very likely that this was being confused with Project IV, for a supply and

workshop boat.) AI u was requested 'together with SK I, to clarify the question whether the construction of a cargo-carrying submarine for commercial purposes could legally be built under the Naval Agreement, and not be included in the military tonnage figures.' However, there is no further mention of this suggestion in subsequent discussions on the development of the German U-boat arm. In any case, the building of a commerce submarine in peacetime would probably have been seen as a questionable and shady business.

In his attitude to the new Type IX, Raeder showed a noticeable reticence. At a further discussion on 9 March 1936, he suggested postponing a decision on it until the following questions had been resolved:

1. Could a further MG/30 be installed?
2. Would it be possible to increase the cruising speed while keeping the same range and displacement by using MAN, double-acting, two-stroke engines?
3. Could quicker reloading be guaranteed by adopting the suggestion of Amtschef MWa relating to the arrangement of the torpedo- or mine-containers beneath the upper deck?

The next day 'A' stated:

'Re. 1. 'A' considers the anti-aircraft weapons as presently envisaged, that is one 3.7cm and one C/30 machine-gun which is greater than the original weaponry by the 3.7cm gun, are satisfactory. The installation of further anti-aircraft weapons would be difficult, people would get in each other's way when using them, and there would be manning problems, all of which adds up to the fact that 'A' cannot recommend them. The armament of one 3.7cm and one 2cm is preferred to an anti-aircraft armament of two 2cm.

'Re. 2. 'A' stresses that the most reliable and fully tested engine installation must be used, which will provide the increased requirements.

'Re. 3. 'A' is not in agreement with the change suggested by MWa, as it will mean forfeiting at least two mine containers (possibly even four). A maximum complement of mines is more important than the ability to discharge mines more quickly

Type IX frame lines.

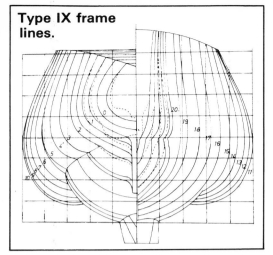

from two or four containers. The reloading of the mines into their shafts can, in any case, only be carried out away from the area of operations and this is only worth doing when a sizeable number — at least four — are to be discharged, so there is no particular advantage to be gained from saving a few minutes only if the minelaying performance is restricted. The discharging of the first two containers according to the arrangement pertaining at the present, will not require any more time than the preparation of the torpedo hatch, derrick and pedestal, all of which take place at the same time.'

In the meantime, however, resistance to the idea of using this new large type for the whole of the U-boat tonnage still outstanding had increased. An essential argument was that, in place of 2 large boats, 3 medium-sized boats of Type VII could be built. The point was also made that the 500-ton boat to be built at Deschimag would require an average of only eight months on the slips. Certainly, on 18 March 1936, the OKM intended that 8 Type IX (*U37–U44*) were to be laid down on 1 October 1936, with completion scheduled for 1 April 1938 (one boat at the end of 1937); yet Raeder delayed the final decision until the summer. 'A's stipulation on the new Type IX and Raeder's indecision resulted in the notorious 1937-gap in German U-boat construction. In a communication dated 8 June 1938, AI took up the initiative again: 'For the initiative of the coming new U-boat constructions, AI makes the following suggestions:

'1. Type IX should be, as planned, laid down as soon as possible on the building slips in a series of 8 and, if possible, 9 boats.

'2. The decision whether the tonnage still outstanding should be used up by further construction of Type IX or whether it should be made up by an improved 500-ton boat can be postponed until experience with the first larger boats has been evaluated. This will possibly be done in the autumn of this year so that, if a decision is made in favour of the smaller boat, the construction of some of these boats could still commence before this year is out. In the meantime, 'K' has received the request to investigate the possibilities of

improving the 500-ton boat in respect of deck housing of reserve ammunition, improvement in engine installation and so on, without any appreciable increase in tonnage.

'*Argument:* Operational considerations demand the completion as soon as possible of Type IX, as these boats are the only ones which could move quickly into the battle area, which, with regard to the tasks at the beginning of a war, is important. This advantage apart, if it should come to a war in the near future, these boats will be the only ones with the ability to carry out operations in distant waters, such as the Central and South Atlantic, the Caribbean, etc., as the radius of action of the 500-ton boats is insufficient for any of these areas. A task for these boats, which has not been mentioned in discussions hitherto, is, in the opinion of AI — and great stress should perhaps be laid on this — the use of the Type IX in direct protection of our own commerce. Through their high cruising speed and their large radius of action, these boats are ideal for the taking over of the tasks of U-cruisers, for example, to accompany important cargo ships across the Atlantic, or to protect trade routes in these waters, in other words, exactly those tasks which normally fall to surface warships. In the opinion of AI, the new type represents a happy amalgam of all the different qualities that various U-boats should have. It also seems of doubtful value to AI to continue the construction of the 500-ton type further, before experience with larger U-boats is available. This enables us to thoroughly evaluate the new boats, quite apart from the consideration that, as far as AI can see, the question is still not clear whether the immediate continued building of these additional boats is practical from the point of view of providing crews and training.

'AI is further of the opinion that experience of the larger U-boats will be to hand by the autumn, with the result that account can be taken of the wish of the Supreme Commander-in-Chief of the Navy to make a quick start to the building of these boats and, in any case, to lay them down before the end of this year. An initiation to build more 500-ton boats is also still possible in the course of this year, should experience with them make it desirable to use up the outstanding tonnage for the boats. AI pleads strongly that the placing of contracts for the building of at least 8 and, if possible, 9 boats of Type IX should not be delayed by considerations concerning the further construction of 500-ton boats, and that it be suggested to the Supreme Commander-in-Chief that the final decision as to whether Type IX boats or 500-ton boats be built before the end of the year could be deferred until the autumn.'

Following these arguments, which to some extent represented a somewhat unreal concept on the part of the AI as to the operational capabilities of the boat, Raeder decided that in the 1936 Estimates 8 U-boats of Type IX (*U37–U44*) corresponding to construction drawings available should be put in hand. The question of the AA armament was deferred, to be settled when the Naval Weapons Office (MWa) had carried out experiments and come to some conclusions as to which was the best gun.

In order to speed the development of the U-boat arm, and to acquiesce in the Commander of U-Boats' desire for the smaller boats, Raeder further requested, on 9 June 1936, that results obtained with the first Type IA and Type VII U-boats be evaluated with the utmost speed, so that by approximately the beginning of October 1936 the implementation of a further six 500-ton boats, with improvements suggested by these results, could be decided on. 'K' was now requested, as a precaution, to make a careful consideration of the possibilities of improving the 500-ton boats by: (a) deck storage for torpedoes and mines, if necessary, by dispensing with above-water stern tubes and (b) improvement of speed and range by using superchargers, etc., without any appreciable increase in displacement. Because the Commander of U-Boats had expressed his concern at Fleet Command regarding the manoeuvrability of medium and larger boats, 'K' was requested (a) to make comparative tests of the turning circles of 250-ton, 500-ton and 712-ton boats at different speeds, and when submerged, and (b) to test possible improvements in the manoeuvrability of Type IX and in the projected improved versions of the 500-ton boats.

However, shortly afterwards, Raeder expressed his doubts concerning the ordering for construction of the 8 Type IX U-boats, but decided finally on 22 June 1936: on 29 July 1936, the first 4 boats of Type IX (*U37–U40*) were contracted to Deschimag. On 28 September 1936, projected specifications for the new Type IX were as follows.

Designated waterline length:	75m.
Maximum beam:	6.5m.
Mean draught with keel:	4.25m.
Standard displacement:	740 tons.
Speed surfaced:	20 knots.
Speed submerged:	8.5 knots.
Range surfaced:	11,000 nautical miles at 10 knots.
	15,000 nautical miles at 8 knots.
Armament:	six torpedo tubes (four submerged bow, two submerged stern); twenty-two torpedoes (twelve in pressure hull, ten in pressure-tight containers on deck); one 10.5cm U-boat gun, one 3.7cm gun, one C/30 MG.
Crew:	40.

Improvements to Type VII: Type VIIB

On 6 April and 11 May 1936, Type IA boats *U25* and *U26* came into service, followed on 25 July by the first Type VII boat, *U33.* The U-Boat Trials Commission (EAU) were to carry out numerous tests with these boats during the next few months, and these resulted in a definite preference being expressed by both Dönitz (Commander of U-Boats) and the EAU for the smaller, manoeuvrable Type

VII: in this, no doubt the wartime experience of Dönitz and Bräutigam played its part. In a report comparing the 712-ton and 500-ton U-boats, Dönitz finally came into conflict with the Command Office regarding the use of U-boats, in the event of a war with France. Among other points, he stated:

'Compared with the speed reached by surface warships, the U-boat — even if it achieves 17—20 knots — is a relatively slow craft. In this respect, the U-boat is at an even greater disadvantage than was the case during the war: the submerged speed of a U-boat has remained the same, while the speed that surface vessels can attain has become notably greater. The prospects for U-boats in unrestricted sea space to attack opponents — even slow merchantmen — are poor unless the U-boat is, at the beginning of the attack, in a favourable position in the line of approach of the enemy ship. It is not a practical proposition for a U-boat to improve matters by making an approach on the surface, for it then exposes itself to observation from the air and to the risk of attack by surface escort ships forcing it once more below the surface. The simple corollary is this: the U-boat can best attack when it is in a stationary position, as near as possible to strategic focal points for enemy commerce, and as near as possible to enemy bases; there it must wait, having taken up a good submerged position. Its attack prospects consist of: (a) being in the appropriate line of approach that opponents must take, and (b) in the use of as large a number of U-boats as possible.

'*Inference:* individual U-boats used for torpedo purposes, in these times of limited U-boat tonnages, should be as small as is practical; for the greater the number of boats at our disposal, the greater the number of sea lanes that we can invest with our U-boats; this means a greater likelihood that our opponents will have to cross our positions. When used as a torpedo carrier, the U-boat must have good offensive qualities; above all, it must handle well when submerged. This calls for: short diving time, simplicity of installations, which reduces the risk of mishaps when repeated alarms cause frequent diving, good depth-keeping properties, noise reduced to the lowest possible level, small turning circle; then, for night attacks, manoeuvrability, low silhouette, short diving time. It is the smaller boats that have these properties in the greatest measure.'

Dönitz then went on to compare the prepared data of the U-boat types in detail. The turning circles were unsatisfactory: surfaced at full speed and full rudder, *U26* 325m, *U33* 305m; submerged at full rudder, *U26* 280m, *U33* 360m. By using double rudders, which would be more affected by propeller wash, it was calculated that considerably improved results could be achieved, especially in the case of the shorter, 500-ton boat.

The 500-ton boat was superior in diving time, and could be taken to a depth of 10m in 20 seconds from maximum speed, if Ballast Tank III were already open (opening time 8—10 seconds) and with forward hydroplanes at 25°, below and behind at 0°, and trim down by the head to a maximum of 10°. It was

Left: Commissioning of *U28*, September 1936.

107

calculated that an improvement to the aperture bars would bring the diving time down to 25 seconds from the time of giving the alarm. By comparison, the 712-ton boat at a maximum speed and with 6 tons negative buoyancy required 40 seconds to reach a depth of 10m. When moving in a forward direction, both boats maintained depth well. However, depth-keeping was a much more arduous business in the case of Type IA than in Type VII. In Type IA, when submerged, the dynamic centre of gravity was not in the control room, but had moved, depending on the speed, to a point up to 6m forward of the control room. Another point was that the ventilation system of the fuel bunkers did not work absolutely reliably. According to the trim, the air bubbles wandered forward or aft, and the volume changed according to the depth kept. (Also, what very possibly influenced Dönitz in his evaluation of the depth-keeping properties of Type IA was a diving operation that went seriously wrong, while he was on board, when a faulty connection in the electrically-operated forward hydroplanes caused the boat to bottom almost as far as the gun position.) Nevertheless, the good depth-keeping properties of the 500-ton boats were specially mentioned by both the EAU, and the Commander of the U-Boat Flotilla at Saltzwedel, Fregattenkapitän Scheer:

'The superiority of the medium boat with regard to depth-keeping is reflected not in statistics alone. I had the feeling with the 500-ton boat that the very effective hydroplane functioning and its tautness under the surface give one a very reassuring feel in the hand, in all situations and to a degree that I have not experienced hitherto in any other boat: in this respect it is very superior to the 712-ton boat.'

The surface qualities of both types were regarded as satisfactory, although at maximum speed the 712-ton boat was considerably bow heavy. Tests in adverse weather had not yet been carried out: when these had been made, the Type VII showed an unwelcome tendency to instability. Boats of this type took so long to recover from rolling that the functioning of the diesel engine could be interrupted.

Needless to say, in terms of range and surface speed, the 500-ton type came off worst. To the question of how these defects could be improved, without materially affecting the construction of the boat, the EAU stated:

'Any increase in the fuel supply will necessitate alteration to the saddle tanks in order to compensate for the reduced height of the transverse metacentre at 'F' which occurs through the increase in weight causing the boat to be lower in the water. It is assumed that the highest point of the saddle tanks will then be approximately 5.2m below the waterline and the tank will curve in underneath to the existing ship's outline. The contents of the saddle tanks can be increased by approximately 50 per cent by this means. The improved surface stability when the tanks are blown (i.e., at approximately 25–30m^3 residual buoyancy) will be an additional advantage. No matter how the additional fuel is arranged, a diminution of the maximum speed will be

occasioned, which we estimate to be approximately 0.5 knots. None the less, a decrease in the reserve displacement of approximately 10 per cent is to be reckoned with, which means a reduction of the buoyancy in the case of damage at sea.'

Saddle tanks were suggested as the best means of storing additional fuel, although a significant advantage of Type VII as planned hitherto (no oil traces if the outer skin were damaged because the fuel bunkers were inside the pressure hull) would be forfeited. The Commander-in-Chief, U-Boats, gave his support to the suggestion, so that the only interior diving tank should be retained, so as not to lose too much reserve displacement. The fuel supply could be increased by 40m^3, by storing in the saddle tanks and by lengthening the boat.

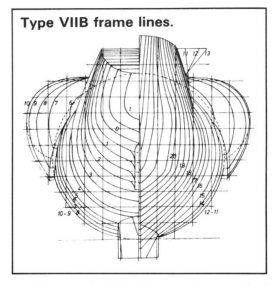

Type VIIB frame lines.

Dönitz regarded the inferior surface speed of Type VII, as compared to IA, as of no significance. While Type VII had a greater number of torpedoes in relation to the number of torpedo tubes, if one expressed torpedo armament in terms of relative displacements, both types were equal.

In order to effect an improvement in Type VII, it was suggested that, in place of the stern tube above the waterline in the outer ship, with its many disadvantages (no maintenance or reloading facilities and no surface firing!) two tubes should be included in the pressure hull, together with two reserve torpedoes. (A single interior torpedo tube, with only one torpedo, would not be worth the expenditure of alteration.) If this relatively strong armament should make the boat too heavy at the stern, with the result that she would lose some of her favourable submerged qualities, the original armament would be reverted to, and in this event two further reserve torpedoes could be accommodated in the bow compartment without any great changes. Dönitz did not suggest that any torpedoes be stowed outside the pressure hull in the outer ship.

These suggestions had a considerable effect on the evolution of Type VIIB (as it was officially

named from 24 November 1936), which was in progress in 'K' Office. First priority was given to increasing the Type VII's surface range, the surface speed and the torpedo supply. The first and third of these were to be attained by increasing the length of the boat by 2m and by fitting larger saddle tanks, as had been suggested by EAU. To be sure, this increased the surface displacement of the boat by 120m^3 (120 tons), but it only increased the standard displacement of this type from 500 tons to 517 tons, a point of great importance in the tonnage limitation of the Anglo-German Naval Treaty. As had been done with Type IX, the steering was improved by fitting a twin rudder in place of the single blade, and this arrangement also benefitted the stern torpedo tube, which was now situated in the pressure hull. The torpedoes could be ejected between the rudders. The torpedo complement was increased from eleven to fourteen by the provision of two additional torpedoes in pressure-tight containers in the upper deck and a further torpedo in the stern compartment. The performance of the diesel installation was increased by 20 per cent by the inclusion of superchargers, which meant that the maximum surface speed was greater by approximately 1 knot, despite the increase in size. Nevertheless, even with the improvement in profile and positioning of the side bulges, and increased streamlining of the full bow, the C_W values, with the exception of the minimum at 12 knots, could not be improved.

'K' Office now saw as its first task the repair of the existing gap in U-boat building, by securing an immediate decision as to how to use the outstanding tonnage. As an indication of the gap, GW, for example, had received no contracts since 25 March 1935. The very short building times that had been achieved up to now, as a direct consequence of diligent initial preparation and the pre-assembly of all necessary components, were no longer to be attained, and this meant an interval of more than a year in the building up of the U-boat arm. In a letter dated 7 October 1936, 'K' Office asked for the decision to be expedited in time for GW to be given a new contract in October 1936. It requested, additionally, that in the future Type IX should only be built at Deschimag, and Type VII only at GW, this to prevent further lengthy delays. On 27 October, the Supreme Commander-in-Chief of the Navy discussed means of allocating the remaining tonnage. While, in the opinion of the Commander-in-Chief, U-Boats (Dönitz), and Bartenbach, the remaining 6,666 tons should consist of 13 boats of the improved Type VII, 'A' demanded that 6 boats of the new Type IX be built, and only 4 of the improved Type VII. Raeder made the decision of Solomon: 4 Type IX boats and 7 boats of improved Type VII. Told by 'K' that a building time of two years should be allowed, Raeder ordered 'special and express aid for the U-boat construction programme as an urgent armament measure', but did not consider that organizational measures (along the lines of the special U-Boat Department BU of 1935 under Bartenbach) would be helpful. He contented himself, therefore, with an urgent written comment to all appropriate official parties.

On 21 November 1936, 4 Type IX boats, *U41–U44*, were contracted to Deschimag, and the 7 Type VIIB *U45–U51*, to GW. Raeder had not chosen to make decisions based on one or other of the conflicting opinions as to practical and strategic use of the U-boats. It was to be expected, therefore, that when a new distribution of tonnage was made, the tug-of-war between the champions of Type IX and Type VIIB would begin once more.

On 17 July 1937, a modified Anglo-German Naval Treaty was signed. With certain modifications, it corresponded to the British-French-American naval treaty (London Naval Treaty) of 1936, regarding qualitative limitation of naval rearmament. It gave Great Britain 70,000 tons in submarines until 1942, and Germany 31,500 tons.

On 8 July 1937, AI (Marschall) presented a memorandum that solved the mystery of why an additional 9,450 tons had been acquired from the new naval negotiations. It proceeded directly from the potential enmity presented by France and Russia, who had been bound together by a non-aggression pact since 1935. It was regarded as the chief task of the German Navy to protect trade shipping in the Baltic and North Sea. In view of the strong dependence on these sea lanes in the event of a war on two fronts, 'A' took the attitude that absolute priority should be given to this, rather than to operational measures against enemy lines of communication, and demanded that the number of small 250-ton U-boats be increased. It was calculated that in the Baltic 8 U-boats would be needed permanently; for the North Sea, up to a line Brest-Orkneys-Central Norway, 6 boats of 250 tons plus 3 of 500 tons were reckoned to be necessary for control of the outer waters. These figures, however, could not be achieved with the 24 boats of 250 tons built hitherto. It was essential, therefore, to augment this class of boat by 9 small U-boats.

The remaining tonnage was to be used for operational U-boat warfare in non-German waters. For the nearer operational theatres, e.g., the western Mediterranean, off the North African Atlantic coast and in the White Sea, the new Type VIIB seemed the most appropriate; but of this type, only 7 were currently under construction. AI suggested an increase of 5 boats of this type, so that 4 could be stationed permanently in these theatres. For more remote operations, especially minelaying, in the eastern Mediterranean and mid-Atlantic, Type IX was envisaged, and 8 of these were under construction. To these could be added both boats of Type IA. In order to have 4 boats permanently in these theatres, 2 more Type IX were held to be absolutely necessary. All this meant new demands from AI to the following total.

9 U-boats of 250 tons	= 2,250 tons.
5 U-boats of 517 tons	= 2,585 tons.
2 U-boats of 740 tons	= 1,480 tons.
Total	6,315 tons.

In the opinion of AI, the remaining 3,200 tons should be used to build 2 larger U-boats, and these, depending on how planning was functioning at the time, could either be one large minelaying U-boat and a U-cruiser, or 2 large minelaying U-boats.

In response to this, the Supreme Commander-in-Chief of the Navy placed the first 4 additional

Above: *U60* being lifted into the water at DWK, 1939.

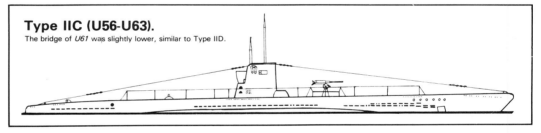

Type IIC (U56-U63).
The bridge of *U61* was slightly lower, similar to Type IID.

250-ton U-boats in contract to DWK on 17 June 1937. They were not regarded as being of great urgency, and were to be inserted into any gaps in construction. They were to be built according to a somewhat enlarged version of the Type IIB. In order to provide more space for communications equipment in the control room, the length of the boat was to be increased by the distance between two frames. At the same time, the fuel bunker beneath the control room was to be enlarged by approximately 1m³, and this slightly increased the range. This new model was given the designation Type IIC.

In anticipation of the tonnage increase, two VIIB boats had been contracted to GW on 15 May 1937 to help fill the building gap. On 30 June 1937, with regard to the outstanding tonnage, the Naval Command Office made the following suggestion, which took account of the new requirements of AI that had been made on 8 June.

4 boats Type IIC	= 1,000 tons.
2 boats Type VIIB	= 1,034 tons.
2 boats Type IX	= 1,480 tons.
Total	3,514 tons.

This took no account of the ninth IIC and the fifth VIIB boat, in order that approximately 4,000 tons would be available for the proposed building of the 2 large U-boats (a minelayer and a U-cruiser). This suggestion was approved by Raeder and appropriate contracts were awarded; on 16 July 1937, 2 Type VIIB to GW and two Type IX to Deschimag; and on 21 July, four Type IIC to DWK. The two new Type IX boats, *U64* and *U65*, were to be built according to an improved design, and were to bear the designation Type IXB. They were noteworthy principally for the fact that the outer ship was made wider, which allowed for an increased fuel supply. The only external difference was that the large gun was shifted from its position forward of the entry hatch to a point aft of this hatch and forward of the conning tower.

This apportionment of types, however, was not at all to the liking of the Commander-in-Chief, U-Boats, who in the early part of 1937 had repeatedly called for the U-boat tonnage to be heavily weighted (up to 75 per cent) in favour of the medium-size Type VII. In December 1937, the outstanding tonnage (approximately 4,000 tons) for further boats of available types, were placed in contract. Again, Dönitz' desire that preference be given to Type VIIB went unheeded, and the distribution was as follows: 4 boats of Type VIIB

(*U69–U72*) and 3 of Type IXB (*U66–U68*). This meant that the permitted tonnage to 1942 was now completely accounted for.

On 21 January 1938, it was decided that, with effect from 1 October 1939, a new chain of command would control this U-boat fleet, which would total 72 boats (a number that coincidentally corresponded exactly with provisional U-boat estimates made on 19 March 1934!):

U-Boat Headquarters, Kiel. (Operational Control of U-boats in outer home waters).

Baltic:
Commander of U-Boats East, Kiel (later Rügenhafen).

1st U-Flotilla (Kiel, later Rügenhafen). *U7, U9, U11, U13, U15, U17, U19, U21*; Escort Ships: *Donau, Memel* and *T23*.

3rd U-Flotilla (Kiel, later Rügenhafen). *U8, U10, U12, U14, U16, U18, U20, U22, U24*; Escort Ships: *Weichsel, Mosel* and *T156*.

5th U-Flotilla (Kiel). *U56, U57, U58, U59, U60, U61, U62, U63*; Escort Ships: (A merchant ship, yet to be purchased).

7th U-Flotilla (Kiel, later Rügenhafen). *U45, U46, U47, U48, U49, U51, U52, U53*; Escort Ships: *I* and *T157*.

North Sea:
Commander of U-Boats North, Wilhelmshaven.

2nd U-Flotilla (Wilhelmshaven). *U25, U26, U27, U28, U29, U30, U31, U32, U33, U34, U35, U36*; Escort Ships: *Saar* and *T158*.

4th U-Flotilla (Emden). *U50, U54, U55, U69, U70, U71, U72*; Escort Ships: *III* and a torpedo-boat.

6th U-Flotilla (Wilhelmshaven). *U37, U38, U39, U40, U41, U42, U43, U44, U64*; Escort Ships: *II* and *T155*.

8th U-Flotilla (Wilhelmshaven). *U65, U66, U67, U68*; Escort Ships: *IV* and a torpedo-boat.

When it came to the consideration of how the available new U-boat tonnage should be apportioned, it became clear that the 45 per cent ruling represented only a little more than the number of boats required for defensive purposes off the German coast. The remaining tonnage available for offensive purposes against the two potential enemies, France and Russia, was wholly inadequate, no matter what tactical measures were used. During the Anglo-German Naval Treaty negotiations of 1936–37, it became obvious that the Soviet-French non-aggression pact had greatly changed the strategic position at sea, and that the German Fleet now faced greater problems than had been the case during the negotiations for the treaty of 1935. In a report to the Supreme Commander-in-Chief dated 18 November 1937, it was recommended that it be proposed to the British Government that German U-boat tonnage (compared to the treaty of 1935) be increased to parity with British submarine tonnage. The resultant loss in surface tonnage was to be taken into consideration, but it was assumed that Britain would react with some sensitivity to any such increase in the German U-boat fleet.

Larger U-boat designs: Types X–XII
The abandonment of the Type III had not completely driven consideration of the large

minelaying U-boat from the thoughts of the Operations Department. Certainly, the development of torpedo-mines TMB (length 230.6cm, weight 740kg, explosive charge 580kg) and TMC (length 338.5cm, weight 1,115kg, explosive charge 1,000kg) made it possible for mines to be ejected through 53.3cm-diameter torpedo tubes; this meant, in effect, that any U-boat could become a minelayer. These mines were essentially mines with remote detonation (mostly magnetic, some acoustic), designed only for a depth of water of up to 20m.

The development of the torpedo anchor-mine with remote detonation, TMA, which had been planned with Type III in mind, and which could be used in water up to a depth of 270m, proceeded slowly. However, although of the same length as the TMC, its anchor weight resulted in its charge being reduced to only 215kg. It seemed advisable, therefore, to evolve a minelaying U-boat suitable for laying larger anchor mines — a special mine, Sonder-Mine A, or SMA (length 215cm, diameter 133.1cm, weight 1,600kg, explosive charge 350kg), with magnetic remote detonation having been chosen. At the beginning of 1937, 'K' Office was given the task of designing a large minelaying U-boat that could carry these mines. Initial planning with types designated 'X' and 'XA' harked back to a considerable extent to the large minelaying U-boats, *U117–U126*, of the First World War. In these boats, mines were carried in a stern compartment in dry housing, and were expelled through two chutes. In addition to this method, plans now envisaged a row of lateral shafts next to the pressure hull, each containing two SMAs in wet storage. To suit this method of housing, the submarines would be given an almost rectangular cross-section. The forward part of the boat was to have a torpedo installation, with four bow tubes. Design 'XA' differed from Design 'X' in having a greater beam and, consequently, a greater displacement.

Dry storage for mines was thought to be necessary because, at the time these boats were being planned, it was not yet possible to adjust the detonating mechanism inside the wet storage shafts. But the mines took up a lot of room, being very bulky with their anchors. Wet storage presented a better proposition in as much that it was only necessary to compensate the negative buoyancy on a weight basis. When, subsequently, the problem of adjusting wet-stored mines had been solved, Project 'XA', which had proceeded quite some way, was dropped in favour of a smaller design with wet-stored mines only. This replaced dry mine storage in the stern by six shafts in the forward section of the boat, each containing three wet SMA mines. The torpedo armament was reduced to two tubes, and these were positioned for defensive purposes in a stern compartment. The space and weight gained in the after part of the boat helped provide a stronger diesel installation and, therefore, an increased surface speed. This design was given the designation 'XB'.

On 25 September 1937, it was decided that a boat of this type should be started at GW on 1 October 1938, with completion scheduled for 1 October

Table 9. Specifications of Types X, XA and XB

	X	XA	XB
Form displacement surfaced (tons)	2,284.1	2,500*	1,710
Length (metres)	103.2	103.1	89.8
Beam (metres)	8.85	9.52	9.20
Draught (metres)	4.41	4.41	4.20
V_s (knots)	14	14	18
C_w	190	201	181
N_w (shp)	2,523	2,392	3,854

*Approx.

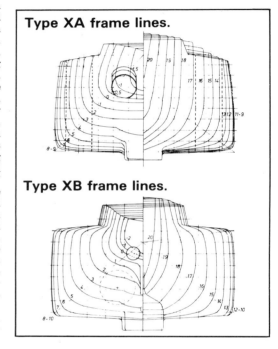

Type XA frame lines.

Type XB frame lines.

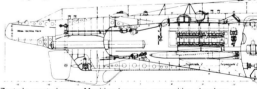

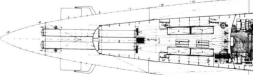

Glossary: Wasserdichtes Heck, watertight stern; Trimmzelle, trimming tank; Torpedozelle, torpedo tank; E.-Maschinenraum, electric motor room; Dieselmotorenraum, diesel engine room; Wasch u. Trocken-raum, laundry room; Kühlschr., cold storage; Küche, galley; Akkuraum, battery room; Turm, conning tower; Zentrale, control room; Munitionskammer, ammunition chamber; Kommandant, commander; Proviantraum, store room; Offizierraum, wardroom; Oberfeldwebelraum, warrant officers' quarters; Mannsch. R., ratings' quarters; Bugminenraum, bow mine compartment; Hecktorp R., stern torpedo room; Regenzeug Schr., oilskin locker; Nische F. Regenzeug, recess for oilskins; Funkraum, radio roo[m]

Above: *U116* (Type XB) before launching in May 1941.

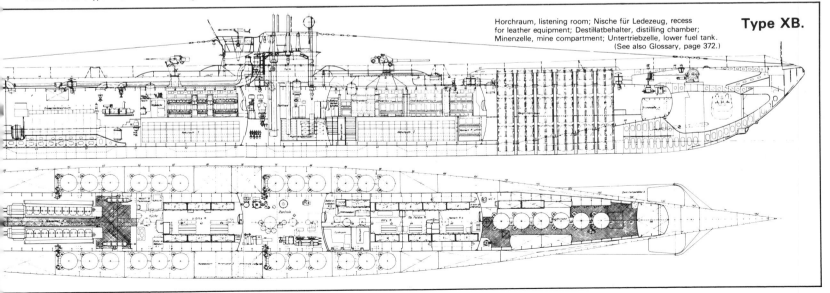

Horchraum, listening room; Nische für Ledezeug, recess
for leather equipment; Destillatbehalter, distilling chamber;
Minenzelle, mine compartment; Untertriebzelle, lower fuel tank.
(See also Glossary, page 372.)

Type XB.

1940. Building costs would be in the region of 7.5 million marks.

The desire of the Naval Command Office for a balanced fleet, called for a U-cruiser with a strong gun armament (for distant operations), as well as the large minelaying U-boat. In a letter dated 24 March 1937, the following requirements for the U-cruiser were stated:

'1. Tasks: offensive operations against merchantmen in distant waters. The U-cruiser has to be able to take over the rôle of a surface ship, and have the firepower of an auxiliary cruiser or escort ship, when protecting or attacking merchantmen. Her diving abilities should be such that:

(a) She can evade strong enemy action, so that she can be used in offensive operations without support of her own surface vessels.

(b) She can appear suddenly and unexpectedly when approaching, leaving or changing from one operational zone to another, and can evade enemy reconnaissance forces.

Compared to a normal-sized U-boat, the U-cruiser can make the enemy split up his forces very considerably, her offensive power being very much greater. The greater the distance from the epicentre of the sea war that she can be employed, the greater the disruptive effect will be.

'2. Operational territory: Consequently, in the event of a war with France and Russia, the U-cruiser will be used to best advantage in the following zones: in places adjacent to all theatres of war where, because of weakly-organized anti-submarine defence, she can function as a U-boat, and which are so important to the enemy that he has to adopt special countermeasures. The principal territories that come into this category are:

(a) The American and African shores of the Atlantic, with the exception of French European coastal waters, and the seas outside well protected African harbours such as Casablanca and Dakar.

(b) The north European coast as far as the White Sea (blockade against Russian sea-routes, protection of German ore routes from northern Norway).

(c) The eastern Mediterranean, if the political situation makes operations necessary there.

'3. In order to fulfil 1 and 2, the following requirements must be met:

(a) Gun armament capable of effectively engaging an auxiliary cruiser or escort at distances greater than 10,000m. Stress is laid on the ability for rapid firing and good gun-laying. The U-boat must be able to open fire immediately on surfacing and, when necessary, must be able to submerge very rapidly without the need for lengthy preparations. With regard to what may be expected from possible opponents, an armament of approximately four 15cm guns, or five 12.7cm guns is required.

(b) AA artillery against low-level attacks. As a U-boat presents a relatively small target, a special defence against high-level attacks is not absolutely essential. As this kind of boat is not likely to be used in theatres where heavy air attacks are expected, two 3.7cm guns mounted singly or in a twin turret are sufficient.

(c) Torpedo armament. The U-cruiser must be capable of dealing with superior enemy units by

Type XI and XIA frame lines.
------ The widened stem of Type XA, suggested by HSVA

Type XIB frame lines.

underwater attack. Armament of four bow torpedo tubes is therefore necessary; corresponding storage space for reserve torpedoes and/or mines must be provided.

(d) A long-range RT with direction-finding apparatus which allows full evaluation of our own radio signals.

(e) Speed: 20 knots cruising speed. Good seaworthiness on the surface.

(f) Radius of action: 25,000 nautical miles at 10 knots.

(g) Quarters and supplies suitable for tropical service.

(h) The strength of the U-cruiser must lie, above all, in its diving properties and weaponry.'

On 24 June 1937, 'K' was asked to carry out preliminary design work for this U-cruiser, which was to receive the designation Type XI. Meanwhile, required specifications were made more specific. First, four 15cm guns were demanded (with performance similar to the 15cm C/28) in twin turrets (not watertight or pressure-tight!), and positioned in one of two ways: with one turret forward of and one abaft the bridge, or with both

turrets forward of the bridge. Whichever was chosen, it was essential that a good arc of fire forward and aft be achieved from both gun turrets.

The new Anglo-German Naval Treaty, which was now ready for signature, mentioned in Article 7 the following limitation for U-boats: 'No submarine should exceed 2,000 tons (2,032 metric tons) standard water displacement, or be fitted with a gun of greater calibre than 5.1 inches (=13cm).' Consequently, on 7 July 1937, the armament was changed to four 12.7cm guns, either in twin turrets or twin mountings. It was suggested that investigation be made into the possibility of an armament consisting of six 12.7cm guns, in several turrets or in triple mountings. Certain requirements were set out in connection with this installation:

(a) Fire control to be contained within the pressure hull; capability of remote control of elevation and depression; special ignition device to compensate side movement of gun barrel during discharge.

(b) Mechanical handling of ammunition directly to each gun from ammunition storage in the pressure hull. Rate of fire: 10 rounds per barrel per minute. Munition supply: if possible, 250 rounds per barrel.

(c) Fire control apparatus to be the same kind as in Destroyer Type 34.

The required AA armament consisted of two 3.7cm guns in a single mounting with 2,000 shells per gun. The torpedo armament was to consist of four bow tubes and, later, a stern tube, with a total of twelve to thirteen torpedoes. Other required specifications were:

Speed surfaced:	20 knots.
Maximum speed surfaced:	23—25 knots for several hours continuously.
Maximum speed submerged:	6—8 knots.
Range surfaced:	20,000—25,000 nautical miles at 10 knots.
Range submerged:	approximately 100 nautical miles at 3 knots.
Diving depth:	100m; if possible, 120m.

Pressure-tight division into three safe compartments. Therefore, as many watertight bulkheads as possible to be provided, so that surface buoyancy would still be feasible if complete flooding of one of these watertight compartments should take place.

Table 10. Specifications of Types XI, XIA and XIB

	XI	XIA	XIB
Form displacement surfaced (tons)	2,659	2,725.4	2,830.4
Length (metres)	105.3	110.3	115.0
Beam (metres)	9.20	9.20	9.50
Draught (metres)	5.73	5.73	5.52
V_s (knots)	21	21	21
C_e	407	451	495
C_w	237	—	—
N_w (shp)	7,819	—	—

An attempt should be made to protect the conning tower against direct hits by 13cm shells striking at

Type XI, 13 April 1939.

0 2 4 6 8 10 12 14 16 18 20 m

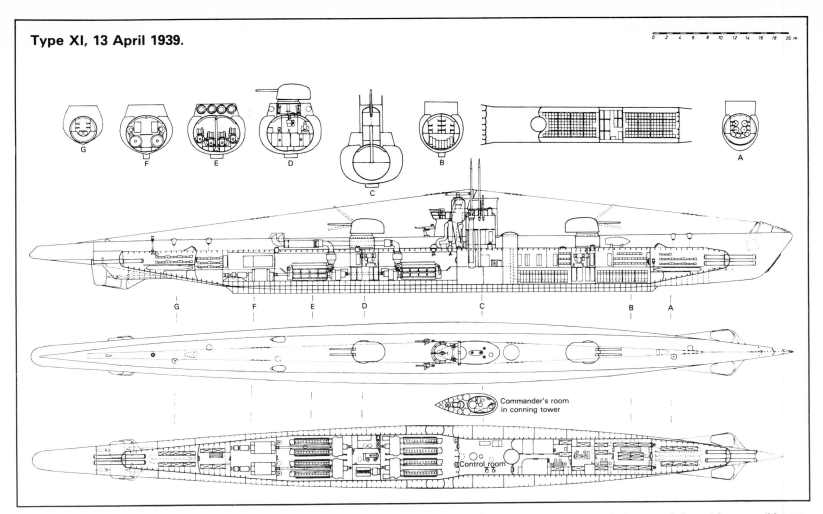

G F E D C B A

G F E D C B A

Commander's room in conning tower

Control room

an angle of 60°, and to protect the pressure hull from splinter damage down to one metre below the surface of the water. A diving time of up to one minute would be acceptable. Good surface and submerged stability were, however, essential. Further requirements concerned installations for living quarters, corresponding to lengthy operational cruises.

Design work started in 'K' Office in the summer of 1937, and Type IX was taken as the starting-point. To achieve the required high maximum speed, a powerful diesel installation was necessary, and this occasioned a special pressure-hull shape in the after section of the boat. Now, for the first time in a German U-boat, the double-circle cross-section was to be used. The two pressure-hull cylinders, set side by side, formed one compartment, 6.8m wide and 5.4m high. In each cylinder it was possible to install four large MWM, twelve-cylinder, RS38Zw diesel engines. Two diesels were coupled to one gearing. In all, the eight diesel engines should give the boat a maximum of 17,600hp. To render this large engine housing pressure-tight brought a host of problems to the designers, and these were solved

by providing interior frames and intermediate girders. Apart from the forward and after sections of the boat (only interior frames), the pressure hull was stiffened by interior frames at the top and with exterior frames overall.

The large boat now had many appendages and, in order to give it an acceptable submerged speed of 7 knots, the storage battery consisted of 2×124 cells of the largest accumulator type used by the German Navy, AFA 28 MAL 1000W (12,000 amp.hr, with 20 hours discharging). This was situated in the forward sections to counterbalance the massive diesel installation.

The torpedo armament was similar to that in Type IX, four forward and two stern torpedo tubes. The number of torpedoes carried was less: the lack of provision of exterior storage limited them to twelve. What was unique in this type was the proposed artillery armament, which was disposed in two enclosed twin-turrets forward and aft of the conning tower, so placed as to be able to fire over it. Rangefinding equipment was placed in an armoured action-station on the bridge. Gun turrets and action-station could be reached from the interior of

the boat, which ensured the quickest possible state of preparedness for firing, and as great as possible independence from weather conditions.

The AA armament fulfilled the wishes of 'A': two 3.7cm guns in single mountings on the upper deck abaft the bridge, and a single 2cm C/30 on the bridge. In order to provide the large gun crews with entry and exit facilities, two conning-tower hatches were provided. The bridge was of the same shape as that in Type IX, but was rather higher, and the conning tower, which formed part of it, was divided into two storeys; the upper one being the observation platform, with two periscopes for submerged control of the boat, and two special periscopes for artillery spotting; the lower storey forming the commander's quarters. Later, the bridge was given a roofed surface-control platform with portholes, similar to those used in Italian and Japanese submarines.

Two special features of the design were, the half-submerged facility, and a small reconnaissance seaplane. The half-submerged facility had been proposed to Igewit by Chief Engineer Hans Vogel as early as 24 August 1935, without any particular interest being aroused at the time. In the event of surface attack, the half-submerged condition was achieved by an installation which could take the boat down to a depth where the upper edge of the pressure hull was one metre below the surface of the sea. Vogel had demonstrated that shots from opposing vessels very quickly lost their velocity in a small amount of water. Thus, without any additional armour, the pressure hull would be safe from splinter damage. This 'swimming situation' was achieved by buoyancy chambers, placed low down at the sides of the boat, remote from the danger of shell damage.

For reconnaissance purposes, a small unarmed seaplane (an Ar 231) was to be carried on board. The aircraft was so constructed that it could be contained in a pressure-tight tube, 2.25m wide and 7.50m long. A special method of construction enabled the 1,050kg aircraft to be assembled by hand on the upper deck: a folding crane on the starboard side helped to prepare the aircraft, and was then used for swinging it out and recovering it. The range of the seaplane was 500km. Use of the machine, however — as tests with six experimental prototypes had shown — was only practicable in good wind and sea conditions. The method of housing, in a tube placed vertically in the boat's hull, was regarded as a very satisfactory solution to a problem that had troubled the builders of foreign submarines; the German method required no further construction on the upper deck, save a single enclosing-hatch.

On 25 September 1937, it was planned to start building this type and Type XB on 1 October 1938, with completion scheduled for 1 October 1940. Deschimag was proposed as the building yard, and costs were reckoned at 7.5 million marks. However, as with Type X B, the design of this complicated and costly boat took longer than had been expected. On 1 October 1938, Naval Construction Adviser Aschmoneit was given special responsibility for Type XI, which was now to have special significance in the Z-Plan (see below).

Finally, in 1938, the Naval Command Office demanded a special, large Fleet U-boat, for operations in conjunction with surface raiders. Type IX had originally been designed for this, but its maximum surface speed of 18.2 knots was considerably below the 20 knots that had been requested. A new design was deemed necessary. Sketches for a boat of approximately 2,000 tons displacement were given the designation Type XII. In outer form, this corresponded to Type IX. It was to have a maximum surface speed of 22 knots and a submerged speed of 10 knots with a range of 20,000 nautical miles at 12 knots, performances to be achieved by using two ten-cylinder, 3,500hp GW diesel engines and two 840hp electric motors. (It is doubtful, however, if this total capacity of 7,000hp would have enabled the boat to reach its required surface speed. As a comparison, the similarly-sized, British *Thames* class submarines, according to the British fleet handbook, required 10,000hp to attain 22.5 knots.) Apparently, the boat was also to be given an additional diesel-electric propulsion unit, in order to achieve the considerable range required. Storage batteries were to be 2 × 62 cells

28 MAL 1000. The armament was to be similar to that of Type IX. The construction specification was as follows.

Length:	92.35m.
Beam:	8.50m.
Draught:	5.40m.
Total displacement surfaced:	2,040.8 tons.
Speed surfaced:	18 knots.
Ce:	487

At the commencement of hostilities in 1939, however, this project was still in the planning stage in 'K' Office.

CONSTRUCTION PLANS TO 1939 AND THE FUTURE OF THE U-BOAT

The Z-Plan of January 1939
The early part of 1938 was notable for the considerable political tensions that arose. Britain was now seen as a potential enemy, and had to be included in operational considerations. On 12 April 1938, Raeder declared, in discussions during War Manoeuvres 'A': 'We must now have to take

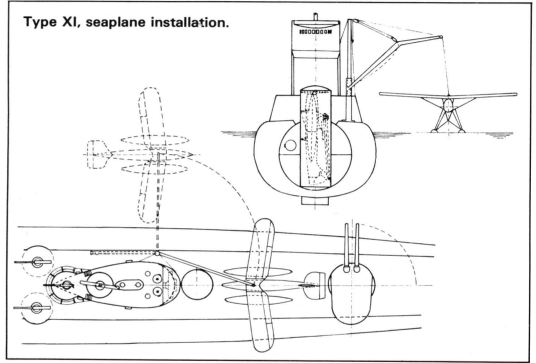

Type XI, seaplane installation.

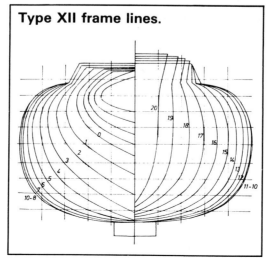

Type XII frame lines.

account of England also, if it comes to a war against France, which means that the basis on which the waging of a sea war depends is altered.' After the Czechoslovakia crisis of May 1938, even Hitler, who all along had desired in all circumstances to avoid a conflict with Britain, was convinced that in the event of war British intervention must be expected. Prior to discussions with the Supreme Commander-in-Chief of the Navy on 27 May 1938, he desired clarification of the possibilities of accelerating the building programme for the Battle Fleet, and of the following points:

'(d) Quick completion of 100 per cent of U-boats, once the word of command has been given.

'(e) Design priority for U-cruisers and, when the designs are satisfactory, rapid construction of a considerable number.

'(f) Against the contingency of mobilization, the most rapid assembly of a considerable number of medium boats (Type VIIB) by disposition and ordering of parts and components at various yards (e.g., Howaldt Yard, Hamburg).'

Type VIIC, 1940.

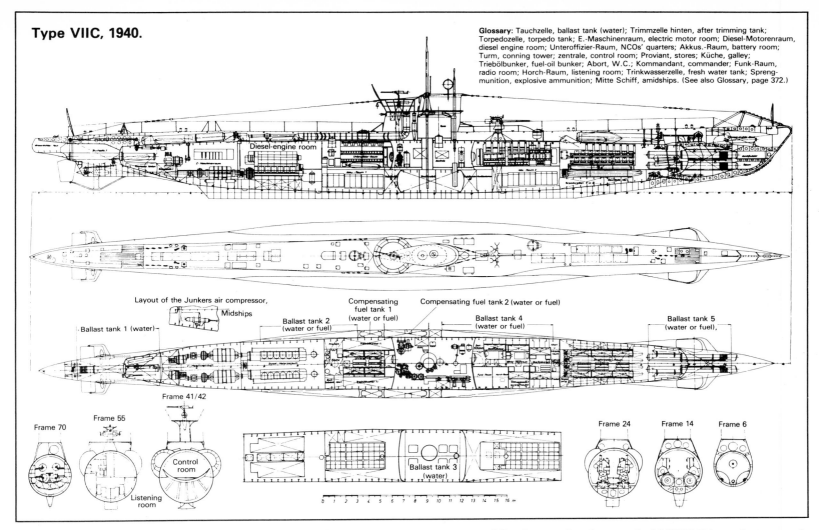

Diesel-engine room

Layout of the Junkers air compressor, Midships

Ballast tank 1 (water)

Ballast tank 2 (water or fuel)

Compensating fuel tank 1 (water or fuel)

Compensating fuel tank 2 (water or fuel)

Ballast tank 4 (water or fuel)

Ballast tank 5 (water or fuel),

Frame 41/42

Frame 55

Frame 70

Control room

Listening room

Ballast tank 3 (water)

Frame 24

Frame 14

Frame 6

Consequently, at a preliminary conference at Supreme Naval Command on 25 May, it was stated:

'Re (d). Negotiations with Britain concerning this point are to begin on 1 October 1938, and be concluded by the end of 1938, so that building could actually start on 1 January 1939. Prudently, engines and periscopes have already been ordered. A V (Fuchs) is of the opinion that if the yards were to employ more people, 36 boats could be built yearly instead of 24. However, in that case, it would be necessary to see that the yard got the right type of workers. From 1941, boat deliveries could be as follows: Bremer Vulkan 8 U-boats, Flender-Werke 8, Deschimag 10 and GW 10. At the Howaldt-Hamburg Yard, it will first be necessary to make certain alterations to existing workshop facilities. This means that by 1942–43, 129 U-boats [=100 per cent] will be available.

'Re (e). A V states that 2 large minelaying U-boats are being built at GW, and 2 U-cruisers at Deschimag. A larger number of U-cruisers would considerably disturb other building projects.

'Re (f). According to existing mobilization planning, 4 Type II, 4 Type VIIB and 2 Type IX boats are planned each month. The Head of BW is of the opinion that the building of these boats, necessary for mobilization, can be accelerated if we involve smaller yards in initial preparatory constructional work before war begins.'

Based on this, an outline 'Improved Reconstruction Plan for 1938–1945' (27 June 1938) was increased in scope in view of the imminence of the conclusion of the Anglo-German Naval Treaty. In the U-boat sphere, it restricted itself to a desire to attain only the hoped-for 100 per cent limit. By the end of 1941, it was planned to have in service 98 U-boats, comprising 32 Type II boats, 2 Type IA, 10 Type VII, 31 Type VII B/C, 21 Type IX, 1 Type X and 1 Type XI. In anticipation of the desired increase to the 100 per cent parity in U-boats, 8 Type IXB boats (U103–U110) had been placed in contract with Deschimag on 24 May 1938, and 8 new Type VIIC (U93–U100) with GW on 30 May. At the beginning of June 1938, there followed

orders for a total of 8 VIIB U-boats for two yards new to U-boat construction, Bremer Vulkan, Vegesack (U73–U76), and Flender-Werke, Lübeck (U84–U87). On 8 August, a further Type IX boat (U111) was added at Deschimag, while at Flender the export order of Hapro for a 500-ton submarine was taken over by the German Navy, as U83.

The stimulus for going over to Type VIIC, was the planned installation of an effective sound-detection device (S-Gerät, or Special Apparatus), which involved increasing the size of the control room by the distance of half a frame forward of, and half a frame aft of, the periscope. This meant that the boat was 600mm longer, and involved the following improvements:

1. Enlarging the rather inadequate dimensions of the conning tower in VIIB by 60mm in width and 300mm in length.

2. Inclusion of two pressure-tight negative buoyancy tanks, one on the port side and one on the starboard side, forward of the compensating tanks, to improve diving, especially in heavy seas.

3. Enlargement of the interior fuel-oil bunkers by 5.4m^3.

The engine installation was to be improved in the following ways:

1. Inclusion of an engine-oil purifying installation, to increase reliability and to economize in the use of lubricating oil.

2. Replacing the starboard electrical compressor by a Junkers Compressor, to reduce consumption of electrical current. An important innovation was the replacing of the BBC control panels with knife switches, which had been used in U-boats since the First War, by AEG handwheel switch gear.

The ideas of the Naval War Staff for 'the prosecution of naval war against England, and the concomitant strategic aims and the building-up of the Navy' necessitated a 'balanced fleet' for the lead-up to war: 'The waging of warfare against merchant shipping by all types, from U-boat to the heaviest capital ship, and including air-force units, will make a stronger impression than such warfare waged by restricted types . . . From an offensive sea operation carried out with U-boats only, not a great amount of success is to be expected.' Reasons for this last statement were given as follows: the progress made by the British in the field of U-boat detection (Asdic), and the possibility that, under the terms of the naval treaty, U-boat warfare would have to be waged according to Prize Ordinance Regulations.

At a meeting of a special Planning Commission in October 1938, the steps necessary for a building-up of the Fleet were sketched out — significantly, no representative of the U-boat arm nor the Air Force (Luftwaffe) belonged to this body. On 1 November 1938, Raeder presented Hitler with three alternative plans for the building-up of the Fleet to the end of 1947. Hitler approved the third plan, which gave a certain building priority to heavy naval units, and to U-boats. He made the further demand that, by the end of 1943, the 6 battleships of Type H and 4 new pocket battleships be given absolute building priority. On 24 November, in line with this modified, third construction plan, U-boat

Table 11. The Z-Plan, third version: U-boat deliveries

Type	By end of 1943	Chief of Naval War Staff demands	By end of 1945	By end of 1947 (full amount)
IA	2		2	2
II	48	(33)	60	60
VII	10		10	10
VIIB/C	69	(90)	90	90
IX	26	(60)	44	60
XB	4	(9)	9	9
XI	7	(9)	9	9
XII	8	(9)	9	9
Total	174		233	249

Table 12. Yard planning, 16 December 1938

Type	Nos.	Yard	Delivery dates
IIC	1—8	DWK	(—1.11.39)
IID	1	DWK	(1.4.42—1.1.44)
	2—13	DWK	(1.4.42—1.1.46)
	14—28	DWK	(1.4.44—1.1.48)
VIIB/C	1—15	GW	(—20.8.40)
	16—25	GW	(10.5.38—1.11.42)
	26—39	Br-V	(2.6.38—15.10.42)
	40—53	Fl-W	(2.6.38—15.10.42)
	54—61	Br-V	(1.9.41—1.1.44)
	62—69	Fl-W	(1.9.41—1.1.44)
	70—80	Br-V	(1.4.42—1.9.45)
	81—90	Fl-W	(1.4.42—1.9.45)
IX	1—13	Deschimag	(—20.3.39)
	14—22	Deschimag	(29.5.38—5.5.41)
	23—28	Howaldt, Hbg	(1.4.41—1.1.44)
	29—32	GW	(1.4.41—1.1.44)
	33—44	Howaldt, Hbg	(1.4.42—1.1.46)
	45—56	GW	(1.4.42—1.1.46)
	57—60	Howaldt, Hbg and GW	(1.4.44—1.1.47)
XB	1—3	GW	(1.4.39—27.10.41)
	4	GW	(1.4.41—1.12.43)
	5—9	GW	(1.4.42—1.9.45)
XI	1—4	Deschimag	(1.4.39—1.8.42)
	5—6	Deschimag	(1.10.40—1.12.43)
	7—9	Deschimag	(1.4.42—1.12.45)
XII	1—3	Deschimag	(1.9.39—1.4.42)
	4—6	Deschimag	(1.10.40—1.10.43)
	7—9	Deschimag	(1.4.42—1.6.45)

(Plus 12 U-boat escort ships at Howaldt, Kiel.)

Type IID.

Glossary: Tauchzelle, ballast tank (water); Oberkante flutschlitzen, overhead flooding slits; Trimzelle hinten, after trimming tank; klosett, W.C.; Spreng patronen behälter, explosive cartridge container; Motorenölvorratstank, engine-oil tank; Trebölbunker, fuel-oil bunker; Regelbunker, compensating fuel tank; Trinkwasserzelle, fresh water tank; Munitionbehälter, ammunition compartment; Echolotbehälter, echo-sounding compartment; Torpedorohr, torpedo tube. (See also Glossary, page 372.)

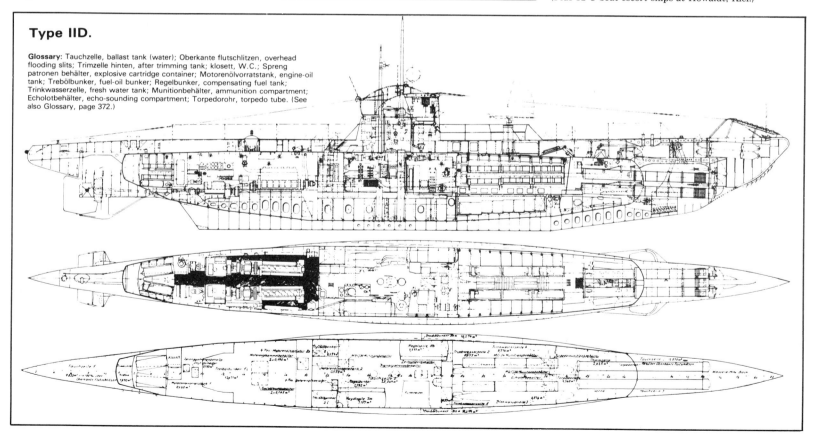

Type VIIC frame lines.

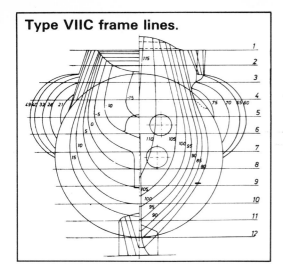

Type IID frame lines.

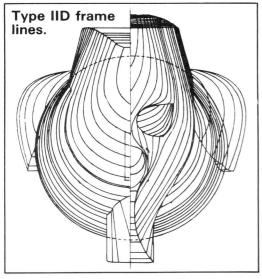

deliveries — if yards worked to full capacity — were established as shown in Table 11.

The 28 additional Type II boats were along the lines of IIC, but with saddle tanks. This provided an increase in surface range to 5,680 nautical miles at 8 knots, which permitted operations off the west coast of Britain. As had been noticed in Type VII, the saddle tanks reduced resistance in the higher speed range (9–12 knots). The bridge was kept to a low profile, and this meant that when submerged, despite the increased displacement, there was no penalty in performance. These boats were given the designation Type IID. As shown in Table 12, yard planning for the period from 16 December 1938 showed only minimal delays.

On 10 December 1938, the negotiations with Great Britain that had been planned during the spring began; these concerned the 100 per cent parity in submarines. On 30 December, the British Admiralty acceded to German wishes, but

requested an agreement by which this increase in submarine tonnage would be carried out in stages. The German negotiator was not prepared for this, but stated (without giving any guarantee) that by the end of 1939, only 65 per cent at most would be achieved. The first orders for the new programme followed in January 1939: 13 Type VIIC (Bremer-Vulkan *U77–U82*, Flender-Werke *U88–U92*, GW *U101–U102*); 3 Type XB (GW *U116–U118*); and 4 Type XI (Deschimag *U112–U115*). This meant that a total of 64,573 tons had been allocated, so the 100 per cent (70,000-ton) figure had still not been reached.

On 17 January 1939, Raeder placed the final draft of the Z-Plan, as the modified third construction plan was now designated, before Hitler; the latter reiterated the priority for battleship construction and demanded that six ships of Type H be completed by 1944. At this, Raeder appointed the erstwhile Head of the Fleet Command (A V) and architect of the plan, Konteradmiral Fuchs, to be Special Delegate for this immense battleship building programme. However, in spite of the special powers that Hitler had granted to the Naval Rearmament Programme, it seemed doubtful if it could be fulfilled in the time required. During the first months, considerable difficulties were noticeable in the provision of labour and materials, despite the very involved personal efforts of the responsible Naval Officials.

The office known hitherto as the 'Construction Office' now became the 'Office for Warship Construction', with complete responsibility for the building and punctual delivery of all new ships. In June 1939, Konteradmiral Fuchs was appointed to be its head.

With preparations starting for the third Type H battleship, the question of abandoning the Anglo-German Naval Treaty became acute. Although, in reality, there was no pressing need, the Navy was desirous of a speedy rejection of the treaty so that, without let or hindrance, a total re-armament could be carried out. Nevertheless, when Hitler repudiated the treaty on 28 April 1939, it came as a complete surprise to Raeder.

Final U-boat planning in the framework of the Z-Plan is shown in Table 13. For organizational purposes, these U-boats were to be assembled by 1948, in 22 flotillas and a training flotilla. From this U-boat planning, by the outbreak of war on 1 September 1939, a total of 136 U-boats were under building contract, and only 57 (30 small 250-ton boats, 10 Type VII, 8 Type VIIB, 2 Type IA and 7 Type IX) were actually in service. The ten IXC U-boats of new construction, which had been placed in contract on 7 August 1939, differed from Type IXB principally in their increased displacement, although they had much the same dimensions. This was the result of an altered cross-section shape. Although of the same beam as Type IXB, the outer

A Type IID boat in dock. Note the Kort nozzle to the left of the starboard propellor.

Type VIIC.

Glossary: Tauchzelle, ballast tank (water); Tauchbunker, ballast tank (water or fuel); Hecktorpedoraum, stern torpedo room; Treibölbunker, fuel oil bunker; E.-Maschinenraum, electric motor room; Dieselmotorenraum, diesel engine room; Regelbunker, compensating fuel tank (water or fuel); Regelzelle, compensating tank (water); Zentrale, control room; Untertriebzelle, negative buoyancy tank; Funkraum, radio room; Horchraum, listening room; Offz. Raum, ward-room; Luke, hatch; Kücke, galley; Schr., locker; K. Sehr., main periscope; Oberfeldwebelraum, warrant officers' quarters; Unteroffizierraum, NCOs' quarters; Bugtorpedoraum, bow torpedo room; Trimmzelle, trimming tank; Torpedozelle, torpedo tank; Trinkwasserzelle, fresh water; Lenz, bilge; Munitions kammer, ammunition compartment; Motorenölvorratstank, engine-oil storage tank; Schmutzwasserzelle, bilge water; Akkumulatorenraum, accumulator room; Flurboden, floor.

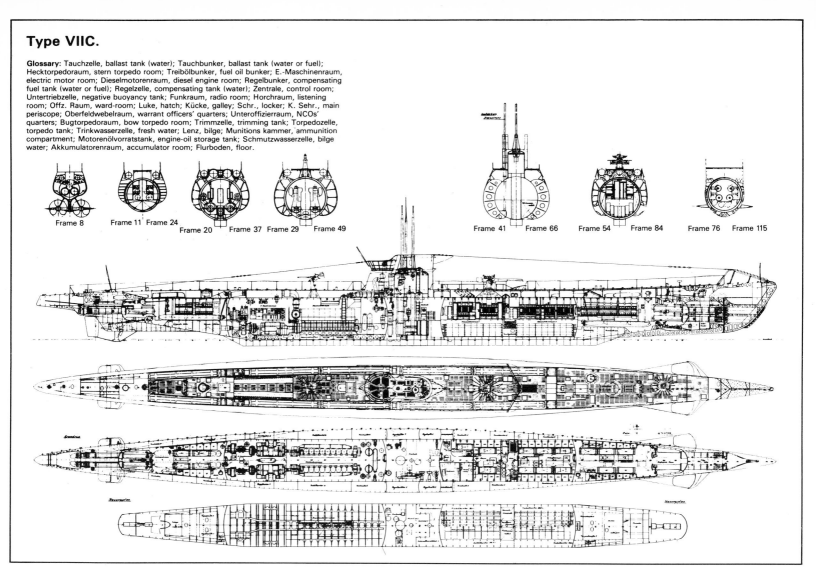

Frame 8   Frame 11 Frame 24   Frame 20   Frame 37 Frame 29   Frame 49   Frame 41   Frame 66   Frame 54   Frame 84   Frame 76   Frame 115

ship was carried farther downwards, to almost meet the upper edge of the keel. From the point of view of water resistance, it would have been better if the outer ship had been drawn down to the lower edge of the keel, although the large ballast keel would not then have been so accessible. On the other hand, the loss in surface speed brought about by this form was negligible, as the surge impedance of the boat was the dominant factor. The wider outer hull meant an increase in fuel storage by approximately 43 tons, and this increased the surface range. The control-room periscope was eliminated.

Mobilization contingency plans, 1933–39

At the end of 1932, it had been decided that until further notice the Naval Rebuilding Programme would restrict itself to two U-boat types, E1 and CV707, and that in the event of mobilization these would be the only two types for which quick completion could be expected. The results of a discussion on 13 October 1933, concerning 'A' New Constructions' was that in the event of mobilization work done to date on the 2 large and 6 small U-boats would immediately be completed. Then, following a certain lapse of time in initial building, further large boats would be completed 'commensurate with the utmost production capacities of building yards that would be used', i.e. 6 small boats per month. On 12 March 1934, the monthly delivery quotas for mobilization building of large boats was fixed at 5, which meant a monthly building of 5,250 tons in the event of mobilization. With regard to the small boats, it was especially noted that efforts should be made to shorten these delivery times. On 26 November 1934, BSt prepared a plan for ''A' — New Construction for 1934' together with a distribution of mobilization U-boats among different yards:

Large U-boats (Type IA) 5 boats per month (B&V 2, Deschimag and Bremer-Vulkan 2; reserve KMW Wilhelmshaven).
Small U-boats (Type IIA) 6 boats per month (DWK 3, GW 3).

To follow on from this timetable of U-boat production, in the early part of 1935 it was necessary to set out a new construction plan for mobilization. However, according to a resolution of A I, Type IA was to be discontinued, and a further problem was that the anticipated number of deliveries as stated in the new construction Mobilization Plan of 1934 had to be reduced in accordance with the restricted output capacities of the yards and on account of an anticipated increased demand for destroyers and torpedo-boats in the event of mobilization. Following a discussion at A II on 25 September 1935, it was established: Large U-boats (Type VII) 4 boats per month.

Small U-boats (Type IIB) 4 boats per month.

In place of Type IIB, a special mobilization boat of 600 tons was to be produced later. Conjecturally, this project would have involved U-boat Type VIII, but no exact details were issued, nor are any available. In the planning that followed, however, the point did not arise again.

On 27 January 1936, BWi presented a new Construction Mobilization Plan for 1936, which corresponded with the 1935 Plan in its monthly delivery quantities. From a projected 4 Type VII boats per month, 2 were to be delivered by Deschimag, 2 by Bremer-Vulkan; of 4 Type IIB boats, 2 were to be delivered by DWK and 2 by GW. It was further established that in the event of mobilization, if necessary and for the length of time it took to fit-out the proposed auxiliary boats, the proposed construction of *U37–U44* could be suspended, but must subsequently recommence with all priority.

Following the decision in favour of U-boat Type VIIB, on 25 June 1937, BWi presented a new 'New Construction Plan for Mobilization 1937–38':
U-boat Type VIIB 4 boats per month (Deschimag 2, GW 1, Bremer-Vulkan, Vegesack, 1).
U-boat Type IIB 4 boats per month (DWK 1.5, GW 2, Flender-Werke 0.5).
Compared with the previous plans, this timetable covered a longer period, a consequence of the increased size of contracts awarded to each yard.

On 24 September 1937, it was decided that in the event of mobilization the completion of the following vessels would be speeded up: *U56–U63* (Type IIC, DWK); *U52–U55* (Type VIIB, GW); *U64* and *U65* (Type IXB, Deschimag); the U-boat Testing Dock (Flender) and the experimental ship for the projected Type X (GW). Finally, consideration was being given at BWi for a new Construction Mobilization Plan for 1939. It was proposed that the new Type IIC should replace Type IIB. A I urged an extension of the existing new plan for 1937–38, by a further 4 Type IX boats. It was also decided that future mobilization plans take account of the projected U-cruiser (Type XI) and the large, minelaying U-boat (Type X). On 17 January 1938, BWi put out two alternative proposals for a new Construction Mobilization Plan for 1939:

'Proposal A':
U-boat Type VIIB 4 boats per month corresponding to 1937–38 Plan.
U-boat Type IIC 4 boats per month corresponding to 1937–38 Plan.

'Proposal B':
U-boat Type IX 2 boats per month (the first boat after sixteen months).
U-boat Type VIIB 3 boats per month (the first boat after fourteen months).
U-boat Type IIC 2 boats per month (the first boat after ten months).'
A decision, however, was not taken on this.

The increased possibility of war (Case 'Green'), ushered in a number of additional measures (proposals for accelerating the construction programme, deferment of yard laying-down times, etc.). However, a new New Construction Mobilization Plan, which in the event of war would replace the ambitious Z-Plan, was not presented by BWi until 18 February 1939. It was to be valid from 1 April 1939 to 31 March 1941, and called for the following monthly deliveries of U-boats:
U-boat Type IX 2 boats per month (Deschimag 1.5, Seebeck and Wesermünde).
U-boat Type VIIC 4 boats per month (GW 1.25, Flender-Werke, 1.25, Bremer-Vulkan 1.5).
U-boat Type IIC 3 boats per month (DWK 1.5, GW 1.5).
This plan could be carried out with normal yard manning. With an increase in yard personnel, peacetime contracts for types embodied in the Mobilization Plan, which are outlined in the mobilization preparations, could be accommodated. If, however, other and specially-demanded larger warships were required on the outbreak of war and were given building priority, the assumed timetable could not be met, and delivery delays would occur in all the above monthly predictions.

Table 13. U-boats in the Z-Plan, final version

	1939	1940	1941	1942	1943	1944	1945	1946	Ult. 1947
U-boats for coastal waters	32	32	32	32	33	39	45	52	60
U-boats for distant operations (Type IA, VII, IX)	34	52	73	88	112	133	157	161	162
U-boats for special tasks (Type XB, XI, XII)	—	—	6	10	16	22	27	27	27
Totals	66	84	111	130	161	194	229	240	249

Table 14. U-boat organizational intention as at 17 May 1939

	Number of boats*	Types	Establishment date
1st U-Flotilla (at Kiel until 1943, then at Rügenhafen)	9+2	II, IIB	Operational
2nd U-Flotilla (Wilhelmshaven)	9+2	VII, VIIB	Operational
3rd U-Flotilla (at Kiel until 1941 then at Pillau)	9+2	IIB	Operational
4th U-Flotilla (at Wilhelmshaven until 1941, then at Emden)	9+2	VIIB/C	1.10.39
5th U-Flotilla (at Kiel until 1943, then at Memel)	9+2	IIB/C	Operational
6th U-Flotilla (Wilhelmshaven)	9+2	IXA/B	From 3.6.39
7th U-Flotilla (Kiel)	9+2	VIIB/C	From 4.6.40
8th U-Flotilla (at Wilhelmshaven until 1941, then at Bremerhaven)	9+2	IXB	1.10.40
9th U-Flotilla (at Kiel until 1943, then at Rügenhafen)	9+2	VIIB/C	1.4.41
10th U-Flotilla (Emden)	9+2	VIIC	1.4.42
11th U-Flotilla (Kiel)	9+2	VIIC	Middle 2.43
12th U-Flotilla (at Wilhelmshaven until 1942 then Cuxhaven)	9+2	IXB	Beginning 1942
13th U-Flotilla (Rügenhafen)	9+2	IXB	1943
14th U-Flotilla (Bremerhaven)	9+2	VIIC	1943
15th U-Flotilla (Rügenhafen)	9+2	VIIC	1943
16th U-Flotilla (Emden)	9+2	IXB	1945
17th U-Flotilla (Rügenhafen)	9+2	IID	1944
18th U-Flotilla (Cuxhaven)	7+2	XB	1944
19th U-Flotilla (Pillau)	9+2	IID	1946
20th U-Flotilla (Wilhelmshaven)	7+2	XI	1944
21st U-Flotilla (Kiel)	7+2	VIIC, IXB	1945
22nd U-Flotilla (Bremerhaven)	7+2	XII	1943
Training Flotilla (Neustadt)	15	IA, IIA, VII	?

*In the 'number of boats' column, the second figure indicates reserve boats, which would not be manned initially.

Table 15. The New Construction Plan for Mobilization, 1934

Delivery after month

	8	9	10	11	12	13	14	15	16
Type IA	—	—	—	1	2	3	4	5	
Type IIA	1	2	4	6	6	6	6	6	6

Table 16. The New Construction Plan for Mobilization, 1935–1936

Delivery after month

	8	9	10	11	12	13	14	15
Type VII	—	—	—	—	1	2	3	4
Type IIB	1	2	4	4	4	4	4	4

Table 17. The New Construction Plan for Mobilization, 1937–38

Delivery after month

	9	10	11	12	13	14	15	16	17	18
Type VIIB	—	—	—	—	—	1	2	3	3	4
Type IIB	1	3	4	4	4	4	4	4	4	4

Table 18. The New Construction Plan for Mobilization of 18 February 1939

Delivery after month

	10	11	12	13	14	15	16	17	18
Type IX	—	—	—	—	—	—	1	2	2
Type VIIC	—	—	—	—	1	1	2	3	4
Type IIC	1	3	3	3	3	3	3	3	3

Fürbringer and Dönitz on U-boat tactics and defence

After the disbanding of BU and the distribution of its personnel to various other departments of the Supreme Command, only Werner Fürbringer was later to make his presence felt by several suggestions concerning the development of U-boats. His particular concern was that the special advantage that the U-boat enjoyed, namely that of being invisible when submerged, would be nullified by the British development of effective underwater detection equipment. He saw it as a hopeless task for U-boats to expect to blockade Britain without corresponding anti-detection devices. In a memorandum from the early part of 1939 entitled 'Which development projects and which operational preparations should be given priority in order to prepare for a U-boat blockade against England?', among other points he stated:

'At the present moment, U-boat blockade of England has very little prospect of success for Germany. Any contradictory opinion, which takes comfort in the large number of our U-boats or in the idea that the English U-boat defence will not be effective far out into the Atlantic, can be dismissed as misleading. It can be taken as proven that every English convoy, no matter whether it operates along the coast or on the high seas, will be secured by defensive forces, fully capable of destroying with certainty any attacking U-boat, even under the surface.'

On the other hand, it was abundantly clear to Fürbringer that the U-boat blockade of Britain represented the sole means of striking a decisive blow against her. Therefore, in his opinion, it was absolutely essential to reinforce efforts to find a method of protecting U-boats from underwater detection and to remedy their defencelessness against attack by escort vessels and submarine-chasers. As early as 1936, he had championed the development of the so-called Positive Buoyancy Bombs (Wasserauftriebsbombe, or WAB.) These were small explosive charges that, ejected from a U-boat, would rise towards the surface and explode beneath the keel of a pursuing vessel. But, in a letter dated 14 March 1936, the Naval Command Office turned this proposal down as impracticable. Their basic objections were the lack of accurate detection means (Vertical Direction Finding); the inadequate effect of the suggested 10kg bombs; the discovery of, and great danger to, U-boats in the event of unsuccessful attack with WAB; the limited possibility of U-boat activity during defensive moves at minimum speed; and the excessive risk of almost-certain discovery if U-boats carried out offensive attacks at speed. A decent alternative was suggested in the shape of a homing acoustic torpedo to be used as a defensive weapon.

On 11 March 1938, Fürbringer made a further proposal for a defensive weapon. In his opinion, the acoustic torpedo had the disadvantage 'that one's opponent, as soon as he realizes that the torpedo is homing in on him, can throw overboard an object capable of emitting noise'. He proposed therefore:
1. A remotely-controlled, small torpedo, running on the surface, which could be aimed by radio (an aerial on the periscope). (Incidentally, this idea was not a new one: as early as 1906, the Siemens Schuckertwerke AG was working on a radio-controlled torpedo which was to have a range of 20km.)
2. A small torpedo with rocket propulsion. (In connection with this, some preliminary work was being carried out at the firm of Walter.)
3. A small torpedo with cable or wire linkage. (Advantage: no chance of the opposing vessel interfering with it.) Aiming would be carried out either by visual means (observation through the periscope) or by direction-finding.
4. Floating mines, which could be jettisoned in the path of the opposing ship.

In a considered opinion delivered on 27 September 1938, BN (Kleikamp) lent support to Fürbringer's views on the dangers of underwater detection; he also went on to emphasize that 'any use of radio by a U-boat gave an opportunity to the enemy for detection, whether on the way to the sphere of operations or on the return journey and, therefore, use of radio was to be avoided unless absolutely essential'. He too acknowledged the necessity for some defensive weapon to be provided for U-boats. Of Fürbringer's suggestions, he saw the small torpedo with cable or wire linkage as the best means of providing this defence.

A further suggestion of Fürbringer's was that success in the U-boat campaign would be more easily achieved by close liaison with naval aircraft. In his memorandum, he expressed himself as follows:

In any future war, the tasks of naval aircraft are so integral a part of naval operations that, immediately war breaks out, both naval aircraft and warships must be fused together as one force if serious mishaps are to be avoided.'

Fürbringer considered it a further danger that, as in the First World War, Britain might well succeed in cutting Germany off from the Atlantic by laying minefields. If this were to happen, the U-boat offensive against merchant shipping would soon disintegrate, unless supported by reinforcements. As a solution, he suggested the use of large supply U-boats. Each would provide a floating base in the Atlantic for 5–10 U-boats. These bases would be replenished by large flying-boats, escorted by special fighter flying-boats. Fürbringer admitted that this idea was somewhat fanciful. However, in his overall evaluation of future possibilities, Fürbringer rightly saw various weaknesses in current thinking concerning a future U-boat campaign, and suggested possible solutions that later — mostly too late — were proved true. On the other hand, he underestimated the scope for U-boats that would be available during the opening phase of the coming war.

In anticipation of the fact that efforts to nullify underwater detection of U-boats, and the provision of a suitable defensive means could not be achieved in a short period of time, he suggested finally in his memorandum that construction of a new type of 'commerce-destroyer' be started, one that could be rapidly built, and which could take over the task of the U-boat, but in different ways. Fürbringer had in mind the Engelmann high-speed boat, whose spindle-shaped hull lay almost entirely beneath the surface. The boat was controlled from a small superstructure that protruded above the surface. On 15 November 1937, Korvettenkapitän (E) Max Valentiner, an experienced and reputable U-boat commander from the First World War, had drawn the attention of the Naval Command Office to this invention, in which Construction Adviser Fenselau of the Construction Office had been much involved. On 22 December 1937, the Naval Command Office gave it as their opinion that a boat of this kind had a limited application for coastal work only, where its seaworthiness would be better than the existing motor torpedo-boat. A continuous speed of 30 knots with a range of 500–1,000 nautical miles was demanded.

By order of the Supreme Commander-in-Chief of the Navy, following trials on a test model built in accordance with Engelmann's suggestions, at the beginning of 1939 a large test boat was placed in contract with Deschimag. The commencement of hostilities, however, meant that all constructional work was interrupted and the project was postponed. Fürbringer nevertheless took this as his starting point in a further item of correspondence, which, having the approval of Head Office 'B', carried considerable weight: he emphasized that, in his opinion, this type of boat had considerable possibilities in a blockade of Britain. A 600-ton Engelmann-type boat should have the following properties:

'Its radius of action should approximate to that of a U-boat, so that it can be used around the coast of England or at even greater distances. Its maximum speed is to be more than double that of a U-boat and, similarly, its cruising speed. . . . Its torpedo armament should be similar to that of a U-boat of similar size. . . . Possibly two 10.5cm guns can be installed. . . . The low profile and the almost completely submerged characteristic of the Engelmann boat makes it much less visible than a U-boat. If a ballast tank is built into the vessel, the boat can be flooded and rest out of sight on the bottom. Almost the entire hull shape of the boat is beneath the surface and is thereby protected from artillery hits. The fact that very little of this boat is above the waterline means that it needs only light armoured protection. . . . The Engelmann boat is especially good for night attacks against convoys.'

There is no doubt that Fürbringer overestimated the capabilities of the planned test vessel and its potential worth. The 'K' Office replied in these terms on 18 September 1939:

'The Engelmann boat, in the light of recent preliminary tests, would seem to be capable of taking over the tasks of motor torpedo-boats, with an increased radius of action and ability to function in inclement weather. The Engelmann boat has a further advantage of being less easily visible by the enemy and being harder for their artillery to hit. Concerning the further proposals made by 'B', there is at the moment little prospect of further development. . . .'

In 1940, however, an unarmed test boat of approximately 250-tons was placed in contract with Deschimag and was completed on 10 April 1941. Concerning the trials that followed, Appendix 7 (Supreme Command Document 1591/41), read at a meeting of the Supreme Commander-in-Chief of the Navy with Hitler on 13 November 1941, stated:

'With the test boat the following questions were to be investigated:
1. Can a favourable towing-curve be attained with the actual boat?
2. Is the hoped-for good handling in heavy seas actually a fact?
3. Are the doubts concerning the longitudinal stability, with regard to the small amount of ship above water, justified?

'The present tests have shown that a favourable result is to be expected concerning all points. The conclusion of the tests is imminent. However, in the higher speed ranges the following has emerged: as the boat has one propeller only and no basic stability on account of the small amount of the boat above the waterline, the propeller torque causes a listing effect, which at high revolutions amounts to 13°. At this point, the vertical rudder begins to act as a hydroplane, so it has not been possible to run the boat at top speed. Up to now, a speed of approximately 28 knots has been achieved. However, the results of the test boat show that a boat with twin propellers would reach the required specifications and rectify the vertical rudder problem. The turning-circle of the test boat is too large. It seems possible to us that an enlargement of the boat by 100 tons would enable it to be used as a motor torpedo-boat in adverse weather conditions. Other possibilities for use of this type of boat in the Warship Construction Programme have not yet been evaluated. . . .'

Appropriate further development was not continued, presumably because in constructional terms the expenditure did not seem justified by the performance that could be obtained. Another factor may have been the increasing significance of the high-speed Walter U-boat (see page 168).

Meanwhile, the available U-boats had demonstrated that, despite their considerably lesser speeds, they were able to achieve success in night surface attacks. Night attacks had been employed against British convoys with good results at the end of the First World War. After examining Kapitänleutnant Marschall's researches into 'Surface attacks carried out by submarines, and the requirements that arise from them', Kapitänleutnant Wassner, stated the view of the Supreme Naval Command on 21 July 1922:

'In my experience, surface U-boat attacks in the last years of the war were amongst the most successful. . . In September 1918, while carrying out surface attacks on two nights, I was successful in obtaining nine shots at targets, three of these in a period of twenty minutes. It is very costly in terms of time for a single U-boat to search for convoys in open waters, and it must be considered that the use of a boat in this way is unwise (uneconomic). In the future, it will be essential for convoys to be hunted by sizeable numbers of U-boats acting together, and this will require further increases in signalling techniques.'

He agreed with Marschall and Mellenthin that the best U-boat type was the medium Type UBIII. He considered the most important technical improvements to be the wakeless torpedo and the long-range, doubling-back torpedo, which could be shot without any tell-tale bubbles and so increased the chances of success in daylight attacks against convoys.

As early as 1922, Wassner had elaborated the principles which the Commander-in-Chief, U-Boats, Kapitän zur See Dönitz, believed were necessary for a successful U-boat blockade of Britain. There was no doubt in his mind that when war was declared the convoy system would be introduced immediately. Above all, hunting by U-boats in packs, in open seas without mutual reporting of positions and tracking signals was almost unthinkable. However, the main objection of the Supreme Naval Command to this, was the use of radio. They considered it important for U-boats to maintain radio silence.

As a consequence of U-boat manoeuvres during the winter of 1938/39, Dönitz demanded 300 operational U-boats for a convoy war against Britain (at any one time, 100 to be in the process of fitting-out and overhaul; 100 to be on the way to, or returning from, their operational sector; and 100 to be actually operating). 75 per cent of these should be of the handy, medium-sized Type VIIB or VIIC. This demand had the support of the Fleet Commander, Admiral Böhm, but had little influence upon the planning already embodied in the Z-Plan, which, without consulting the Commander-in-Chief, U-boats, had opted for a 'balanced fleet' in which the large U-cruisers, large U-boats (Type IX) and medium-sized boats (Type VIIB/C) were equally represented. However, Dönitz kept to his opinion, which he had made the basis for all U-boat training. He was able to demonstrate the probable success of hunting in packs during a large convoy exercise that took place from 11 to 15 May 1939 between Cape St. Vincent and Ushant, and in which 20 U-boats took part. As complete long-distance control of the U-boat groups in the operational zone was not possible at that time, and it was probably better to judge the situation from close by, it was decided that a number of U-boats then in course of construction should be fitted with special, operationally-effective communications equipment, and these boats would subsequently be used as the leaders of U-boat packs. As a result of this suggestion, it was decided that 13 of the Type IXB/C boats being built should be given appropriate equipment as so-called 'communications U-boats'.

The impending war with **Britain** stimulated Dönitz, at the end of August 1939, to set down his 'Thoughts on the Development of the U-Boat Arm' and to communicate these in a memorandum to Raeder on 1 September 1939. Taking the same attitude as Fürbringer, he considered that in the event of a war with Britain 'the Navy and especially the U-Boat Arm will simply not be in a position to carry out the tasks that will be demanded of it. Although we hope that war will not break out, we must not assume that the political climate between England and Germany will not change greatly in the next few years. . . . The most significant weapon that can be prepared quickly — compared with the time a Fleet would take — is the U-boat.' Dönitz then went on to repeat his demand for 100 boats to be ready for operations at all times; this meant a minimum of 300 operational U-boats of Types VIIB/C and IX in the ratio of 3:1.

'In addition to these boats, which will bear the main burden of the U-boat war, there will be a further requirement for approximately 18 artillery U-boats and 30 boats of Type XII for operations in the more distant seas, to serve as long-distance reconnaissance vessels liaising with U-boat groups in the Atlantic, and as Fleet U-boats. This overall force is absolutely necessary if a successful war against England is to be waged. With the numbers of boats we have at present, and with those embodied in the Construction Plan as formulated at the moment, this aim is simply not to be achieved. The Supreme Naval Command must therefore examine carefully which building tasks can be put back, the better to serve the interests of the U-boat Construction Programme; which yards can be released for U-boat construction; which supply industries can be used to bolster further U-boat construction; and whether a high-speed construction programme, with special regard to Types VIIB/C and IX, is possible.'

To assist his recommended priority construction of the U-boat arm, Dönitz requested the formation of a central office with wide-ranging powers, and directly responsible to the Supreme Commander-in-Chief of the Navy.

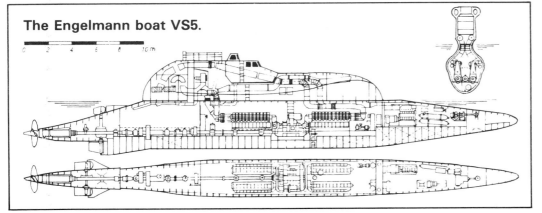

The Engelmann boat VS5.

0 2 4 6 8 10 m

5 WAR CONSTRUCTION, EXPERIENCE AND DEVELOPMENT, 1939–1943

CONSTRUCTION PROGRAMMES AND PROBLEMS, 1939–43

The Enlarged Programme of October 1939

With the commencement of hostilities, the Mobilization Programme of 1939 got under way. Apart from new constructions of motor torpedo-boats and motor minesweepers, this called, after the initial building time, for the yearly delivery of 24 destroyers, 48 torpedo-boats, 132 minesweepers, and 108 U-boats (24 Type IXC, 48 Type VIIC and 36 Type IID). During the initial phase, the major combatants *Bismarck*, *Tirpitz*, *Graf Zeppelin*, *Prinz Eugen* and *Seydlitz*, whose building had proceeded considerably, were to be completed. Construction of all other large ships, especially the new battleships of the Z-Plan, was immediately stopped, and partly assembled components were broken down.

When Britain and France entered the war on 3 September 1939, the great fear of Dönitz had materialized — that of facing the greatest sea power in the world without an appropriate fleet. The only sensible measure to be adopted in this situation was the rapid build-up of a large U-boat force, according to the suggestion already made by the Commander of U-Boats. Raeder saw the wisdom of this, and ordered the establishment of a special Group Office of U-Boat Affairs (Seekriegsleitung, or SKL–U) at the Supreme Naval Command. Dönitz wanted to be in the controlling position in this Office, as he considered that only from there could he exert a significant influence on the realization of his plans. Raeder, however, turned him down: in his opinion, the Commander of U-Boats (from October 1939, Commander-in-Chief, U-Boats) should not be diverted from the conduct of operations. He did promise Dönitz that the new Office would carry out, without restriction, all demands made from the theatre of operations; but, sadly, Dönitz was in practice excluded quite extensively from U-boat development and construction right up to 1943. Instead, Raeder chose Vizeadmiral Siemens, who had been Naval Attaché in London from 1937 to 1939; consequently, on taking over his office, he was rather poorly informed about the planning and problems of U-boat construction.

At first, an attempt was made to raise U-boat production in the Mobilization Programme to the maximum without disrupting the other programmes, by ensuring that total works capacity was being used. On 8 September 1939, the Supreme Commander-in-Chief of the Navy (Raeder) received the suggested programme shown in Table 19. This would yield a monthly delivery of 4 Type IID, 9.5 Type VIIC and 4.25 Type IXC, i.e., a total of 17.75 boats per month, or 213 per year. To this figure could be added 4 U-cruisers of Type XI and 2 large minelaying Type XB. As the programme would take time to get into its stride, 6.5 boats were scheduled for delivery in 1939, 99 in 1940 and, finally, 211.25 boats in 1941.

However, even this enlarged programme would be insufficient for Dönitz's requirements, especially

Table 19. The Enlarged Mobilization Programme of 8 September 1939

Monthly deliveries	IID	VIIC	IXC
KMW, Kiel (Howaldt)		1.5	
DWK, Kiel	1.5		
GW		2	
Schichau, Elbing		2	
Danziger Werften	2.5		
DW, Hamburg			2
AG Weser, Bremen			1.5
Bremer Vulkan		1.5	
Seebeck, Wesermünde			0.75
Flender Lübeck		1.25	
Nordseewerke Emden		0.5	
Flensburger SBG		0.75	

if one took into account an estimated monthly loss of 5 per cent. During a discussion at Hitler's Headquarters in Zoppot on 23 September 1939, the Head of Naval War Staff, Admiral Schniewind, called for an enlargement of the programme to 20–30 boats per month, this to be achieved by curtailing less-urgent building tasks and by giving it priority over other sections of the armed services. In addition, he suggested that Russia and Italy be induced to build U-boats for Germany. For political reasons (Hitler's peace overtures), a decision was postponed for a fortnight, but appropriate plans were drawn up immediately by 'K'. The Navy's mobilization planning was again re-examined very

it envisaged U-boat increases as shown in Table 20. This meant that from 1942 an average of 29.3 U-boats (attainment of programme) would be delivered monthly, in the ratio of 1:3 between Types IXC and VIIC. The programme was also to include 16 small, Type IID boats, 4 long-range boats, 4 large minelaying boats and 4 U-boat tankers. In a further pronouncement of 22 November 1939, a plan was formulated for development in U-boat construction, taking into account losses estimated at 10 per cent, as shown in Table 21.

carefully, and U-boat deliveries were raised very considerably at the expense of destroyers, torpedo-boats and minesweepers. 'K' called for the following maximum yearly deliveries: 7 destroyers, 9 torpedo-boats, 60 minesweepers and 275 U-boats, of which 68 would be of Type IXC and 207 of Type VIIC, to

Table 20. The Enlarged U-Boat Construction Programme, 6 October 1939

	1939: small boats	1939: large boats	1940: small boats	1940: large boats	1941: small boats	1941: large boats	1942: small boats	1942: large boats
Jan			1	1	1	12	—	30
Feb			1	2	2	12	—	27
March			1	2	1	17	—	28
April			—	—	1	16	—	31
May			—	2	—	20	—	28
June			2	3	—	18	—	30
July			1	4	—	22	—	29
Aug			2	4	—	24	—	30
Sept			1	5	—	26	—	28
Oct	—	1	2	4	—	26	—	31
Nov	—	2	1	5	—	27	—	28
Dec	1	1	2	8	—	25	—	29
Total Strength	31	33	45	73	50	318	50	667

give the ratio of 1:3 required by Dönitz. This would yield a monthly delivery of 23 U-boats.

At the beginning of October 1939, it was clear that, although German troops had rapidly overrun Poland, Britain would want to continue the war. On 4 October, therefore, Hitler gave top priority in re-armament to a larger U-boat programme, and this now became the most important task for the German Navy. On 7 October, the Naval War Staff, in the presence of all available heads of offices and departments, laid down an 'Enlarged U-boat Construction Programme (to commence 6th October 1939)'. Without taking losses into account,

Table 21. U-boat planned strengths, November 1939 to October 1943*

Date	New arrivals	Total at start of month	U-Boat School and training boats	Boats at disposal of C-in-C, U-Boats	Operational boats	10% losses	Total at end of month
Nov 1939	1	57	12	45	15	5	52
Jan 1940	2	52	18	34	11	3	49
April 1940	3	51	24	27	9	3	48
July 1940	5	51	37	14	5	1	50
Oct 1940	6	63	42	21	7	2	61
Jan 1941	13	88	55	33	11	3	85
April 1941	18	113	55	58	19	6	107
Oct 1941	26	191	75	116	39	12	179
Mar 1942	27	253	75	191	64	19	245
Oct 1942	29	312	75	237	79	24	288
Mar 1943	29	334	75	259	86	26	308
Oct 1943	29	347	75	272	91	27	320

*Taking account of losses at 10 per cent per annum.

In October 1943, therefore, a grand total of 320 U-boats would be available, of which 75 would be training boats. From that date, it was anticipated that losses, which had been assessed at 10 per cent, would rise; but so too would new deliveries, so that a strength of approximately 270 operational U-boats could be maintained. However, the actual monthly losses suffered up to April 1943 were considerably lower than had been anticipated, amounting to an average of 5.7 per cent of operational boats. Consequently, although additional boats were not supplied in the quantities hoped for, the number of available U-boats considerably exceeded the planned number. They amounted, for example, in March 1943 to 426 boats

Below: *U514* (Type IXC) running constructor's trials.

as compared to an estimated 308; however, the 235 U-boats fully available for operational work were less than the plan called for, because the number of training boats required and the duration of training had been very much underestimated.

The implementation of this large plan would mean the complete cessation of merchant ship construction, abandoning the construction of surface ships larger than destroyers (except those that could still be delivered by the end of 1940) and a curtailment of the building of destroyers, torpedo-boats, motor torpedo-boats, minesweepers and motor minesweepers. Compared with the Mobilization Preparation Plan, which, as a result of preparatory work carried out so extensively in peacetime, required no further enlargement of capacity, this Enlarged U-Boat Construction Programme required an additional involvement of yards and subsidiary industries, and could not be achieved without special diversion of personnel and materials. On 10 October 1939, the Supreme Commander-in-Chief of the Navy published the programme at Hitler's Command Headquarters and demanded raw materials and extra labour as set out in Table 22. For the furtherance of the programme, Raeder demanded that absolute priority over all other programmes be secured by a special High Command Decree. Hitler, however, was not at the time ready to accede to this: in the opinion of the High Command of the Armed Forces, the build-up of the Army for the campaign in France should have priority, but it was agreed that a new look at naval requirements should be made in December 1939. Until then, the Enlarged U-Boat Construction Programme should carry on without any special note being made as to its absolute priority. On 23 October 1939, the Head of the High Command of the Armed Forces stated that: (a) the Führer was in agreement with the Navy's plan (the continued construction of 5 large units, the restricted mobilization construction plan and the fulfilment of the suggested U-boat programme) and (b) Generalfeldmarschall Göring would have comprehensive powers for the realization of these plans. Therefore, no special powers would be necessary for the U-boat construction programme. On 25 October, in connection with this, Raeder directed:

'1. Following discussions with Chief of Staff 'B' on 24 October, I have made decisions and communicated them to those offices involved: the new construction programme of 6 October 1939 is to be retained. Any difficulties that arise to December 1939 are to be settled in such a way that the U-boat construction task remains the chief one. Other tasks are — unless indispensable — subordinate to U-boat construction.

'2. Increase in torpedo production: It is essential that this keep pace with the increased U-boat production without any special directives from the Führer.

'3. Skilled workers who have been conscripted into the Army are to be returned to work for the Navy.'

In order to realize the Navy's war programmes, especially the Enlarged U-Boat Construction Programme, the Office for Warship Construction was reorganized in October 1939 and given the new designation of 'Head Office for Warship Construction' (Hauptamt Kriegschiffbau). Administrative sections with special responsibilities for U-boat construction were formed from the various departments of 'K'. Special mention should be made of Department K I U, which was responsible for the overall planning and maintenance of U-boats, under the control of Ministerial Counsellor Dr. Schürer, and Department K II U, responsible for engine and electrical installations in U-boats, under the control of Ministerial Counsellor Bröking.

To achieve smooth-running construction of a series of Type VIIC and IXC boats, it was essential that close liaison be maintained between the various yards. GW (VIIC) and AG Weser (IXC) were to be responsible for main construction, with other yards used for assembly. To co-ordinate the various tasks (supply of materials and assembled construction items, common construction plans, etc.), assembly offices were set up at GW and AG Weser, manned by personnel from the large subsidiary yards. The largest construction programmes went to B&V, which originally had not featured at all in the mobilization programme for U-boat construction. Their task was to produce 52 Type VIIC boats per year, and AG Weser's approximately 30 Type IX boats. It was decided to dispense with Schichau, Elbing, where construction of mobilization torpedo-boats had been transferred. A total of 20 boats was given to each of the large yards: Schichau, Danzig, Bremer Vulkan, Vegesack (Type VIIC), and DW, Hamburg-Finkenwerder (Type IXC). The medium yards, such as Lübecker Flenderwerke and Nordseewerke, Emden, were each required to supply approximately 10 boats. In all, the construction of VIIC boats was distributed among 13 yards, and IXC between 3 yards. From the beginning of the war until the end of 1939, U-boat contracts were placed as shown in Table 23.

Problems: the Restricted Programme

On 22 November 1939, at a conference with Hitler, the Supreme Commander-in-Chief of the Navy reviewed the planned Enlarged U-Boat Construction Programme and indicated that it could be carried out only if certain considerations were met.

1. Fulfilment of all requests for labour.
2. Enlargement of shipyard and industrial capacity through acquisition of necessary workers and raw materials.
3. Priority to be given to U-boat programme in transportation and distribution of machinery and raw materials.
4. Attention to be given to claims for increased repair facilities.

He pointed out that the High Command of the Armed Forces had promised an examination of these points for December. But, as early as the next conference on 8 December 1939, it was clear that in the first quarter of 1940 the Navy would receive neither the 170,000 tons of pig-iron they had asked for, nor the other necessary metals. The approved amount of 140,000 tons meant that the proposed war programme for the Navy could not be reached,

and delays would be absolutely inevitable. Nor had attempts to obtain submarines from Japan and Italy been successful. At an earlier date, a suggestion that boats be purchased from Russia had been rejected by Hitler, for political reasons. So, at the beginning of the war, the only additional strengthening of the U-boat fleet consisted of 3 boats that had been intended for export but had been requisitioned by the Navy (2 small Type IIB intended for China, and a large minelaying boat which had been constructed by the IvS for Turkey and was designated UA after the mine shafts had been altered to fuel tanks).

During the course of that December, the requisite conditions for fulfilling the U-boat programme became even more remote in view of the absolute priority given to the provision of munitions for the Army and the dovetailing of other programmes into the top priority bracket (machine tools, power plants, roller-bearing production, anti-aircraft equipment, etc.). In view of the limited reserves of raw materials (especially tin) held in Germany, the continuous implementation of the Enlarged U-Boat Construction Programme was quite out of the question, and on 30 December 1939, it was announced during a conference at Hitler's Headquarters: 'It has been arranged with the Head of the Armed Forces High Command that in anticipation of the Navy receiving the apportioned metal (tin) in the next few years, a programme can be carried through that, by 1 January 1942, will yield an increase of 316 U-boats over the present number. A final decision as to whether this programme is feasible or whether further delays must take place, can be postponed until May 1940.' This lesser plan was designated 'Restricted Construction Programme'. The delivery quotas of the Enlarged U-Boat Construction Programme were to be reached at all costs by the end of 1941, but, because of the shortage of raw materials, this could only be achieved by accepting delays and postponements of other projects. In connection with this, on 22 February 1940, the Naval Office at Wilhelmshaven stated:

'1. The very unsatisfactory state of deliveries of metals in recent months is certainly going to be with us for some considerable time, and obliges the Navy to agree to the Restricted Construction Plan (deadline 1 January 1942), to make the most use and best possible application of allotted raw materials. This plan will only take account of new constructions which can be completed by 1 January 1942. The Head of 'K' is in agreement with the Chief of Naval War Staff and with 'A', that the construction of U-boats must be ensured, with the most acute restriction of all other ship construction. The establishment of new building yards that could subsequently only build relatively few U-boats will be dispensed with and U-boat construction can be better passed on to other yards.

'2. It is impossible to over-stress the need for an increase in new construction after 1 January 1942, as U-boat losses will have to be reckoned on the basis of 5 per cent monthly.

'3. In spite of all these measures, one must still be prepared for the Navy's restricted building

Table 22. Material and labour requirements plan, 10 October 1939

From the second quarter of 1940 (monthly):

Iron and steel	195,000 tons
Copper	5,850 tons
Lead	3,900 tons
Tin	342 tons
Nickel	274 tons
Aluminium	2,950 tons
Additional labour:	
Ship and engine construction	20,000
Torpedoes and mines	60,000
Instruments and optics	5,000
Other work	35,000
Total manpower required	120,000*

*Of which 35,000 required immediately

Table 23. U-boat contracts, September to December 1939

	23–25 Sept	9–12 Oct	16 Oct	24 Oct	30 Oct	23 Dec
Type IID:						
DWK	16	—	—	—	—	—
Type VIIC:						
GW	4	—	8	—	—	6
Bremer Vulkan	5	—	—	—	—	6
Nordseewerke	4	—	—	—	—	—
Flensburger SBG	4	—	4	—	—	—
Howaldt, Kiel	4	—	8	—	—	—
Danziger Werft	4	—	4	—	4	—
Schichau. Danzig	4	—	4	—	—	—
Blohm & Voss	8	—	4	12	—	—
Howaldt, Hamburg	—	12	—	—	—	—
Stülcken, Hamburg	—	6	—	—	—	—
KMW, Wilhelmshaven	—	12	—	—	—	—
DWK	—	—	—	—	4	—
Type IXC:						
AG Weser	6	—	—	—	—	8
DW, Hamburg	6	6	—	—	—	—
Seebeck	6	—	—	—	—	—

Table 24. The Restricted Construction Programme, 15 June 1940

Type	1940									1941												1942			Totals
	April	May	June	July	Aug	Sept	Oct	Nov	Dec	Jan	Feb	Mar	April	May	June	July	Aug	Sept	Oct	Nov	Dec	Jan	Feb	Mar	
IID	1	1	2	1	2	2	2	3	2	1	1	—	—	—	—	—	—	—	—	—	—	—	—	—	18
VIIB/C	2	1	—	1	2	3	3	3	6	9	9	14	9	17	14	13	14	16	12	15	14	9	5	—	191
VIID	—	—	—	—	—	—	—	—	—	—	—	—	—	—	—	—	1	2	3	—	—	—	—	—	6
IXB/C	—	2	1	—	2	2	1	2	2	3	2	3	4	4	4	6	5	6	6	5	3	2	—	—	65
IXD	—	—	—	—	—	—	—	—	—	—	—	—	—	—	—	—	—	—	—	—	1	1	1	1	4
XB	—	—	—	—	—	—	—	—	—	—	—	—	1	—	—	1	—	—	1	—	—	1	—	—	4
XIV	—	—	—	—	—	—	—	—	—	—	—	—	—	—	—	—	—	—	—	1	1	1	1	—	4
Totals	3	4	3	2	6	7	6	8	10	13	12	17	14	21	18	20	20	24	22	21	19	14	7	1	292

(In addition to this programme, the construction of a further 20 Type VIIC boats was envisaged, without using any of the scarce materials.)

programme to be still further disrupted in terms of delays and curtailments by the further unsatisfactory supply of raw materials.'

This Restricted Construction Programme was promulgated by Raeder on 8 March 1940. In amplification, he stated on 9 March: 'We cannot count on an increase in the numbers provided in the Restricted Construction Programme. The amount that can be assumed to be produced by the Supplementary U-boat Timetable is, at the most, 300 U-boats. As a matter of urgency, allocations for U-boat construction, U-boat torpedoes and mines must be considered. I shall make a decision by 1 June 1940 as to the continuation of the U-boat programme from 1 January 1942.'

In addition to material supply difficulties, the harsh winter of 1939/40 brought further building problems. During U-boat construction, water-pressure tests were delayed or prevented, cables could not be attached to boats lying on the open slipways or in the water, and heavy components could not be installed by crane. Despite ice blasting, it was not always possible to carry out launchings at the appointed time. The proposed completion of the Vulcan shipyard at Stettin was finally abandoned after it had almost come to a standstill at the end of 1939 through shortage of raw materials and workers. This meant that the building of 3 U-boats scheduled to have been completed by 1942 had to be abandoned. Progress on Type IID construction at DWK was delayed because of the numerous auxiliary ship conversions, but cessation of work on the aircraft

carrier *Graf Zeppelin* at the end of April 1940 meant that these delays could be made good, and the delivery dates of the last boats were even advanced. At GW and AG Weser there were also delays, occasioned by changes of mind with regard to the design of the new Types VIID and IXD. It was decided that further placing of contracts should be made in such a way that the total U-boat plan could be finally completed by 1 January 1942. Flender-Werke, Lübeck, were exceptional in that during peacetime they had received sufficient raw materials to cope with their long-term programme up to and beyond 1 January 1942. As an additional measure, it was intended that Flender take in U-boat repairs from the autumn of 1940. The previously mentioned delays could only partly be made good, and led to a non-attainment of delivery quotas so that the number delivered in 1941 fell behind that called for in the Enlarged U-Boat Construction Programme. Table 24 shows the Restricted Construction Programme as at 15 June 1940.

On 1 March 1940, the Chief of Naval War Staff 'U' published a Flotilla Plan for the future U-boats. It envisaged 10 flotillas of Type VIIB/C, 4 flotillas of Type IX, 2 training flotillas and 3 school flotillas. Each U-flotilla should consist of 25 boats, and a new flotilla should not be set up until a full complement of boats was available. It was calculated that a small U-boat would require one month, and a larger boat two months, from commissioning before being ready to join a U-flotilla for operations, and that losses of 4 per

Admiral Werner Fuchs (left) congratulating Fritz Bröking on the occasion of his 65th birthday, 11 March 1942.

cent must be anticipated. From these calculations the following disposition was evolved:

Type VIIB/C:

Ready	No. 7 U-Flotilla at Kiel.
1 March 1941	No. 8 U-Flotilla at Königsberg.
1 May 1941	No. 9 U-Flotilla at Königsberg.
1 June 1941	No. 10 U-Flotilla at Danzig.
1 July 1941	No. 1 U-Flotilla at Kiel (after delivery of the small boats).
1 Sept 1941	No. 11 U-Flotilla at Flensburg.
1 Nov 1941	No. 12 U-Flotilla at Hamburg.
1 Dec 1941	No. 6 U-Flotilla at Danzig (new formation).
1 Jan 1942	No. 5 U-Flotilla at Gotenhafen (new formation).
1 March 1942	No. 14 U-Flotilla at Kiel.

Type IX

1 Oct 1940	No. 2 U-Flotilla at Wilhelmshaven (after delivery of boats Type IA and VII).
1 Jan 1941	No. 3 U-Flotilla at Stettin (new formation).
1 Sept 1941	No. 4 U-Flotilla at Danzig (new formation).
1 Feb 1942	No. 13 U-Flotilla at Kiel.

Training flotillas:

1 Jan 1940	Tactical U-boat operational training flotilla in Warnemünde (9 boats of Type II).
1 April 1940	Training flotilla for gunnery and crew training in Travemünde (only operational U-boats).

School flotillas: For training, initially Type II boats, then Type VII boats from 2nd Flotilla; later, boats from 7th Flotilla.

By June 1940, the Restricted Construction Programme was suffering from inadequate distribution of raw materials, lack of skilled workers and tardy extension of the shipyards. Raeder brought this to Hitler's notice on 4 June, and the Führer promised that when the campaign in France was over he would reduce the size of the Army in order to favour the new points of emphasis — the Air Force and the Navy — and would solve the latter's labour problems. On 20 June, Raeder reiterated the urgent need for immediate distribution of the required means, and stressed that if they were not forthcoming further delays would occur.

Following the capitulation of France, on 29 June 1940 an immediate allocation of the necessary raw materials, workers, works capacity and machine tools was ordered. After France had been occupied, a large supply of raw materials was discovered so that the shortage of non-ferrous metals (especially copper) was eased. This made it possible to continue the Restricted Construction Programme, which scheduled approximately 25 boats per month by 1 January 1942. This number would comprise 18 Type VIIC, 5 Type IXC/D and 2 boats of other types. On 31 July 1940, Raeder asked Hitler for permission to carry on the U-boat programme at this level, which would, however, still require more materials and workers than had been allotted hitherto. The number of workers required would amount to 20,000 (8,000 for new construction and 12,000 for maintenance work). Hitler gave his assent, but absolute priority could not be given to U-boat production at this moment. Preparations for the invasion of Britain (Operation 'Sealion') was now given absolute priority, and shipyards were ordered to provide transports and landing barges at the expense, to some extent, of the U-boat programme.

The shortage of skilled workers created a special bottleneck in the production of torpedoes and torpedo tubes — according to a letter to Keitel, dated 3 August 1940, it was estimated that 2 Type IX and 21 Type VII boats would be delayed by between four and six months because of the shortage of torpedo tubes. On 13 August 1940, the Supreme Commander-in-Chief of the Navy requested that this branch of construction be given first priority over all aspects of the programme, or the entire U-boat campaign would be in jeopardy from October 1940. On 20 August 1940, Hitler ordered a new degree of urgency 'Special Stage' ('SS'), to take precedence over 'First Priority' which had been somewhat diluted through overuse in a multiplicity of programmes. In this 'SS' stage, the war construction plan for U-boats, including torpedoes and torpedo tubes, was included alongside tank construction, anti-tank weapons and construction of aircraft of especially important types. In a new decree dated 20 September 1940, the maintenance and repair of U-boats was included, as well as training in the use and maintenance of torpedoes.

The awarding of contracts for the continuation of the U-boat programme followed on 15 August 1940, and comprised 60 Type VIIC, 18 Type IXC40, 2 Type IXD₂ and 2 Type XIV. (Type IXC40 was a further development of Type IXC, with a somewhat enlarged outer hull and, consequently, an increased fuel supply, and was better equipped.)

Problems: delivery quotas, 1941–42

Because preparations had been inadequate, Operation 'Sealion' was postponed, and in December 1940 it was decided to attack Russia (Operation 'Barbarossa') so as to eliminate this last potential opponent before invading Britain. Once again, it was thought that control of the Continent must take priority over the defeat of Britain, reflecting exactly the philosophy that had obtained at the beginning of the First World War ('. . . it is important that the war on land be waged successfully, then can we think of attacking England' — Reichs Chancellor to Admiralty, 27 December 1914). But, on 27 December 1940, the Supreme Commander-in-Chief of the Navy raised serious doubts as to the wisdom of embarking upon 'Barbarossa' before Britain had been defeated. With regard to the U-boat campaign, he told Hitler: 'The position that U-boat construction has been given in the general framework of total armament production does not correspond to its great importance. Attempts to increase U-boat production are thwarted by the chronic lack of skilled workers. With the number of workers available at the moment, the monthly maximum delivery can be only 18, possibly only 12. It is essential that monthly deliveries total at least 20–30 boats.' Hitler spoke in favour of boosting U-boat production, but also stressed the urgency of the Russian campaign, for which the Army would need to have priority: only then could a full concentration of means be put at the disposal of the Air Force and Navy. However, two new priority stages (S I and S II) should provide some improvement. At this, Raeder noted sourly: 'It is a basic error to allocate non-existent workers. If these are not available, no amount of decrees concerning stages of priority or any other such methods can effect any improvement.'

On 18 March, Raeder tried once more to persuade Hitler to strengthen naval re-armament, and stated clearly the requirements for workers up to the autumn of 1941. The workers being allocated to the Navy in January 1941, following his appeal of 27 December 1940 could arrest only the growing shortage of workers, but not ameliorate the shortage of them that already existed. The decree of 20 December 1940, which exempted from call-up personnel engaged in special work for the Navy and Air Force, was somewhat nullified by a considerably increase in the use of 'S' and 'SS' classifications for many undertakings. Approximately 10,000 workers on leave would have to rejoin their branches of the armed services by 1 April 1941, which meant that the shortage of workers would continue to rise during the coming months.

In the second half of 1940 (following Hitler's decree of 30 June), supplies of raw materials had been adequate, but were still insufficient to meet the increasing demand. Until now, the U-boat programme had been kept going by careful management, but the supplies allocated by the Supreme Command of the Armed Forces for the second quarter of 1941 had been considerably lower than had been demanded, and the efforts of Special Priority Stage 'S' had been successful in obtaining only 45–48 per cent of material sought. The situation with regard to supplies of aluminium and copper was in a similar state.

What most affected U-boat construction was the increasing shortage of workers at the yards. It had to be accepted that in the course of the year the number of deliveries would fall from a high mark of 18 per month in the second quarter to approximately 15. If, however, the desperately needed workers could be made available, the number would rise to approximately 20 per month in 1941, and to 24 per month in 1942. Therefore, three further yards (Stettiner Oderwerke, Stettiner Vulcan and Neptun, Rostock) were taken into the VIIC programme. Following this, steel distribution for the third quarter of 1941 reached the record total of 190,000 tons. Table 27 shows the position as at 15 June 1941. In the light of this stocktaking, the Chief of Naval War Staff — without actually placing additional contracts — investigated the need for further U-boat orders which would yield 212 operational boats by about the end of May 1942, 313 by the end of 1942 and 477 by the end of 1943. In this calculation, however, the estimated average monthly loss of six boats seemed rather low. If orders were to continue at the present level, maintaining the same supposition as to losses, a

Table 25. Manpower shortages, 1941

	Yards	Other naval armament firms	Total naval work strength
Shortage on 1 Feb 1941	8,500	8,000	16,500
Further requirement to 31 May 1941	10,500	12,000	22,500
Further requirement to 30 Sept 1941	9,000	9,500	18,500
Total requirement	28,000	29,500	57,500

Deliveries of Types VIIB, VIIC and C/41.

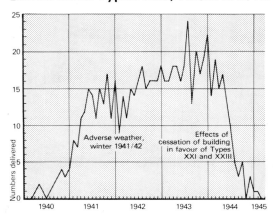

Adverse weather, winter 1941/42

Effects of cessation of building in favour of Types XXI and XXIII

Table 26. Progressive table of iron and steel monthly supplies for the Navy

	4th quarter 1939	1st quarter 1940	2nd quarter 1940	3rd quarter 1940	4th quarter 1940	1st quarter 1941	2nd quarter 1941
Required (tons):	160,000	170,000	150,000	145,000	155,000	180,000	229,000
Supplied (tons):	125,000	140,000	120,000	140,000	155,000	155,000	176,000

Table 27. U-boats under construction on 15 June 1941

	On slip	Fitting-out[1]	In use by UAK: Delivered	Commissioned	Released from UAK control[2]	Ordered but not yet on slips
IA	—	—	—	—	2	—
IIA	—	—	—	—	6	—
IIB	—	—	—	—	20	—
IIC	—	—	—	—	8	—
IID	—	—	—	—	16	—
VII	—	—	—	—	10	—
VIIB	—	2	—	1	21	—
VIIC	127	25	3	15	53	296
VIID	6	—	—	—	—	—
IX	—	—	—	—	8	—
IXB	—	—	—	—	14	—
IXC	24	12	—	3	9	6
IXC/40	2	—	—	—	—	60
IXD₁	2	—	—	—	—	—
IXD₂	6	—	—	—	—	16
XB	4	—	—	—	—	4
XIV	6	—	—	—	—	—

Total boats completed	189	Operational boats	36
Boats under construction	216	School boats	50
Boats projected	382	Training boats	41
Total	787	Total boats available	127

[1] After launch. [2] By 15 June 1941.

strength of 618 boats could be achieved by the end of 1944. In his efforts to persuade Hitler to provide more men and supplies for naval re-armament, Raeder used the much more pessimistic estimates of the 'K' Office, which reflected future development rather more accurately.

Following the postponement of 'Barbarossa' to the summer of 1941, occasioned by the Italians' Balkan venture, 'Sealion' was not thought to be feasible before the early part of 1942 — and then only after a successful 'lightning campaign' in the East. On 25 July 1941, therefore, Raeder took pains to renew his representations on behalf of the U-boat campaign, which was now the only means of hitting at Britain. In addition, he suggested that when the campaign in the East was over, capital ship construction (*Seydlitz* and *Graf Zeppelin*) be recommended. He emphasised the urgent need for monthly U-boat deliveries to total at least 25, because a total of 300 operational boats, which with a monthly increase of 21 boats and 5 per cent losses would not be reached until 1 July 1943, would only represent an effective increase of 6 boats per month. Indeed, if losses were 10 per cent, there would be no increase at all. Therefore, 21 U-boats per month were an absolute minimum if the arm was to carry out its operational tasks.

The chronic labour shortage, amounting at that time to 25,000 men, meant that from the end of 1941 the U-boat programme would only produce approximately 14 boats per month. Therefore, Raeder asked Hitler for a directive to be sent to the Reichs Minister for Armaments and Munitions, Dr. Todt: at the end of the campaign in the East, the Navy must have all the workers it required. Hitler promised he would solve this problem, and promised also to release Army personnel to make up U-boat crews. In a communication dated 31 July 1941 to Keitel and Dr. Todt, Raeder made much of this discussion and Hitler's approval, and stated among other points:

'The Führer and Supreme Commander of the Armed Forces has acknowledged in all respects my representations and decided that the U-boat construction programme must be carried through without restrictions. That involves the construction of 25 U-boats monthly. Furthermore, he confirmed to me expressly that the existing naval strengths as embodied in the U-boat programme will be fully carried out as his directive of 14 July dictates ... Bearing in mind the fact that is absolutely vital for a successful prosecution of the U-boat war that, in the next few months, as many U-boats as possible are brought to a state of operational readiness, I make the request that measures now be taken to reorganize the armament programme in such a way as to secure the U-boat programme and that necessary directives be issued so that matters can start immediately the Russian campaign is over ...'

However, after initial successes, the war against Russia became a veritable Moloch that increasingly consumed the German war economy, and the hope that priority might be given to the Navy's needs became more and more remote. Moreover, as had happened in the First World War, the Battle of the Atlantic moved increasingly westwards and, when the United States began to side more and more with Britain, it was only a matter of time before Germany and America would be at war.

The considerable increase in deliveries of U-boats in the second half of 1941 meant that additional personnel were required for repairs and maintenance and, on 13 November 1941, Raeder renewed his request for workers — 'a minimum of 20,000 immediately!'. Hitler recognized the urgency of the Navy's need, but did nothing to change the situation. The offensive in Russia became bogged down in mud, and the severe frosts that followed brought it to a halt; Soviet resistance consolidated, and a quick success in the East became no longer possible. The U-boat construction programme was also adversely affected by the harsh winter of 1941/42, and the whole situation further exacerbated the anticipated breakdown in production during the early part of 1942. U-boat deliveries now looked as follows:

June 1940	3	May 1941	18
July 1940	2	June 1941	17
August 1940	7	July 1941	15
September 1940	7	August 1941	20
October 1940	7	September 1941	18
November 1940	7	October 1941	25
December 1940	8	November 1941	20
January 1941	12	December 1941	21
February 1941	8	January 1942	15
March 1941	12	February 1942	19
April 1941	15	March 1942	16

With regard to these problems, Raeder, at a conference with Hitler on 13 February 1942 stated: 'If, after adjustment of the construction programme to the reduced distribution of raw materials and re-apportionment of workers for new construction and repairs, the position with regard to workers were to remain stable, the number of U-boats that could be delivered would fall only to 19—20. However, as the number of workers will fall because of conscription into the armed forces, the monthly number that will be delivered in the course of the year will go down to 16—17.'

In addition to the considerable shortage of steel (153,000 tons monthly in the first quarter of 1942, 150,000 tons monthly in the second quarter of 1942) there now occurred serious shortages of copper. Only 1,600 tons monthly were available for the second

Below: Repair and construction work at GW Kiel, 9 July 1942. Right foreground, *U118* (Type XB) undergoing repairs in the floating dock. In the background is *U227* after launching.

quarter of 1942, which was approximately 50 per cent of the requirement. This, together with the intensified equipping of the Army, led to a very considerable curtailment of the Warship Programme. The building of destroyers was especially affected and would have to cease in 1943 — from 1944, the monthly total of surface ship construction amounted to only 1 motor torpedo-boat and 2 motor minesweepers. Even U-boat construction had to be further restricted, and in 1944 only 15 boats (Types VIIC and IXC) or 12—13 boats (Types VIIC, IXC and larger boats) were delivered monthly. On 12 March 1942, Raeder communicated this threatening development to Hitler (see Table 28). Nevertheless, Hitler rejected utterly the request for an increase in the quotas for the Navy, saying that greater quantities than were

being currently delivered could not be supplied, and that copper would have to be withheld from construction where it was not absolutely necessary. In the long term, however, Raeder's dire warnings did have an effect on Hitler and, on 13 May 1942, he spoke out against the suspension of destroyer construction. As a result (through the intervention of Speer), the Navy could now receive an additional 1,000 tons of copper monthly, and Raeder declared himself ready to recommence the building of all suspended vessels from destroyers downwards.

There is no doubt that in the constant tug-of-war for raw-material distribution, Raeder had somewhat dramatized the possible consequences of the shortages, especially for U-boat construction. But a very real bottleneck was the shortage of skilled workers, and it was this that effectively

restricted production rather than the shortage of materials. In order to achieve a delivery quota of 25 U-boats per month, only about 20,000 tons of steel and 450 tons of copper were needed, i.e., a fraction of the allocation. But to build these 25 boats required 60,000 workers out of a total naval work force of about 136,000 in the summer of 1941. Although more and more men were being recruited, the number was never sufficient in view of the rapidly-mounting repair and maintenance tasks. Raeder disagreed with the idea of a radical cessation of all inessential surface vessel building in order to benefit the U-boat campaign. Even Dönitz, who had spoken out in July 1941 in favour of such a step after U-boat workers had been transferred to work on larger surface vessels, opposed Hitler by retaining these ships when he became C-in-C of the Navy. In effect, he thwarted Hitler's command to 'Scrap them!'.

The shortage of labour dominated Raeder's efforts to increase U-boat production during the second half of 1942. On 15 June 1942, he stated that he was lacking 2,200 workers for U-boat overhauls and 1,000 for surface ship repairs. A further 3,641 workers were required for finishing work on *Graf Zeppelin*, conversion work on the battleship *Gneisenau* and overhauls to the heavy cruiser *Prinz Eugen*. The number of workers available at the U-boat yards permitted completion of only 19 U-boats per month, and the call-up of approximately 20,000 workers to the armed forces had to be taken into account. In connection with this, Raeder requested that U-boat construction and repair work, at least, be protected from the call-up. Hitler saw the point that, in the last analysis, U-boat war could be a decisive factor, and suggested that Keitel approach Speer, the new Minister for Armaments, to try to settle the naval requirements. On 26 August 1942, Hitler questioned Raeder concerning the labour situation. Raeder, disagreeing with Speer, thought it quite likely that 8,400 skilled workers from other parts of the armament industry might be given to the naval armament programme in exchange for foreign labour, and suggested additionally, that OT (Organization Todt, the German paramilitary construction organization) workers might be diverted to naval armament.

The increasing importance of the U-boat campaign and the mounting losses made it imperative that U-boat production be increased to 25 boats per month. The planning of the newly-formed Main Committee for Ship Construction (Hauptausschuss Schiffbau, or HAS), under the direction of State Counsellor Rudolf Blohm, forecast only a slow increase (23 boats by the middle of 1943, 25 boats by the end of 1944). The increasing requirement for labour was to be met principally by moving certain aspects of the industry, such as pressure-hull sections and components, to the interior and by bringing about organizational improvements at the yards.

The further reduced distribution of raw materials for the first quarter of 1943 (137,550 tons of steel and 2,082 tons of copper per month) prompted Raeder to appeal again to Hitler on 22 December 1942, announcing serious deficits in completed boats. It was decided, however, that U-boat construction (increased to 25 boats) and U-boat repair must continue at the present production level. Hitler sympathized with the Navy's predicament and hoped that supplies could be improved for the second quarter of 1943, but in view of the critical situation in the East, he could not make any firm promises.

Table 28. The threatened programme, 12 March 1942

	Large U-boats	Medium U-boats	Total
Original production plan[1]:			
Monthly	6	19	25
Yearly	72	228	300
Production plan after curtailment of Dec 1941:			
Monthly	5	15	20
Yearly	60	180	240
Reduced production for the 2nd quarter of 1942:[2]			
Monthly	3	12	15
Yearly	36	144	180

[1]Continuation of the Restricted Plan as authorized by Hitler. [2]Caused by shortages of raw materials.

Table 29. HAS Planning at 1 December 1942

	GW	Br.V	Fl.W	HDW, Kiel	DWK	Danz.W.	Schichau	B+V	Flensb. SBG	NSW	HDW, Hbg.	Stülcken W'haven	KMW, Oderw.	Stett. Vulc.	Stett.	Neptun	Deschimag	DW	Seebeck
Oct	1	2	1	1	—	2	1	5	—	—	1	1	1	—	—	—	2	2	—
Nov	2	1	1	1	—	1	2	4	1	1	1	—	1	—	—	—	3	2	1
Dec	2	2	1	1	2	1	1	6	1	1	1	1	—	—	—	—	2	2	—
Total	20	21	10	8	11	12	16	53	7	7	9	8	5	—	—	—	24	23	4
1943:																			
Jan	2	2	1	1	1	1	2	4	1	—	1	—	1	—	—	—	2	2	1
Feb	1	2	1	—	1	2	2	5	—	1	—	1	—	—	—	—	2	2	—
March	3	2	1	1	1	1	1	4	1	1	1	1	1	—	—	—	2	2	1
April	1	1	1	1	—	1	2	5	—	—	1	1	—	—	—	—	2	2	—
May	1	2	1	1	1	1	2	4	1	1	1	—	1	1	—	1	2	2	—
June	2	2	1	—	2	2	1	4	1	1	1	1	—	—	1	—	2	2	1
July	1	2	1	1	1	1	2	5	—	1	1	1	1	—	—	—	2	2	—
Aug	3	2	2	1	1	1	2	4	1	—	1	1	—	—	—	1	2	2	—
Sept	2	2	1	1	1	1	2	5	1	1	1	1	1	—	—	—	2	2	1
Oct	2	2	1	1	1	2	2	4	1	1	1	1	1	—	1	1	2	2	—
Nov	2	2	1	1	1	1	2	4	—	1	1	1	—	1	—	—	2	2	—
Dec	2	2	1	1	1	1	2	5	1	—	1	1	1	—	—	1	2	2	1
Total	22	23	13	10	12	15	22	53	8	8	10	10	7	2	2	4	24	24	5
1944:																			
Jan	2	2	1	1	1	1	2	4	1	1	1	—	—	—	—	1	2	2	—
Feb	2	2	1	1	1	1	2	4	—	1	1	1	1	—	—	—	2	2	—
March	2	2	1	1	1	2	3	5	1	1	1	1	1	—	—	1	2	2	1
April	2	2	1	1	1	1	2	4	1	—	1	1	—	—	1	—	2	2	—
May	2	2	1	1	1	1	2	4	1	1	1	1	—	1	—	—	2	2	—
June	2	2	1	1	2	2	2	5	—	1	—	—	1	—	—	1	2	2	1
July	4	2	1	1	1	1	2	4	1	1	1	1	—	—	—	1	2	2	—
Aug	4	2	2	1	1	1	3	4	—	1	1	1	1	—	—	—	2	2	—
Sept	3	2	1	1	—	1	2	5	1	1	1	1	—	—	—	1	2	2	1
Oct	3	2	1	1	1	1	2	4	—	1	1	1	—	—	—	1	2	2	—
Nov	3	2	1	1	1	2	2	4	1	1	1	—	1	1	—	1	2	2	—
Dec	2	2	1	1	1	1	2	5	1	—	—	1	—	—	—	1	2	2	1
Total	31	24	13	12	12	15	26	52	9	9	10	9	6	2	—	8	24	24	4
1945																			
Total	26	24	13	13	12	18	26	52	10	9	12	11	13	—	—	8	24	24	4
1946																			
Total	26	24	13	13	12	18	26	52	10	9	12	11	13	—	—	8	24	24	4

Monthly totals: 1942, 238; 1943, 274; 1944, 290; 1945, 299; 1946, 299. Approx. monthly averages: 1942, 20; 1943, 23; 1944, 24; 19145, 25; 1946, 25.

Building U-boats: the construction sequence

Although series production had been agreed upon, after the outbreak of hostilities U-boats — like large ships — were still being built as individual units. In each building hall, metal plates and spars were marked out piece by piece to the drawings issued by the Construction Office, and were subsequently worked on to become sections, tanks, platforms, conning towers and other finished components, to be finally assembled into a complete boat on the slip. The most important step forward from the building methods of the First World War, was the increasing use of arc-welding. Only in a few places on the outer hull and at the conning-tower fairing was riveting carried out, and only then because there were not enough welders available who could carry out perfect welding of the thinly-galvanized metal sheeting. As arc-welding needed protection from the weather and could be carried out more reliably in favourable conditions, more and more parts were built in the workshops instead of on the slips. In this category, the most important single part was the pressure hull, which in Type VIIC consisted of eight sections and in Type IXC of ten sections. Each section was made up of four to six pressure-hull plates, with their shortest sides curved to fit around the circular frames. Their maximum thickness was 18.5mm, except beneath the conning tower where it was increased to 22mm. The plates were welded to the circular supports to make short cylinders, as can be seen in the photograph on the right: this was done by laying the first two plates on roller jacks, with support blocks underneath; the longitudinal seam between these two plates was then welded from the top, i.e., from the inside of the boat. The next step was to place the circular frames on top of the two plates; these were then correctly lined up and attached to the plates. The third plate was now attached to this with bolts and nuts. Now it was possible to rotate the entire structure so that the next longitudinal seam came to the bottom, and this too was welded from the top, again, from the inside. This performance was then repeated until the pressure-hull drum had become a closed cylinder. The last plate had to be cut to fit into the gap. However, this measuring was only carried out for the first two cylinders of each series and then the same sizes were used for the other sections. The outside edges

Table 30. Section lengths in Types VIIC and IXC

	Type VIIC (cm)	Type IXC (cm)
Section 1	600	385
Section 2	350	490
Section 3	550	420
Section 4	710	700
Section 5	910	630
Section 6	720	770
Section 7	790	630
Section 8	310	700
Section 9		770
Section 10		280

Right: Pressure-hull plates being welded on to the frames of *U116* (Type XB). **Far right:** *U98* (Type VIIC) being launched at GW, 31 August 1940.

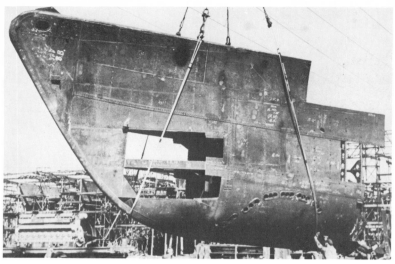

Above, left and right: Sections for Type IXC. On the left, the prefabricated foreship of *U1225* is being manoeuvred into position at DW; on the right is a Section X with forward pressure bulkhead. **Below:** Series production of VIIC boats at GW, with *U94* (right) prior to launching lying beside the pressure hull of *U72*.

of the seams were then also welded from above. A maximum of approximately 250mm were left unwelded at the ends to make it easier to match the sections when on the slip. If a bulkhead occurred within a section, it was assembled together with the circular frames; bulkheads at the end of a section were welded-in before the last plate was fitted. If the section were shut off by a bulkhead at either end, large components such as tanks, decks, walls or flooring were built-in and made temporarily secure before the ends were sealed. The ballast-keel sections were also built in the workshops, and these were assembled from vertical and horizontal keel plates, and transverse girders.

On the slips, these items were first laid on blocks in the slipway, set up and welded together. At first, it was found that the thrust of the vertical, middle keel plate was transmitted to horizontal keel plates several frames' distance away, and this meant that a further row of transverse girders had to be welded in position at the slipway. When work was being done on Type IXB, two thrusts were encountered in the same frame area, but this did not in any way impair the strength of the construction. When it came to Type XI, the builders went a stage further and allowed the thrusts from pressure-hull sections, keel plates and outer hull all to fall in the same area which, in fact, made possible the assembly of these parts as complete crude sections in the workshop.

The various pressure-hull sections were now assembled on the ballast keel. A start was made with the control room section, which established the middle part of the boat. After it had been placed in position it was welded to the keel. Further sections were now added simultaneously forward and aft; to assist in this, a sighting line with a sighting jack was set up at the forward and after ends of the boat. Welding together of margin seams was carried out as a simultaneous operation by several welders in the so-called 'Pilgrims' Step'. After assembly of the pressure hull, the conning tower was set up. This meant that the pressure-tight portion of the boat was now complete, with the exception of the compensating tanks, which were an exterior feature, and the hull could now be subjected to a watertightness test to 3 atmospheres overload interior pressure.

Only then was a start made on the fitting out of the interior, and adding the outer hull. Here, too, work began in the centre, working out from there to each end. First came the heavy pressure-tight interior compensating and ballast tanks with their strong transverse bulkheads; then followed the transverse frames and longitudinal support for the outer ship. The bow and stern sections of the boat, which had similarly been prefabricated to such an extent that they had already received their outer skin, were now attached. Finally, the outer skin of the mid-ship section was welded, plate by plate, to the frames, decks and stringers.

The upper deck was assembled almost entirely from smaller components, and the subsequent fitting had to be carried out hand-in-hand with the engine installation, because it was essential to lay the sizeable tubes and conduits for diesel ventilation, air-intake and exhaust systems first, because these lay between the pressure hull and the upper deck. The latter had a wooden floor of 80mm-wide planks, which were laid by hand with a 20mm space between them. The upper deck trapdoors were first prepared in accordance with the exact positions of the hatches so that they would be a good fit in the deck apertures above them. Normally, building-slip time did not extend to this work and consequently, after launching, a number of workers were obliged to carry out completion work on the upper deck. The conning-tower fairing, on the other hand, had already been completely assembled in the workshops, and had only to be secured like a hood over the conning tower and air-masts.

Items for interior fittings were prefabricated in such a way that they could almost all be brought aboard in sections through the narrow hatch openings. The largest hatch was that for the diesel-engine installation, and all bulky items were brought in through this. As it was desirable to leave this open as long as possible, there tended to be a congestion here after the welding, because the exhaust heads and silencing installations had still to be fitted. In order that electric motors and other large components could be brought into the electro-control compartment, the bulkhead between the diesel compartment and this area was given a large right-angled opening, which was later closed and welded-up. Then such items as thrust bearings, shaft couplings, electric motors, main switchboards, and diesel engines with diesel couplings were set up and installed.

Work was being carried out simultaneously in the other compartments, and it was necessary to formulate an exact timetable so as to avoid one operation hindering another, especially when installing tubes and cables. Although the construction offices issued general drawings for installation of tubes and cables, no precise instructions with exact measurements were furnished, and these had to be worked out on the spot by the engineers and technicians, which certainly saved design-office time, but made more work for the dockyard staff. The after sections of

Above: *U67* (Type IXC) outside the dry bunker at Lorient. **Below, left and right:** Two boats shortly before launching. The Type XB on the left is *U119* in January 1942, and, on the right, is a Type VIIC on Slip 3 at Blohm & Voss.

Various fitting-out processes underway on Type VIIC boats at Flender-Werke, Lübeck, in 1942. The photograph on the far right shows *U970* under construction at Blohm & Voss, Hamburg, in January 1943.

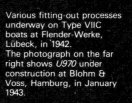

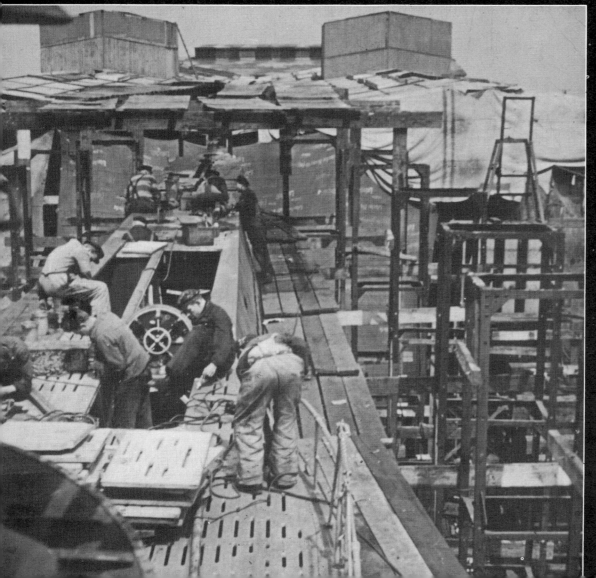

the torpedo tubes were brought in through the torpedo-hatch opening, and then the coamings for these hatches were welded into place. The last sizeable task was the installation of batteries through a special hatch. Launching took place as soon as possible in order to free the slip, but this increased the fitting-out time at the quayside and the distance that material and workers had to travel.

Following delivery and commissioning, all U-boats were given a thorough testing by the U-boat Acceptance Commission (Ubootabnahme-kommando, or UAK), which included, if possible, a pressure-dock test. The pressure dock had been built by Flenderwerke in 1937—38, and consisted of a pressure-cylinder of 12m diameter resting in a floating dock. A U-boat could be taken into the submerged dock, with the cylinder half full of water, and secured; the dock was then raised and the boat was shored up as in a normal floating dock. The dock was then lowered once again, the sluice was opened and the boat was subjected to water compression, which took 90—120 minutes. On board would be 9—12 men, including the commander, the chief engineer and one or two representatives of the UAK. The dock was used to establish any shortcomings in construction and lack of watertightness, but could not of course be used to test and evaluate maximum strength qualities.

From 1941, as a result of the grievous shortage of workers, the construction of sections and outer-hull parts was handed over to steel construction plants outside the yards. In this way, work forces and yard installations in other areas could play a direct part in U-boat construction. The difficulties of transporting longer sections or those with projections, such as longitudinal bulkheads, decks, platforms, etc., resulted in these being redesigned sectionally for assembly on the slip. The transporting of sections and the larger components for the outer hull was carried out by barges on canals.

In 1942—43, a total of 24 steel firms were engaged in section and outer-hull construction for the 16 yards building Type VIIC boats. Almost all production of components had been handed over to firms outside the shipbuilding industry, and this left the shipbuilders free to concentrate on yard assembly work.

These innovations led, notably in the medium yards, to a considerable saving in work time from 1942. For example, the Flensburg Shipbuilding Company required for the first 8 Type VIIC boats (to July 1942) approximately 400,000 yard-hours per boat, when most miscellaneous tasks, excluding work on delivered engines, had to be completed at the yard. Engines were excluded because they were delivered fully assembled. In the case of the ninth boat, by order of the Construction Office, approximately 35,000 hours were subcontracted, and simultaneously the piece-work system at the yard was examined from a time and motion aspect and modified. By the time of the 22nd boat at the beginning of 1944, production methods had been so well improved that no decrease in boat-hours from the existing 240,000 could be expected. At the same time, the best yard, Blohm & Voss, managed with

Type VIIC boats at launching. **Far left:** *U442* at Schichau Werft, Danzig in January 1942. **Left:** A boat leaving Slip 7 at Blohm & Voss. **Below, left:** In the winter of 1943/1944. **Top right:** At the Howaldt Yard, Kiel. **Below:** *U69* on 19 September 1940 at GW. In the left of the photograph is *U70* under construction.

Right: The commissioning ceremony for *U80* (Type VIIC) at the Vegesack Works (Bremer-Vulkan) on 8 April 1941. **Middle:** *U111* (Type IXB) in spring 1941. **Far right:** *U651* (Type VIIC), the first boat from Howaldt Werke, Hamburg, after a submerged trimming test at the beginning of 1941. **Below:** *U205* (Type VIIC) after launching at GW on 20 March 1941.

180,000 hours per boat. Even if this difference in hours per boat was the result of the greater facilities at B&V, and their more comprehensive subcontracting to outside firms, it is still certain that a very considerable portion of the hours saved can be attributed to the considerably larger quota of boats built at B&V, which made possible a more thorough specialization and distribution of work processes. In being called upon to deliver 1 boat per week, the assembly workers were performing similar work at least every seven days, so that total work schedules could be formulated according to an exact timetable, and the course of construction could follow an absolutely inevitable plan. A statement of costs at the large B&V yard at the end of 1943 ran as follows.

Work hours for a single VIIC boat 180,000	180,000 marks (at 1 mark per hour)
State addition 160 per cent	288,000 marks
Materials and delivered finished components including engines	1,420,000 marks
Profit 5 per cent	95,000 marks
Total price	1,983,000 marks

To be sure, the considerable differences in work hours did not affect total costs per boat as much as might have been expected, because the State addition was correspondingly smaller, as a result of the reduced expenditure on works organization, and the subcontracting of certain work to smaller yards, to be carried out in their own workshops, which reduced transport costs.

On 8 February 1942, the Reichs Minister for Armaments and Munitions, Dr. Fritz Todt, was killed in a flying accident and, next day, Hitler named as his successor the 37-year-old Albert Speer, the 'architect' for the redesigning of Berlin. Speer began immediately to organize the armaments industry afresh, taking control of it more positively in his Ministry. His first step was to ensure that various orders, which hitherto had been sent by various branches of the armed forces direct to industry, should now be sent to the Armaments Ministry for distribution to appropriate firms. In order to control procurement. he extended the system of Production Committees, and completed it by setting up bodies which should supply the committees. As early as 20 March 1942, Speer suggested to Hitler that this system be extended to naval armaments, and Raeder agreed with this. Consequently, in the early part of 1942, two main committees were set up, Ship Construction (Schiffbau), under State Counsellor Rudolf Blohm (B&V), and Special Naval Equipment (Marinesondergerät), under Paulus. A special Main Committee for U-Boats was considered by Speer and Raeder, but was not actually formed

The Main Committee for Ship Construction, a civil authority for the industry, was subdivided into lower committees (Special Committees): Warship Construction (Kabelac), Merchant Ship Construction (Scholz), Ships' Engines and Boilers (Immich), Ships' Electronics (Buff), Coastal and River Boats, and small boats (Völker), Special Ships and Amphibious Installations (Wendel). In June 1942, there followed, as an additional body, the Special Committee for Concrete Ships. In place of a Special Main Commission for U-Boats, so-called Work Committees were set up for the most

Table 31. Yard hours expenditure
(Best achievements as at 1 April 1943)

Type	Ship construction	Engine construction	Total
VIIC	147,000[1]	107,000[2]	254,000
VIIC/41	150,000[1]	105,000[2]	255,000
VIIC/42	175,000[1]	115,000[2]	290,000
VIID	271,000[3]	130,000[2]	401,000
VIIF	235,000[4]	125,000[2]	360,000
IXC/40	200,500[1]	141,300[2]	341,800
IXD$_2$	257,000[1]	167,300[2]	424,300
XB	525,000[5]	320,000[6]	845,000
XIV	400,000	164,000[2]	564,000
WK202	133,000	87,500[7]	220,500
XVIIG/B	115,000	85,000[7]	200,000
XVIII	564,000	196,000[7]	760,000

[1] Components made of steel such as ballast keels, pressure-hull sections, forward and after parts of boats, upper decks, conning towers, torpedo hatches and exterior tanks delivered from outside sources.
[2] Without main engines, but including the installation of the electrical system and all tubing.
[3] All steel components prepared at the yard itself.
[4] Steel components apart from Section 4a, upper deck and ballast keel supplied by outside sources.
[5] All steel components built at the yard.
[6] Including manufacture of the main engines (65,000 hours).
[7] Hours excluding time spent on the Walter System.

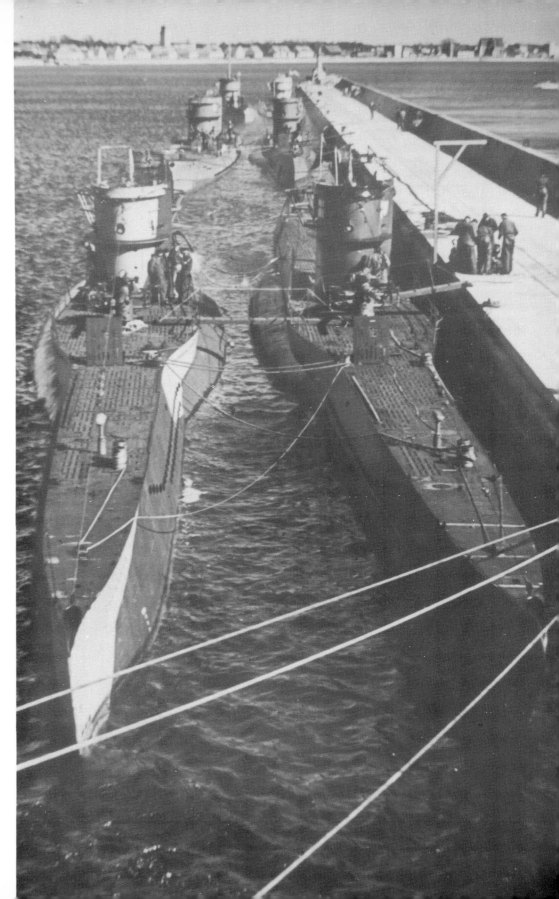

Left and above: Completed Type VIIC boats training in the Baltic, summer 1942.

Work hours on Types VIIC and IXC.

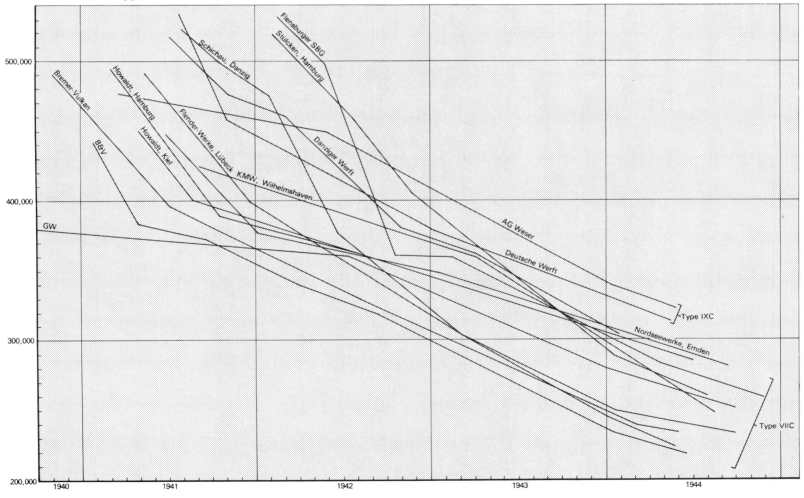

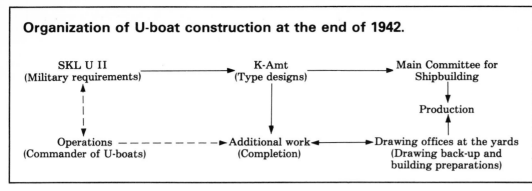

Organization of U-boat construction at the end of 1942.

SKL U II
(Military requirements) → K-Amt
(Type designs) → Main Committee for
Shipbuilding
↓
Production
↓
Operations - - - - - - - → Additional work ← Drawing offices at the yards
(Commander of U-boats) (Completion) (Drawing back-up and
building preparations)

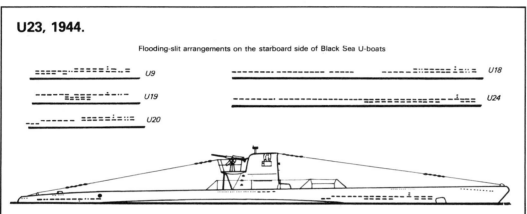

U23, 1944.

Flooding-slit arrangements on the starboard side of Black Sea U-boats

U9 U18
U19 U24
U20

important U-boat types, and these were affiliated to the Special Committees for Warship Construction; there was thus a Work Committee U VIIC under Dir. Cords; Work Committee U IX under Dir. Neeff and, in the early part of 1943, the Work Committee U XX under Dir. Kabelac. At the end of 1942, U-boat construction was organized as shown in the diagram.

U-boats for the Black Sea

As early as 18 March 1941, consideration had been given to the idea of sending small U-boats to Rumania, for use in the Black Sea during the planned attack against Russia. The idea stemmed from the activities of the Germano-American Petroleum Company, which operated tanker barges on the River Danube. However, the voyage would have taken 4½–5 months and, as a relatively short war with Russia was envisaged, it seemed unlikely that the boats would arrive in the Black Sea in time to play an operational rôle. For this reason, the Naval War Staff shelved the plan.

However, in the autumn of 1941, when it had become clear that no decisive blow had been struck in Russia, the use of operational U-boats during the planned offensive against the south Russian front was discussed again. On 12 December 1941, the feasibility and time requirements of transporting U-boats by land and water to the Black Sea were discussed. Investigation established that only Types IIA and IIB would be suitable, as the dead

weight after removing engines, keels, sections of upper decks, conning tower, hydroplanes, propellers and other items of this type would be 140 tons, which could just about be carried overland on two special 70-ton vehicles. The manufacture of simple pontoons for transporting the boats on the Elbe and the Danube was also discussed. The total time from dismantling in the Baltic to a state of readiness for operations in the Black Sea was estimated at approximately ten months, of which approximately six weeks would be spent in transit.

But Hitler decided not to proceed with the long-term project. If the almost complete mastery the Russians enjoyed in the Black Sea were to be challenged, then the rapid transportation of MTBs and minesweepers, Italian miniature submarines, the Finnish small submarine *Saukko* (by rail) and other small vessels was vital. Nevertheless, in the early part of 1942, three 250-ton Type IIB U-boats were allocated for transportation, the intention being to assemble them at Linz, which lies on the Danube, approximately 150km west of Vienna. It was hoped that the time needed to transport them could be shortened. Ministerial Counsellor Dykmann of Supreme Naval Command was given the task of organizing the affair, and the engineer Karl Baumgarten worked out a detailed plan at the Ship Construction Office of DWK. By the early summer of 1942, preliminary work was so far advanced that *U9*, *U19* and *U24* could be taken out of service and broken down by DWK.

The hulls of the boats were dismantled and lightened as far as possible, and were then turned through an angle of 90° to achieve the lowest possible height for travelling. They proceeded from Kiel along the Kiel Canal to Hamburg, and were towed from there along the Elbe to a point near Dresden. As the draught for shipping on the upper Elbe and Danube was limited to approximately 1.2m, each U-boat hull was placed on its side on a raft made from five pontoons, each approximately 3.1m long and 1.4m high. At Dresden, each raft was pulled far enough out of the water for the pontoons to be removed, then each hull was loaded on to two Kuhlemeier transport vehicles, each of which could be steered independently. The vehicles inched their way along the autobahn to Ingolstadt, an operation that was especially critical at curves and when crossing bridges. The vehicles were powered by 150hp Kälble tractors and Luftwaffe Faun engines, and these were used either four in line or in two parallel sets according to the road and weather conditions. On the autobahn, the convoy could achieve a top speed of 8km per hour, and it moved by day and night, even when there was danger of air attack. A breakdown would no doubt have brought about the loss of a U-boat and a lengthy blocking of the autobahn, but the undertaking was carried out with extreme precision and without delays. Meanwhile, the pontoons were sent by rail from Dresden to Ingolstadt, where they were secured to the appropriate hull. As the level of water in the Danube was low, the first boat could not leave the slip-vehicle until additional pontoons had been employed.

In Linz, after the pontoons had been removed, the boats were brought to a normal upright position by flooding its main diving tank. The pontoons were attached once more, and the boats were lifted from the water. Now the dismantled components (engines, batteries, conning towers, etc.), but not the ballast-keels, were reassembled and the boats, in the interests of camouflage and security, were towed between two wherries along the Danube towards Galatz. Here, in a floating dock, the pontoons were detached and the keels were welded on; finally, the completed boats were taken over by their crews. After arriving at the operational base of Constanza, the boats were recommissioned in October 1942.

On 26 August 1942, Hitler spoke in favour of a further 3 small U-boats for use in the Black Sea, as they might have a favourable political effect on Turkish opinion. Raeder agreed with this and gave orders that *U18*, *U20* and *U23* be sent to the Black Sea. These boats were in transit during the winter of 1942/43, which brought additional transport problems, and they came into service in Constanza in May 1943. A total of 6 U-boats were used without loss in the Black Sea until Rumania ceased active participation in the war; although they did not achieve spectacular success, they did exert an important operational pressure on Soviet naval forces, and sank supply vessels and tankers. On 20 August 1944, *U9* was sunk in Constanza harbour by Soviet air attack. *U18* and *U24* were damaged and, four days later, when the harbour was evacuated they were blown up by their crews. *U19*, *U20* and

U23 were in use until their fuel was expended and, after Turkey had refused to purchase them, they were sunk off Turkey on 2 September 1944.

WAR EXPERIENCE: TORPEDOES, DETECTION AND PROTECTION

Torpedoes

At the beginning of the war, both G7a (T I) and G7e (T II) torpedoes were available. Each contained 280kg of gun-cotton 36, which could be detonated by impact fuze (Aufschlagzündung, or AZ) or magnetic proximity fuze (Magnetzündung-Pistole, or MZ-Pi). With MZ, the increased magnetic field surrounding the iron mass of a ship activated a pistol, which exploded the charge under the ship's keel. A switch regulated the pistol's sensitivity to differing strengths of magnetic fields. When the torpedoes were used operationally, however, a multiplicity of premature detonations and failures occurred, and these reached catastrophic proportions during the Norwegian campaign of April 1940. After restrictions on their use had been enforced, an order was given in June 1940 that neither type of torpedo be used except with the AZ impact/contact system. Both the contact pistol and the torpedo's depth-keeping were unreliable — a consequence, in part, of inadequate operational tests by the TVA. The fluctuations in depth-keeping had been recognized by that body, but had been dismissed as of no great importance in the development of the new magnetic torpedoes. Furthermore, new developments of other torpedo types with higher speeds and better depth-keeping qualities, to replace the G7a, were considered to be more important. These new types were the G7a6 (six-cylinder engine, maximum 420hp) and G6a (3km at 50 knots). These specifications according to a statement of 30 October 1934!

During 1941 and 1942, when the U-boats had their greatest successes, only the contact system was used. Because of the uncertain depth-keeping, both types of torpedo were usually set to run fairly shallow, which further reduced the effect of the detonation.

At the beginning of November 1942, a new, improved magnetic proximity fuze, Pi39H (Pi2), which was also effective with contact detonator, was ready for operational use with a specially developed, electrically-propelled torpedo (T III); it was acknowledged that there were still certain weaknesses present in this development. At the same time, a device had been prepared for the G7a that permitted running in circles. The torpedo thus modified was designated G7a Fat (Federapparat, or spring-loaded), and could be set to run in the following ways: circling to right or left, circle long or short and an initial straight run of 500-500m up to 15km, surface speed = 30 knots, running distance 12.5km. The G7a was at first permitted only for night attacks because it left a slight bubble-wake, and its introduction into service was to be concealed for as long as possible.

Although, in the interests of safety, the T III had been envisaged as running at a shallow depth, a series of magnetic detonations at the beginning of 1943 confirmed the efficiency of the new proximity pistol. The introduction of the G7a Fat was also hailed as a complete success by Dönitz who recorded a hit rate of 75 per cent. Meanwhile, the conditions in which U-boats had to carry out attacks had worsened, so that the effectiveness of these new weapons was reduced. It was becoming essential to provide a defensive weapon against the growing offensive power of escort vessels and Support Groups, which were preventing U-boats from approaching convoys.

It had long been thought that accuracy of firing would be improved if an acoustic, homing torpedo were used, but only the development of ultra-sonic receivers and practical amplifiers could make this possible. After the Communications Test Institute (Nachrichtenmittelversuchsanstalt, or NVA) had laid down the physical principles, Atlas, Elac and AEG began work on the development of suitable direction-finding receivers in 1934, the intention being to produce a torpedo with a speed greater than 30 knots for use against warships. Laboratory models were available at these three firms by the beginning of the war. Development was then handed over to TVA-Eckernförde, but progress here was slow, because they were engaged in other work and were short of personnel. The objective was modified so that the torpedo could be used against merchant shipping, which necessitated increasing sensitivity at the cost of reducing the speed of the torpedo to 20 knots. The weapon was tested in 1940, and development was switched to Gotenhafen in 1941, being intensified by the formation of a 'Special Department for Acoustic Torpedoes'. The first model, G7es 'Falke' (T IV), for use against merchant ships was available in the late autumn of 1942. It had a contact fuze, a speed of 20 knots and a range of 5–7km, depending on storage battery heating. The weight of the warhead had to be reduced to 274kg because the sound-detection gear had to be accommodated in the head. It could be used against deep-draught vessels moving at 7–13 knots, from a bearing 0°–180°, but was not suitable for use in the tropics. The first tests under operational conditions took place with 6 U-boats in February-March 1943. As a safety precaution with regard to the lack of a safety-device on the pistol while still in the torpedo tube, its use was restricted to the stern tubes. Only three torpedoes were fired and two of them secured hits. Following certain changes (enlargement of the arming-range, i.e., the distance the torpedo must run before the detonator will function) the 'Falke' was ready for general operational use on 1 July 1943.

The heavy U-boat losses sustained in May 1943 made it imperative that an acoustic torpedo be developed, suitable for use against fast-moving warships. It was necessary that the torpedo have a higher speed and a proximity fuze because the shallow draught of its intended targets and the need to run deeper to avoid sound interference meant that a contact pistol could not be considered. The last-mentioned problem was the most difficult, and the very high incidence of failures indicated

that it would not easily be solved. It was reckoned that this torpedo, designated G7es 'Zaunkönig' (T V) (sound homing torpedo), could not enter service until the beginning of 1944 at the earliest. At this time, however, the state of the U-boat campaign compelled Dönitz to demand that 'Zaunkönig' be ready by 1 October 1943 and, on 13 July, he asked for it to be ready by 1 August. Amazingly, 80 acoustic torpedoes were ready for service on that date. The specifications of the torpedo were: speed 24.5 knots; running range 5–5.7km depending on battery heating; proximity-and-contact pistol. It was suitable for use from any position against any vessel having a speed of 10–18 knots. Unfortunately, the short arming-range made it necessary for the boat to dive deep after firing, which severely reduced the chances of observing the result of the attack, and this led to a considerable over-estimation of the effectiveness of this weapon, as very many near-miss detonations were reported as hits. From 20 to 24 September 1943, of 24 acoustic torpedoes fired only four hit the target, yet reports spoke of the certain destruction of 12 destroyers.

While the main task of the Torpedo Test Establishment (TVA) at Gotenhafen was to test and improve the acoustic torpedo, work was being carried out on a further development — 'Zaunkönig 2' (T XI). This had an improved guidance system which was less vulnerable to jamming from equipment towed behind enemy vessels. At the same time, other firms were carrying out tests on a number of improvements, the most important of which bore such cover names as 'Pfau', 'Lerche' and 'Geier'. 'Pfau' (AEG) was a passive-acoustic guidance system that, in contrast to the 'Zaunkönig's' 'Amsel' (Magneto-Striction Receiver — Amplitude Method), used crystal microphones and a phase-differential method. Development had begun in 1937 — originally for aerial torpedoes (F 5). When the war started, development work was shelved for some time in favour of other projects. 'Lerche' (AEG) had a passive homing-head with a remotely-controlled directional microphone (swivel-mounted magneto-strictive microphone, able to focus critically) connected to the U-boat by a wire. This enabled the torpedo to be steered to a target from a distance of 6km. The steering wire was of hard copper with a dimeter of 0.45mm with Igelit insulation, and ran through the torpedo's hollow propeller-shaft. 'Geier' (Atlas-Minerva) had an active homing-head with two sending and two receiving oscillators. It was difficult to jam, but its sensitivity range was essentially smaller than that of 'Zaunkönig', and it was necessary to steer the weapon, passive-acoustically, to a distance of approximately 250m from the target. A forerunner of 'Geier' was the active homing-head 'Boje', developed by the Luftwaffe.

Other special guidance systems, proposed or actually developed before the war ended were:
1. The 'Ackermann' 'Wake-Homer' (Prof. Ackermann, Danzig Technical College), guidance according to the variable pressure-relationships of vessels' wash; and 'Ibis' (Dr. Grützmacher, Imperial Physical-Technical Institute) guidance through ultrasonic noise echoes in vessels' wake.

2. 'Märchen' (Prof. Schwenkhagen, Danzig Technical College), guidance by magnetic field distortion in the neighbourhood of ships.

3. 'Taube' (S&H), passive-acoustic guidance using very deep natural frequencies (50–100Hz.).

4. 'Fasan' (Dr. Unkelbach, OKM), independent torpedo-triggering using the reflection of ultrasonic impulses in vessels' wake.

5. 'Kondor', a combination of the passive 'Geier' and 'Fasan' for long-range torpedoes.

Further improvements to the G7a and G7e were the development of a reliable proximity pistol for the G7a on the lines of the Italian 'Pi Sic', the incorporation of a circling function and, also in the G7e (Fat II and Lut), the use of high-performance batteries (T IIIa) and the adaptation of acoustic torpedoes (OT I up to 50m and OT II to a maximum of 100m depth firing capability).

The introduction of the G7a with the new magnetic firing (MZ3 and Pi3) followed in August 1943. The G7e Fat II was released at the end of March 1943. In contrast to G7a Fat I, it could be used only with a long loop or as a circling torpedo, because of its shorter range. These operational alternatives, however, were not very successful: the orbit that the weapon described when fired defensively against oncoming destroyers did not result in any hits.

The Lut was a further development of the Fat (spring-apparatus torpedo). By incorporating a new articulation joint in the looping mechanism, the Lut could be made to follow a path parallel to that taken by the enemy in any situation, so that this torpedo could be fired from any bearing. The circling-track took the shape of a zig-zig, and the speed was adjustable between 5 and 21 knots. Lut I was built into the T IIIa, and the torpedo was given a high-performance battery allowing a range of 9km. Trials with Lut were carried out by U970 from 9 October to 9 December 1943, and 60 torpedoes in a total of 233 firings were used. The results were stated to be 'very satisfactory'. T IIIa with Lut I became operational in February 1944 and, by 1 July, approximately 50 operational boats had been equipped with the new torpedo. A true evaluation had not yet been made, however, and it is doubtful if the good results suggested by the trials were achieved during operational use where harsher conditions obtained. Just as keel-wash detonations had presented problems in the use of Zaunkönig, so now the new torpedoes with magnetic detonators of the G7c and G7e series, detonated frequently at the end of their run and often prevented a true assessment by the U-boat.

From 15 April 1944, a Type VIIC U-boat operating in the Atlantic had the following options for torpedo armament (according to Ordinance 40):
1. Forward: three T V, two Fat I, three T III Fat II (or five T IIIa Fat II); Aft: two TV.
2. Forward: three T V, five T IIIa Lut; Aft: two T V.
Lut II, with four armatures in the gyroscopic apparatus (GA), was provided for the faster G7a. This allowed changes of course of over 180° to be made in the looping-path, which permitted the torpedo's speed to be significantly reduced during the first stages of its approach, which was necessary when engaging convoys with fast

torpedoes. A small number of G5e (a 5m-long electric torpedo with one battery only and correspondingly shorter range) were made available for the small Walter submarines (see page 175). These boats were also to be equipped with the fast Walter torpedoes, which were propelled by special turbines.

Walter torpedo development began in 1938 with the preparation of project studies on engine and pulse-jet drive. The intention was to produce a high-speed, long-range torpedo which left no track. The first result was the G7u 'Klippfisch' with the G7a piston engine. It was driven by a gas/steam mixture from the 'hot Walter process' instead of by paraffin burned in compressed air, and had a range of 6.5km at 40 knots. In 1942, it underwent trials at Eckernförde and Gotenhafen, but was not put into service because the turbine-drive principle offered better performance — the G7ut 'Steinbutt' gave 8km at 45 knots. However, the very complicated installation of such a turbine gave rise to a multiplicity of problems which delayed production. By the time that trials of one version had been concluded, improvements had so advanced that basic work had to be undertaken once again, so that G7ut 'Steinbarsch' torpedoes were not ready for operations until the end of the war. On the other hand, a very much simplified 'Butt' torpedo, without negative buoyancy, was in series production by the end of the war. Designated 'K-Butt' (T XIII), its range was 3km at 45 knots, and it was intended for use by midget submarines. The last development stage of the Walter torpedoes was that of the long-range 'Wal' and 'Schildbutt'. By using sea-water injection, the otherwise essential feed-water would be dispensed with, allowing a larger supply of 'Ingolin' (Hydrogen Peroxide, H_2O_2) which increased the range considerably — in the case of 'Wal', to 21km at 45 knots.

A different propulsion method for a high-performance torpedo that left little detectable trail was provided by the Otto closed-cycle engine. As early as 1927, the TVA of the Research Institute for Vehicles at the Berlin Technical High School had been given the task of developing a torpedo engine based on the exhaust gas–oxygen overcharge process of Prof. G. Becker. Work was controlled directly by Prof. Becker until 1932 when Dr. Kauffmann took over; by early 1933, a reasonably satisfactory stage of development had been achieved. The propulsion section consisted of an eight-cylinder, water-cooled carburettor-motor in a 90° V-form, with a total capacity of 7.45 litres and maximum 134hp at 2,200rpm in the air operation. Cooling of exhaust gas was carried out by injected water, which was then led through two water extractors. The exhaust gas remaining in circulation was enriched with oxygen and led back to the carburettor. At a charging pressure of 1.4 atm, 120hp at 2,200rpm were achieved in the circulation; at 2.7 atm, as much as 250hp was achieved. The reliability of the regulators was good, and fire in the carburettor hardly ever occurred. Then racial pressures caused Dr. Kauffmann to leave Germany, and experiments were discontinued.

In 1937, work on the 'closed-cycle torpedo' was recommenced, this time at the firm of Junkers. Here, Dr. O. Hohlfelder carried out similar development work for the Supreme Naval Command. The objective was to produce a high-performance torpedo with a circuit-drive in the shell of a G7a. After extensive studies, based in part on the research of Prof. Becker and Dr. Kauffmann, an eight-cylinder V-engine of a maximum 425hp at 4,500rpm and a cylinder capacity of only 4.3 litres was developed, and was given the designation KM 8. Trials began in 1941 and, at a charging pressure of 2.5 atm, 0.68kg/hp/hr oxygen and 290g/hp/hr fuel in circulation, yielded 300hp at 3,800rpm. The first firings of this new torpedo, designated G7m, took place at Neubrandenburg in the summer of 1943, and at the same time trials began at Eckernförde. Ranges of 12km at almost 40 knots were achieved, but the regulating apparatus was too primitive and presented severe co-ordination difficulties, so that operational reliability had not been established by the time the war ended. Development was suspended by the fourth meeting of the Midget Weapons Commission on 2 February 1945.

Underwater detection and protection

The most important device for detecting underwater noise was the Gruppen-Horch-Gerät (GHG), or Group Listening Apparatus) which had been installed in all German U-boats since 1935. At first, the receiving diaphragms were integrated in the outer skin near the forward diving tanks. Eleven receivers were positioned on each side of the boat, in the form of an arc with its open side underneath. In time, the number of receivers was increased and, in Type IXC, numbered 23 on each side of the boat. To avoid welding problems, the receivers were now no longer set singly into the outer skin, but were assembled on a common flange to provide two or three listening chambers. These flanges were so cast that their shape exactly followed the curved outer skin and there were no projecting parts. An electric pulse-timing compensator enabled this arrangement of receivers to provide a crude directional sounding in which the time differences of noises reaching the various receivers could be levelled at a determined setting, and a maximum volume could therefore be obtained in a head-set connected with the equipment. From the settings of the compensator could be read the bearing of the received noise.

At the beginning of 1943, an attempt was made with a Type IXC boat to determine whether receivers set lower down would be more effective and whether listening would be possible in a surfaced boat. Initially, the receivers were simply built into the ballast-keel, which was made somewhat wider at this point, but subsequently 2 x 24 receivers were collected into a special gondola (balcony) in front of the keel. This arrangement proved extraordinarily successful, and critical bearings could be obtained from all directions with the exception of an angled segment aft of 150°–210°. The installation was retained and, in fact, was being further developed long after the original requirement had become obsolete. Following the rewarding experience with the balcony on Type IXC, an almost identical arrangement was envisaged for new types of boats. In 1944, balconies for group listening apparatus were built into some VIIC boats.

In order to provide adequate listening in the fast Walter U-boats (page 16|8), and to be able to listen at higher submerged speeds, a much larger number of receivers was built into the Type XXVI. In this case, the balcony was built as a bow-bulge, with 8 x 12 receivers arranged one above the other on each side of the boat (i.e., a total of 192 receivers). In order to increase the effectiveness of this arrangement in a rearwards direction, the bulge was given a pronounced S-curve and was tapered almost to the line of the keel. A provisional fitting was made to the conning tower of *U38* and was tested in 1944. Subsequently, Dr. Maas, the Head of the Development Group 'Listening Devices', had the bow of a mock-up of Type XXVI built to its original measurements, and tried out the group of

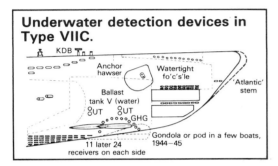

Underwater detection devices in Type VIIC.

receivers incorporated in it in Lake Constance. This experiment showed that an arrangement of 3 x 48 receivers invariably gave better bearing responses, with higher vertical focussing, than the arrangement of 4 x 48 receivers.

Before the balcony arrangement had been introduced, the group listening installation had not given very exact bearings, but many VIIC and IXC boats had an additional item built into the forward part of the boat, in the form of a swivel hydrophone (Kristall-Basisgerät or KDB). This contained six crystal receivers arranged on a swivelling base of approximately 50cm length. By turning to and fro, a maximum listening accuracy of ± 1° could be achieved. Using this 'deck hydrophone', a U-boat lying on the bottom could register an exact bearing, but the range of the apparatus was nothing like so large as with group listening apparatus. Given favourable circumstances, using GHG, single ships could be heard at a distance of 20km and convoys at a distance of 100km. The range over which listening was possible, however, changed considerably according to the acoustic conductivity of the water. Consequently, the strength of an audible bearing gave no certain indication of the distance of a target. On one occasion, Kapitänleutnant Prien detected what was thought to be a bombing attack on his *U47*: it turned out to be German aircraft attacking a British naval formation 100 nautical miles away (*War Diary*, 9 April 1940, 16.21 hours). Another kind of listening device with very exact bearing-recognition was the SP apparatus

(S-Analage passir, or SP-Anlage) designed for passive short-range detection astern. It was intended as an aiming-device for underwater missiles (Project 'Ursel'), which were to be used against pursuing U-boat hunters, and consisted of a crystal swivel-base, with two receiving components of the active echo-ranging installation; with the help of this, the horizontal and vertical angles of incidence of propeller noise could be determined. Using one's known submerged depth, the exact position of a pursuing ship could be evaluated. The range of this gear corresponded to approximately five times the submerged depth. The swivel receiving-base was mounted under a streamlined, hooded fairing on the after part of Type XXI U-boats (see page 209). Although the underwater missiles were still in the development stage at the end of the war, the echo-sounding devices had given good results during trials.

An additional listening device destined for new U-boats was the torpedo-warning and indicating equipment (Torpedowarn- und -anzeigegerät, or TAG) produced by NVK/Atlas and Elac. This equipment consisted of 2 x 6 receivers in the bow. Using four delay-members, four receiving-directions (35°, 120°, 240° and 325°) were made available. A rotating scanning-device gave automatic warning through four lamps and there was, additionally, a loudspeaker for acoustic warning and observation.

The incorporation of a submerged detection installation activated by the U-boat was envisaged as early as 1938, when the Type VIIC U-boats were being built — the so-called S-Gerät (Sonder-Gerät für aktive Schallortung, or 'Special Equipment for Active Sound Location'). However, work on this 'horizontal sounder', which was designed to measure the distance and direction of objects in water by using the echo process for sound impulses, suffered delays. Not before the beginning of the war was a 'Mobilization Echo-sounding Apparatus' with a two-strip base suitable for U-boats ready for mass production, and in the course of the war it was replaced by an improved SZ-Apparatus (SZ=S-Apparatus for destroyers) with a four-strip base. This equipment worked on 15kHz impulses of 20m/sec length. The output of the transmitter amounted to 5kw. Again, the detection ranges were strongly influenced by water conditions, and varied between 5 and 10km in the case of large objects (when proceeding slowly while submerged). However, this equipment was very seldom used by U-boats because it was essential for bearings to be taken continuously in order to determine an opponent's exact position. Allied detection devices could pick up these impulses at a far greater range than U-boat noise, which meant that the U-boat revealed her position before she had located the enemy.

Subsequently, more space was needed for radar equipment, so the echo-sounding devices were removed from U-boats because installations for the more essential surface operations were given priority. Later, an improved echo-set, with the designation SU-Apparatus (SU=S-Apparatus for U-boats), 'Nibelung', was projected for the enlarged Type VIIC/42 (page 157): this could pinpoint the exact position and approximate speed of a detected

object, using only a small number of impulses, which made it almost impossible for an opponent to take a bearing on it.

When emphasis changed to the new U-boats, whose travel was predominantly underwater, the echo-ranging gear became increasingly important as a navigational aid and as an aiming device, especially for planned 'direction-finding deep-shooting'. In the Type XXI boats, the forward edge of the bridge provided a very favourable position for the swivelling base with its 2 x 4 magneto-strictive oscillators. These provided a bearing of from 0° to ± 100°. The directional accuracy of ± 0.5° was good. In the Walter Type XXVI boats an even better position was found. The swivel-base was situated beneath a streamlined hood on the forward section of the boat, making it possible to take bearings in almost all directions (except for a segment aft). Of course, the new SU-Apparatus was not available until the end of 1944, when a small number were fitted immediately in some Type XXI U-boats (page 209). Tests of the new installations were made by Test Group 'Sultan' and, at the end of January 1945, an exercise using 13 ships in convoy was carried out in the waters around Bornholm. The following tactics were employed: initially, group listening apparatus was used, and the target was detected as accurately as possible at long range. When the sound was being received sufficiently loudly, the echo-ranging installation was switched to 'listen' and the swivelling base was brought into the correct direction as indicated by the GHG. When reception had increased in strength to the point when propeller noise could be detected on the cathode-ray tube, the volume was turned down and an impulse was transmitted by depressing a key. Given favourable circumstances, only three impulses were needed to determine the distance, course and approximate speed of an opponent.

To translate measurements on the echo-ranging apparatus into torpedo firing calculations, coupling equipment was being developed. By the addition of 'Sarotti' to the echo-sounding gear, panoramic presentations on a picture-tube (i.e., the simultaneous presentation of several objects on the screen) would be possible. This would mean that in the future, without using a periscope, the U-boat would have at all times an exact view of what was taking place on the surface. However, the war ended before this could be brought to fruition.

Up to about the end of 1942, the Supreme Naval Command regarded the British Asdic device as the most dangerous anti-submarine weapon, and the development of protection against acoustic detection was therefore pursued by the German Navy with corresponding vigour. It concentrated on two processes, 'Alberich' and 'Bold'. 'Alberich' was a 4mm-thick layer of rubber, which muffled echo reflections in the range of 10—18kHz up to approximately 15 per cent, but not at all diving depths. Practical evaluation was impeded because it was difficult to make comparative tests at sea. Exact location of a boat was not determined by the rubber covering alone, but the air content, temperature and salt content of the sea water all had to be taken into account. The first tests with a hull of synthetic rubber coating (Oppanol) followed in the early part of 1940, with the NVK test boat *U11*. In 1941, a larger boat, *U67*, was similarly clad. Tests with this boat were considerably influenced by the fact that the covering did not stick very efficiently to the hull; when parts of the covering came loose, they set up eddies and noises in the current caused by the boat's passage, which had the opposite effect of what was desired. Trials of a similar nature were then made with the former Dutch submarine *O26 (UD4)*, but difficulties were again experienced with the covering material and it seemed that this process could not be used as a general measure. Attention was now directed more strongly at an increase in diving depth as a means of securing improved underwater protection.

Not until the advent of the schnorkel in 1944 (page 19|8), did 'Alberich' take on renewed significance as an operational possibility for use in shallow, off-shore waters. The first operational U-boat to be so equipped was *U480*, and she reported positive results during Channel operations in August 1944. On 11 July 1944, it was decided to cover some of the Type XXIII coastal U-boats. It was hoped that at least two or three of these boats could be treated each month, and at least two per month were to be completed by the end of 1944. However, a suitable hall or hangar where the boats could be dealt with while completely protected from the elements was not available, so the first boat to receive the 'Alberich' treatment, the Type XXIII *U4709*, was not ready until February 1945. Furthermore, the Navy wanted 'Alberich' applied to the Walter Type XXVI medium boats, but delays occurred and the programme was not implemented. The 'Alberich' cladding would have added a total of 5,000-6,000 work hours to the production of each boat.

Another kind of protection system was the releasing of objects designed to deceive the enemy. 'Bold' was a container with positive buoyancy, filled with calcium hydride. With a diameter of 10cm, it could be expelled from a tube similar to that used for torpedoes. It floated in water at a depth of approximately 30m, producing hydrogen bubbles intended to present a false target to Asdic while the endangered U-boat made its escape. This relatively simple equipment was installed in U-boats from 1942 and was considerably successful. Preparations were also being made for a 'Bold 5', which would work in greater depths up to 200m.

Towards the end of the war, two further means of protection were envisaged: 'Sieglinde' and 'Siegmund'. The first of these was a 'noise-deceiving body'; the second, a 'noise-disturbing body'; both were intended to be ejected by the U-boat. 'Sieglinde' emitted the noise of a U-boat proceeding underwater at a speed of approximately 6 knots, and was switched on at the same time as a 'Bold' was released. 'Siegmund' produced a series of detonation-noises designed to block the enemy's listening devices so that, for a short time, the U-boat could proceed at top speed without being detected. The 'Siegmund' installation was planned initially as a series-production item for Type XXVI U-boats.

PROJECTS AND DEVELOPMENTS, 1939—43

In a letter to the Supreme Naval Command on 8 September 1939, Dönitz made the following suggestions regarding U-boat types.

'1. Continuation of building Types VIIC and IX, in the ratio suggested by the Commander-in-Chief, U-Boat's Secret Memorandum 172 dated 1 September 1939.

'2. No construction of small U-boats, as their use is basically restricted to home waters, and no operational application in the Baltic seems likely in the foreseeable future, and their use in the North Sea seems doubtful. The latter function could, however, be undertaken by boats of Type VIIC. This type could also be used for Atlantic duties (Azores).

'3. Continuation of building the Type XB boats that have been placed in contract. The prospects of minelaying in more remote waters are very rewarding (Capetown, Simonstown, Colombo, Singapore). (For the last two ports, see No. 6. re U-boat tankers.)

'4. Continuation of building Type XI. The main value of this type lies in applying strategic pressure in very remote territories. The opportunities of using its artillery are rather doubtful. The Flag Officer, U-Boats, suggests reducing the artillery armament to provide a high-speed boat with a very large radius of action. This boat could then be used in the Atlantic together with torpedo-carriers. (It could be used to locate convoys near their departure point, America, being better adapted for tracking and maintaining contact than a slower boat, and could lead waiting torpedo U-boats to convoys on the eastern side of the Atlantic.) It could also be used as a Fleet U-boat. It is suggested it be given the designation 'Long-Range U-boat'.

'5. This would make superfluous the construction of the Type XII Fleet U-boat, which has been proposed earlier. In any case, it is doubtful if Type XII could reach the required specifications of speed and range. Type XI would seem to be better adapted for fulfilling these aims.

'6. Construction of 3 submarine tankers to carry fuel and supplies; these to be of approximately 2,000 tons — low-speed boats, but equipped with all necessary means for effective transferring of fuels and supplies to U-boats.

'Summary: The following list of U-boats consequently represents those that we feel are worthy of construction.

(a). Torpedo-carriers; boats of Type VIIC and IX.

(b). Long-range minelaying boats of Type XB.

(c). Large, high-speed, long-range boats.

(d). U-boat tankers.'

These demands by Dönitz were considerably to influence future type development.

Type VIID

At the beginning of the war, the torpedo anchormine TMA was still not ready for operational use.

Above: A Type VIID at GW, 1941/42. **Below:** *U216* (Type VIID) being launched on 23 October 1941.

The 4 large Type XB minelayers, which carried SMA mines, had been designed specially for minelaying in distant seas, but there was a lack of medium-sized operational boats that could also carry SMA mines for use off the coasts of Britain and France. As the Type VIIB/C had shown itself to be especially suitable for minelaying in coastal waters, the idea was born of developing the VIIC boat as an SMA minelayer. By incorporating an additional pressure-hull section between the NCO's compartment and the pressure-tight bulkhead that formed the control room's aftermost frame, sufficient space was made for the fitting of five vertical mine shafts to contain fifteen SMA mines; the shafts ended in a narrow superstructure projecting above the deck abaft the conning tower. This section lengthened the boat by 9.8m, and the saddle tanks were correspondingly lengthened, which allowed the inclusion of an additional compensating tank, an additional diving tank and an additional diving bunker. The enlargement of the fuel supply was an unlooked-for bonus, which increased considerably the operational possibilities of the boat.

The mine shafts were covered at the top by Venetian-blind-type sheeting, slatted or pierced, to provide effective ventilation; at the bottom they were open. The use of the VIIC drive installation affected speed very little. On 16 February 1940, 6 boats of this type, designated Type VIID, were placed in contract with GW; the laying-down of the first boat, *U213*, followed on 1 October 1940.

Type VIID

Glossary: Wasserdichte Hecht, Watertight stern; Tauchzelle, ballast tank (water); Trimmzelle hinten, after trimming tank; Torpedozelle, torpedo tank; E.-Maschinenraum, electric motor room; Diesel Motorenraum, diesel engine room; Küche, galley; Unteroffizier-Raum, NCOs' quarters; Akku-Raum, accumulator room; Treibölbunker, fuel-oil bunker; Zentrale, control room; Munitionskammer, ammunition compartment; Kettenkasten, chain cover; Wasserdichte Back, watertight forecastle; Durchfluteter Raum, flooding compartment; Mitte Torpedo Rohr, middle torpedo tube; Schuss, section; Schmutzwasser, bilge water; Waschwasser, fresh water; Minenzelle, mine compartment; Knick, break; Proviant Raum, stores; Bugtorpedo-Raum, bow torpedo room; Mündungsklappen-vorn, forward opening flaps; Tiefenruder, hydroplane; Kmdt. Raum, commander's quarters; Horch-Raum, listening room; Zentrale, control room; Brüche, bridge; Druckkörperachse, pressure hull axis; Hauptachse, main axis; Turm, conning tower; Bb. port; Stb. starboard; Kielsohle, keel bottom.

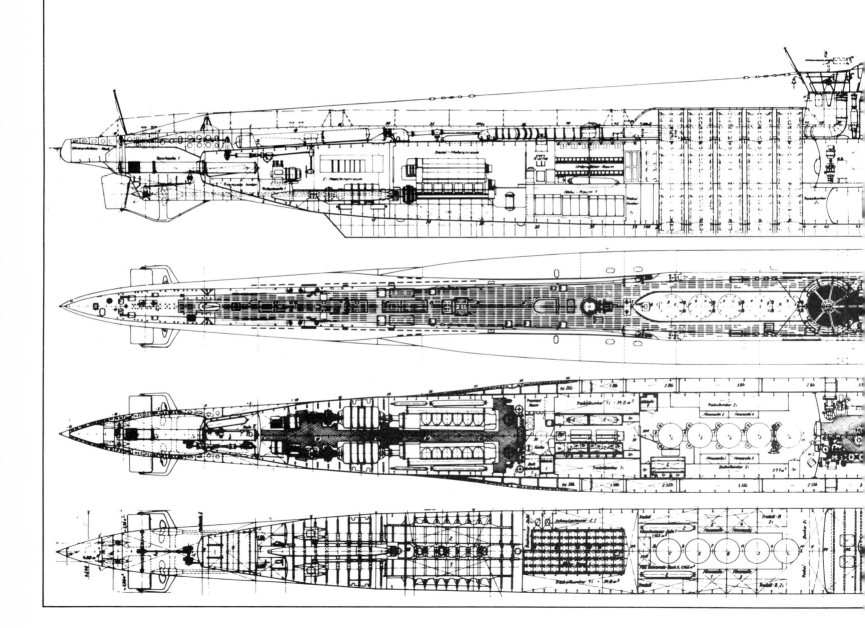

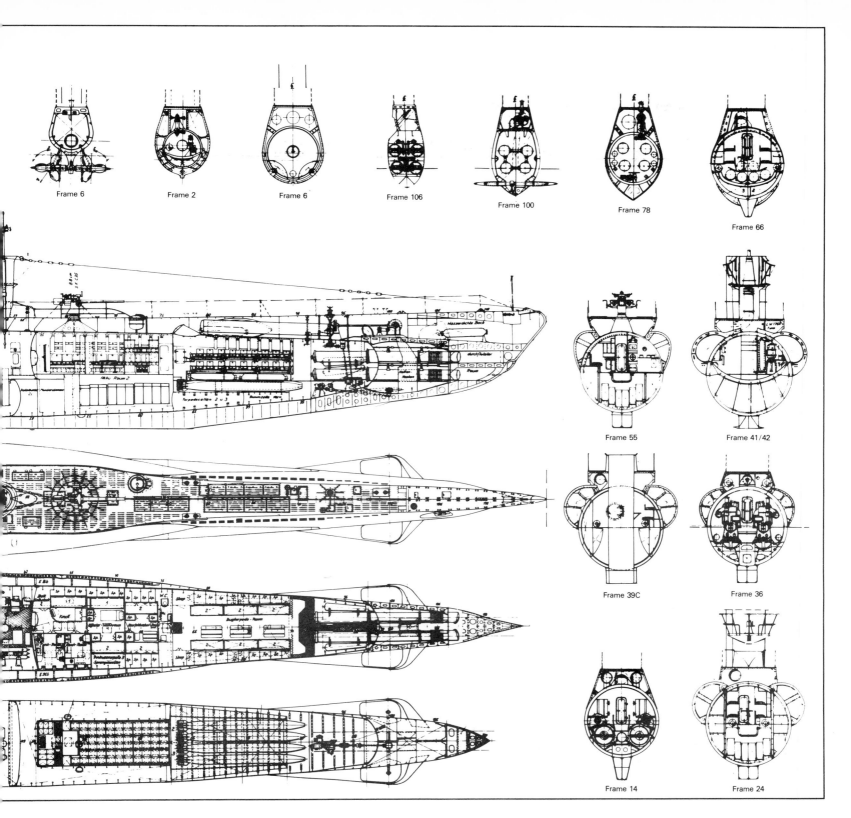

Frame 6

Frame 2

Frame 6

Frame 106

Frame 100

Frame 78

Frame 66

Frame 55

Frame 41/42

Frame 39C

Frame 36

Frame 14

Frame 24

Types IXD₁ and IXD₂

The suggestion by Dönitz concerning the further building of Type XI as a long-range and Fleet U-boat, but minus the characteristic, heavy artillery armament, would certainly have been too costly and would have overloaded the already-stretched capacity of the yards. A completely new working-out of the design based on Type XII would certainly have delayed considerably the commencement of construction of such U-boats. Ideally, the long-range boats should be built as cheaply and as quickly as possible, so an attempt was made to enlarge Type IXC into a U-boat with a higher surface speed and an increased range. In order that the displacement should not become too large, these requirements were sought not in a single boat, but in different projects, which would differ only in the disposition of the engine compartment. Type IXD₁ would be given a large installation of six 1,500hp motor torpedo-boat diesels for a high surface speed (20.8 knots); Type IXD₂ would receive the normal Type IX propulsion unit, but with a diesel-electric addition for increased range. The pressure hull had the same strength and the same diameter as Type IX. Apart from the diesel compartment, the fittings corresponded approximately to those of Type IX, but the living quarters and stowage space were considerably enlarged to meet the requirement for greater endurance. The outer hull, however, was rather wider and higher, and now enclosed the whole pressure hull.

At the bow, the S-curve of Type IX was avoided by using longer torpedo tube flaps, and this lessened the formation of spray at the bow. The stern was now drawn-out in a very slim profile, and the torpedo tubes now were more effective at the otherwise unencumbered stern. In the upper speed ranges, the longer boat had — from 18 knots — more favourable C_w — values, so that even in Type IXD₂, a higher maximum speed was attained than in Type IX. The first 4 boats of Type IXD (3 of Type IXD₂ and 1 of IXD₁) were contracted to AG Weser on 28 May 1940, being intended as a replacement for the suspended U-cruisers of Type IX.

While Type IXD₂ was quite successful with the conventional engine installation, the heavy diesel concentration with fresh water cooling in Type IXD₁ caused such serious problems during trials

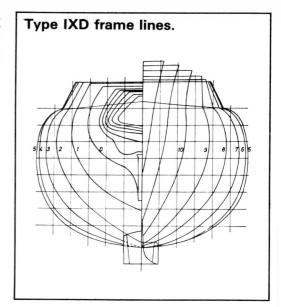

Type IXD frame lines.

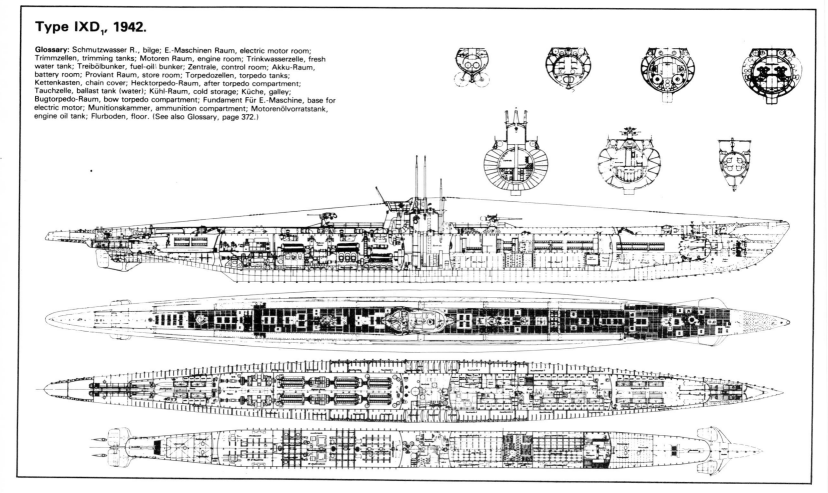

Type IXD₁, 1942.

Glossary: Schmutzwasser R., bilge; E.-Maschinen Raum, electric motor room; Trimmzellen, trimming tanks; Motoren Raum, engine room; Trinkwasserzelle, fresh water tank; Treibölbunker, fuel-oil bunker; Zentrale, control room; Akku-Raum, battery room; Proviant Raum, store room; Torpedozellen, torpedo tanks; Kettenkasten, chain cover; Hecktorpedo-Raum, after torpedo compartment; Tauchzelle, ballast tank (water); Kühl-Raum, cold storage; Küche, galley; Bugtorpedo-Raum, bow torpedo compartment; Fundament Für E.-Maschine, base for electric motor; Munitionskammer, ammunition compartment; Motorenölvorratstank, engine oil tank; Flurboden, floor. (See also Glossary, page 372.)

and on her sole operational voyage — strong build-up of exhaust smoke, leakages in the cooling-water installation, lack of space and high temperatures in the engine compartment, leaking exhaust outlets, etc. — that this installation was removed.

Type XIII

At the beginning of the war, designs were also prepared for a larger coastal U-boat for North Sea operations, with similar tasks in mind as had been carried out by the UF type of the First World War. It was to have a displacement of 400 tons, a heavier armament (4 bow torpedo tubes), an increased surface speed (approximately 15 knots) and a greater range than Type II. This project, designated Type XIII, probably owed its origination to the Flag Officer, U-Boat's refusal to continue construction of the small Type II boats of the Mobilization Programme, but it did not get further than the outline design stage.

Types XIV—XVI

In his letter to Naval Headquarters, Dönitz had requested the construction of 3 submarine tankers for fuelling and supplying offensive U-boats. This request prompted 'K' Office to develop Type XIV. The exterior shape was taken from that of the long-range IXD, which was being designed at the same time, but the ratios of length:beam and length:draught were considerably reduced (by approximately 60 per cent) so that the proposed size would provide sufficient storage capacity for an additional 432 tons of fuel-oil, approximately 45 tons of provisions and four torpedoes, plus a sufficiently wide and dry upper deck for the easy transfer of supplies at sea.

The first towing tests of the Type XIV 'shape' followed as early as February 1940. The very bad c_e values in the Froude-Numbers range, 0.26—0.34 $\triangleq$ 13—16 knots, of the Supreme Naval Command's design were considerably improved by a greater sharpening of the bow lines in the modified HSVA (Hamburg Shipbuilding Test Institute) Model 2119. On the basis of these findings, the original official design was reworked and, on 15 April 1940, had the following main specifications.

Length overall:	67.10m.
Maximum beam:	9.3m.
Mean draught (loaded):	6.52m.
Pressure-hull diameter:	4.9m.

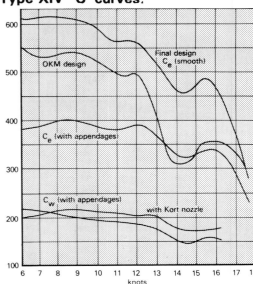

Type XIV 'C' curves.

Type IXD₂, 1943.

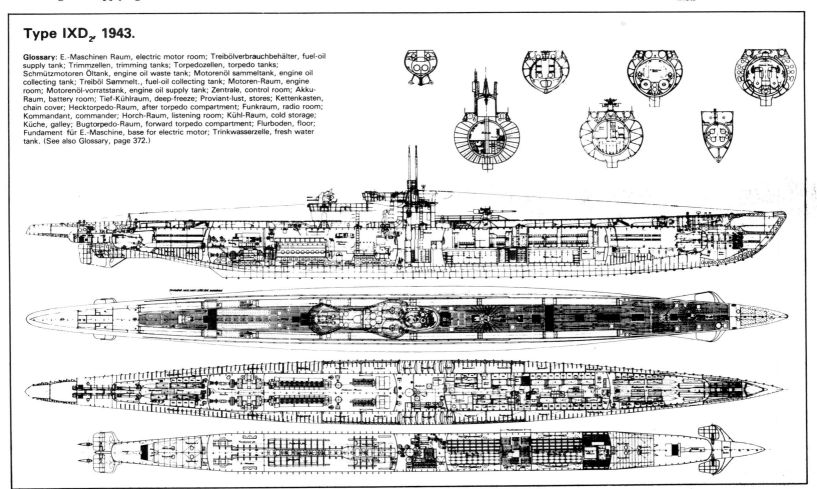

Glossary: E.-Maschinen Raum, electric motor room; Treibölverbrauchbehälter, fuel-oil supply tank; Trimmzellen, trimming tanks; Torpedozellen, torpedo tanks; Schmützmotoren Öltank, engine oil waste tank; Motorenöl sammeltank, engine oil collecting tank; Treiböl Sammelt., fuel-oil collecting tank; Motoren-Raum, engine room; Motorenöl-vorratstank, engine oil supply tank; Zentrale, control room; Akku-Raum, battery room; Tief-Kühlraum, deep-freeze; Proviant-lust, stores; Kettenkasten, chain cover; Hecktorpedo-Raum, after torpedo compartment; Funkraum, radio room; Kommandant, commander; Horch-Raum, listening room; Kühl-Raum, cold storage; Küche, galley; Bugtorpedo-Raum, forward torpedo compartment; Flurboden, floor; Fundament für E.-Maschine, base for electric motor; Trinkwasserzelle, fresh water tank. (See also Glossary, page 372.)

Type XIV frame lines.

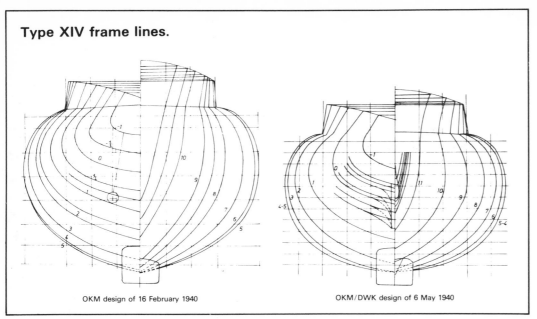

OKM design of 16 February 1940   OKM/DWK design of 6 May 1940

Displacement surfaced (loaded):	1,670 tons.
Displacement submerged:	1,922 tons.
Hull displacement:	2,300 tons.
Engine installation:	as in Type VIIC.
Battery:	as in Type XII (2 × 62 Z. 28 MAL 1000).
Speed surfaced:	14.5—15 knots.
Range surfaced:	10,000 nautical miles at 10 knots.
Speed submerged:	6 knots.
Range submerged:	76 nautical miles at 3 knots.
Crew:	51.

In order to effect a further improvement in the propulsion, it was proposed that Kort nozzles (conical shrouds fitted around the propellers) be fitted, but this was not carried out.

The relatively light-weight cargo of fuel made possible something that had been proposed for Type XI, the use of stronger sheet metal for the pressure hull, to a maximum of 21.5mm (as opposed to 18.5mm in Types VII and IX), which meant a greater margin of safety from depth-charges for this U-boat, which did not have torpedo armament. The surface armament was restricted to a reasonably heavy anti-aircraft defence consisting of two 3.7cm quick-firing C/30U guns forward and aft of the bridge and a 2cm C/30 machine-gun on the bridge. In addition to the propulsion unit, various features were borrowed from the series production of Type VIIC, including hatch closures, pumps, anchor winch, etc. The conning tower derived from that of Type IX. This design, therefore, eased itself, without great difficulty, into the current U-boat construction programme. The design work was given to DWK, who received a contract on 14 May 1940 for 4 U-tankers of this type, and the first boat, *U459*, was laid down on 23 November 1940.

Type XIV.

Key: B, bunker; BT, ballast tank; C, compensating tank; F, fuel-oil bunker; N/B, negative buoyancy tank.

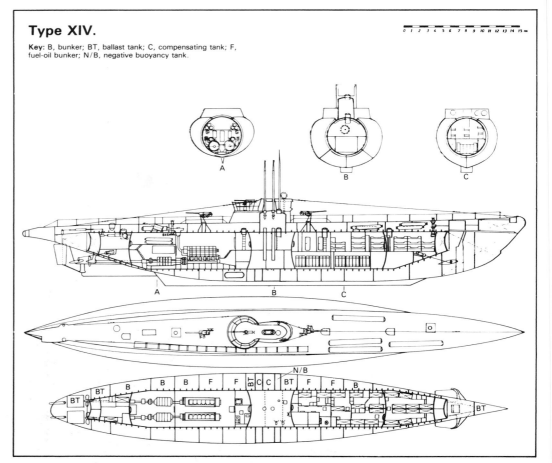

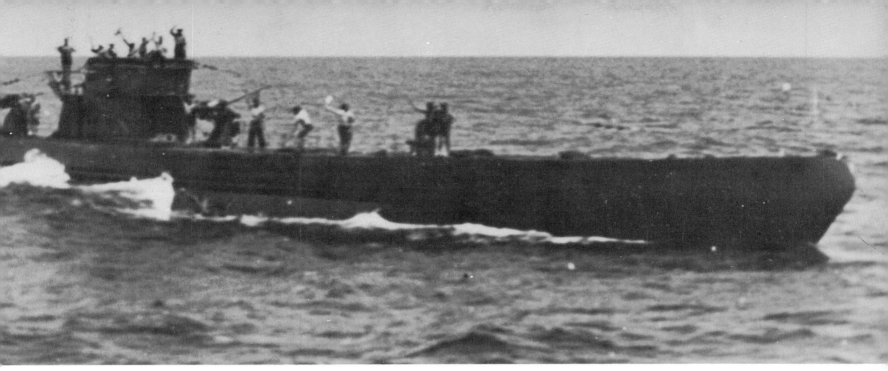

Above and below: Type XIV supply boats. The top photograph shows *U459* on operations in mid-Atlantic.

After the First World War, Germany had no foreign bases and, when consideration was being given to the planning and building-up of a new U-boat fleet, requests were made for large supply and workshop U-boats, which would not only increase considerably the radius of operational U-boats by supplying fuel-oil, provisions and ammunition, but would be able to undertake small repairs and give technical assistance. It was considered that such mobile and submersible U-boat bases should be capable of remaining at sea for at least three months. In 1939, Fürbringer reiterated this suggestion as he feared that the German Fleet might find itself cut off in the 'wet triangle' (the German Bight). After hostilities had commenced, together with Type XIV, large workshop U-boats on these lines were projected with the ability to carry out simple technical repair and overhaul tasks for operational U-boats in calm seas. Two projects were discussed concerning a

Below: The commissioning ceremony for *U1171* (Type VIIC/41) at Danziger Werft on 22 March 1944. **Far right:** *U995* (Type VIIC/41) being set up as a U-boat memorial at Laboe on 13 March 1972.

2,500-ton (Type XV) and a 5,000-ton (Type XVI) boat, the pressure hulls for both of which should be considerably wider to accommodate workshop machinery and spare parts. To achieve this, a cross-section of a horizontal three-cycle shape was suggested, after the fashion of Flamm's U-cruiser projects. As with Type XIV, constructional components were wherever possible to be drawn from those in current use, so it was intended that the propulsion unit of the Type VIIC be installed in these boats, although this would have provided inadequate speeds for such large and complex vessels. Because of their size, neither project found much favour, and both were rejected by Dönitz. With the fall of Norway and France, and the consequent acquisition of well-situated U-boat bases on the Atlantic seaboard, the need for them was no longer so pressing.

Developments based on Type VIIC: C/41, C/42 and C/43

On 27 February 1942, at the request of 1. SKL/Ib Supreme Naval Command (Planning), the Chief Engineer of *U157*, Oberleutnant (Eng.) Kiesewalter,

compiled a memorandum on 'Technical Development of the U-boat in the Light of War Operations'. The main theme was his concern that U-boats available at that time would soon no longer measure up to the requirements of the U-boat campaign and that, therefore, new developments were necessary, even at the expense of current production. Ideally, these new U-boats should be ready for operations in two years to replace the present Types VIIC and IXC.

The stated demands for the new boats corresponded to the prevailing offensive tactics and operational experiences at that time. No attention was paid to the development of radio high-frequency detection or to aircraft surveillance. As a result, his prime consideration was to increase surface speed to 22 knots, because the boats — especially the VIIC — were too slow for surface attack against convoys. As a quick means of improving this problem, he suggested the installation of a second diesel unit in a lengthened VIIC. Experiences with Type VIID suggested that this could be achieved in one year. However, to cope with the increased surface performance, a jaw

clutch would need to be installed in place of the friction clutch and, because of the considerable discrepancy between high surface revolutions and slow submerged revolutions, a set of gears or variable-pitch propellers would have to be used. Furthermore, the hull shape would need to be modified for the increased surface speed. At the very least, the watertight forecastle should be enlarged, and the external torpedo tube flaps of the Type IX should be changed because their streamlining left much to be desired. As a further means of bringing about an increase in performance, especially in Type IXC, consideration should be given to supercharging the MAN engines.

The next requirement concerned an increase in the diving depth. On this point Kiesewalter stated: 'If we cannot actually succeed in concealing U-boats from detection by ultrasonics, then only two possibilities remain: either one dives to 300 metres and waits until depth-charging is over, or one must be equipped with an attacking weapon such as an acoustic torpedo with which to destroy the pursuer. Something on these lines must be developed!' '. . . Efforts must be made to enable a boat to dive to 300 metres. At that depth, the effect of depth-charges is greatly restricted and, furthermore, the time it takes for depth-charges to descend to such a depth enables a boat to take avoiding action.'

Concerning armament, he stated:

'The torpedo armament is sufficient in terms of numbers. There is no need to lay special emphasis on a more reliable, faster and deadly torpedo which could reach 50 knots, because this has been brought up often enough. For the medium Type VII boat operating in the North Atlantic, gun armament is not necessary apart from anti-aircraft armament on the bridge. The tactical and weather conditions in this region allow the use of artillery only very seldom.'

(U157 was sunk by depth-charges in the Gulf of Mexico on 13 June 1942, with the loss of all hands, including Kiesewalter.)

In an opinion expressed by the U-Boat Department (Amtsgruppe Ubootwesen SKL-U) on 5 May 1942, it was established that certain important suggestions made by Kiesewalter were already in development or test stages, but that it 'was completely out of the question to complete the planning and construction of a new U-boat type in two years to the extent that series-production could commence at the end of this time'. After considering the arguments, the Supreme Naval Command came down firmly on the side of continued further development of the current U-boat types, especially of the successful Type VIIC, which meant an avoidance of risks in a completely new development programme and avoidance of impairing current production. Long-term development was seen in terms of the Walter U-boat.

The first further development of Type VIIC manifested itself in Design VIIC/41. In this, the question had been posed: how far can one develop Type VIIC in respect of increased diving depth without disturbing current production lines? The main problem was one of weight. In the first instance, the weight requirement was overestimated by the KIU. A more thorough calculation then showed that an increase in diving depth of 20 per cent was possible without stability

being affected too greatly. Subsequent calculations concerning the weight of the engine installation, simplification of the electrical installation and of weight-saving in other ways, showed it possible for 11.5 tons to be saved; this meant that the strengthened pressure hull could increase by approximately 10 tons without any significant reduction in the effective ballast. The maximum thickness of pressure-hull plates would now amount to 21mm compared to the present 18.5mm. The constructional diving depth now rose from 100m to 120m, the test diving depth (60 per cent of the destruction diving depth) from 150m to 180m, and calculated destruction depth from 250m to 300m.

This altered constructional plan was designated Type VIIC/41, because the final decision on it had been made in the year 1941, and more complete working-out of details was then undertaken. The concept, however, was an older one. The first contracts for this new type were placed on 14 October 1941, with the first boats being delivered in August 1943. The boats were given the enlarged forecastle ('Atlantic Stem') demanded by Kiesewalter, which increased the length of Type VIIC by 13cm.

Following the unsatisfactory state of affairs with measuring the effectiveness of the 'Alberich' boat, *U67*, in the autumn of 1941, Chief Naval Construction Adviser Aschmoneit suggested to Ministerial Counsellor Dr. Schürer (Head of KIU) to abandon further efforts with this Asdic-avoidance device and press on with the doubling of the diving depth for Type VIIC, something which was also desired by the Chief of Naval War Staff; this would give a threefold benefit:

1. Shielding from Asdic by a considerable depth of water.
2. Obliging the enemy to use a greater number of depth-charges.
3. Making the pressure hull more resistant to rupture.

It was recognized that echo-sounding gear worked much less well with any increase in depth. Early in the war, experience had also shown that a slow U-boat could avoid detection by diving deeper. U-boats had repeatedly escaped by sinking to the destruction diving depth at 200m. The required doubling of the diving depth, however, implied so great an extra weight that, without enlarging the boat, compensation could not be achieved. Designs were therefore prepared for constructional depth to be 200m, test-diving depth 300m and calculated destruction diving depth 500m; the proposed construction resulting from these demands was given the designation VIIC/42. The metal-rolling facilities at the yards and at most of the sub-contractors permitted a maximum pressure-hull skin thickness of only 28mm to be worked, which meant that normal U-boat steel St 52 KM could not be used for doubling the diving depth. Specially tempered, armour-plated Krupp steel CM 351 was therefore envisaged for the pressure-tight components. CM 351 contained 0.17 per cent C, 0.3

per cent Si, 1.23 per cent Mn, 0.1 per cent V, 0.13 per cent Cr and had a strength of 55–70kg/mm², a yield point of 45kg/mm², a 60 per cent reduction of area and an expansion of 28 per cent. The provision of this significantly stronger pressure-hull skin increased the weight of a Type VIIC boat pressure hull by 68.3 tons to 154.3 tons. This was to be compensated by increasing the pressure-hull diameter from 4.70m to 4.90m, later to 5m.

In order to realize the design as quickly as possible, Chief Naval Construction Adviser Aschmoneit urged that, apart from essential modifications, as little as possible of Type VIIC be changed. In the course of time, however, more and more demands were made on the Type VIIC/42, and it was accepted that a speedy realization of the basic requirements was no longer possible. As

Christoph Aschmoneit.

convoy operations were now dispersed over a wider area, and the speed of convoys had increased, the VIIC boats increasingly required the surface performance of the larger Type IXC. It was hoped that the proven six-cylinder MAN diesel engines M6V40/46, with incorporation of effective supercharging would give the required high performance. The six-cylinder MAN engines were already used in Type VII U-boats and, without charging, had a performance of 1,050hp at 470rpm and, with simple charging, 1,400hp at 490rpm. High-charging would increase these values to 2,200hp at 530rpm. The installation of the various auxiliary engines required for this uprated performance meant that the length of the diesel compartment had to be increased by 80cm. The final design for Type VIIC/42 increased its length by 1.54cm over Type VIIC. After towing tank tests

had been made, a maximum surface speed of 18.6 knots was calculated (compared to 17 knots in Type VIIC).

The large surface range of 12,600 nautical miles at 10 knots (50 per cent more than that of Type VIIC) was made possible by larger saddle tanks and interior bunkers, which, together with the greater diameter, increased the beam to 6.85m. The Supreme Naval Command imposed more conditions and expressed further wishes concerning the installation of other equipment, only partly dictated by the increased diving depth and the better surface performance. In particular, the following points were mentioned to the VIIC Work Committee at GW, which had taken over the design work in the summer of 1942:

1. A strong and common base for diesel engines and electric motors.
2. Hydraulic clutch between diesel engines and electric motors.
3. Sufficient space to be provided for the interior exhaust-gas installation and the supercharger.
4. The shaft must rotate smoothly in the stern sleeve, even at considerable water pressures.
5. Attention to be paid to increased water pressure in the thrust bearings.
6. As compared to Type VIIC, the shaft-sleeve to be extended far enough outside for the distance of the propeller circle from deadwood to be 200mm instead of 170mm.
7. Two Junkers air compressors and an electric compressor.
8. Bilge-pumps. Three centrifugal pumps envisaged, all of the same size, made by Amag-Hilpert (working pressure 30 atmospheres overload at 15m³ per hour required performance); to be installed in the bow and stern compartments and in the control room.
9. Trimming, preferably by an IMO spindle pump or by compressed air (double trimming tanks!).
10. Increase of compressed-air supply over that in Type VIIC.
11. Compartment ventilation to be that of the Dräger (Lübeck) system, with compartment-ventilators and turbo-ventilators of the quietest possible type. Compartment heating by exhaust gas and electrical heating; all this to be made possible by recirculation of the compartment air-cooling and drying installation ('thermal pump').
12. Naszogen installation with Naszogen (Oxygen) cartridges made by IG-Farben.
13. Cooling installation with three similar BBC cold air compressors for deep freezer, refrigerator, potato storage compartment and compartment air-drying installation.
14. An autogenous welding unit to be installed.
15. Main periscope and night navigation periscope in the conning tower (with no periscope in the control room!).
16. Simplification of the electrical network, by dispensing with three transformers and reducing the constant-voltage network.

The wish was also stated for an arrangement whereby the main switch panels could be manned from the front instead of from the central passage. This would offer a number of advantages in operating and servicing as well as making for a

Type VIIC/42 frame lines.

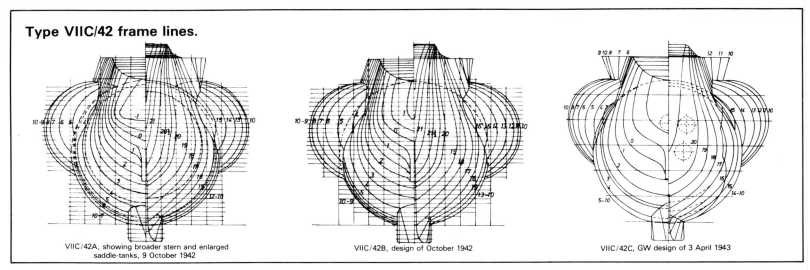

VIIC/42A, showing broader stern and enlarged
saddle-tanks, 9 October 1942

VIIC/42B, design of October 1942

VIIC/42C, GW design of 3 April 1943

Type VIIC/42 structural layout, 2 April 1943.

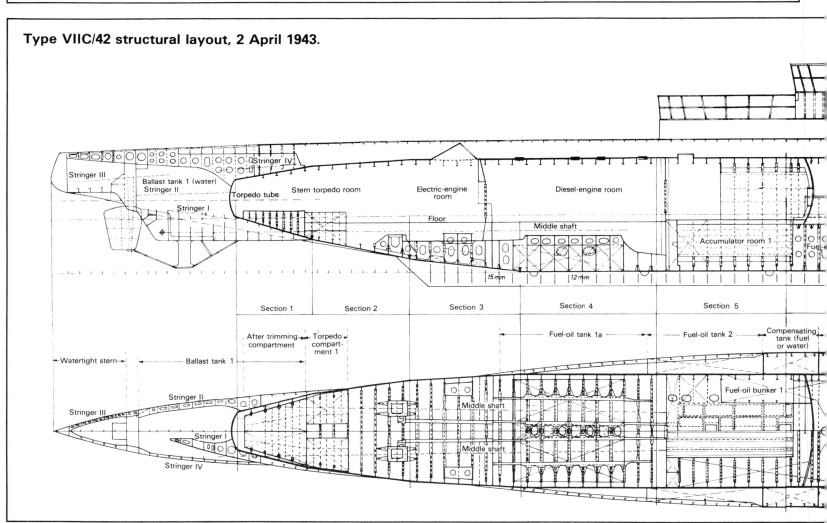

more compact layout, but the idea was not employed until AEG installed their cam-operated switchgear in the Walter U-boats. In their system, the switch elements were activated by cams and could be programmed to perform specific functions. Developments along these lines were carried on by AEG and BBC as prototype panels for Type VIIC/42. In other respects, compartment division and fittings corresponded to those in the Type VIIC boats.

In June 1942, the first drawings were available from GW for the hull shape of Type VIIC/42: length 68.73m, beam 6.46m, pressure-hull diameter 4.9m. On 16 July 1942, GW were given an initial contract for 12 boats (*U1069–U1080*), the first boat to be delivered on 1 August 1944. The large B&V yard was to deliver its first boat (*U1423*) on 1 November. However, at this time, the boat's ultimate dimensions had not been settled because of the many additional requirements that had been called for. Two counter-projects (VIIC/42A and VIIC/42B) were being worked on by the Supreme

Naval Command and these had larger dimensions. On 15 August 1942, they declared that Design VIIC/42B with a length of 73.4m and a beam of 6.92m, would be more appropriate, and B&V made the point that the building sites used hitherto for VIIC would be too narrow for these boats. On 10 November 1942, the Main Committee for Ship-building Construction decided in favour of Type VIIC/42A, with a length of 68.73m and a beam of 6.7m. This led to the final design VIIC/42 early in 1943. Naturally, the changes delayed completion of the drawings. GW was now to deliver the first boat on 29 August 1944, and B&V would deliver their first boat three months later. A further series of five VIIC/41 (*U1435–U1439*) was to be added.

The discussion on 10 November 1942 had taken account of fabrication problems. It had been intended to put as much work as possible to outside firms so that the yards, suffering from acute labour shortage, might be spared some part of the burden; however, Counsellor of State Blohm made the point that one should not lose sight of transport

problems and the increase in work hours at these other firms. The pressure hull of Type VIIC/42 was to be assembled from ten sections, and it was thought advisable that one efficient delivery body be responsible at any one time for each section; however, this was regarded as inadequate for the 13 proposed yards, if one took into account the transport routes. It was especially emphasized that the risky sea transport of sections be avoided if possible.

A subsequent discussion on 20 January 1943, at Krupp AG of Essen, established that Krupp could produce a maximum of 2,150 tons of tempered CM 351 steel per month — sufficient for only 10 boats. As the timetable for the series production called for a monthly total of 21 boats, either other rolling mills must produce appropriate tempered steels (and possibly French armour-plate firms could be used for this), or the remaining boats would have to be built from ordinary 52 KM steel with correspondingly reduced strength. As the establishment of new installations to produce tempered steel could

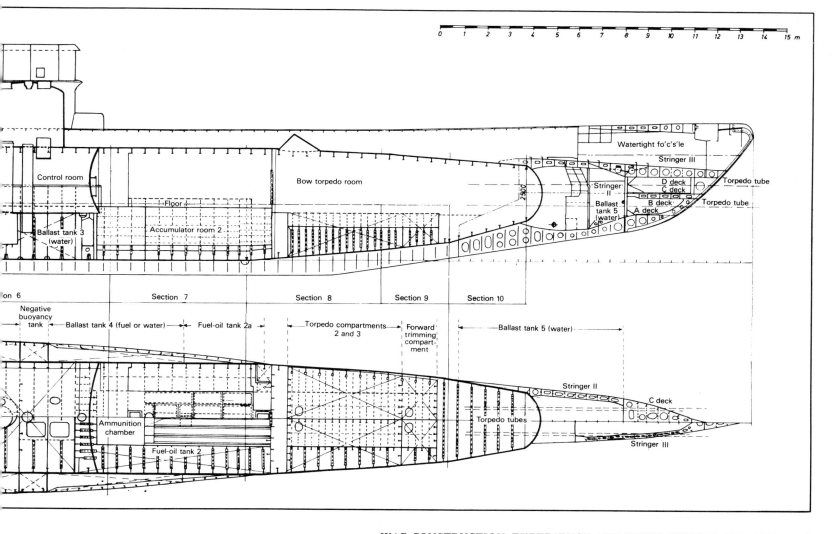

not be achieved quickly, particularly in view of the shortage of labour, Director Cords, the head of the VIIC Work Committee, suggested on 26 January 1943 that the 10 boats that could be constructed from CM 351 be distributed between GW, B&V, Bremer Vulkan, KMW Wilhelmshaven and Kiel (Howaldt), while the other yards should build their boats from 52 KM steel. It was further suggested that GW use 52 KM steel to start with, as Krupp would not achieve full production before October 1943.

On 22 February 1943, the first large allocation of contracts for Type VIIC/42, totalling 42 boats, was distributed among six yards. On 4 March 1943, therefore, appropriate quotas were allocated to the steel firms. Notes of authority for the iron were to be prepared twelve months prior to keel-laying, as between four and six months were needed for production and delivery of materials, one month for

for Type VIIC to 30 weeks, it was thought possible to deliver a yearly total of 66 boats, i.e., one boat every 5½ days instead of the current 1 boat every 7 days. The intended subcontractors for pressure hulls and outer-hull construction are shown in Table 32.

In the meantime, 'K' Office, in response to operational demands for a U-boat with the greatest possible number of torpedo tubes ready to fire at all times, had projected a version of the Type VIIC/42 with six bow torpedo tubes and two stern tubes, but with otherwise identical dimensions, and this was designated VIIC/43. During the course of 1942, it had become increasingly difficult for U-boats to reposition themselves suitably after the first attack, and it seemed essential that, when a U-boat found itself in a favourable position, as many torpedoes as possible should be fired. Obviously, in the long term, a large number of tubes would be

but to complete towing tank tests with this project.

On 17 April 1943, a further contract was placed with all of the 13 yards chosen for the building of Type VIIC/42; in all, 174 boats were ordered, with B&V receiving the largest allocation of 24 boats. On 29 May 1943, building notes were sent from Supreme Naval Command to the yards. Detailed design work now proceeded apace, but various requests for changes continued to delay completion. On 8 June 1943, for example, 50 per cent of the completed engine-floor drawings were scrapped and had to be redrawn. By 14 July 1943, approximately 80 per cent of the constructional work had been decided upon, but in the meantime, the operational conditions which had demanded a boat of this type had changed significantly.

However, after the Supreme Commander-in-Chief of the Navy had decided in favour of large series production of the new Type XXI (see page 208),

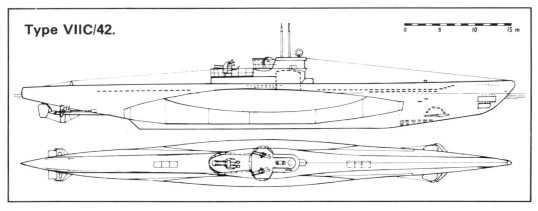

Type VIIC/42.

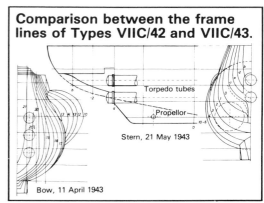

Comparison between the frame lines of Types VIIC/42 and VIIC/43.

Torpedo tubes

Propellor

Stern, 21 May 1943

Bow, 11 April 1943

bending of metal and spars, three months for construction of sections and one month for transport. Sections should be ready at the yards one month before assembly. However, during the initial phases of production it was acknowledged that the sections due to arrive at the yards between February and April 1944 would require a period of up to 15 months.

At B&V, 38 sites were planned on the building slips for the series production of Type VIIC/42. By shortening the slip time from the current 38 weeks

preferred to a good supply of torpedoes. On 3 April 1943, Director Cords suggested that, in order to avoid a second type change, an immediate change to the new Type VIIC/43 be made at the expense of further VIIC/41 boats. But constructional details for C/43 had not yet been formulated, and Cord's suggestion would inevitably have delayed the building of the urgently required deep-diving boats, which would have been wholly undesirable at this critical phase of the U-boat campaign. On 11 May 1943, it was resolved not to pursue Type VIIC/43,

General Director Merker, the new head of the Main Committee for Ship Construction, suspended all work on the Type VIIC/42. All contracts were withdrawn on 24 July 1943. Attempts were still being made in October 1943 to save the extensive preliminary work that had been done on VIIC/42, in the hope that work could continue until the Type XXI programme began, with construction from then on being undertaken by those yards not involved in the Type XXI programme (H.C. Stülcken Sohn, Hamburg, and Nordseewerke, Emden). But this was all to no avail, and the cessation of work was final.

By the end of the war, 572 Type VIIC and 87 Type VIIC/41 boats had been delivered. These bore the main brunt of the U-boat campaign and, at first glance, it is difficult to understand why, following the decision to favour the electric U-boat, with its increased submerged performance, no attempts were made to redesign Type VIIC to meet new requirements. Very possibly, even if inessential construction and appendages had been removed, and a more streamlined bridge shape adopted, no significant increase in submerged speed could have been achieved by the rather poor performance of existing electric motors. This opinion is supported by post-war trials carried out by the Norwegian Navy using the former *U926* redesignated KNM *Kya*. Using the reshaped bridge style of the Walter

Table 32. Subcontractors for Type VIIC/42 construction

Pressure-hull section		Length	Max. diameter	Subcontractor
1		3.3m	3.29m	Thyssen, Mülheim
2	Electric motor compartment	4.2m	4.42m	Thyssen, Mülheim
3		4.8m	5m	Carl Spaeter, Hamburg
4	Diesel compartment	5.9m	5m	Carl Spaeter, Hamburg
5	After battery compartment	5.6m	5m	J. Gollnow Sohn, Stettin
6	Control room	9.1m	5m	Dortmunder Union/Krupp, Stahlbau
7	Forward battery compartment	5.9m	5m	Krupp-Druckenmüller, Berlin
8		5.85m	4.33m	Eggers & Co., Hamburg
9	Bow compartment	2.95m	3.757m	Thyssen, Mülheim
10		3.3m	2.5m	Thyssen, Mülheim
Ballast keel				Thyssen, Mülheim
After-ship (length 8m)				Ottenser Eisenwerke AG
Fore-ship (length 9.85m)				Ottenser Eisenwerke AG
Upper deck				Carl Spaeter, Hamburg
Diesel floor				Carl Spaeter, Hamburg
Conning-tower construction				J. J. Sietas and Carl Spaeter

U-boats, instead of the usual VIIC bridge (minus 'wintergarden', the AA platform behind the bridge, and armament), only an insignificant increase in speed (38 revolutions per knot as opposed to 40 revolutions per knot) resulted, but the depth-keeping properties were greatly improved.

A decisive improvement could only be brought about by changing the shape of the outer ship and enlarging the battery capacity and submerged power unit. As early as the summer of 1943, in an 'investigation into the increase in submerged speed of the VIIC/42 boat', suggestions were made concerning the trebling of the submerged power in Type VIIC. Additional battery capacity was to be obtained by removing the surface armament, by a reduction of the four reserve torpedoes and of the interior fuel-oil bunkers. A further proposal was the installation of larger battery cells even at the cost of accessibility. A more difficult problem would have been the provision and installation of appropriate electric motors giving a higher performance. Almost certainly, the entire engine installation would have had to have been changed, and it would have been simpler to have incorporated variable pitch propellers, giving an increased number of revolutions from an increased voltage in the normal electric motors. (Without any change of shape of the outer skin, an increase in the submerged speed to approximately 12 knots was calculated.) In any event, such conversions would have taken up a significant part of yard capacity and, inevitably, would have delayed the Type XXI programme, and this would have been totally unacceptable.

Supply U-boats: Type VIIF

Until the summer of 1941, it had been possible to replenish U-boats operating off Freetown and in the South Atlantic from fleet auxiliaries, but, after the battleship *Bismarck* had been sunk, the British eliminated the auxiliary-ship network that supplied surface commerce raiders. The final attempt at a supply operation by surface ship in the Atlantic ended in November–December 1941, with the loss of the auxiliary cruiser *Atlantis* and the supply vessel *Python*. In the Indian Ocean, on the other hand, supplying by surface vessel was possible until the beginning of 1944.

On 13 September 1941, the first two Type XIV U-tankers left the slipway at DWK. They were subsequently commissioned on 15 November and 24 December 1941, just when their employment had become a matter of urgency because of the failure of surface-ship supplying, and because of the entry of the United States into the war, which necessitated an immediate extension of U-boat operations to the east coast of America. During trials, the boats were difficult to keep on a straight course – which was hardly encouraging in view of their intended rôle – but which could, however, be eased by enlarging the stern deadwood. On the other hand, despite their wide upper deck, depth-keeping was satisfactory.

The first U-tanker, *U459*, sailed at the end of March 1942, under Korvettenkapitän von Wilamowitz-Möllendorf, to a rendezvous south of the Newfoundland Banks. Aboard was Chief Naval Construction Adviser Grim, representing 'K'

Office. The experience gained from this first operation is embodied in a report, here quoted in extract, which set out the problems encountered by supply ships:

'Fuel was supplied in quantities of 20 to 55 cubic metres. Lubricating oil was requested only in one instance, and was supplied in two instances only. Time to supply fuel varied according to weather conditions, the amount and the nautical and technical skills of the boats involved; variation was between 1 hour 35 minutes and 5 hours. . . . Weather conditions varied between wind and sea 1–2 and 4. The higher figures are the limit at which efficient execution of the supply operation is possible. During the replenishment of supplies, a speed of 3–4 knots on electric motors was achieved. Present equipment would not seem to allow any greater speed. . . . In the case of eight boats, mishaps occurred causing greater or lesser delays, through

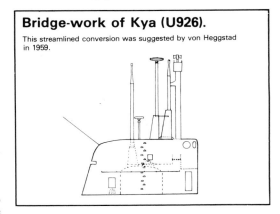

Bridge-work of Kya (U926).

This streamlined conversion was suggested by von Heggstad in 1959.

hose leakages caused by poor manoeuvring, by repeated passing-over of hoses, by inept handling on deck (chafing and tearing because of the lack of chafing mats and such like) or through hooks on the hydroplanes. The apparatus would then have to be hauled in, mostly by me, and the torn length of hose changed and, in one case, it had to be disconnected on the deck of the receiving boat. While the hoses were being passed over, one boat fouled the hoses with its forward hydroplanes, tore the hawser and both hoses away and, when this was cleared, let go the whole equipment. Very much to be regretted was the fact that out of 15 boats, of which 13 came from their bases, only 5 had knowledge of the oil-transferring procedure, although this had been given to the flotillas by the Second-in-Command, U-boats, on 23.3.1942. Although I gave preliminary instruction, it is impossible to state just how many abortive manoeuvres took place and how many technical delays occurred . . . which shows that the instructions were not understood. The operation of taking into tow (necessary for oil-provisioning) did not go at all well with the Type IXC boats. In the case of *U108*, the slip-hooks kept giving; in the case of *U103*, in quite a light swell, the towing-cable parted at the *U459* end. With the VIIC boats it went well on one occasion, badly on others. We proceeded in echelon formation. That made the heavy hawser unnecessary. . . . In heavy seas and in

conditions of high or steep swell, the boat lay very well in the water with only a small amount of movement and little shipping of water at the conning tower. What is disadvantageous in my opinion is the unexpectedly high loss of speed in a head sea, amounting to approximately 40–50 per cent. The crew behaved magnificently in these operations, which were often most difficult, pushing themselves to the limit of physical endeavour. For example, the provisioning of 4 boats in a period exceeding 16 hours in one day; on another day, working 8 to 10 hours with lifelines attached, with seas and breakers constantly washing over them. Severe injuries did not occur, but this must be ascribed to Fortune smiling on us. . . .

'On board our vessel in about 10 hours, approximately 80 fresh loaves each of 1kg can be baked. Some 800 of these loaves were baked at night, were then distributed to various boats and received with great joy. Additionally, approximately 250 loaves were baked for our own use. The rye-bread that we produced has an excellent taste, is nourishing and keeps well. . . . [In toto] 14 boats were supplied with 13,100kg of provisions for 137 days. . . . It had been thought that the 6m rubber dinghy would serve as a means of transporting provisions from one boat to another. Just how it should have performed this task was not clear. Large iron davits were provided at all deck hatches for the hoisting up of provisions. However, during the entire operation conditions permitted the hatches to be used on only one day, and that while homeward bound. Otherwise, only the conning-tower hatch could be used. On this one favourable day, the rubber dinghy might have served as a means of transporting goods if it had not been lost during the first supply operation. I am fully convinced that, even on calm days, handing over provisions by means of rubber dinghy would have taken four times as long as my well-tested rope method which could be used in any conditions of weather: the receiving boat would come to a distance of 25–40m with the sea somewhat astern and wind to the port side. Through pennant-pistol, a line-connection is made of about 300m of manila hawser, 5–6cm circumference, with a central round-thimble with 0.5m steel-wire pennants, with 2–3 spring-hooks attached. Goods are sent over in packages (sea-sacks which can be quickly slit open), mesh-nets the size of a mesh hammock. For articles that could be damaged by water, transport containers made of light metal 30 × 35 × 50 with watertight closures. . . .

'Above all, the handing over of provisions is an operation to involve all personnel; seamen on deck; off-duty stokers on the lower deck attending to provisional tasks in the control room, all attending to packing of supplies according to the pre-conceived plan.'

At about the same time, *UA* (the ex-Turkish *Batiray*, taken over on the outbreak of war) and, just a litttle later, the first large minelayer, *U116*, could be used for supply purposes. Because of the continuing embargo on SMA mines for U-boat operations (page 110), Type XB could not be used for its designed task. Later, too, XB boats – even after mine operations had been resumed — were still used as auxiliary supply vessels.

Now, in quick succession, six Type XIV boats (*U459–U464*) were ready for operations and, in 1942, they noticeably improved the effectiveness of the VIIC and IXC boats, despite increased defensive measures by the enemy, and they contributed initially to successes off the American coast and in the large convoy battles of this, the most successful year of the U-boat campaign. Each U-tanker's supply of fuel-oil could replenish twelve VIIC boats with four weeks' supply, or five IXC boats with eight weeks' supplies. These successful operations led on 22 September 1942 to a further contract with DWK, for 6 and, on 17 April 1943, for 8 Type XIV boats, which brought the total number ordered to 24. In fact, only *U491–U493* were laid down.

In addition to replenishing fuel-oil, the supplying of torpedoes was also very important. Time and again, in conditions of the greatest difficulty, boats that had quickly exhausted their torpedoes were forced to re-arm from other U-boats whose fuel supply was running low; alternatively, such boats would hand over their fuel, and this too was a complicated operation. Even Type XIV could carry only four torpedoes in upper deck housings, and the larger Types XV and XVI (page 154) were not further developed to any extent. In the summer of 1941, it was decided summarily to modify the well-proven Type VIIC as a torpedo transporter by incorporating an additional pressure-hull section, 7.8m long, abaft the control room. As early as 1940, a similar modification of Type VIIC had resulted in the medium minelaying Type VIID for fast operations with SMA mines (see page 147). Apart from this, on 13 August 1941, the Chief of Naval War Staff's U-Boat Department demanded the development of a torpedo transporter of a size similar to Type XIV, but this project did not get beyond the initial planning stages and, like the very large Types XV and XVI, was rejected on account of 'unwieldiness'. The only prospect now for torpedo transporters lay in a vessel based on VIIC, which was designated VIIF. This, apart from additional storage for twenty-one torpedoes, incorporated considerably widened saddle-tanks for a large fuel supply and a roomy deck abaft the bridge to accommodate the transferring parties. On 22 August 1941, four of these boats were placed in contract with GW, but their delivery was not expected before the beginning of 1943. In order to have a torpedo transporter available as soon as possible, it was decided on 9 September 1941 to fit out the captured Dutch submarine *O27* (*UD5*) as a makeshift. In addition, the Type XB boats could carry nine reserve torpedoes, six of which were stored in upper-deck housings.

During the first year of supply operations, the rendezvous appointed for U-boats were beyond the zones of enemy air-surveillance, and losses were slight; only one (outward-bound) U-tanker, *U464*, was lost up to May 1943. In the summer of 1943, however, when the Allies adopted an offensive rôle against U-boats, the U-tankers' mid-Atlantic network was torn to pieces. Meanwhile, the Americans had begun to provide air-cover from escort-carriers on the convoy routes from the

United States to the Mediterranean. Having encountered U-boat supply groups by accident, the Allies thereafter sought them out systematically. Once detected, these large, slow boats had little chance of evading a combined air and sea attack. July 1943 was an especially unlucky month for supply boats. On the 13th, during her maiden voyage, *U487* was detected by the enemy and destroyed by five aircraft from the escort-carrier *Core*. On 24 July, her replacement, *U459*, was bombed. The next attempt to put to sea in a group, from Bordeaux on 27 July, was a complete fiasco. Three days later, north-west of Cape Ortegal, *U461* and *U462* with the operational *U504* were intercepted and destroyed by Allied aircraft working in conjunction with a submarine-hunting group. On 4 August, *U489* was sunk south of Iceland on her maiden voyage.

The situation for a homeward-bound U-boat, short of fuel, was extremely critical, and the solution to its problem seemed to be the replenishing of its fuel while submerged. In his book *U977 66 Tage unter Wasser* (Wiesbaden, 1950, p. 135), Heinz Schaeffer describes the initial trials of a submerged oil-supplying operation involving *U445* and the supply U-boat, *U460*, on 7 December 1942. The boats proceeded in line astern connected by a hose for three hours, at a depth of 50m. Course and speed signals were exchanged by underwater telegraphy. It is astonishing that this system was not used more often; in fact, it was not thoroughly tested until the trials held with *UD4* in the Gulf of Danzig in September–October 1943. In these trials, *UD4*-Dutch *O26*, travelling on the surface at a constant speed of 2–3 knots ahead of the U-boat that was to receive the fuel, first released a buoy with a 96m towing hawser, hose and telephone cable. The hose was filled with air so that both it and the hawser connected to it floated. The telephone link was found to be more reliable than underwater telegraphy, and a pressure-tight socket for the telephone had been obtained from the captured British submarine *Seal*. The buoy was taken aboard the receiving boat and stowed on the bridge, the towing hawser was made fast and the hose was connected. Both boats went to periscope depth, with the supplier maintaining a constant speed and towing the receiver. After repeated practice, the time from releasing the buoy until diving was reduced to about nine minutes. The boats now dived to about 30–35m, with the towing speed increased to 3–4 knots. In the absence of a special pump, *UD4* had to use water pressure to force the fuel through the hose. The transfer of 80m³ took approximately four hours, after which both boats surfaced simultaneously. The receiving boat let go the buoy and turned directly to port, which took about three minutes with an experienced crew.

In August 1943, with the cessation of work on all older-type vessels in favour of Type XXI, further construction of Type XIV at DWK was also terminated. Even after this contract had been transferred to GW, U-tanker construction was not restarted, and the loss of *U490* on her first operational voyage on 11 June 1944 meant that no more boats of this type existed.

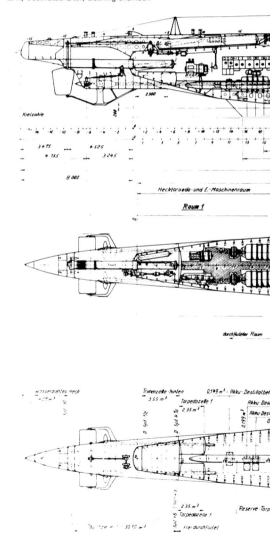

Type VIIF.

Glossary: Treibölhochbehalter, high fuel oil container; Mitte Torpedo Ausstossrohr, middle torpedo exit tube; Hecktorpedo und E.-Maschinenraum, stern torpedo and electric motor room; Dieselmotorenraum, diesel engine room; Unteroffiziersraum hinten, NCOs' quarters after; Torpedolagerraum, torpedo store-room; Kombüse, galley; Zentrale, control room; Offiziers und Oberfeldwebelraum, ward room and warrant officers' quarters; Bugtorpedoraum, bow torpedo room; Rohr, tube; Frei durchflutet, free-flooding compartment; Wasserdichte Back, watertight forecastle; Treibölbunker, fuel-oil bunker; Tauchbunker, ballast tank (water or fuel); Untertriebzelle, negative buoyancy tank; Regelzelle, compensating tank (water); Regelbunker, compensating fuel tank (water or fuel); Tauchzelle, ballast tank (water); Kettenkasten, chain cover; Trimmzelle, trimming tank; Torpedozelle, torpedo tank; Trinkwasserzelle, drinking water tank; Torpedozelle, torpedo washing water; Dete-Anlagerraum, detection equipment room; Akkumulatorenraum, accumulator room; Schmutzwasserzelle, bilge water tank; Munitionskammer, ammunition compartment; Drucköldbehalter, pressure-oil container; Kartoffellast, potato cargo; Gefechtspistolen, contact pistol; Motorenölvorratstank, engine oil storage tank; Gummboot, rubber dinghy; Sammeltank, collecting tank; Destillatbehälter, distilling chamber.

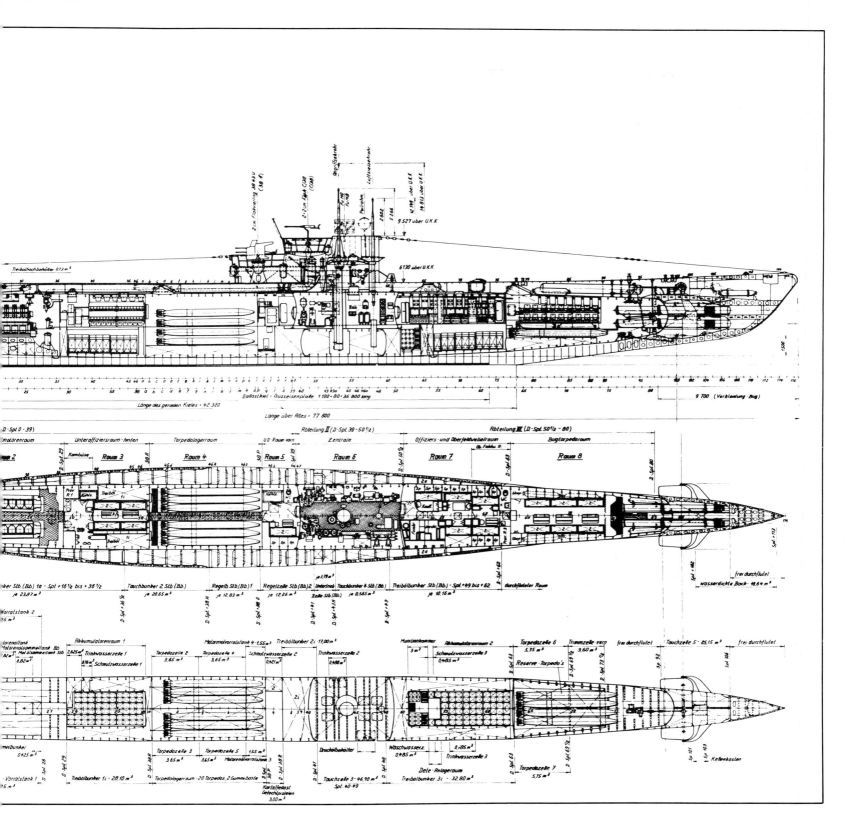

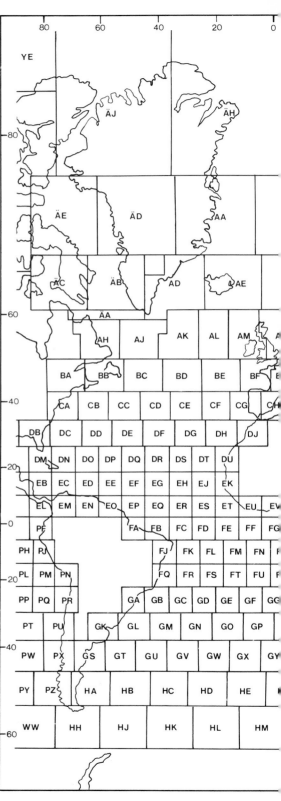

Above: *U1060* (Type VIIF) before launching in April 1943. **Right:** A standard German naval chart showing the supply U-boats' broad areas of operation. (See pp. 166-167 for a brief explanation of the system and a summary of operations.)

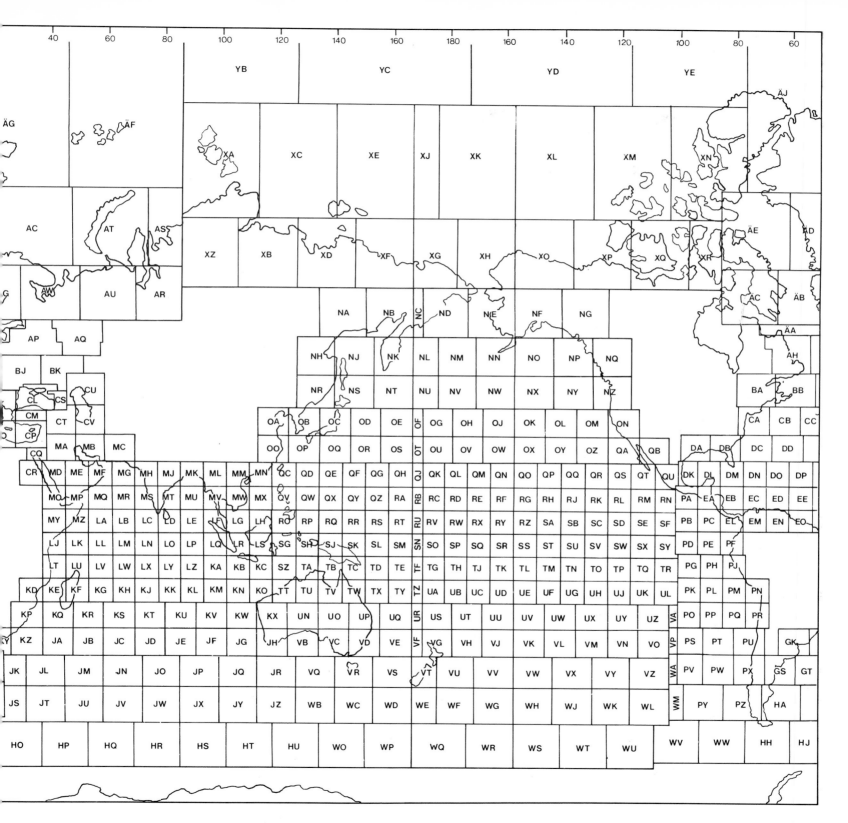

Table 33. Summary of operations carried out by supply U-boats
(Compiled from material from BdU war diaries, amplified by Prof. Dr. Rohwer).

Boat	Op. No.	Duration of operation	Main supply territory	U-boats being supplied
U459[1]	1	21 March 1942–15 May 1942	CC	U108, U98, U333, U582, U352, U564, U571, U566, U594, U558, U69, U572, U751, U103, U753.
	2	6 June 1942–20 July 1942	CC	U558, U566, U594, U571, U106, U84, U107, U575, U502, U437, U203, U134, U432, U653, U135, U754.
	3	19 Aug 1942–5 Nov 1942	GG (Cape Town operation of the 'Eisbär (Polar Bear) Group)	U68, U504, U172, U159, U333, U552, U107, U125, U174, U506 (on the return trip this boat was, in turn, supplied by U462).
	4	20 Dec 1942–8 Mar 1943	GG (Africa boats)	U506, U509, U516, Cagni in FD and U160, U161 in FU.
	5	21 April 1943–4 June 1943	AK/BD	U306, U258, U648, U168, U381, U226, U260, U378, U709, U454, U466, U402, U448, U569, U650, U129, U403, U92.
	6	22 July 1943 left Bordeaux with U461 and U117. U461 had to put back because of damage. The other two boats were escorted by three destroyers to BF 4751. From here they carried out their individual operations alone. On 24 July 1943, after being damaged by bombs from two aircraft of 172 Squadron, U459 scuttled herself. Some of the crew were taken prisoner.		
U460[1]	1	7 June 1942–30 July 1942	BD (Originally intended for Brazilian operation)	U89, U132, U406, U173, U96, U576, U171, U402, U458, U202, U584, U126, U509, U508.
	2	2 Sept 1942–14 Oct 1942	DF/DT (Freetown boats)	U201, U202, U511, U332, U109, U406, U107, U333, U87, U590, U507, U160.
	3	16 Nov 1942–19 Dec 1942	BD	U224, U84, U43, U106, U608, U383, U663, U623, U445, U611, U373, U67, U183, U606, U518, U303, U358, U405.
	4	30 Jan 1943–12 Mar 1943	AK/BC	U707, U632, U594, U414, U608, U135, U402, U454, U89, U614, U456, U606, U303, U403, U525, U607, U226, U223, U186.
	5	24 April 1943–26 June 1943	ES (Freetown boats)	U515, U118, U123, U126, U154, U105, U511, U513, U92.
	6	30 Aug 1943–5 Oct 1943	CE (Zaunkönig boats) then in BD	U338, U645, U386, U305, U260, U448, U610, U603, U422, U170.
		After an additional refuelling of U264, U460 was attacked by several carrier-borne aircraft. A defensive action lasting 30 minutes ensued, after which U455 and U264, which were also present, made their escape. U460 was then sunk by 3 aircraft from the carrier Card. There were no survivors.		
U461[1]	1	28 June 1942–19 Aug 1942	CC/CD	U332, U454, U43, U607, U552, U597, U71, U161, U704, U86, U437, U379.
	2	7 Sept 1942–18 Oct 1942	BC	U594, U92, U411, U218, U96, U380, U91, U211, U404, U407, U584, U171, U164, U217, U558.
	3	19 Nov 1942–3 Jan 1943	DG/DS	U753, U606, U126, U174, U128, U134, U176, U129, U154, U159, U161, U163, U172, U508.
	4	12 Feb 1943–22 Mar 1943	DG/DF	U522, U202, U558, U382, U87, U707, U106, U521, U504.
	5	20 April 1943–31 May 1943	AK/BD	U631, U610, U267, U706, U108, U598, U532, U266, U662, U707, U413, U552, U264, U221, U666, U642, U603, U228, U217.
	6	27 July 1943 sailed from Bordeaux with U504 and U462. At 10.00 on 30 July the group was attacked by aircraft of 502 Squadron. At 11.57 U461 reported herself under attack from 5 aircraft in BF 7124 and requested air support. She was sunk soon afterwards. There were no survivors.		
U462[1]	1	23 July 1942–22 Sept 1942	CD	U161, U94, U558, U373, U569, U176, U755, U596, U135, U512, U516, U98, U600, U66, U163, U173.
	2	18 Oct 1942–7 Dec 1942	DG/EH	U459, U125, UD5, U516, U156, U107, U590, U87, U332, U134, UD3, U505, U552.
	3	Planned for mid Jan 1943, but damage forced boat to return. Intended territory DF 19 Feb 1943–25 April 1943	BD	U332, U603, U383, U753, U226, U91, U653, U621, U600, U468, U598, U358, U454, U707, U134, U303, U306, U381, U415, U438, U604, U628, U631, U523, U186.
	4	1. First operational departure on 20 June 1943. Saw U462 attacked and damaged by 5 aircraftr in BF 81. Put back. Entered Bordeaux on 6 July 1943. 2. U462 became non-operational on 13 June 1943 through bombing attacks and U847 had to supply the 'Monsoon' U-boats. 3. 27 July 1943 sailed with U461 and U504. On 30 July the group was attacked by aircraft (see U461). U462 was sunk with the loss of one man.		
U463[1]	1	11 July 1942–3 Sept 1942	CD	U84, U564(2x), U654, U658, U510, U598, U600, U129, U125, U154, U217, U164, U134.
	2	28 Sept 1942–11 Nov 1942	BD	U216, U661, U620, U382, U260, U662, U706, U610, U442, U437, U356, U69, U753.
	3	6 Dec 1942–27 Jan 1943	CD	U130, U103, U653, U86, U442, U436, U575, U381, U571, U620, U225, U336, U406, U455, U615, U628, U664, U123, U524.
	4	4 March 1943–19 April 1943	BD	U409, U591(2x), U89, U758, U664, U91, U230, U615, U84, U642, U641, U333, U336, U440, U666, U373, U590, U527, U526, U305, U523, U610, U86, U618, U228, U616.

Boat	Op. No.	Duration of operation	Main supply territory	U-boats being supplied
	5	12 May 1943 sailed from Bordeaux, assigned quadrant BD. Destroyed by bombers of 58 Squadron south-east of the Scillies on 15 May.		
U464[1]	1	4 Aug 1942–20 Aug 1942. Supply assignment in AJ. Sunk by US aircraft on 20 Aug south-east of Iceland with loss of two men.		
U487[1]	1	27 March 1943–11 May 1943	AK	*U260, U270, U168, U584, U662, U630, U571, U415, U84, U618, U257, U404.*
	2	15 June 1943–13 July 1943 Sunk (29 survivors) by 5 aircraft from the carrier *Core* in DF 99 on 13 July.	DF ('Monsoon' boats)	*U382, U195, U598, U406, U604, U662, U591, U382, U359, U466.*
U488[1]	1	18 May 1943–8 July 1943	CE	*U641, U603, U221, U608, U228, U211, U666, U558, U951, U953, U435, U232, U642, U336, U193, U590, U618, U571, U306, U653, U358, U634, U732, U257.* Large supply capacity resultant on embarking the remaining fuel from *U199, U536 U171* and *U535.*
	2	7 Sept 1943–12 Dec 1943	CE/DE	*U68, U155, U214, U103, U402, U378, U641, U758, U220, U129, U530, U193, U731.*
	3	22 Feb 1944–26 April 1944 Sunk with all hands at her supply point by US escorts *Frost, Huse, Barber* and *Snowdon.*	DR	*U123, U543, U843, U537.*
U489[1]	1	22 July 1943–4 Aug 1943 Bombed and sunk (1 man lost) by aircraft of Canadian 423 Squadron south of Iceland on 4 Aug.	CD	
U490[1]	1	6 May 1944–11 June 1944 After lengthy training and trials, sunk on 11 June north-west of the Azores by 2 aircraft from the carrier *Croatan* and escort destroyers *Frost, Inch* and *Huse.* Crew rescued.	CD and Indian Ocean	
UA	1	14 March 1942–24 April 1942	CC	
U116[2]	1	15 May 1942–9 June 1942	CC	*U203, U202, U84.*
	2	27 June 1942–23 Aug 1942	BE	*U590, U406, U94, U124, U569, U96.*
	3	22 Sept 1942–Oct 1942 Last report on 6 Oct then missing in North Atlantic.	BD	*U582, U752, U572,* also five (?) VIIC boats (*U130*) during her southbound passage.
U117[2]	1	Oct 1942–23 Nov 1942	BD after minelaying off Reykjavik, Iceland.	*U618, U356, U221, U258, U43, U106.*
	2	24 Dec 1942–8 Feb 1943	BD	*U753, U454, U402, U381, U438, U89, U624, U606.*
	3	30 March 1943–15 May 1943	DG after minelaying off Casablanca and Fedala.	*U628, U615, U591, U435, U336, U662(2x), U260, U706.*
	4	22 July 1943–7 Aug 1943 Minelaying off New York, before supplying *U66* in CD. Then scheduled to take over supplying of north-bound boats in DF 14, in place of the unavailable U-tanker *U489.* But on 7 Aug the refuelling of *U66* in CD 64 was interrupted and *U117* was sunk with all hands by 3 aircraft from the carrier *Card.*		*U516, U185, U506, U68, U509, U183, U460, U160, U518.*
U118[2]	1	19 Sept 1942–18 Oct 1942	AK	*U410, U607, U216, U615, U599.*
	2	11 Nov 1942–13 Dec 1942	DH	*U564, U653, U86, U92, U519, U124, U105, U160, U185, U91.*
	3	25 Jan 1943–26 Feb 1943	DH after minelaying off Gibraltar.	*U175, U558, U258, U202, U214, U87, U264, U514, U217.*
	4	25 May 1943–12 June 1943 Sunk (5 survivors) in DG 47 by 8 aircraft from the carrier *Bogue.*	DG after minelaying off Halifax.	
U119[2]	1	6 Feb 1943–3 April 1943	BD after minelaying off Reykjavik.	*U608, U377, U359, U659, U405, U448, U566, U603, U638, U616.*
	2	25 April 1943–24 June 1943	AK/BD then minelaying off Halifax.	*U92, U954, U628, U584, U614, U383.*
		Homeward bound, supplied *U603* in CD. In company with bomb-damaged *U449* and *U650* depth-charged and rammed by HMS *Starling.* No survivors.		
U219[2]	1	16 Oct 1943–1 Jan 1944 Original assignment: minelaying off Cape Town and Colombo, then to Penang.	AK/EH ('Monsoon' boats).	*U91, U510, U170, U103, U172.*
	2	As a transport U-boat after receiving schnorkel. Sailed from Bordeaux on 1 Sept 1944, arrived Djakarta on 11 Dec 1944. Taken over by the Japanese in Singapore as *I505* on 8 May 1945.		
U220[2]	1	8 Sept 1943 left Bergen for minelaying off St. John's. She was then to carry out supplying in BD. To this end, *U220* was to embark the remaining fuel from *U455* and *U488.* On her way to the rendezvous, *U220* was sunk with all hands in BD 61 by 2 aircraft from the escort carrier *Block Island.*		

[1]Type XIV boats. [2]Type XB boats. The Type XB boats, *U233* and *U234*, were not used subsequently for supplying (*U233* was lost while minelaying off Halifax in CB 34 on 5 July 1944; *U234* was to proceed to the Far East as a transport U-boat).
Note. All abbreviations shown in the table above refer to the grid system used by the Germans on their standard naval charts (Marine-Quadratkarte). Letters such as DG, CD and BC denote broad areas. Precise positions within these areas may be recognized by the four-digit numbers (eg BF 7124) after the letters.

6 THE DEVELOPMENT OF SINGLE-DRIVE U-BOATS

THE WALTER PROCESS

In the early thirties, the German engineer, Hellmuth Walter, was involved with the Germania Yard, Kiel, in the design of a gas turbine, which was to have an effective performance of 2,000hp. It occurred to him to develop a thermal engine as the single propulsion unit for a high-speed U-boat, which would obtain necessary oxygen through the disintegration of hydrogen peroxide (H_2O_2) when submerged. One kilogramme of 80 per cent H_2O_2 solution contains approximately 0.38kg of O_2 (i.e., a quantity that in normal conditions is usually found in 1.15m^3 of air). This would enable 0.1kg of fuel to be burned. At that time, however, the normal commercial solution contained a maximum of only 45 per cent H_2O_2. The use of hydrogen peroxide, as opposed to oxygen gas in U-boat technology seemed to offer possible advantages in that it required lower container weight (4.5kg steel for 1kg of O_2 at 400 atmospheres) and lent itself to easier storage on board.

At first, Walter regarded H_2O_2 only as a convenient and pure carrier of oxygen. He was hoping that a diesel engine could be driven by the circulation of exhaust gas enriched with oxygen obtained from catalytic disintegration, and intended to test the principle with an available 250hp diesel engine using commercially available H_2O_2. His aim was a high-speed submarine with an underwater speed of 25–30 knots — an attacking weapon that, with the aeroplane, would revolutionize warfare.

In March 1933, Walter contacted the Electro-Chemical Works in Munich, which produced industrial H_2O_2, requesting information and delivery possibilities, and succeeded in arousing the interests of Albert Pietzsch, the founder of the firm. He also made simultaneous representation to the Naval Office, and here Laudahn's successor, Chief Naval Construction Adviser Brandes, took the matter up. In a communication to the Naval High Command dated 5 October 1933, Walter set out a detailed suggestion for his high-speed boat:

'Design for a High-Speed Submarine
The following design arises from the efforts to increase surface and submerged speeds of U-boats to the point where they can work with fleets in all contingencies. The U-boat must also be capable not

Professor Hellmuth Walter.

only of keeping up with fleets at fighting speeds but of attaining speeds which will enable it to take up a favourable attacking position against fast opponents. Discussions with representatives of the Supreme Naval Command have established that a boat with approximately the following specifications would be suitable for these requirements:

Displacement:	surfaced 300 tons, submerged 320 tons.
Maximum speed:	surfaced 26 knots, submerged 30 knots.
Maximum power of main engines:	surfaced 4,800hp, submerged 7,500hp.
Total range of action:	2,500 nautical miles at 15 knots, of which 20 per cent is carried out submerged = 500 nautical miles at 15 knots.

The propulsion system and hull construction at present in use do not permit the attainment of these

figures. One looks, therefore, to the use of a light-weight closed-circuit engine, impelled by air on the surface and by a carbon dioxide/oxygen mixture when submerged. For reasons of operational expediency and weight, the oxygen is to be carried in the form of hydrogen super-oxide. In the best interests of engine layout and weight considerations, of armament and manning, the following design is most appropriate for a high-speed U-boat. Obviously, we can only give a broad sketch, but from this one can shape a judgement on how one may best dispose the various compartments and weights.

'General Description
The outer casing is shaped like a fish, with a completely smooth exterior presenting no sharp projections. A small amount of positive buoyancy is present when the boat is travelling on the surface, and the boat does not break surface in the usual sense of the term, i.e., it does not travel 'on the water'. In effect, it 'sticks its essential organs up through the water-surface' — those organs that are necessary for suction of air, for combustion and for navigation. As the normal U-boat weight-allotment for the casing would be unacceptably high for high-speed boats, such boats would be over-pressurized internally when submerged, so that the thickness of casing-walls can be kept thin. These could then withstand pressures of 2–10 atmospheres, depending on wall thickness and method of construction. The crew and life-support equipment are situated in a special pressure hull which is always at normal pressure. The main engines are arranged one above the other, as it is essential to achieve a two-fold purpose: a low water resistance and a narrow and high cross-section in the interest of the centre of gravity. The boat will be only 32m in length, and so its manoeuvring properties should be adequate. The exhaust-gas cooling system, the oxygen-producing equipment and the absorbers are situated in the same compartment as the forward engine, with the rear engine in a similar compartment abaft this. Hydrogen super-oxide is stored as far forward and aft as possible, with the fuel supply in a centrally-placed compartment. The tanks containing hydrogen super-oxide are only two-thirds full, because the specific gravity of this substance is approximately 1.4 and this weight must be balanced by sea water after the fuel has been consumed. Various empty compartments,

which in normal vessels would contain air, will be kept under pressure during submerged travel, as will also, for example, half-filled tanks and crank casings for main and auxiliary engines to the extent that they can be made effectively air-tight. In the interests of more effective working at high revolutions, as well as helping to achieve a smooth hull outline, the propellers will be housed in shrouds. Hydroplanes and rudders will be placed abaft these shrouds so that the stream of water can act against them and send the boat in the desired direction. The boat's hull is designed to withstand a slight outside over-pressure of approximately 1 atmosphere, and a very strong internal over-pressure, which may amount to a figure of up to 8 atmospheres.

'The following methods of travelling are possible:

'On the surface with air; the conning-tower (air-shaft) is raised. In this condition, one can travel either with the boat's hull under pressure, or, if it suits the requirements of the situation, with the hull freely ventilated. In the first of these cases, the boat is completely ready for diving at all times; in the second case it can, however, dive to a maximum depth of 10m. To this depth one can keep the boat at a pressure of 1 atmosphere and carry out functions inside the boat's hull. Repairs can therefore be carried out both in a surfaced position and in a condition of moderate submergence.

'When the boat's hull is under a high internal over-pressure, for example at 8 atmospheres, and this is maintained, the boat may be taken at will to depths of 0–90m. If one had time to put the interior of the boat under sufficient pressure and if the pressure hull were built with sufficient resistance, it would be possible to achieve even greater depths, and the boat would be able to move as quickly at such depths as on the surface. However, the attainment of such depths in the North Sea and the Baltic could only have minimal significance.

'The switching from air to oxygen drive will be an automatic process, and will be controlled automatically by closure of a slide-valve in an air-duct of the conning tower, and activated by increases in water pressure. This will also directly control the chemico-technical apparatus. It is essential that we succeed in so arranging the switching process as to be automatically activated by the diving of the boat, that is, to have the switch linked to the hydroplanes. At the commencement of

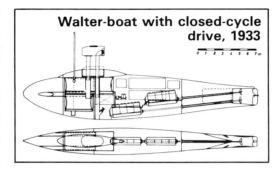

Walter-boat with closed-cycle drive, 1933

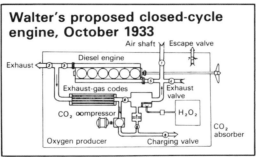

Walter's proposed closed-cycle engine, October 1933

travelling, air will be circulating through the engine and in the boat, and it will therefore be necessary, by repeated charging and exhausting, to drive off the nitrogen in the engine and replace it by soluble carbon dioxide. All kinds of thermal engines could be used, combustion gas engines, gas turbines or steam engines.

'The sketch represents a method of circulating the propulsion agent, using diesel engines in a coupled arrangement. For surface travel, fresh air is taken through the aspirating pipes via Valve 1 into the engines, leaving again as exhaust gas through Valve 3 and through Exhaust Valve 2 to the outside of the boat. If, during surface travel, the boat's hull should be loaded up, the exhaust gas compressors take some of the exhaust gas in through Valve 6, which in the meantime has had its temperature reduced in the coolers, and this is forced through Valve 8 into the engine compartment (which is separate from the accommodation area). For this to be accomplished,

however, Valve 1 must be closed and air aspirated through Valves 4 and 5, i.e., through the body of the boat itself.

'In submerged travel, i.e., when hydrogen peroxide is being used, exhaust gases are in circulation in the closed circuit. Nitrogen is then gradually replaced by carbon dioxide. In this circulation process, one is not tied to the pressure of the outer atmosphere as an aspirating means, and as one is likewise not tied to the oxygen content of the air, it then becomes possible in submerged travel to achieve considerably increased speeds with conventional engines. What helps this process is the fact that the specific heat of carbon dioxide is greater than that of the air, which means that the engines require less heat, leading in turn to the engines giving a considerable increase in performance at identical heat. An increased performance of 56 per cent over surface travel is calculated.

'In submerged travel, the exhaust gases from the engine pass from Valve 3 (Valve 2 being closed) into the cooler and, from there, through Valve 6 and past the oxygen-generator once again, into the engine. At Valve 6, the exhaust gas compressor sucks in the carbon dioxide that is constantly being formed by combustion, and forces it through Valve 8 into the body of the boat, or through Valve 9 into the absorber, in which the carbon dioxide is dissolved and the surplus oxygen collected and led back once again into the oxygen generator. In this section the exhaust gases are enriched again with oxygen. This takes place through the fact that a continuous supply of H_2O_2 is passed by a pump, rigidly connected to the fuel pump, into the oxygen-generator where it is disintegrated by a catalyst. The introduction of fuel takes place in conventional ways, by pump to the engine or to the separate cylinders. Exhaust Valve 7 serves to reduce the over-pressure in the interior of the boat.

'Another species of propulsion plant is a steam installation driven by the circulation-process. In this, the large exhaust-gas cooler is unnecessary, as the temperature at which gases enter the boiler can be high. Additionally, the exhaust-gas compressor for the loading of the boat's body is dispensed with; first, because a boiler, even with a high initial pressure, can be driven; and, second, higher performances are attained; and another benefit accrues — loading takes place automatically through carbon dioxide build-up. The pressure difference before and after the supercharging is so considerable that the frictional resistance of the circulation system is just exceeded. The employment of a second circulation system (gas and water) and the provision of a larger fuel supply, and division into compartments, are all possible; however, tests with steam should first be undertaken.'

At the end of 1933, as a result of these suggestions, Walter was given permission to undertake an appropriate project-study for a high-speed boat with a displacement of 300–400 tons, a submerged top speed of 24 knots and the following ranges: 2,000 nautical miles at 15 knots surfaced and 400–500 nautical miles at 15 knots submerged. This project, which was designated Type V by the Naval Office, was to include work on a diesel engine propulsion system in addition to steam propulsion. With the higher H_2O_2 concentration (initially 60 per cent, later up to 85 per cent) it turned out that the disintegration was accompanied by a considerably increased build-up of heat. At 80 per cent of H_2O_2, the disintegration heat amounted to 552Kcal/kg, i.e., approximately 50 per cent of the amount of heat that resulted from the combustion with released oxygen. This considerable extra heat, however, could not be used in an engine installation; rather, it worked to the disadvantage of this system. After further consideration it became obvious that the steam installation was preferable, that is, an installation in which the combustion circulation is separated from the propulsion component.

On 15 March 1934, Walter laid an appropriate design before Chief Naval Construction Advisers Brandes and Bröking of K II. On 10 April, the Commander-in-Chief of the Supreme Naval Command authorized GW to work out a tender for a test steam installation (to consist of a combustion chamber with burners, a gas circulation system with supercharger and an oxygen-generating installation) and to carry out as soon as possible its own evaluation and presentation of a carbon-dioxide absorption installation.

Following further research, Walter decided to abandon the exhaust gas-circulation operation, this being unnecessary in view of the dilution of oxygen that occurred in the steam arising from the disintegration. This simplified considerably the entire structure: the disintegrated H_2O_2 was led into a combustion chamber and burned with injected fuel. In the 'Direct Process', more water was simultaneously injected, which had the effect of reducing the very high combustion temperature, from approximately 2,100°C to approximately 550°C, and approximately doubling the amount of steam available for the operation. In the 'Indirect Process', the exhaust gas from the combustion chamber gave its heat to a secondary circulation in which steam was produced. In the final engine process, the disintegrated H_2O_2 was cooled to approximately 100°C, and was then led as 'intake air' into the working cylinders of the diesel engine.

The simplest solution was the 'Direct Process', in which the steam-exhaust gas mixture was led, at an approximate temperature of 550°C and 35

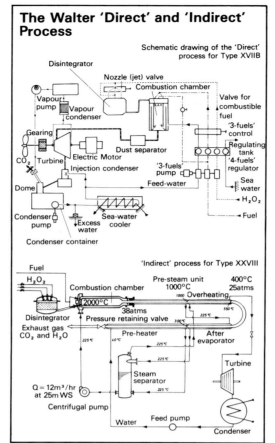

The Walter 'Direct' and 'Indirect' Process

Schematic drawing of the 'Direct' process for Type XVIIB

'Indirect' process for Type XXVIII

atmospheres over-pressure, into a gas turbine and, depending on the working arrangement, condensed in a combined injection and surface cooler. The condensed water could be partly used again as injection water, while the CO_2 was led outside the boat by its own pressure or by using an exhaust gas compressor. The CO_2 dissolved readily in water — which, of course, was useful when one did not wish to leave any trace of the submarine's passage. The 'Indirect Process' raised considerable problems connected with the high-combustion chamber temperature of approximately 2,000°C, and of providing a suitable heat-exchanger. Nor was any great progress made with the development of the engine process. The heavy onset of water into the lubricating oil, and other problems, caused operational difficulties that delayed its general development. On the other hand, as early as 1936, GW could report that a 4,000hp turbine installation, built according to the Direct Walter Process, had been installed on a test-bed and proved successful. The process had passed its test.

In the summer of 1936, Walter left GW and, with a rapidly increasing staff, set up his own research establishment in an old gasworks in Kiel-Wik. His sphere of interests proliferated: apart from the Navy, the Luftwaffe was greatly interested in his new, high-performance research. However, the

high-speed U-boat remained his favourite brainchild. The design progressed slowly. The first step came at the beginning of 1939 with the contract for a small test vessel (V80) of approximately 80 tons, to test speed-keeping and steering capabilities at high submerged speeds. This vessel was not to have a 'Hot Installation' with combustion chambers, but a disintegrator with a rear-connected turbine. The oxygen bubble trail from this vessel would have prevented its operational use, but it was used for checking the results of further trials. V80 was built at GW in 1939–40, on slipway V, behind a high wooden screen. After completion, she underwent trials in the Schlei Estuary. Her base was a covered dock. The converted tanker John Rehder, renamed Polyp, was used as combined living quarters and supply-ship, and a small motor-boat, Ingo, was provided as an escort. The trials were conducted from April 1940, under great secrecy, and the results were considerable — even sensational.

The hull shape of V80 harked back to Walter's first designs of 1933. Vertical rudders and hydroplanes were controlled by an original dual-control unit taken from a Ju 52 aircraft. At high speed, the boat steered well with dynamic surfacing and submerging. With the aid of depth-control apparatus taken from a torpedo, automatic depth-keeping was possible. The high number of revolutions (20,000rpm) of the 2,000hp turbine was reduced, for the first time ever in ship-construction, by a Stoeckicht-Planetary Gearing, to 1,000rpm. For the H_2O_2 (cover-names: 'Aurol' for ship propulsion units, 'T-Stoff' (literally, T-Substance) for aircraft engines and 'Ingolin' for torpedo propulsion units) an excellent storage medium has been found, using plastic bags surrounded by sea water. Just as with fuel-oil, H_2O_2 could be forced into the interior of the boat by water pressure, and its weight could be compensated by the sea water. The shallow water of the Schlei Estuary restricted submerged speed to 14 knots. Not until the test centre was moved to Hela in the autumn of 1940 could the maximum submerged speed be attempted in the Gulf of Danzig, where 28.1 knots were achieved. The crew of the boat — a maximum of four — were all civilians. Walter usually took charge of the boat himself, together with his right-hand man, Heinz Ullrich, the Test Engineer of the Walter Works, who made 100 voyages in V80, and 200 voyages in the Walter U-boats that followed.

The next step was to build a test boat for the 'Hot Installation' and in January 1940 GW were ordered to produce such a design. In 'K' office of the Supreme Naval Command, Walter's suggestions and the commissions he received were worked on faithfully by Dr. Pflaum (1933–34), Dr. Piening (1934–38) and lastly, until the end of the war, by Engineer Waas. These engine-builders were supporters of Walter's ideas, were inspired by his élan and gave him all possible support. In a memorandum of February 1940, Waas suggested that, in order to assist in a wide-ranging system of trials for the new propulsion unit, an immediate start should be made with the construction of a series of 6 small Walter U-boats. If the production of 12 U-boats from current building could be sacrificed, then in three years the trials of Walter

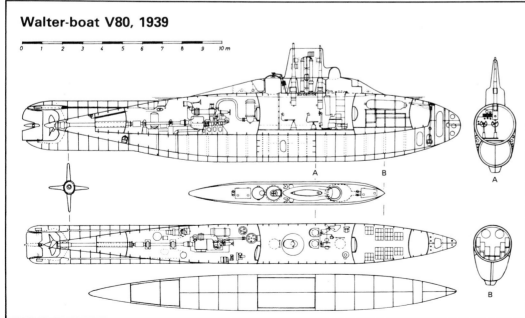

Walter-boat V80, 1939

0 1 2 3 4 5 6 7 8 9 10 m

Above: *V80* under construction behind a wooden screen at Germaniawerft in early 1940. **Below:** A stern view of *V80* in the covered floating dock at GW.

Above: *V80* preparing for a trial.

U-boats could be completed to the extent that operational use of them would then be possible. In addition to using experienced U-boat builders, personnel would have to be employed whose minds were open to innovations. Personnel could also be used from the aviation sphere. The most appropriate development centre would seem to be at B&V. However, conditions at that time were not in favour of such far-reaching planning: there existed in the U-Boat Departments of the Supreme Naval Command a certain scepticism regarding a quick, operationally-reliable realization of the Walter-Drive, and there was also a reluctance to sacrifice current production of U-boats that were urgently needed. The Heads of the U-Boat Department, Schürer and Bröking, were of the opinion that the reliability of the new installation should first be proved in a land installation; only when it had proved itself satisfactory in all respects should it be tested fully on board a test boat; and only then could the reponsibility be taken for interrupting the current construction programme of conventional U-boats. Consequently, a test boat only should be placed in contract with GW. Admiral Fuchs, the Head of the 'K' Office, decided that no departure from well-tested construction principles

should be made, but instead of the procedure with *V80*, administerial direction should remain in the U-Boat Department of the Supreme Naval Command. To co-ordinate Walter's ideas with the views and experiences of U-boat building staff at GW, an office, 'K/W' (Krupp/Walter), was set up in the new Walter Works in Kiel-Wik.

The evolution of Types XVIIB, XVIIG and XXII

The first design for the test boat, designated 'V300', envisaged a small U-boat of 320 tons, with the typical 'Walter' shape, which, with two turbines producing a total of 4,000hp, would reach an underwater speed of 25 knots. However, in Design II of 30 September 1940, the boat had become considerably larger. This second design took thorough account of the basic principles of conventional U-boat construction and the requirements necessary to bring about the higher submerged speed. The propulsion installation consisted of two diesel engines developing a total of 600hp for surface travel, two turbines developing a total of 4,000hp for fast submerged travel and two small electric motors for quiet, slow travel. Walter had also intended that the diesel installation be made suitable for use with Aurol, to facilitate an economic cruising speed when submerged, but the engine system had not been developed sufficiently

for this to be considered. All these propulsion systems were to work through two sets of gearing on only one propeller shaft. As with *V80*, forward hydroplanes were dispensed with. Steering was to be carried out with one control-stick for lateral and depth purposes. The boat's shape and speed would make possible dynamic surfacing and submerging (i.e., at full speed without additional ballast-water, using hydroplanes only). A conning tower was not envisaged, which meant that the bridge could be kept to a low profile. The armament consisted of two 7m-long torpedo tubes and four torpedoes.

In the final version of 16 September 1941 (Design III), the size had increased to over 600 tons. The boat had a conning tower and forward hydroplanes, and the bridge was now enclosed, but the underwater shape of the body and bridge had become so large that the calculated submerged speed using the intended turbine installation amounted to only 19 knots. On 18 February 1942, GW was given a contract for a test boat (*U791*) of this type, but, in the light of its anticipated submerged speed, it no longer corresponded to Walter's idea of a high-speed boat. Therefore, in collaboration with his colleagues, he developed in the autumn of 1941 his own ideas for a small U-boat of approximately 220 tons, with two 2,500hp turbines and a submerged speed of 26 knots. Walter

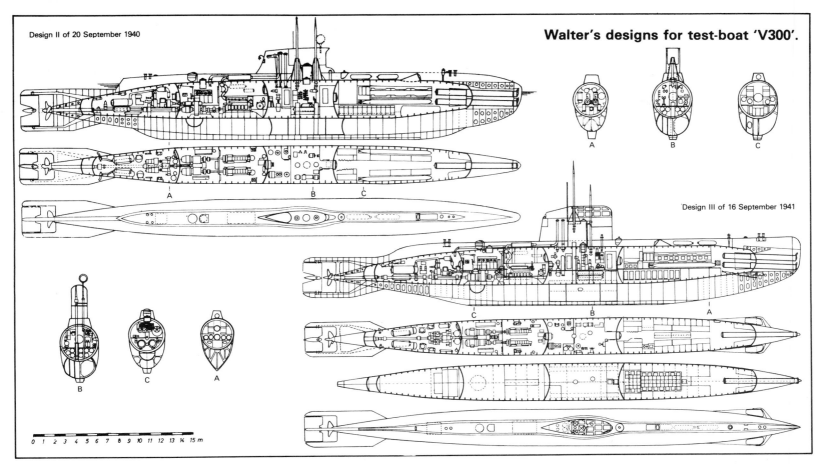

Design II of 20 September 1940

Walter's designs for test-boat 'V300'.

A B C

Design III of 16 September 1941

B C A

0 1 2 3 4 5 6 7 8 9 10 11 12 13 14 15 m

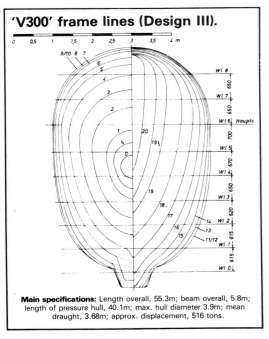

'V300' frame lines (Design III).

0 0,5 1 1,5 2 2,5 3 3,5 4 m

9/10 8 7
6
5

4

3

2

1
20
19½

19
18.
17
16
15

WI 8
650
WI 7
650
WI 6 Hauptc
700
WI 5
670
WI 4
650
WI 3
620
14 WI 2
615
13
11/12 WI 1
615
WI 0

Main specifications: Length overall, 55.3m; beam overall, 5.8m; length of pressure hull, 40.1m; max. hull diameter 3.9m; mean draught, 3.68m; approx. displacement, 516 tons.

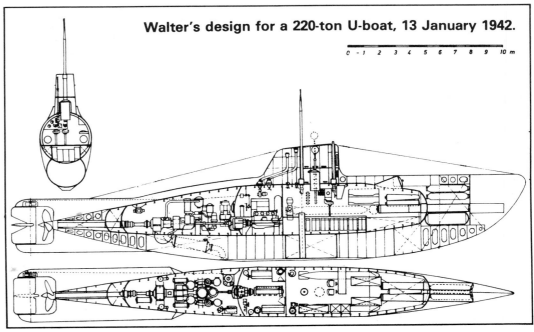

Walter's design for a 220-ton U-boat, 13 January 1942.

0 - 1 2 3 4 5 6 7 8 9 10 m

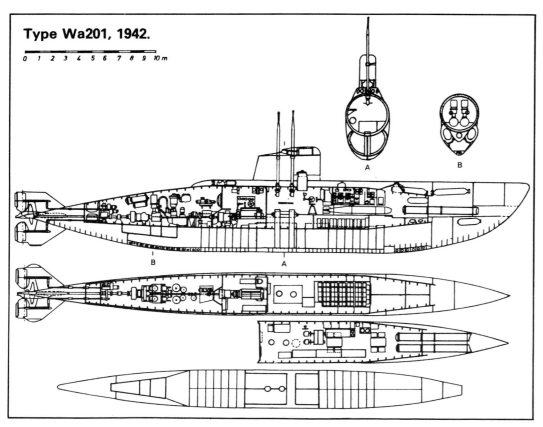

Type Wa201, 1942.

0 1 2 3 4 5 6 7 8 9 10m

and Waas were convinced that this small boat could be built quickly and be available in quite a short period of time for fundamental testing of the 'Hot Walter Installation'.

In order to win over the Supreme Naval Command to these ideas, they offered a demonstration of *V80* at Hela on 14 November 1941, which Grand Admiral Raeder and Admiral Fuchs (Head of 'K' Office) attended. Although Raeder showed great interest, the desired approval from the decisive bodies within 'K' Office was not forthcoming. On 3 January 1942, therefore, Walter and Waas made representations to the Commander-in-Chief, U-Boats, in Paris. At this discussion, Dönitz declared that 'the gift of a high speed which had been bestowed on him overnight, as it were, by the Walter-Process' would justify his doing everything he could to make boats of this kind available. What was most significant for him was the high submerged speed, which far outweighed all other considerations. What he saw as most important was a large, high-speed boat for Atlantic use. If, however, a small boat of this type could be built quickly and in large numbers inland and without any hindrance to the Naval Programme, there would be nothing at all against this, especially if this small boat could also attain a sufficiently high speed. The radius of action, however, would have to be sufficient for boats to be able to operate to the north of the British Isles from the existing bases. The ability to carry at least four torpedoes

was, in all circumstances, absolutely necessary.

In a telex to the Supreme Naval Command on 18 January 1942, Dönitz requested emphatically that the Walter U-boat be developed in accordance with the foregoing points. But 'K' Office continued to show reluctance and, in a letter dated 23 February, stated that it was imperative to concentrate efforts on the production of the standard Types VIIC and IXC, in view of the critical state of the U-boat sector. The introduction of any special type would disrupt the smooth progress of series production. Finally, however the Head of the 'K' Office, Admiral Fuchs, did consent to provide yard capacity for a test construction of the new small Walter boat — not as Waas had suggested at B&V, but at the Lübecker Flenderwerke. Only when it became obvious that conditions there were not suitable for such a complex task were B&V and, later, GW (after cessation of the V300 project) involved.

GW's boat was designated 'WK201' (Walter-Krupp), B&V's, 'Wa201' (Walter). Walter's original design, apart from the sharper and more sloping bow to give better surface travel, was strongly reminiscent of *V80*. The working-out of the basic shape, the distribution of compartments and the engine installation were carried out by the yards. However, the fin-cross (the horizontal and vertical fins) was no longer included in the outer hull, but was separated from it and positioned on the spindle-stern. The GW design had normal balanced

rudders with hydraulic steering, while the B&V boats had balanced rudders with additional Flettner ancillary rudders to minimize the effort needed to steer at high speeds. Additionally, an SAM (Siemens Apparate und Maschienen GmbH) installation for course and depth-keeping was planned for the Wa201 boats, but this required such complicated electrical impulses to be sent to the guidance-engines, resulting in such frequent interference that in later series-production of B&V only hand-steering with servo-engine assistance was envisaged. As with *V80*, forward hydroplanes were dispensed with, the firm of Walter being of the opinion that what applied to aircraft applied equally to the high-speed U-boat.

The first designs were ready in March 1942. GW's WK201 was 34.03m long; the B&V design, Wa201, was 35.9m long. Models of both designs were thoroughly tested at the HSVA (Hamburgische Schiffbau-Versuchsanstalt GmbH, or Hamburg Shipbuilding Test Institute), and the steering and depth-keeping properties of the proposed rudders and hydroplanes were measured in a wind tunnel at the LFA (Luftfahrtforschungsanstalt 'Hermann Göring, Braunschweig' or Hermann Göring Aviation Research Institute, Brunswick). This proved Wa201 to give significantly better results. Compared with the value of a rotating body of the same volume and at the same submerged depth, the resistance value at 20 knots was 20 per cent higher in Wa201 and 35 per cent higher in WK201, which was attributed to the influence exerted by the differing appendages on each boat — in Wa201 an enclosed bridge, while WK201 had an open bridge with wind protection, and different fin and rudder shapes. At 24 knots, the B&V design had a considerably better total propulsion ratio than WK201, 75 per cent against 57 per cent, and this could have resulted from the better outline provided by the fins and rudders and by the better propeller design. Measured screw-performance in model tests amounted, at 24 knots, to a converted 2,400shp of Wa201, while WK201 required approximately 70 per cent more, at 4,120shp. (It should also be mentioned that in Wa201 the original spade-rudders were under-dimensioned.)

In order to improve the rather unsatisfactory results achieved with WK201, a number of model tests were carried out with different bridge versions and rudder shapes. These showed that, with a closed bridge, an 18 per cent improvement in performance could be expected. Rudder tests showed that the rudder-cross (the vertical rudder and after hydroplane in a cross arrangement) adversely affected the propeller, reducing the performance by 952shp at 24 knots. Later, a more favourable rudder shape was devised for better streamlining of the spindle-stern; this arrangement had a movable Kort nozzle as lateral rudder and a deep-set hydroplane with a small fin. These deeper-set rudders and fins gave an increase in performance at 24 knots of approximately 7.5 per cent, and the Kort nozzle provided a further gain of 6.5 per cent. The total propulsion ratio correspondingly increased by 70 per cent. However, these findings came too late for the GW design,

Type WK202, 1942.

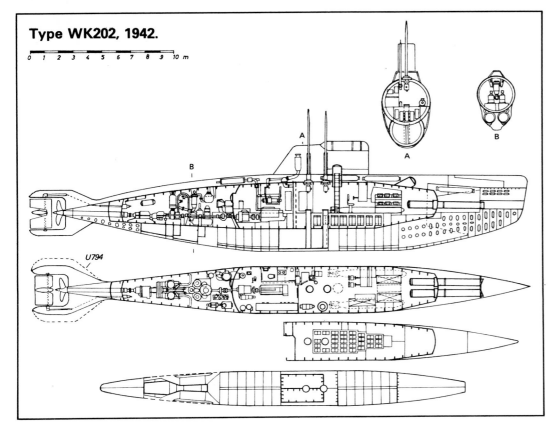

0 1 2 3 4 5 6 7 8 9 10 m

U794

Type WK202 frame lines.

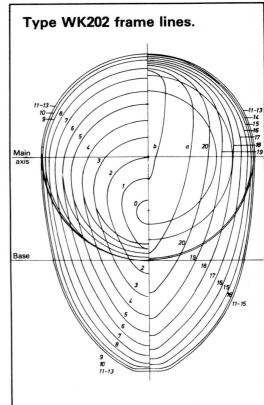

'C' values, Type WK202.

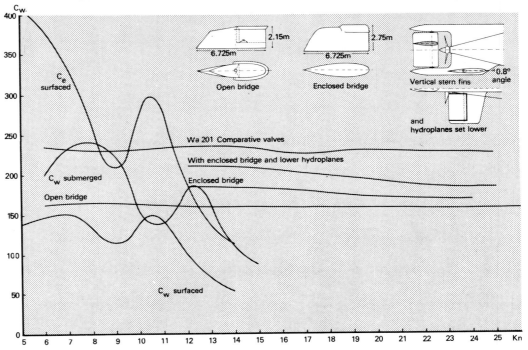

which, during further development work, had been given the designation WK202 to further distinguish her from Wa201.

To keep the boats as small as possible, only two 5m-long torpedo tubes and four torpedoes were envisaged. The restricted range of the 5m torpedoes was regarded as satisfactory for these high-speed and manoeuvrable small U-boats. Additionally, torpedoes equipped with Walter-Turbine propulsion suitable for 5m tubes, with a range of 3.8km at 45 knots, were being specially designed for the Walter U-boats, under the cover-names 'Goldfisch' and 'Goldbutt'.

In the summer of 1942, building contracts were awarded for the final versions of Wa201 (length 37.15m), and WK202 (length 34.64m). But the extensive development that had been hoped for would not be achieved with these four boats. Six of each type seemed the minimum if war experience were to be obtained in respect of production, testing, handling, training, and experience in handling H_2O_2 on land and at sea. However, only after various interventions by Dönitz was it decided in the autumn of 1942 to award contracts for a series of 24 small boats of this kind, as soon as results with the new Walter installation were available. On 4 January 1943, these boats were ordered in equal quantities from B&V and GW. Enlarged and developed for operational use, Wa201 and WK202 were given the designations 'Type XVIIB' and 'Type XVIIG' respectively.

U1405-U1409 (Type XVIIB).

Glossary: Trimmz., trimming tank; Tauchz., ballast tank (water); Tiefenruderleitung, main hydroplane; Turb. R., turbine room; Sammeltank, collecting tank; Seitenruder, side rudder; Treibölbunker, fuel oil bunker; E.-Masch. u. Diesel, electric motor and diesel; Treibstoffbunker, fuel (motor) bunker; Regelz., compensating tank (water); Kombüse, galley; Bugtorpedoraum, bow torpedo room; Wd. Back, watertight forecastle; Zentrale, control room; Schnitt, section; Druckkörper, pressure hull; Kond. Kuhler, condenser cooler. Bb., port; Stb., starboard; Hauptachse, main axis.

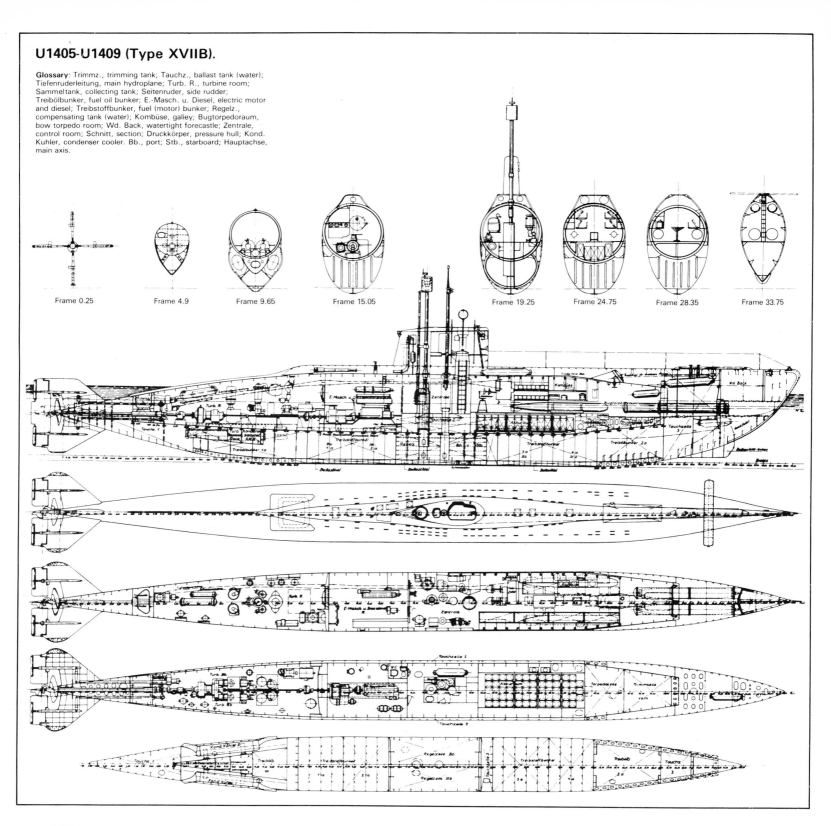

Frame 0.25   Frame 4.9   Frame 9.65   Frame 15.05   Frame 19.25   Frame 24.75   Frame 28.35   Frame 33.75

Walter Type XVIIG, 1943.

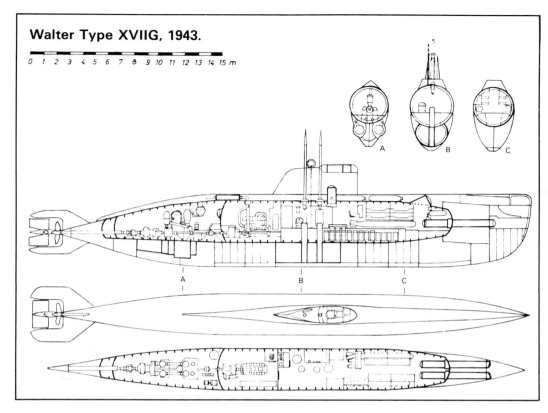

0 1 2 3 4 5 6 7 8 9 10 11 12 13 14 15 m

Walter Type XXII, 1943.

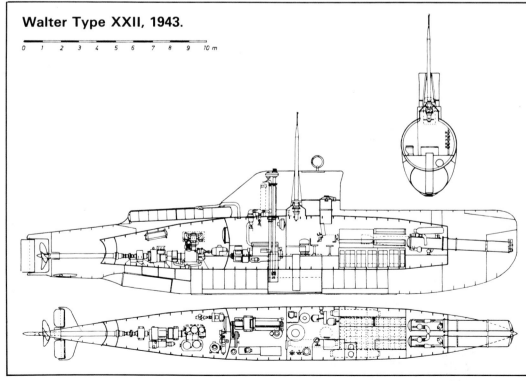

0 1 2 3 4 5 6 7 8 9 10 m

Left: Professor Ulrich Gabler. **Right:** Dr. Karl Fischer.

Dr. Karl Fischer and the engineers Heinrich Heep and Ulrich Gabler, who had joined Walter's firm for U-boat development in the early part of 1943, soon recognized that a bottleneck in the production of the complicated turbine installations would occur. Corresponding to this, they considered the Wa201 installation of $2 \times 2,500$hp as too complicated a unit for further development. If a Walter U-boat were required quickly for operational trials, only a small, simply-built coastal U-boat would be possible, bearing in mind the engine problems in the current series production. In line with this, in the early part of 1943, the Walter Works originated a design for a small Walter U-boat of 155 tons displacement, with only one Walter-Turbine of approximately 1,850hp. As with the existing Walter design, the boat's shape was distinguished by having the H_2O_2 bunker under the pressure hull. This gave the boat's cross-section the shape of an upright ellipse. In contrast to Wa201 and WK202, however, the stern was projected as a knife-edge, with fin and hydroplane set low down beneath the rush of water from the screw. The knife-edged stern was intended to increase the surface waterline and, hence, the sea-keeping properties of the short boat; propulsion was to be increased by the deeper-set hydroplane. As the boat was to be kept as small as possible, once again only 5m-long torpedo tubes were considered, and these formed protuberances in the outer casing of the sharp bow outline. A further torpedo tube was considered for a position in the outer hull abaft the bridge. It was only possible to load torpedoes from the outside. Surface propulsion of the boat was to be diesel-electric. The surface range of 1,200 nautical miles at 8 knots and the extremely narrow internal measurements considerably restricted operational possibilities. The use of an exhaust-gas compressor was intended to increase the efficiency of the turbines, consequently increasing considerably the range, especially at greater depths of travel. This boat was designated 'Type XXII'.

The construction of the four test boats of Type Wa201 and WK202 had begun on 1 December 1942 at B&V, and at the beginning of February 1943 at GW. During the course of construction, the B&V boat had to be enlarged, by the distance between three frames, to a length of 39.05m in order to allow sufficient space for the turbines.

Above: *U793* (Wa201) at the Howaldt Yard, Kiel, in the summer of 1945. **Below:** *U794* being raised from the slipway on 7 October 1943.

In April 1943, the test-bed for the first boat of Type Wa201 was almost ready. The complete propulsion unit was mounted in a U-boat mock-up. In order to save Aurol, a battery of six small Henschel high-pressure boilers was prepared especially for the test-run, and this assembly was to drive the installation with steam. First tests began in May 1943. The construction of the four small boats proceeded slowly, but one should take into consideration the fact that no special priority declaration had been given to the undertaking. Furthermore, the difficulties that occurred were part and parcel of the construction of any completely new U-boat, and enemy air attacks interrupted building. Not until October 1943 were the first two Walter Boats *U792* and *U794* delivered by B&V and GW respectively.

The development of Type XVIII
In a discussion with the Commander-in-Chief, U-Boats, in Paris on 3 January 1942, Dönitz emphasized his preference for a large high-speed boat suitable for Atlantic use. Given the project designation 'V301', constructional preliminaries began immediately at the Walter Works for a test boat of this kind. An initial rough outline envisaged a U-boat of approximately 800 tons, with a surfaced speed of 15 knots and a submerged speed of 26–27 knots. The surfaced range would correspond with that of Type VIIC, and a torpedo armament of four tubes with a total of sixteen torpedoes was envisaged. It was obvious that a boat as large as this with a high submerged speed would require a considerably more powerful Walter-Drive installation than all previous high-speed boats. This meant that the test U-boat *U791* (V300) no longer had any significance in the future development of Walter U-boats suitable for the Atlantic: after relatively few building preparations at GW, it was scrapped on 15 July 1942.

The very numerous design tasks that were an integral part in the new development of a large U-boat and a new engine installation gave Walter's firm considerable personnel problems. Naval Construction Adviser Waas had hitherto tried in vain to obtain from the constructional and development offices specially qualified and operationally experienced officers to serve as permanent advisers in constructional matters and to act as collaborators. However, the Personnel Office at Supreme Naval Command was unwilling to weaken the operational sector by granting this request. Furthermore, the interest aroused by the pronouncement of Dönitz in January 1942 was beginning to fade. It was clear that a new emphatic declaration by the Commander-in-Chief, U-Boats, to the Supreme Naval Command was necessary to keep interest alive.

In June 1942, therefore, at a further discussion with Dönitz in Paris, Walter and Waas attended with Admirals Kleikamp (as Representative of the Head of 'K' Office) and Gutjahr (as Chief of the Torpedo Office). The points for discussion were the new Walter ocean-going U-boat, the 5m-long torpedoes suggested for Walter projects, and personnel problems at Walter's firm. Dönitz demanded twin-shaft drive for the large boat, six torpedo tubes for 7m torpedoes, and anti-aircraft armament. The importance he attached to the new Atlantic Walter boat could be measured by his granting immediate permission to Waas to make use of highly-qualified operational officers. (Subsequently, the U-boat engineering officers, Heep and Gabler were seconded from U-boat operations to the firm of Walter. Heep was requested by Walter on the recommendation of Dr. Pflaum, and began work in October 1942; on the recommendation of Heep, Gabler joined the firm at the beginning of 1943.) In line with the general tone of the discussion, Dönitz declared, among other points, on 24 June 1942 in a lengthy report to Supreme Naval Command: 'The quickest development trials and, finally, the speediest construction for the Walter U-boats of large dimensions are of major importance for decisive war operations.'

During a discussion at Hitler's headquarters on 26 August 1942, in Appendix 5 of a speech made by the Supreme Commander-in-Chief of the Navy, it was stated:

'In the interests of providing U-boats suitable for Atlantic operations and with a high submerged speed, for the time being it was necessary to continue work on V300 and the building contract given to GW in February 1942. This boat was thought of as a boat to train crews to try out weapons and their usage. The year 1942 has seen the introduction of new building methods and new knowledge concerning engine installations for small boats (Wa201), and these suggest the suspension of work on V300, because in the light of the present situation this boat no longer represents a stage along the path to providing a large boat suitable for Atlantic use. The construction of a boat suitable for Atlantic use must therefore be approached in a new way. Planning at the firm of Walter and subsequent drawing-up of plans at a ship construction yard (if needs be, Germania and Blohm & Voss in competition) will take approximately six months; after that, a decision can be made as to whether one of these constructional plans for an appropriate boat should be put in hand as a building task. Planning at the firm of Walter is suffering currently, among other problems, from a shortage of personnel. The 20 engineers who have been requested by name by the firm of Walter should, if possible, be released by the Navy. Tests continue.'

Special priority was not granted to Walter U-boat development. Dönitz acknowledged that his efforts in the Supreme Naval Command on behalf of the Walter U-boat had not had the desired result. He therefore informed Hitler's Naval Adjutant, Kapitän zur See von Puttkamer, that he was greatly concerned at the development of the enemy's air-surveillance which would soon be effective throughout the Atlantic, and added a request that this danger be met by an acceleration in development and completion of Walter U-boats. This was communicated by von Puttkamer to Hitler, who ordered that an appropriate report be made to the Navy. This took place in the Reichs Chancellery on 28 September 1942: apart from Hitler, the participants included Keitel, Raeder, Dönitz, Fuchs and Waas. After introductory

remarks by Hitler on the necessity of bringing new technical developments to a prompt state of practical implementation, Dönitz declared in a report on the existing situation in the U-boat campaign and prospects for the future:

'Technical improvements in U-boats and U-boat weapons are required, not because losses have climbed to the degree they have, but so that in tactical terms, in spite of the increase in anti-U-boat measures, we may retain at least the same successes as we have enjoyed hitherto. Most important of all is the requirement that underwater speeds be increased and this is possible by the introduction of the Walter boats. A U-boat with high underwater speed has a greater chance of getting into a good firing position against a convoy despite enemy protection vessels. It would also mean that a U-boat would be more readily capable of evading its pursuers.'

Hitler gave his approval to these ideas and stated that, in his opinion, the introduction of a U-boat with a high submerged speed would mean incontrovertible success. At the close of the discussion, there followed a special treatment of the development of Walter U-boats to date. Raeder reported that 2 boats of the smaller type had been placed in contract with B&V and 2 with GW; that a prototype design for the larger type was being developed by the firm of Walter; and that in about two months' time, a decision would be made concerning series-production for the larger type. Regarding the small type, a series of 24 boats should be placed in contract as soon as possible.

This discussion led to a complete change of heart inside the Supreme Naval Command. From then on (i.e., some six months before the total collapse of the U-boat campaign in the North Atlantic), enthusiasm was rekindled in the construction staff, who until then had viewed their task as that of merely effecting improvements to current types. Admiral Fuchs now strove to take all possible decisions to support Dönitz. The most important question now was the actual construction of the large Walter U-boats, which were given the Project Designation 'Pr476' at the firm of Walter, and the designation Type XVIII at Supreme Naval Command. On 10 October 1942, Walter presented its Design II for an Atlantic high-speed boat.

Length overall:	67.7m.
Maximum beam:	5.75m.
Draught:	6.25m.
Pressure-hull diameter:	5.1m.
Maximum pressure-hull thickness:	26mm.
Interior frames:	220 × 15 at 800mm distance.
Hull displacement:	1,524.25 tons .
Displacement submerged:	1,181.7 tons.
Propulsion:	two × 6,000hp at 7,500rpm BKC-Walter turbines. two × 1,200hp at 700rpm Deutz T12 M133 diesel engines. two electric motors.
Aurol:	175 tons.
Fuel-oil:	136 tons.
Battery:	two × 62 type 33 MAL 800W cells.
Maximum speed surfaced:	14 knots.
Maximum speed submerged:	26.8 knots.
Range surfaced:	11,500 nautical miles at 8 knots; 8,500 nautical miles at 10 knots.
Range submerged:	243 nautical miles at 25 knots.
Constructional diving depth:	130m.
Armament:	six 5m bow torpedo tubes, twenty G5u torpedoes. one twin 2cm AA.
Crew:	45.

The lines of the large boat, Pr476, were based on those of Wa201 (designation Pr477), which meant that the available towing tank results could be used as a basis for calculation for the new design. As in Wa201, forward hydroplanes were not provided, but in their place cross-shaped stabilizing surfaces were attached to the finely tapered spindle-stern. In contrast to Wa201, however, in Pr476 a decision had been made in favour of a twin-screw drive, for greater reliability on distant voyages. The propeller shafts lay within the horizontal stabilizing surfaces, with the lateral rudder on the vertical fins, but still forward of the propellers. Especially noteworthy in this design was the low bridge superstructure (no conning tower!) with a collapsible bridge screen. On the forward side of the bridge was an observation point, pressure-tight to a depth of 130m and with a cross-section of 1.6m. This was covered on top by a Plexi-glass cover of a similar pressure-tight quality. Initially, anti-aircraft armament was not envisaged, but, at the request of Dönitz, planning later envisaged a two-barrelled 2cm anti-aircraft gun on the bridge superstructure.

The Walter-installation differed from that of Wa201 principally through the use of an exhaust-gas compressor so that the turbines no longer needed to work against the counter-pressure of the depth of water. Additionally, the electric switching apparatus for the turbine system had been simplified by dispensing with voltage regulating. The steering installation in the rear compartment was to be hydraulic, using oil pressure; steering impulses from the control room were to be transmitted electrically. Torpedo armament was concentrated forward so that the favourable streamlined properties of the stern would not be impaired by projecting torpedo tubes. As in the small Walter boats, the tubes were of the air-expelling type, i.e., without piston ejection. This was to ensure that even with the most rapid firing of torpedoes, with 2.3 seconds between each, movement of the boat would be so slight that compensatory trimming would be unnecessary. As the boat did not have a jumping wire to prevent the conning tower fouling a net, an extensible rod aerial was provided.

In November 1942, Walter, Schürer, Bröking and Waas visited Dönitz in Paris, taking with them appropriate basic drawings. The design of the boat

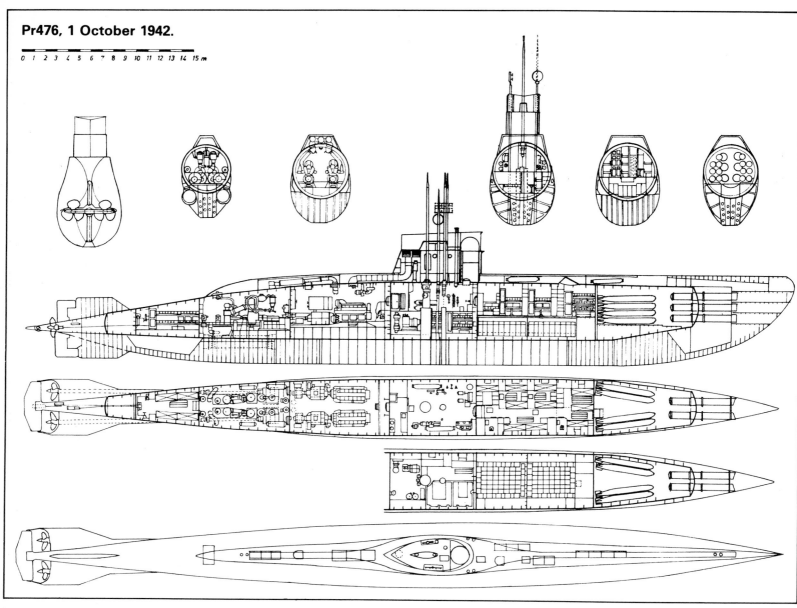

Pr476, 1 October 1942.

0 1 2 3 4 5 6 7 8 9 10 11 12 13 14 15 m

met with his approval apart from certain alternative wishes (7m torpedoes and pressure-tight conning tower). Dönitz demanded that yards capable of such work should, as soon as possible, be given a change of tasks to accommodate this new type, and that the production of a large series be commenced. Bröking and Waas made the immediate point that the engine installation was not yet ready for such series production, and even Walter, who was usually over-optimistic, hesitated on this point. Waas declared that the more-quickly built Type XVII would need to have adequate time spent on it before the large Type XVIII, but there was argument for initiating the building of two boats of the large type immediately. These could

take account of results obtained at the end of 1943 with the Type XVII boats, but no large series could be initiated before these were to hand. This meant that a delay in series production of at least a year was unavoidable. At this meeting, Waas also mentioned that while the production of H_2O_2 had in fact begun in Bad Lauterberg, an essential item for the future changeover to Walter boats, the second works in Rhumspringe (planned a considerable time previously), had still not been built. At this time, the Navy was concerned to secure only those amounts of H_2O_2 necessary for U-boat contracts already awarded and, as far as could be seen, the production of H_2O_2 for the Walter boats would rise only slowly. This question would have to be cleared

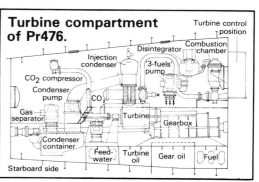

Turbine compartment of Pr476.

Turbine control position
Injection condenser
Disintegrator
Combustion chamber
'3-fuels' pump
CO_2 compressor
Condenser pump
CO_2
Turbine
Gas separator
Turbine
Gearbox
Condenser container
Feed-water
Turbine oil
Gear oil
Fuel
Starboard side

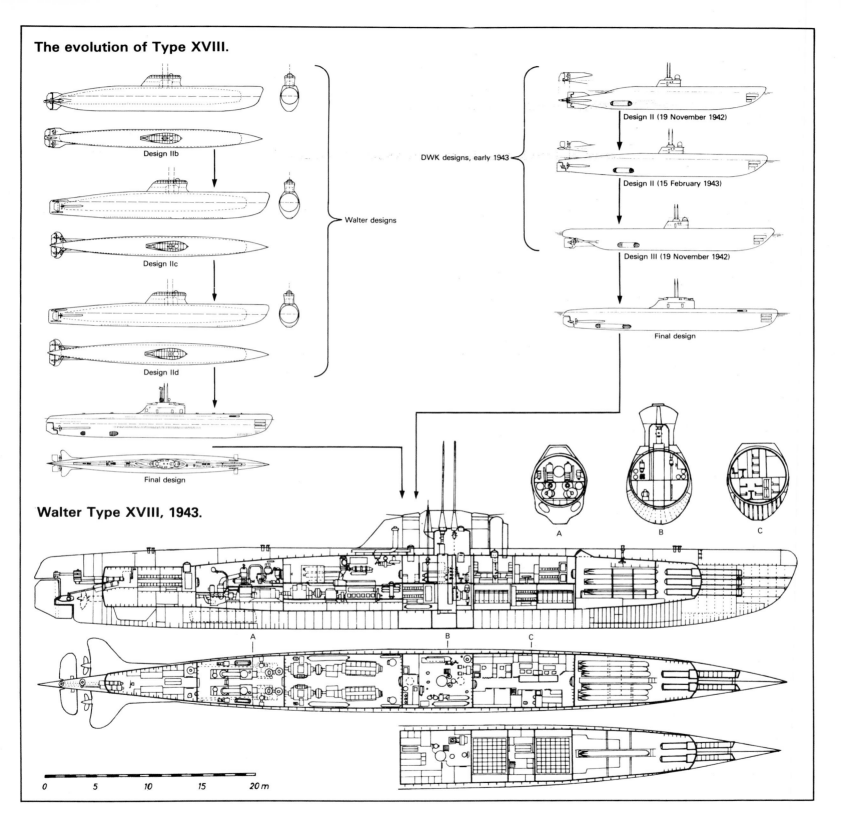

The evolution of Type XVIII.

Design IIb

Design IIc

Design IId

Walter designs

Final design

DWK designs, early 1943

Design II (19 November 1942)

Design II (15 February 1943)

Design III (19 November 1942)

Final design

Walter Type XVIII, 1943.

A

B

C

A

B

C

0   5   10   15   20 m

up before a decision was made on series production. The meeting ended with Dönitz urgently requesting that pressure be applied in appropriate quarters to provide, in addition to the proposed 24 Type XVII boats, at least the 2 suggested Type XVIII boats; and that H_2O_2 procurement should be investigated in the light of all future aspects and requirements.

The working-out of constructional details was now given to DWK. The requirement concerning a conning tower and 7m torpedo tubes altered the outer hull considerably. In order to make good the loss of stability brought about by this, the diving tanks were placed higher up and the stabilizing surfaces were widened, which gave the boat a more pronounced double-hull shape. As the length, despite the 7m torpedo tubes, was not to be altered, the battery compartments had to be made shorter. This could be done by going over to external frames, which was now possible, and this resulted in several further advantages for the layout of the boat's interior. A further step was that the bunker capacities were enlarged. The engine installation was also somewhat changed. Instead of the previously intended 1,200hp Deutz T12 M133 engines, 2,000hp MWM Type RS12 V26/34a were used. This four-stroke engine was preferred to the Deutz two-stroke because it was better able to blow the diving tanks. The main specifications for this new Design IIb (15 January 1943) were as follows:

Length overall:	67.7m.
Maximum beam:	5.8m.
Draught:	6.57m.
Pressure-hull diameter:	5.1m.
Maximum pressure-hull thickness:	25mm.
Outer frames:	260 × 14 at 800mm distance.
Hull displacement:	1,836.7 tons.
Displacement submerged:	1,453.1 tons.
Propulsion:	two × 6,000hp at 7,500rpm BKC-Walter turbines. two × 2,000hp at 85rpm RS12 V26/34a MWM diesel engines. two electric motors.
Aurol:	245 tons.
Fuel-oil:	247 tons.
Battery:	two × 62 type 33 MAL 800W cells.
Maximum speed surfaced:	17 knots.
Maximum speed submerged:	24 knots.
Range surfaced:	18,500 nautical miles at 8 knots; 15,000 nautical miles at 10 knots.
Range submerged:	270 nautical miles at 24 knots.
Constructional diving depth:	130m.
Armament:	six 7m bow torpedo tubes, twenty torpedoes. one 2cm AA.
Crew:	47.

On 4 January 1943, the building contract for two boats of this type was handed over to DWK, with the Yard Designation 'K330/331' (*U796–U797*).

In the detailed working-out of plans, a further enlargement of the boat was made, the spindle-stern changed to a knife-edge, a closed, roomy bridge and conning tower were provided and forward hydroplanes that could be swung out were installed. In versions IIc and IId, the design had a length of 69.35m, a beam of 6.2m and a pressure-hull diameter of 5.3m, but similar draughts. Initially, both versions were given a lateral rudder between two horizontal stabilizing fins abaft each propeller; later, this was changed to a semi-balanced rudder positioned amidships and a stabilizing fin placed level with the propeller shafts. The knife-edge stern was intended to increase the surface speed: in surface towing tests carried out at the HSVA in the early part of 1943, this had proved a more successful shape than the spindle-stern. Comparative surface measurements with a model corresponding to Design II showed that, at 17 knots, the spindle-stern required 2,748shp and the cut-away stern only 2,682shp. A noteworthy result of the trial was that in the version with knife-edged stern, the forward part of the boat was not awash at 16 knots, but remained dry — so, despite the enlarged size, a maximum speed of 18.5 knots was anticipated, and the Chief of Naval War Staff requirements were met beyond any question.

However, to meet the required maximum submerged speed of 24 knots, a sizeable increase in performance was necessary in view of the larger size, and it was hoped to achieve this by increasing the performance of both BKC-Walter turbines to 7,500hp at 10,000rpm for each turbine.

In the final version, which was to have been submitted in about May 1943, Type XVIII had a length of 71.7m, a submerged displacement of 1,652 tons and a form displacement of 1,887 tons. The bridge had been changed once again. It now had an open control position on the bridge deck, and two anti-aircraft turrets, placed forward and aft, each with two 3cm anti-aircraft guns (see pages 208 and 246).

THE EXHAUST-GAS CLOSED-CYCLE PROCESS

Development at FKFS, 1940–43

In December 1940, Dr. Heinrich Dräger gave the Research Institute for Motor Vehicles and Vehicle Engines at the Stuttgart Technical College (Forschungsinstitut für Kraftfahrwesen und Fahrzeugmotorenbau an der TH Stuttgart, or FKFS) a development task for a closed-cycle diesel engine. The firm of Dräger, Lübeck, which produced oxygen equipment among other items, was greatly interested in an 'oxygen-engine', which it regarded as having special significance for small U-boats. In one composite experiment they had compared various thermal engines working under conditions in which air was shut off. The item showing the most favourable results and which seemed to promise the simplest realization was the so-called

'oil-oxygen engine'. Conditions of secrecy meant that they knew nothing of the Walter-drive.

In March 1941, the FKFS began building a single-cylinder test installation for the closed-cycle operation. Under the control of Professor W. Kamm (Institute Head) and Dr. L. Huber (Department Head), a staff of engineers and scientists had been formed, and they approached this task with enthusiasm and scientific zeal. The initial closed-cycle operation of this engine showed that much might be expected from it. The engine ran very stiffly (too low an inlet-temperature) and, compared with air-operation, a fall-off in performance was observed. Tests with CO_2 absorption then followed. In May 1941, the closed-cycle operation was shown to representatives of the Dräger Works, and in June there followed an hour-long running of a

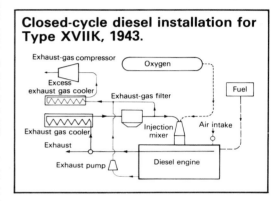

Closed-cycle diesel installation for Type XVIIK, 1943.

closed-cycle operation under partial loading. This very successful beginning prompted the Supreme Naval Command to give a development task to the FKFS on 3 July 1941: 'To investigate the possibilities of a working-process for a diesel engine for underwater operation and achieve a state of development that would make it suitable for use on board a vessel'.

The first closed-cycle operation under fully-loaded conditions showed that either higher compression or a greater concentration of oxygen was necessary, as the compression-exponent is less in closed-cycle than in air. In August 1941, the single-cylinder, closed-cycle engine was demonstrated to representatives of the Supreme Naval Command. It was shown, furthermore, that the unwanted exhaust gases could be absorbed in fresh water completely and without trace. In all, seven different processes for removing unwanted exhaust gases were discussed.

It seemed as though development of a closed-cycle engine for U-boats could be developed rapidly, so on 1 October 1941, Dr. Dräger added to his 'small U-boat' research programme two projects of 70 and 120 tons, to be 'oil-oxygen operated with exhaust-gas connection'. Both small boats were to be equipped with a large 'attacking diesel' of 800–1,000hp, developed in closed-cycle and giving an underwater speed of 16–18 knots. For cruising purposes, an additional small diesel engine of 60hp was envisaged. The armament would consist of two bow torpedo tubes (5m long and 45cm in diameter).

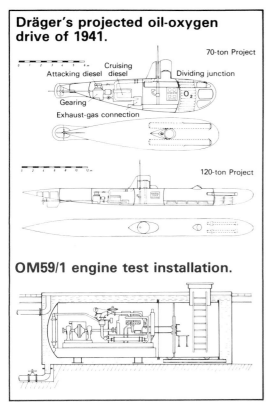

Dräger's projected oil-oxygen drive of 1941.

70-ton Project

Attacking diesel Cruising diesel Dividing junction

Gearing

Exhaust-gas connection

O_2

120-ton Project

OM59/1 engine test installation.

Further tests at the FKFS showed that conditions leading to better operations were to be achieved by an increase in closed-cycle temperature, and that an exhaust gas cleaning unit was necessary. The development of an automatic regulating system for the operation of the installation was handed over to the closed-cycle specialist, Dr. W. Rixmann, Construction Head of the firm of Kienzle AG, Villingen.

In November 1941, the FKFS commenced the planning of a U-boat engine incorporating the closed-cycle operation, and for this they chose the 1,400hp MTB engine of Daimler-Benz, MB502, a sixteen-cylinder, four-stroke diesel engine with fresh-water cooling. Additionally, so that further extensive basic testing could be carried out, a closed-cycle installation was constructed using a 53hp four-cylinder motor-car engine OM59/1. The necessary exhaust-gas compressor came from Ljungström, Sweden, whose Lysholm screw compressor was also considered suitable for a similar purpose in the Walter-Drive. In January 1942, the OM59/1 was to be seen in operation, initially without regulating mechanism. However, a considerable setback was experienced by the withdrawal of the Supreme Naval Command's contract. They justified this step by the shortage of raw materials and especially by the 'considerable progress that has been made in other solutions, in other places'. This meant, more particularly, the Walter-Drive, which at that time, was also having to fight for its existence.

In March 1942, the Dräger Works, which had aroused little interest by its suggestions for small U-boats, also withdrew its support. Research now made very halting progress, partly through lack of urgency, partly through a shortage of skilled staff. Nevertheless, the test-bed with the MB502 diesel engine was ready in June 1942. After considerable effort by the FKFS to obtain new authority for future work, they received on 13 July 1942 a priority requirement from the Army Ordnance Office, for test-bed trials of a diesel engine in the exhaust-gas, closed-cycle process, and the definitive development and testing of an automatic mixture-regulating installation. In November 1942, a contract arrived from the Reichs Office for Economic Development, Stuttgart, for the evolution of a diesel unit working independently of air, and this involved renewed Dräger participation.

In November 1942, the mixture-regulating installation of Dr. Rixmann could be put into use with engine OM59/1 (initially without load-dependency). Following this, it was possible to develop a mixture-regulating installation with temperature control mechanism which was adjusted by the uncooled bypass air current. At the beginning of 1943, work began on a mechanically- and hydraulically-operated pre-exhaust gas valve which was installed in the test engine in March 1943. The first trials showed that a complete expulsion of excess exhaust gas was achieved, and the endurance running time exceeded thirty hours. Further tests showed that increasing the closed-cycle pressure was only economic in conditions of full-loading and over-loading.

A second closed-cycle test-bed, incorporating an OM59/1 diesel engine built into a boiler, was prepared on 20 July 1943, and was given its tests only two days later under conditions in which air was completely excluded. On 16 October 1943, a running time of more than ten hours in the enclosed boiler was achieved without interruption. This meant that the installation had, at this stage, achieved forty-six hours of closed-cycle running without any attention to the engine. The final step was the incorporation of the OM59/1 boiler test-bed in a water trough so that information could be collected as to its behaviour in fully-submerged conditions, and in the interests of further research.

Trials at Deschimag and Germaniawerft: Type XVIIK

At the beginning of 1943, the Navy showed interest once again in the 'closed-cycle drive'. This interest was stimulated by Deschimag, who, at a much earlier date, had been experimenting with advanced processes (project for a caustic-soda/steam U-boat in about 1912, and the construction of the Engelmann high-speed boat of 1940–41). On 11 January 1943, theoretical evaluations were available from Deschimag (Obering, Eckert) concerning the exhaust gas-oxygen, closed-cycle operation in submarines. On 9 February 1943, Deschimag presented the Supreme Naval Command with the preliminary sketch for a high-speed, closed-cycle U-boat of approximately 350 tons, with two MB501 diesel engines, each developing 1,500hp, which in certain respects resembled the Engelmann boat. There is no doubt

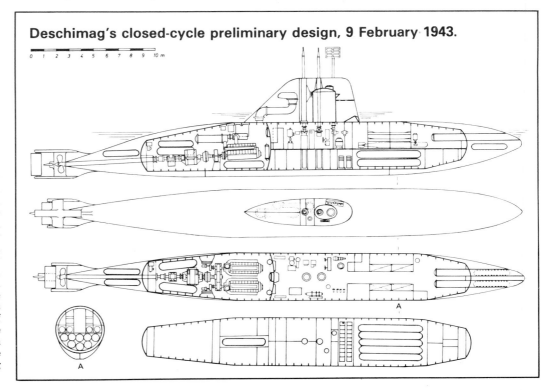

Deschimag's closed-cycle preliminary design, 9 February 1943.

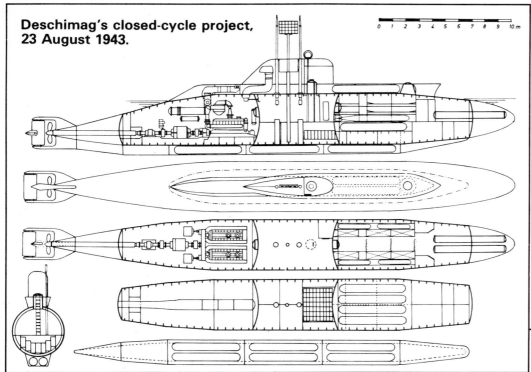

Deschimag's closed-cycle project, 23 August 1943.

Form displacement surfaced:	352.3 tons.
Form displacement submerged:	400.7 tons.
Propulsion:	two 1,500hp at 1,500rpm MB501 diesel engines (closed-cycle). one 50hp electric motor.
Fuel-oil:	30 tons.
Oxygen:	12 bottles (total 9.6 tons at 400 atmospheres).
Battery:	two × 62 cells and 2,100amp.h at 1.5 hours discharge.
Maximum speed surfaced:	15.75 knots.
Maximum speed submerged:	22.5 knots.
Diving depth:	150m.
Armament:	two 5m torpedo tubes; four torpedoes.

When the decision had been taken to switch U-boat construction to the new 'electric' U-boat Types XXI and XXIII (page 216), the outlook for a

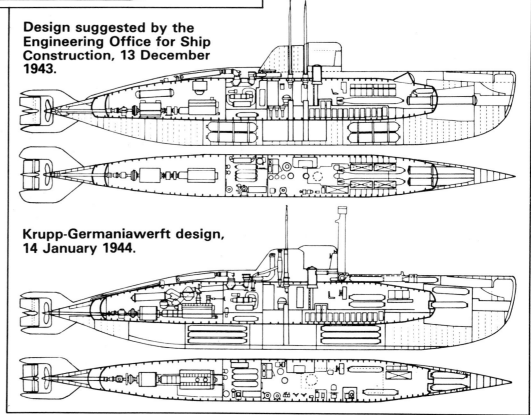

Design suggested by the Engineering Office for Ship Construction, 13 December 1943.

Krupp-Germaniawerft design, 14 January 1944.

that Deschimag, which was not involved with Walter U-boats, was influenced in producing this 'competitive project' by the interest shown by the Navy in the high-speed Walter U-boat. Their boat was to travel on the surface (half-submerged) at a maximum speed of 23 knots and, when submerged, a closed-cycle installation would enable it to achieve 22.5 knots. The oxygen supply amounted to approximately 7.5 tons and was stored in 10 pressure bottles at 400 atmospheres. It was armed with two bow torpedo tubes and five 5m torpedoes.

In March 1943, the Supreme Naval Command decided, as a result of this, to have a test boat built along these lines by Deschimag and Daimler-Benz in collaboration. The FKFS was therefore instructed to supply information on the closed-cycle process as applied to the MB501 diesel engine. In May 1943, the undertaking was given the 'SS' priority designation by the Supreme Naval Command, and in June at their request, the Reichs Minister for Armament and War Production, gave it the 'DE' (Dringlichkeitsstufe, or highest priority) designation.

All conditions now pointed to a prompt construction and testing of a full-sized installation. On 20 June 1943, Daimler-Benz delivered an engine, MB501C, with a converted suction line, and various regulators were completed for it. The Dräger yard provided the pressure-reducing apparatus.

In the meantime, work on the design of the boat had made progress. As planned in August 1943, the main specifications were as follows.

Length overall:	37.9m.
Maximum beam:	4m.

supreme development effort, bearing in mind the fact that yards were already working to capacity, seemed bleak. On 7 August 1943, at the instigation of the Ship Construction Commission, Deschimag had to suspend all work on its closed-cycle test U-boat. Three days later, Daimler-Benz had likewise to terminate work on its contract for the propulsion unit. However, the FKFS continued its research as far as circumstances permitted. An improvized test-bed was made for Engine MB501C, and the trials with the OM59/1 engine continued. At the request of the FKFS, representatives of GW inspected the closed-cycle test facilities on 22 September 1943. GW was not directly involved in the large, electric U-boat construction programme, but had been obliged to take over the more essential U-boat contracts that had been suspended from other yards. For this reason there was the possibility of an individual test construction by them.

After completion of the improvized test-bed for the MB501, there followed, on 5 November 1943, the first air- and, on 9 November 1943, the first closed-cycle operation. On 15 November, the installation was demonstrated to the HAS-Director, Otto Merker. Merker was very impressed and promised to try to bring about a change of mind on the part of the Ship Construction Commission and to plead for a continuation of the tests with Engine MB501C.

Then on 6 December 1943, the Supreme Naval Command looked once again at the project for a closed-cycle U-boat. A test boat was to be built so that the operation could be tested aboard, and then fully developed. Additionally, the safe storage of oxygen at high pressure (400 atmospheres) could be investigated, and other ideas could be tried out on board, such as hydraulic rudder gear driven by high-revolution engines (a development of the Test Institution for Air Travel at Berlin-Johannisthal) and a relatively high-performance schnorkel with special safety fittings.

GW, which was greatly interested in the construction of this test boat, wanted to use the hull of the Type XVIIG Walter U-boat, which had been designed but was as yet unbuilt. By 13 December 1943, a first suggestion of the Engineering Office for Ship Construction, Lübeck (Engineer Ebschner), for the necessary amended construction was available. As compared with Type XVIIG, the following changes were made:
1. An Aurol bunker to be used for the storage of oxygen bottles, positioned in the lower outer hull.
2. Lubricating-oil tanks, water tanks and coolers for the Aurol operation to be removed from the lower, outer hull, which would make some space for oxygen storage.
3. Stowage of ballast to be changed.
4. Forward torpedo tubes to be removed, to make space for oxygen storage.
5. Compressed-air containers in the upper deck to be removed to bow compartment and auxiliary engine compartment. Space to be used for oxygen storage.
6. Schnorkel to be installed on the forward edge of the conning-tower superstructure and in the upper deck.

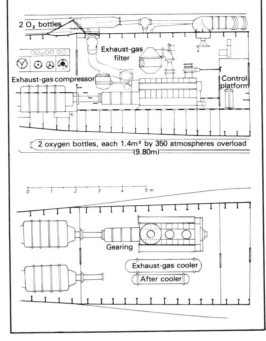

Closed-cycle conversion for Type VIIB, 15 January 1944.

2 O₂ bottles

Exhaust-gas filter

Exhaust-gas compressor

Control platform

2 oxygen bottles, each 1.4m³ by 350 atmospheres overload (9.80m)

Gearing

Exhaust-gas cooler

After cooler

7. The forward periscope to be dispensed with.
8. Engine compartment bulkhead to be repositioned further forward in the pressure hull by the distance of 2.5 frames and to be made to serve as a watertight, upright bulkhead (gas-tight).
9. Living quarters to be simplified.
10. Engine insulation to be changed fundamentally.
11. Hydroplane control-position in the control room to be provided on the starboard side.

Equipped with an MB501 closed-cycle engine, the boat was to reach a maximum surface speed of approximately 14 knots and a maximum submerged closed-cycle speed of approximately 16 knots. By using large 400-atmosphere high-pressure bottles, an oxygen supply of approximately 10 tons was calculated, sufficient for submerged travel of 120 nautical miles at 16 knots. The electric motor was to be developed from the AEG-type GU4463/8 of the Type XXIII (page 210). As the number of revolutions that this developed was too high, some modifications would be necessary.

On 21 December 1943, verbal contracts were given to GW by the Supreme Naval Command for a closed-cycle test boat; to Daimler-Benz for the MB501C engine, and to FKFS for the appropriate closed-cycle installation. On 23 December 1943, an endurance-running of ten hours was now achieved in the closed-cycle operation with the available MB501C test motor. In accomplishing this, the engine had achieved a total of 48 hours' closed-cycle operation, and seventy hours' air operation without any significant interruption.

The task of co-ordinating the development and construction of the planned experimental closed-cycle boat was given to Chief Naval Construction Adviser Kurzak of the Supreme Naval Command. At a discussion on 20 January 1944 between Kurzak, representatives of the FKFS and Daimler-Benz, the question was raised of finding the quickest way of setting up a second test-bed for the closed-cycle testing of the first engine actually to be used on board a vessel and due for delivery in May. The improvized, closed-cycle test-bed of the FKFS was too open to air attack and, in any case, was only fitted with provisional coolers. When the new test-bed was ready, trials were to take place under conditions resembling, as closely as possible, those on board ship. The most appropriate seemed to be one of the three air-screw test facilities under construction in Wendlingen. These were inspected on 26 January 1944 and the necessary conversions and installations were established. They included the erection of a building to house a container with a capacity of 25m³ of liquid oxygen, a 400-atmosphere oxygen pump with an evaporator, and four high-pressure bottles for storage of the gaseous oxygen at 400 atmospheres.

Daimler-Benz took over construction of the complete installation, while FKFS organized delivery of necessary items for the closed-cycle operation — regulators, fittings and measuring equipment. Exhaust-gas coolers and exchanger flaps were to be supplied by GW (who had prudently been carrying out such work from the autumn of 1943). Steel high-pressure bottles were procured from the Zeppelin Airship Company; normally used for helium transportation, these were 10m long and held 1,200 litres. The oxygen apparatus, liquid containers, pump and evaporator were produced by the IG-Farbenindustrie, Autogen Works. The high-and middle-pressure reducers were to be delivered by the Dräger Works, while the regulators necessary for the closed-cycle operations were to be produced by the firm of Kienzle.

The work of completing the test installation progressed so well that, as early as 28 February 1944, an ordinary MB501 diesel engine could be given preliminary trials in air-operation. At GW, the working-out of constructional details proceeded well. On 15 January 1944, for purposes of comparison, a plan was also discussed for a test boat using a closed-cycle installation that could be produced quickly, by converting a Type VIIB training boat. The oxygen bottles would be carried in the upper deck (three bottles forward, in place of the capstan, and two bottles aft, near the torpedo hatch) and four in a widened ballast keel. By these means it was hoped that a total 12.6m³ of oxygen at 350 atmospheres could be stored.

However, the Supreme Naval Command decided in favour of a test boat with the more useful high submerged speed provided by the hull shape of Walter's Type XVIIG, and this was designated Type XVIIK. Type XVIIG's shape lent itself better to the incorporation of the closed-cycle installation, once the parallel midships section had been lengthened by 1.8m, but of course the already-available hull would not necessarily provide a perfect housing for a new installation of this kind.

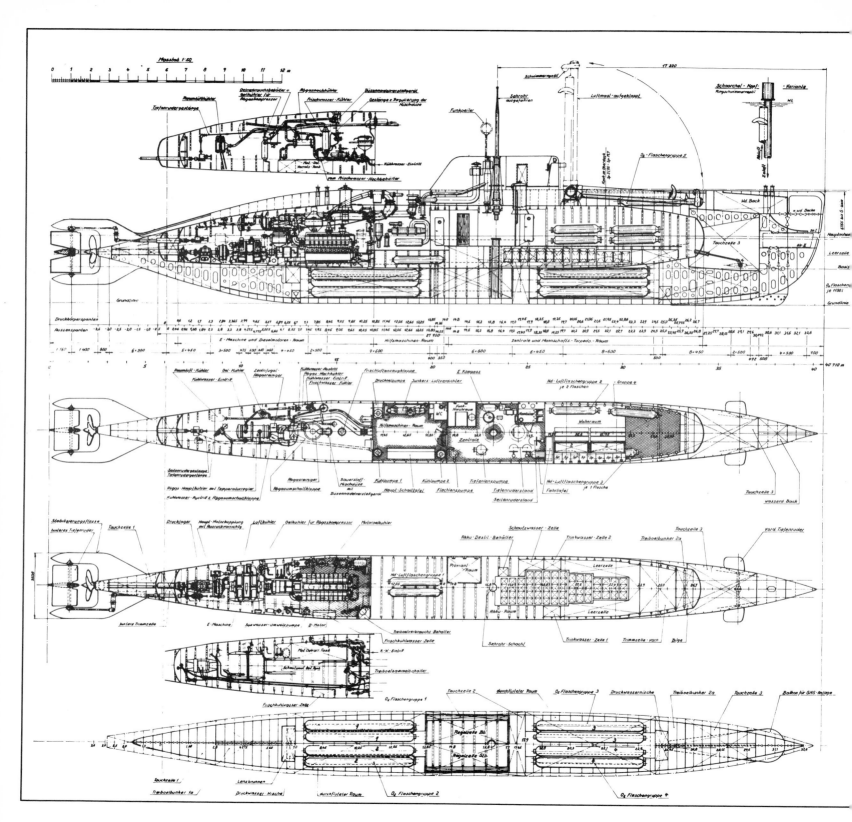

Type XVIIK.

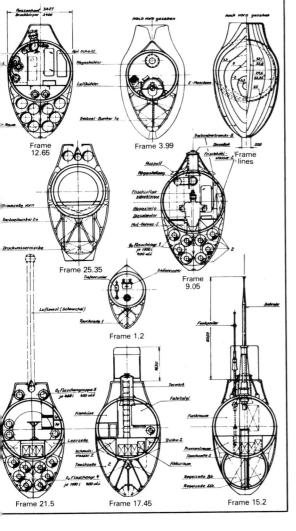

Glossary: Tiefenrudergestänge, hydroplane rods; Oelverbrauchsbehalter, oil supply tank; Oelkühler, oil cooler; Abgaskompressor, exhaust gas compressor; Frischwasser, fresh water; Kühler, cooler; Raumluftkühler, air conditioning; Mot. Oel Vorrats Tank, engine oil storage tank; Düsennadel verstellgerät, nozzle adjusting equipment; Gestänge z. Regulierung der Mischduse, articulated rod for regulating the blending nozzle; Funkpeiler, radio beam; Seerohr, periscope; Schwimmventil, floating valve; Luftmast, air mast; Schnorchel Kopf, schnorkel head; Flaschen, bottles; Wd. Back, watertight forecastle; Zuluft, air intake; Tauchzelle, ballast tank (water); Turmluk, conning tower hatch; Kombüse, galley; Funkraum, radio room; Proviantraum, stores; Regelzelle, compensating tank (water); Schmutzwasser Z., bilge water tank; E.-Kompass, electric compass; Luftverdichter, air compressor; Druckoelpump, pressure-oil pump; Zentrifugal-Abgasreiniger, centrifugal exhaust-gas purifier; Haupt-Schalttafel, main switch panel; Flachlenzpump, level bilge pump; Tiefenruder, hydroplane; Seitenruder, side rudder; Sauerstoff, oxygen; Hilfsmaschinen-Raum, auxiliary engine room; Drucklager, thrust bearing; Kuppling, coupling; Wohnraum, living quarters; Zentrale, control room; Funk-Horchraum, radio listening room; Leerzelle, empty compartment; Umwalzpumpe, revolving pump; Suswasser, fresh water; Lenzbrunnen, bilge well; Sammelbehalter, collecting tank; Druckwasser, pressure water; Trimmzelle, trimming tank; durchfluteter Raum, flooding compartment; Treibölverbrauchs-Behälter, fuel-oil storage tank; Auspuff, exhaust.

(For example, a special property of the closed-cycle drive is that the surface speed is relatively high because the air-power of the engines is determined by the power of the closed-cycle. This demands a good hull shape for full attainment of surface potential, and this was not present in the available Walter boat type, whose floating waterline was too short.) Nevertheless, for the envisaged test purpose, the boat's hull was adequate. Armament, the second periscope and special communications installations could be dispensed with because it was intended only to test the propulsion unit.

On 15 February 1944, the official contract was placed with GW under the construction number 'G787' (U798). The materials were gained by ceasing work on the sixth B&V Walter U-boat U1410 (Type XVIIB), and the work force was acquired by postponing completion of the large Walter U-boat U797 (Type XVIII) by six months. Once the keel had been laid on 23 April 1944, construction began in the roofed slipway at GW. When the detailed construction design had been completed, delivery was envisaged on 12 September 1944.

The Walter Works, which (not without reason) feared a considerable delay in its own submarine programme, expressed itself in critical terms concerning the 'competitive' closed-cycle drive (Report S71 dated 5 February 1944). Special reference was made to the more favourable storage facilities for Aurol and the better performance-to-weight and performance-to-size ratios of the Walter turbine as compared with a diesel engine. While a diesel installation, as in Type XVII, would yield only approximately 1,500hp, use of a Walter-Turbine could provide 5,000hp. If, however, one looked at the submerged range rather than the submerged top speed, the closed-cycle drive seemed superior, as Kurzak confirmed in his report 'The Ranges of U-Boats with Drive supplied by Closed-Cycle Diesel Engines and by Walter-Turbines, using Oxygen and Aurol' dated 4 May 1944. The ranges for a Type XVIIB with a 1,500hp installation at a diving depth of 30m were as follows:

Walter-Turbine without compressor:	340 nautical miles at 8 knots, or 225 nautical miles at 17 knots.
Walter-Turbine with compressor:	490 nautical miles at 8 knots, or 305 nautical miles at 17 knots.
Closed-cycle diesel with gaseous oxygen at 400 atmospheres:	720—800 nautical miles at 8 knots, or 184—208 nautical miles at 17 knots.
Closed-cycle diesel with liquid oxygen:	1,080 nautical miles at 8 knots, or 284 nautical miles at 17 knots.
Closed-cycle diesel with Aurol:	1,160 nautical miles at 8 knots, or 396 nautical miles at 17 knots.

In the meantime, the closed-cycle installation using the MB501 test engine had been set up in Wendlingen. The exhaust-gas coolers were available as early as the middle of February 1944, but deliveries of certain conduits from Daimler-Benz and of an exhaust-gas filter from Mann & Hummel were delayed considerably by air raids.

The exhaust-gas filter was destroyed by fire and a new one had to be made by Daimler-Benz. Consequently, in March, construction of the closed-cycle installation was making but slow progress. As delivery of the high-pressure bottles and appropriate fittings and connections was delayed by air raids, construction and assembly could not begin until the latter part of April. On 10 May 1944, the installation was ready and trials could begin. On 16 May, it was run for the first time in an hour-long, closed-cycle operation, but closed-cycle pressure could not be increased, and its temperature was controlled by hand. Several slight changes and improvements followed. These preliminary trials were concluded on 21 May, after which the test engine was removed and the MB501C engine, intended for the boat, could be installed on the test bed with its exhaust-gas pump. This twelve-cylinder exhaust-gas pump had been developed by Daimler-Benz from a petrol engine and was electrically driven. It was tested in air conditions to the desired back-pressure of 10 atmospheres. On 30 May 1944, tests were continued with this engine, and with temperature- and closed-cycle pressure regulators, which had been tried-out on the FKFS test-bed. Meanwhile, the 400-atmosphere oxygen pump with vaporizer and the high-pressure reducer, had been delivered and installed so that, on 1 June 1944, as planned, the complete installation could be set into operation up to the operating pressure of 400 atmospheres.

After necessary test adjustments, the complete installation in closed-cycle operation was demonstrated to the directors of Daimler-Benz AG on 5 June 1944 and a day later to representatives of the Supreme Naval Command, when it ran for four hours without interruption. On 12 June 1944, the double-gearing was installed and tried out. On this occasion, the crank-case exhaust process was carried out using the Dräger-Lysholm compressor, but the results were not as expected because too large a quantity of oil collected in the crank-case. Following the acceptance and approval of the installation for operational use, the engine was dismantled and prepared for despatch to the actual U-boat. After a water-pressure test on 15 June 1944, the boat was ready to receive it, but in the meantime GW had become involved in the Type XXIII Programme (page 224) and the Type 127 Midget U-boat Programme (page 288), both of which were considered more urgent in view of the critical war situation. In consequence, considerable delays and cessation of work occurred, so that even by the autumn, the test boat still lay incomplete on the slip.

During an armament discussion on 6 December 1944, it was stated that a figure of 90,000 work-hours still remained to be done on U798; i.e. 63 men would have had to work on the boat in order to make it ready for the new date of 1 June 1945. In view of the events of that time, it is most unlikely that any resumption of work on this boat was undertaken. It had been intended to put the boat into the water on 16 February 1945, but at the end of the war she lay in an overturned position in the yard, alongside the oxygen pressure bottles intended for her use.

7 THE MOVE TO HIGH SUBMERGED SPEED

SURFACED U-BOATS: PROBLEMS AND SOLUTIONS

Improved anti-aircraft armament

From 1940, the first change from peacetime armament in all Type VII U-boats had consisted of a widening of the bridge for the 2cm C/30 machine-gun positioned there. This was rarely used against aircraft, however, as commanders deemed it more prudent to evade air attack by diving. By 1942, however, the growing threat of air attack and detection by radar, and the unreliability and limitations of the C/30 machine-gun led to a request by the Commander-in-Chief, U-Boats, on 16 June 1942, for a strengthening of the armament by two twin 15mm MG151, and the designing of a 3.7cm twin mounting for U-boats.

The Supreme Naval Command required, therefore, two twin MG151 on the existing bridge and a 2cm twin anti-aircraft mounting on a platform half the height of the bridge and situated abaft the conning tower (in what was known as the 'winter garden'). Special pressure-tight box mountings had to be designed for the 15mm MG151s which were not pressure-tight. As, at that time, the 2cm twin mounting was not available, initially only one 2cm gun was used on the platform. This was Bridge Conversion I. *U553*, fitted out in this way, was tested in the autumn of 1942, but the installation was unsatisfactory, especially because of the lack of penetrating power of the MG151. At the end of January 1943, the boat was lost in the North Atlantic, cause unknown, and in the meantime the improved 2cm anti-aircraft C/38 introduced in December 1942 offered better results. A modification of Bridge Conversion I, involving two twin 13.2mm Breda machine-guns and one 2cm anti-aircraft gun on an enlarged bridge (without 'winter garden'), was built into certain Mediterranean U-boats and used operationally in 1943 (*U81* and *U453*). Following the testing in October 1942 of two quadruple 2cm C/38 Army-type machine-guns for suitability in U-boats, a discussion with the Commander-in-Chief, U-Boats, on 14 November 1942 resulted in the following anti-aircraft installations being called for:

Bridge Conversion II: one 2cm C/38 on the bridge and a similar one on the anti-aircraft platform.

Bridge Conversion III: two 2cm C/38 on a widened bridge (especially necessary for Type VIID) so that the mine-shafts would not be overhung).

Bridge Conversion IV: two twin 2cm C/38 on the bridge, and one quadruple 2cm or an automatic 3.7cm anti-aircraft gun on the platform abaft the bridge.

Bridge Conversion II was intended only as an intermediate solution until the 2cm twin, the 2cm quadruple and the new automatic 3.7cm anti-aircraft guns were ready for operational use, and Bridge Conversion IV was to be the final solution. Bridge Conversion II began in December 1942. Following some teething troubles, the first two quadruple 2cm mountings were fitted to two operational U-boats (*U758* and one other) for trial purposes in April–May 1943. (Originally, one boat should have received the new 3.7cm anti-aircraft gun M42U for comparative purposes, but this was not ready for use.) However, because of the high losses through air attack, it was not expedient to await the operational findings of these two boats and, from May 1943, the quadruple 38/43U was produced as a series and, from June 1943 fitted in all current production.

From 27 April 1943, the removal of the 8.8cm gun was authorized, because there were very few opportunities to use it and, furthermore, the necessity was borne in mind for balance in the weight-momentum and height-momentum. Only the Mediterranean and Polar boats were allowed to keep these guns, if specially applied for. Some large U-boats retained their 10.5cm gun, or exchanged it for another 3.7cm quick-firing C/30U, the position of which, abaft the bridge, had to make way for the new 'winter garden'. In the summer of 1944, for operations in the Gulf of Finland, a few VIIC boats had their 8.8cm gun refitted.

From 14 June 1943, no U-boat was allowed to go into action without an increased anti-aircraft armament (at least two 2cm). Following the delivery of the first 40 twin M38 guns on 15 July 1943, no boat was allowed to be used in operations from August 1943 without Bridge Conversion IV. Initially, the two twin 2cm guns were mounted without a protective shield; only when they could be placed farther apart were protective shields provided, and these were welcomed by operational crews.

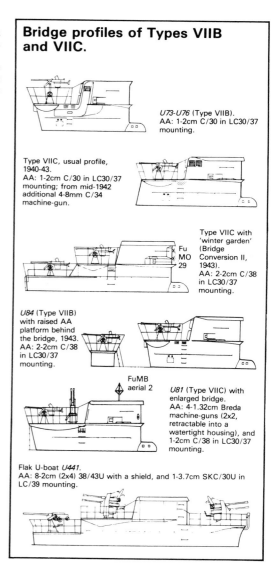

Bridge profiles of Types VIIB and VIIC.

U73-U76 (Type VIIB). AA: 1-2cm C/30 in LC30/37 mounting.

Type VIIC, usual profile, 1940-43. AA: 1-2cm C/30 in LC30/37 mounting; from mid-1942 additional 4-8mm C/34 machine-gun.

Type VIIC with 'winter garden' (Bridge Conversion II, 1943). AA: 2-2cm C/38 in LC30/37 mounting.

U84 (Type VIIB) with raised AA platform behind the bridge, 1943. AA: 2-2cm C/38 in LC30/37 mounting.

U81 (Type VIIC) with enlarged bridge. AA: 4-1.32cm Breda machine-guns (2x2, retractable into a watertight housing), and 1-2cm C/38 in LC30/37 mounting.

Flak U-boat *U441*. AA: 8-2cm (2x4) 38/43U with a shield, and 1-3.7cm SKC/30U in LC/39 mounting.

Right: *U81* (Type VIIC) with longer bridge and two extra twin 1.32cm Breda machine-guns, 1943. **Far right:** A 2cm quadruple 38/43U on *U745* (Type VIIC), 1944.

Left, top: *U1108* (Type VIIC/41) with twin 3.7cm AA, May 1945.
Below: Mock-up of a new bridge shape (Bridge Conversion I) to accommodate increased AA armament on *U236*, autumn 1942.

Opposite page, top: *U673* with increased AA armament (Bridge Conversion VI).
Below: Series production of new bridges (Bridge Conversion IV) at KMW, 1943/44.

o

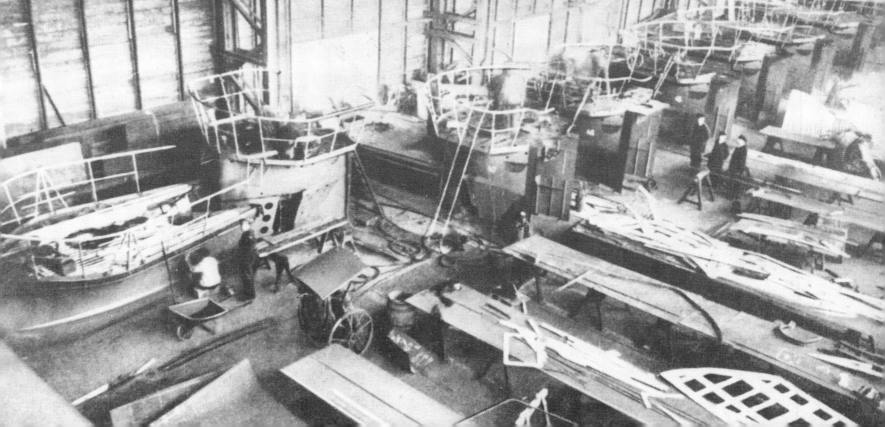

The enlarged bridge of 'Flak' U-boat *U441*. **Above:** Model under construction at GW, early 1943; below, on operations after conversion. **Opposite page:** *U362* with Bridge Conversion V.

In October 1943, 4 U-boats could be equipped for the first time with the new 3.7cm automatic M42U in mounting LM43U. As the quadruples, even in the improved M43 version made by Hanomag, did not fully come up to expectations, an exchange of the 2cm quadruple with the more effective 3.7cm automatic was ordered on 15 October 1943. However, because of delivery problems, some U-boats (approximately 20 per cent) remained equipped with either the 2cm quadruple or a single 3.7cm quick firing C/30U.

As a further strengthening of the anti-aircraft armament, on 14 August 1943, tests were ordered of an additional anti-aircraft platform forward of the bridge. These Bridge Conversions V and VI (differing versions for the forward platform) provided: aft above, two twin 2cm M38; aft below, one 3.7cm M42; and, on the forward platform, a twin 2cm or a further 3.7cm M42. The first two test boats, *U973* and *U673* (Conversion VI) were intended for the Polar regions. Additionally, *U362* (Conversion V) was similarly fitted-out. The added structure did not prove satisfactory, however, and had an adverse effect on stability. Finally, as Bridge Conversion VII, around the bridge itself a raised platform was provided, on which two anti-aircraft guns were placed side by side forward of the bridge, and a similar two abaft it.

These Bridge Conversions V—VII should not be confused with the conversions to the so-called anti-aircraft, or 'Flak', U-boats. These had different offensive tasks (protecting groups of U-boats) from those of normal VIIC U-boats and were provided with only five torpedoes, but their anti-aircraft armament was considerable (two 2cm quadruple and one 3.7cm gun). The repair boat *U256* was the first to serve as a Flak U-boat, but its fitting-out suffered considerable delays and, on 16 April 1943, a speeded-up conversion of *U441* to a Flak U-boat was ordered. In the period ending 20 May 1943, 7 U-boats (*U441*, *U256*, *U621*, *U211*, *U953*, *U271*, *U263*) were ordered to be converted. However, the first operation of *U441* showed that even these strongly-armed boats were no match for the Allied air superiority in the Bay of Biscay and, for more distant operations, their fuel supply was inadequate and their torpedo supply too meagre. On 11 November 1943, the re-conversion of all Flak U-boats to normal operational boats with Bridge Conversion IV was ordered.

Parallel with the strengthening of the anti-aircraft armament, an armoured shield for the bridge crew was ordered. From July 1943, the initial all-round armouring was replaced by anti-splinter shelters to port and starboard, but these were not popular and were hardly ever used. Their removal, therefore, was ordered on 31 October 1943.

By the end of 1943, it was obvious that all attempts to win back a measure of surface 'battle-power' for the U-boats, by increasing their anti-aircraft qualities, were in vain. Nevertheless, until the end of the war, all larger U-boats proceeding on operations carried a heavy anti-aircraft armament, which considerably hampered the submerged qualities of the boats. The Chief of Naval War Staff made it a significant requirement, even for the new, large U-boats whose development went back to the spring of 1943, that they possess a strong anti-aircraft armament, so that when making rapid changes of position over considerable distances, which even the Walter U-boats could only do on the surface, they should not be defenceless. On the other hand, it was necessary that the anti-aircaft weaponry should not create too great a submerged resistance for the envisaged high submerged speed. Therefore, in the case of Type XVIII, a plan was formulated for the construction of enclosed anti-aircraft towers streamlined into the conning-tower superstructure, initially only aft, but later both forward and aft. These towers, which could turn, were entered either from the bridge or from above by bascule-type doors, and each was served by a 3-man crew. The armament for each tower consisted of two 3cm Flak M44 in LM44 with 3,800 rounds and a hydraulically-operated aiming device. It was then decided to use this item of weaponry for Type XXI, but the development of these new weapons took longer than had been expected, and special difficulties with their pressure-tight qualities arose. As a result the well-tested 2cm twin Flak C/38 were installed in the anti-aircraft towers, which meant that the new boats were under-armed compared to the old U-boats. Then again, the towers were unpopular because they were not particularly accessible and they delayed the diving-process. They may have had some psychological significance, but they were of very little practical use.

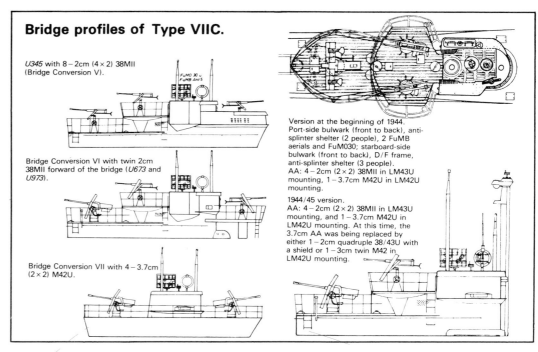

Bridge profiles of Type VIIC.

U345 with 8 – 2cm (4 × 2) 38MII (Bridge Conversion V).

Bridge Conversion VI with twin 2cm 38MII forward of the bridge (U673 and U973).

Bridge Conversion VII with 4 – 3.7cm (2 × 2) M42U.

Version at the beginning of 1944. Port-side bulwark (front to back), anti-splinter shelter (2 people), 2 FuMB aerials and FuM030; starboard-side bulwark (front to back), D/F frame, anti-splinter shelter (3 people). AA: 4 – 2cm (2 × 2) 38MII in LM43U mounting, 1 – 3.7cm M42U in LM42U mounting.

1944/45 version. AA: 4 – 2cm (2 × 2) 38MII in LM43U mounting, and 1 – 3.7cm M42U in LM42U mounting. At this time, the 3.7cm AA was being replaced by either 1 – 2cm quadruple 38/43U with a shield or 1 – 3cm twin M42 in LM42U mounting.

Below: *U2502, U3041, U3515, U170* and *U1108* alongside the torpedo-boat *Panther* at Horten, May 1945. **Opposite page, top:** *U515* (Type IXC) with increased AA armament (six 2cm and one 3.7cm), autumn 1943. **Opposite page, below:** Type VIIC boats in the shelter at Trondheim, May 1945.

At the end of 1940, the British began to equip their aircraft with a new detection device working on a wavelength of 1.5m — ASV (Air to Surface Vessel) radar. By April 1941, 110 aircraft of Coastal Command had been so equipped and, from early in 1942, all aircraft operating against U-boats had this equipment installed in them. From the summer of 1942, U-boats increasingly reported unexpected attacks by enemy aircraft even at night, when they would suddenly be illuminated by strong searchlights. Radio observation had already shown that the cause was to be sought in radio detection equipment (radar). With all speed, VHF-heterodyne receivers, made by the French firms of Metox-Grandin and Sadir, together with a primitive wooden frame aerial ('Biscay Cross') were fitted to U-boats. The detection beam was indicated by a loud 'pinging' in the receiver.

From August 1942, all U-boats were given this equipment, and losses in Biscay declined sharply; however, the Allies possessed new radar equipment operating on much shorter wavelengths that the Germans did not think could be successfully employed. German industry was requested to produce an operationally-effective observation equipment for the range of 3—0.75m wavelength. The result was a pressure-tight, all-round dipole, designated FuMB29 'Bali' (FuMB being short for Funkmess-Beobachtungsgerät, or 'Radar Observation Equipment'), and the Butterfly aerial 'Palau' (already tried on surface vessels) with direction-finding. At first, the receiver to go with this was to be the VHF-heterodyne receiver 'Samos' made by Rohde & Schwartz.

When, therefore, in the early part of 1943, U-boats were once again subjected to unexpected air attack by night, and illumination by search-lights without the evidence of any detection equipment, it was assumed that the enemy were now using a higher impulse-sequence which could not be detected acoustically. As a counter-measure, the Metox equipment was fitted with a 'magic eye' from March 1943. The catastrophic U-boat losses in May, however, showed that the detection problem besetting U-boats was nowhere near solved. One consequence was the dismissal of the Head of the Naval Communications Arm, Vizeadmiral Maertens, and his replacement by Konteradmiral Stummel. High-frequency research in the field of U-boat operations was greatly widened and intensified. The scientific control of this was handed over in December 1943 to Professor Karl Küpfmüller. Nevertheless, the months that followed were still characterized by uncertainty and underestimation of the enemy's detection processes.

At the end of July 1943, it was believed that the cause of the high U-boat losses lay in the fact that the enemy could zero-in on the intermediate frequency of the heterodyne receivers carried aboard U-boats. This led in August to an order forbidding the use of Metox, and the resumption of U-boat operations in the North Atlantic was postponed until designated U-boats had been fitted with new detection receivers. (Certainly the British knew that the Metox emitted radiation, but this factor was never actually used in detection.) The first low-radiation observation and warning device was that produced by Hagenuk and installed from August 1943. This was the automatic search receiver FuMB9 'Zypern' (also called W. Anz g 1) which was intended especially to detect the erroneously-assumed short impulses. The equipment consisted of a heterodyne receiver with indicator valves in series. When used for automatic frequency-scanning, using a movable condenser activated by a motor, the radiation issuing from this apparatus was quite slight.

FuMB aerial 2 ('Biscay Cross').

The first boat fitted with W. Anz g 1 ('Wanze') was U161, which proceeded through the Bay of Biscay without attack. Following this, and successive possibly fortuitous experiences with the W. Anz g 1, the U-boat Directorate concluded: 'After the switching-off of Metox and the introduction of "Wanze" hardly a single boat has been sighted or attacked. Thus, the anti-detection position has changed basically.' However, at the beginning of September, despite being equipped with 'Wanze', U386 was surprised and attacked by an aircraft at night, without any evidence of detection. Only gradually did the Chief of Naval War Staff realize that a completely new detection process with a significantly shorter wavelength (i.e., in the centimeter range), could be responsible for the failure of the warning installations. Thinking, however, was still obsessed by the fear that the enemy could zero-in on German heterodyne receivers, and this led to the replacement of W. Anz g 1 by W. Anz g 2 which was less prone to emission. Additionally, the completely emission-free, untuned detector adaptor FuMB10 'Borkum', introduced by NVK/Telefunken, using an attached NF-impulse amplifier, formed a wide-band receiving installation with a relatively large frequency spread (up to approximately 20cm wavelength), but with a somewhat restricted range.

Early in 1943, an aircraft was shot down over Rotterdam and was found to contain one of the new British radar installations, H2S, with a 9cm wavelength. Only after thorough investigation and reconstruction of this equipment was the full extent of the new danger realized, and the development of a suitable warning device began immediately. In June 1943, the prototype of a simple detecting receiver, designated FuMB 7 'Naxos', was available from NVK/Telefunken. An impulse amplifier was used as a receiver. The first U-boats were furnished with this installation at the end of 1943, but its range of approximately 5km was too low to provide security from sudden air attack, which left the situation very much as before. Not until the advent of the sounding combination, FuMB26 'Tunis', with dipole aerial 'Fliege' for a wavelength of 9cm, and the horn radiator 'Mücke' for the new American 3cm radar, did the position improve. This new warning system was incorporated into U-boats from May—June 1944 and attained ranges of up to 70km. The aerials, however, were not pressure-tight. For surface travel, they were simply incorporated into the direction-finder frame and rotated with it. Only at the end of the war was a pressure-tight cm-wavelength aerial with an extensible mast available operationally for the 9cm and 3cm ranges, with a rough direction-finder installation; it was designated FuMB35 'Athos'. The next step followed on 12 September 1944, with the decision to introduce a combination of 'Athos' and 'Bali', designated FuMB37 'Leros'.

Apart from the development of warning devices, experiments were carried out with little success in disguising U-boats against high-frequency detection (e.g., with the Bachem 'net', a wire net of 120 ohms resistance, set a quarter of a wavelength from the boat's hull). More success was seemingly offered by the idea of disguising certain smaller components, e.g., the schnorkel head, with detection sumps. Swimming bodies ('Thetis') and balloons ('Aphrodite') with reflectors were intended to deceive by providing apparent targets. Even the supposed infra-red detection was investigated, and tests were carried out on certain U-boats. A significant measure against the infra-red emission given out by a boat was the re-positioning of the exhaust under the surface of the water. All these strivings were carried out almost wholly to defeat the enemy's radar equipment. Right up to the end of the war, it was not comprehended by the German U-Boat Command that the homing-in of even short W/T messages on short-wave with the aid of the

British HF-DF equipment (high-frequency direction-finding) represented, at the very least, a considerable danger for U-boats, and was often the precursor of an exact detection by radar and asdic, followed by an accurate attack on the U-boat, or the surrounding of it by convoy escorts. It has recently been made known that the British had been in possession of a German Enigma machine throughout the war, and their systematic deciphering of German radio transmissions greatly assisted them to find and destroy U-boats.

As early as the summer of 1939, two U-boats were to have been fitted for test purposes with an active radar equipment (Dete-equipment). Various discussions between the NVK and the U-Boat Command took place, in which a general basis for the installation of such apparatus was thrashed out. On 3 November 1939, a letter from the U-Boat Command to the NVK stated:

'The general basis for the installation of Dete-equipment in U-boats worked out in the previous discussion is confirmed and stated below. Chief of Naval War Staff — U estimates a maximum range of 6—7,000m. Without any special expenditure, the detection accuracy that can be attained with the help of a maximum detection of 2° is regarded as adequate. In these installations, care must be taken that all opportunities be taken to avoid an increase in the silhouette of the U-boat or at least any increase must be kept to a minimum. At the moment, there is no objection to the intention to make the complete aerial structure either collapsible or to make certain components portable. Chief of Naval War Staff — U has taken note that a provisional test on *Störtebecker* or on a similar vessel is envisaged for December of this year.'

However, there was no move to install such apparatus in U-boats, presumably because of the considerable amount of space that would be taken up and the general lack of urgency at the time. It was not until June 1942, at a conference with the Commander-in-Chief, U-Boats, concerning the problems of U-boat detection by aircraft, that Dönitz demanded that boats be fitted with an active detection equipment. This led to the conversion of the Naval FuMO (Funkmess-Ortungsgerät, or Radar-Detection Equipment) made by GEMA for U-boat use: Designated FuMO30, the equipment consisted of 2 × 4 dipoles on a turntable installed in the bridge superstructure. The aerial assembly had to be specially reduced in size, but the frequency of 368MHz (82cm wavelength) was retained. It did not give very accurate information. In certain U-boats, a fixed aerial with 2 × 6 dipoles was fitted forward of the bridge (FuMO29). Installation began in the autumn of 1942, but the results were not satisfactory.

More was hoped for from the Luftwaffe ship-detection gear FuMG 200 'Hohentwiel', made by Lorenz in the summer of 1942. It had a frequency of 556MHz (56cm wavelength) and allowed the disposition of 4 × 6 dipoles on an assembly of 1 × 1.4m². The Naval designation was FuMO61

Right: A Type VIIC bridge with FuMO30 radar and armoured conning tower.

'Hohentwiel U'. By 20 September 1944, 64 operational boats had been fitted with 'Hohentwiel', and it was intended to install a further 32 in Type VIIC and Type IX boats. On 17 September 1944, *U862* reported from Penang: 'FuMO Hohentwiel has worked well throughout the voyage. The range against loaded freighters in the tropics amounts to 7.2km. No impairment of performance has been occasioned by the tropical climate.' A further 16 boats used the installation successfully as an active air-warning gear, but these were almost certainly exceptional cases. As boats hardly ever operated on the surface now, and their commanders hardly ever switched on the equipment for fear of being themselves detected, it was rarely used on the few surface voyages and its efficiency seems highly doubtful, as does that of its later development, FuMO65 'Hohentwiel-Drauf' which was fitted to all new Type XXI boats.

FuMO65 'Hohentwiel'-Drauf radar aerial on a Type XXI.

At the end of the war, two items of active detection equipment that could be used at periscope depth were still in the test stage. These were the German 9cm FuMO84 'Berlin II', which had a stern emitter in a pressure-tight casing on an extensible mast, and the active surveillance apparatus for use against aircraft, FuMO391 'Lessing' (2.4m wavelength) with an extensible vertical aerial. These were intended for new U-boats from the summer of 1945.

The schnorkel
Walter's first proposal for a high-speed U-boat in October 1933 included an installation for introducing atmospheric air while the boat was just below the surface, through an extensible air-shaft. The reason for the latter was that the boat, having a fish-shaped hull without upperworks, was awash on the surface even at low speeds. At about the same time, Lieutenant-Commander J. J. Wichers of the Royal Netherlands Navy took out a patent for

an extensible air mast in an attempt to facilitate the use of diesel engines when submerged. Possibly this was prompted by the wish to be able to undertake diesel-powered voyages, in the flooded condition, in the very considerable heat of the Dutch East Indies: the calm seas that prevail in that part of the world meant that a relatively short air-mast could be used.

Wichers improved the concept several times, and planned an automatic head-valve for the air-mast, with a spherical float (valve seating and counter-spring) as an intermediate cushioning for pressure variations. In the interior of the boat, he proposed a special air container with connections for air-mast and oxygen bottles. For test purposes, his air-mast was fitted in Dutch submarines from *O19*. In 1939, *O19* and O20 had air-masts with automatic head-valves and a motor-drive for lifting and retracting it. The exhaust-gas mast was not retractable. *O19* used her air mast during the war against Japan, but it is not known whether lengthy submerged voyages using the diesel engines with this arrangement were undertaken. *O21–O27* had an improved installation in which the exhaust-gas mast could be extended and retracted by hand. A more comprehensive design, of 1940, even envisaged an automatically extensible, two-section air-supply and air-expulsion mast.

Both the German and British Navies knew of these installations through submarines captured or handed over, but showed no particular interest in them. In fact, the air-masts for *O21–O24* were dismantled in 1940 by the British Navy, supposedly at the suggestion of a Dutch officer. In 1941, the air mast of *O26* (*UD4*) was subjected to tests by the UAK. Certain problems were encountered, but at the end of 1941, despite Chief Naval Construction Adviser Aschmoneit's protests, the trials were discontinued, and the air-masts were dismantled from the captured submarines *O25–O27*. It was considered that, in the turbulent European and Atlantic waters, the air-mast could be used, at best, to supply air while surfaced in heavy seas, but the German diesel air-masts were preferable for this. The authorities decided that there was no future in trying to develop an apparatus for introducing fresh air while submerged.

Not until the early part of 1943 was the idea taken up again, on the initiative of Hellmuth Walter. On 2 March 1943, Walter and Dönitz discussed the future development of the Walter U-boats, the difficulties of the U-boat campaign and the severe losses sustained. Walter suggested that U-boats should travel submerged, even when using their diesels, taking in air for the diesels through a tube — this would inhibit radar and make the enemy's task more difficult. Walter illustrated his proposal with a sketch, relating it back to his original idea of 1933. Dönitz was immediately intrigued and asked Walter to develop the idea. At Kiel, Walter handed the concept to his collaborators, principally to the U-boat specialists Gabler and Heep, who took account of the Dutch spherical float for the automatic head-valve. The vital point that made possible the use of the air-mast in the rough Atlantic seas was the principle of

using the entire interior of the boat as an air cushion from which the diesels could freely aspirate. On 19 May 1943, Walter reported progress of the work in a letter to Dönitz:
'Dear Grossadmiral,
When, on the occasion of my visit on 2.3.43, I asked for the Construction Director, Dr. Fischer, who incidentally has taken up his task zealously and with success that is already apparent, I mentioned the possibility of running engines during submerged travelling at periscope depth by the taking-in of air through a tube. In the intervening time I have put this proposal to 'K' Office. A fresh-air tube and an exhaust tube will be extended and retracted like a periscope. When water washes over the top, the tube will open and close itself automatically. At a speed of 7 knots, the engine can draw air from all compartment air for about 60 seconds. The spray that is sucked in by this operation can be ejected by a special water-remover.

'The increasing threat to U-boats from the air has led me to these thoughts, which have been in my mind for some time. What we would achieve by using these means would be:
1. The outward and return journeys could proceed almost without any danger. The detection of periscopes and air-tubes by radar installations would only be possible at close range and, on the high seas, would probably not occur at all. Additionally, the reflection qualitities of these tubes could be eliminated without great expenditure. Visual detection from aircraft would be difficult in normal sea conditions and, in any case, would be possible only at distances at which the U-boat would have spotted the opponent.
2. The exact position of U-boats in operational territories will be impossible for the enemy to determine. I am assuming that the enemy is currently able to establish the whereabouts of most of the hostile U-boats through his air-reconnaissance network using radar. Even if a boat should be obliged to surface for a time and proceed at top speed, subsequently and to a considerable degree, it will be able to change its position by submerged travelling, and then will also be able to recharge its battery for purposes of slow travel.

'The air-tube could be of considerable worth to the high-speed underwater boat. From a technical viewpoint, this would then not need to travel on the surface at all. From a military viewpoint this would be necessary for detection of the enemy, but the use of radar and sound-location would mean that surface travel could be kept to a minimum. Type XVIII fitted with an air-tube and suitable location devices would come very near to the ideal U-boat. The value of artillery armament for U-boats of this kind represents more of a problem, as the resistance of the boat would be thereby increased by 20–25 per cent, so its use would endanger a boat more than its non-use.

'I suggest the following for full evaluation:
1. A IIB boat with an air-tube in place of one periscope.
2. A similar arrangement with one of the Type XVII test boats when one of them has been delivered.

'Following favourable outcome of these trials, individual boat types could be fitted with the air-tube. In the above short outline I have omitted, to be sure, several disadvantages that, from a military aspect, could give rise to criticism. As an engineer, I see the project in an 'avowedly single-minded' light. I request you, dear Grossadmiral, to ascribe that sentiment to me in the best way possible.

Yours sincerely, Walter.'

On 27 May 1943, Dönitz replied:

'Dear Herr Walter,

I thank you for your letter and for your suggestion, which I shall immediately have thoroughly tested out. You and your collaborators will be able to take part in the tests. It is a matter for conjecture how things will turn out; however, at all events we shall proceed to investigate each possibility with energy. For this reason I welcome all such 'single-minded' proposals.   Yours, Dönitz.'

Walter continued to concern himself with the further development of the air-tube, which was given the suggestive name of 'Schnorchel' (generally spelt 'schnorkel' in English). At a conference in Wolfenbüttel, he suggested reducing the size of the schnorkel head by the incorporation of electrical switch elements (an electro-pneumatic head-valve).

In March 1945, Walter received the highest Order of Merit that could be given to a civilian in wartime, the 'Knight's Cross for War Services, with Swords' — not only as Dönitz said in his introductory note, for his 'considerable services in the development of the Walter U-boat', but also 'for the introduction of the schnorkel'.

Meanwhile, the first schnorkel with a floating valve at its head had been placed in contract with DWK. On 8 June 1943, the constructional drawings were available for a test version, which was to replace the after periscope in the training boats *U57* and *U58*. Directors Middendorf and Immich of DWK worked on this undertaking with such energy that the first schnorkel was ready in only three weeks. In August 1943, the initial tests were successful and showed that, if travelling were undertaken carefully, damage to health need not occur. A collapsible air-mast forward of the bridge was envisaged for Type VIIC boats, and this was fitted for test purposes in the repair boats *U235* and U236 as early as September 1943. Although the test journeys that followed were similarly successful, conservative technical circles remained sceptical and operational crews refused it. Schnorkel-travel seemed too ponderous and too risky, for it was thought that only a slight error in depth-keeping might lead to the poisoning of the entire crew.

The installation of schnorkels in further boats began very tentatively during the winter of 1943/44. The differing structural features of the various U-boat types meant that different locations were necessary for the collapsible schnorkel. Wherever possible, it was sited on the starboard side abreast the conning tower, at approximately

Left: The head of an extensible schnorkel fitted in *U2518* (Type XXI).

Above: The schnorkel being fitted in *U235*, November 1943.

the height of the after periscope (Types IXC and XIV) or abaft the periscopes (Types XB); the best arrangement was a position amidships abaft the periscopes, but this was only possible in boats developed after Type XXIII; the worst arrangement was that in Type VIIC, in which the schnorkel head and exhaust vapour obscured forward observation by the periscope.

The first 20 VIIC schnorkels had been ordered as early as 12 August 1943. On 24 September 1943, the Naval Arsenal at Kiel and the KMW (Kriegsmarinewerft Wilhelmshaven) were required to produce, as a matter of urgency, a further 100 schnorkels for the VIIC in service, and 40 for the IXC and IXD boats in service. With effect from 27 September 1943, it was similarly ordered that various new boats be equipped as quickly as possible. In a letter to GW and AG Weser dated 15 November 1943, Bröking, the head of K II U stated: 'The completion of these schnorkel installations for operational boats and new boats is to be accelerated by every means. In the discussions at Supreme Naval Command, it has been expressly stated that no delays must occur in the delivery programme through efforts to bring about improvements in the first installations'. Nevertheless, production proceeded slowly, and schnorkel installations remained a bottle-neck until the summer of 1944.

This led, in the early part of 1944, to the decision that schnorkels should be fitted as a priority to operational boats, then to other service boats and, only then, to newly-constructed boats. (Meanwhile, the first operational boat to be fitted with a schnorkel, *U264*, was lost in the North Atlantic on 19 February 1944 during her first operational trip, which did nothing to increase 'enthusiasm' for the schnorkel in operational circles.) Information sent by the Arsenal at Kiel to the Supreme Naval Command showed that, up to April 1944,

Head of a schnorkel with a floating valve (for Type VII).

Schnorkel installation for Type XVIIB.

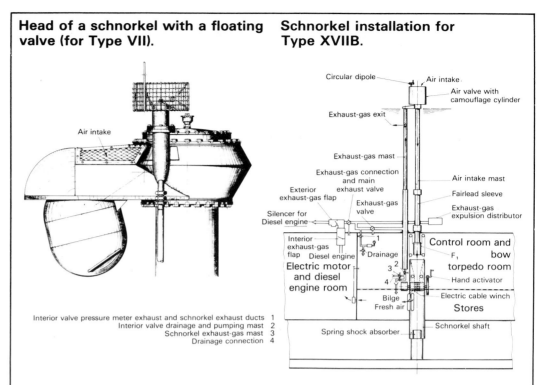

Interior valve pressure meter exhaust and schnorkel exhaust ducts 1
Interior valve drainage and pumping mast 2
Schnorkel exhaust-gas mast 3
Drainage connection 4

Design and operation of a schnorkel system with an electro-pneumatic head-valve for Type IID.

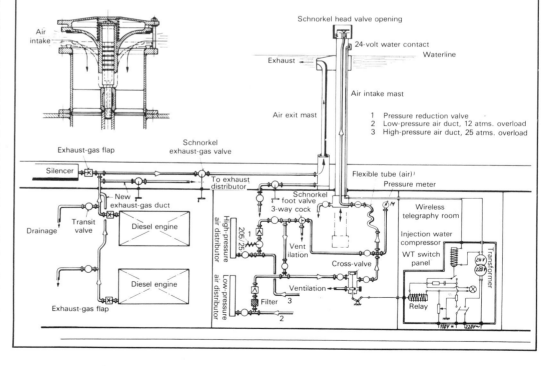

1 Pressure reduction valve
2 Low-pressure air duct, 12 atms. overload
3 High-pressure air duct, 25 atms. overload

The folding schnorkel on *U889* (Type IXC/40), May 1945.

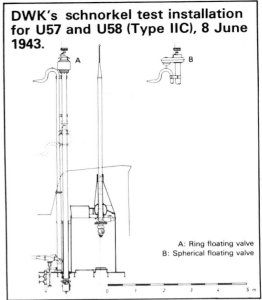

DWK's schnorkel test installation for U57 and U58 (Type IIC), 8 June 1943.

A: Ring floating valve
B: Spherical floating valve

0 1 2 3 4 5 m

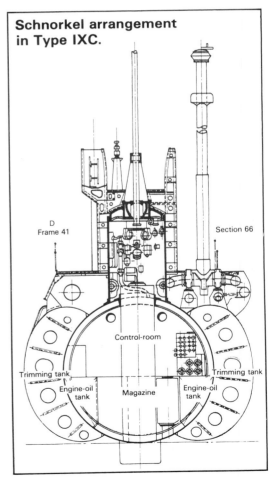

Schnorkel arrangement in Type IXC.

D
Frame 41

Section 66

Control-room

Trimming tank

Trimming tank

Engine-oil tank

Engine-oil tank

Magazine

The schnorkel layout in Type IXC.

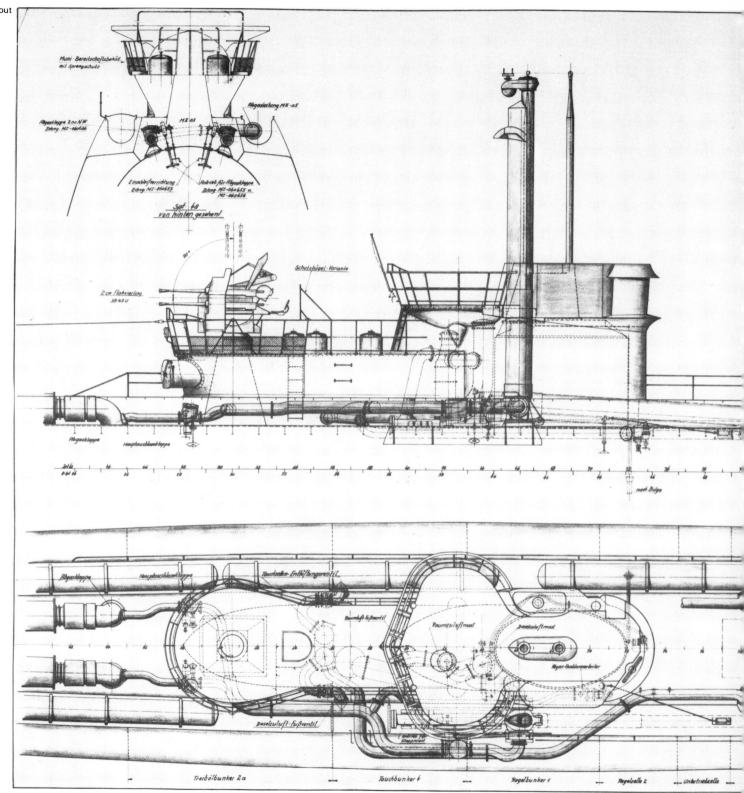

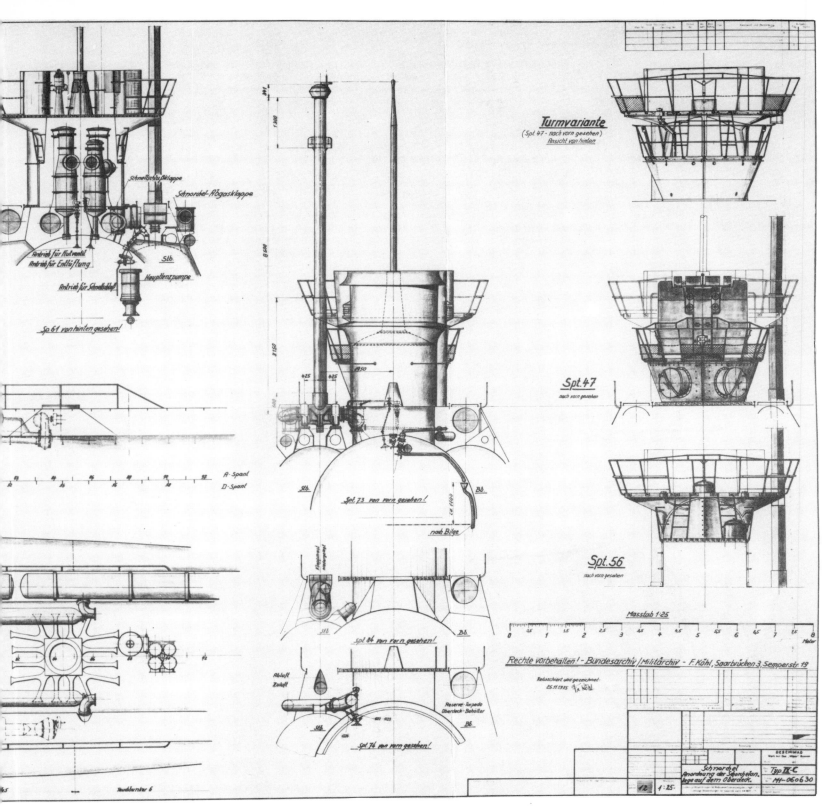

Turmvariante
(Spt. 47 - nach vorn gesehen)
Ansicht von hinten

Schnellschlußklappe

Schnorchel-Abgasklappe

Antrieb für Flutventil
Antrieb für Entlüftung   Stb.

Antrieb für Schnellschluß   Hauptlenzpumpe

Sp.61 von hinten gesehen!

Spt.47
nach vorn gesehen

A-Spant
D-Spant

Spt. 73 von vorn gesehen!

nach Bilge

Spt.56
nach vorn gesehen

Stb.

Klappenschließ
Spt. 86 von vorn gesehen!   Bb.

Masstab 1:25

0   0,5   1   1,5   2   2,5   3   3,5   4   4,5   5   5,5   6   6,5   7   Meter

Rechte vorbehalten! - Bundesarchiv/Militärarchiv - F. Köhl, Saarbrücken 3, Semperstr. 19

Retuschiert und gezeichnet:
25.11.1985 Fr. Köhl

Abluft
Zuluft

Reserve-Torpedo
Oberdeck-Behälter

Spt. 74 von vorn gesehen!

DESCHIMAG

Schnorchel
Anordnung der Schnorchel-
lage auf dem Oberdeck.

Typ IX-C
M-060630

1:25

Tauchbunker 6

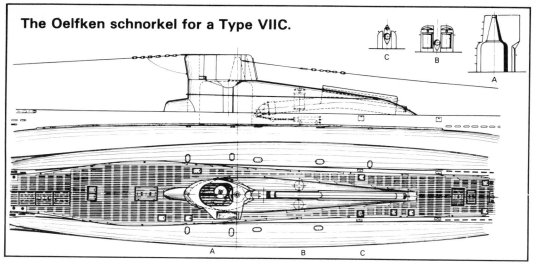

The Oelfken schnorkel for a Type VIIC.

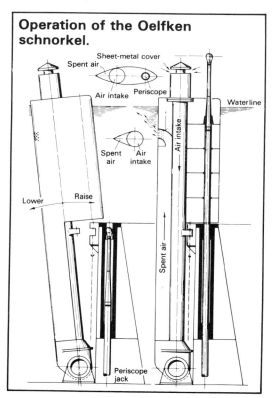

Operation of the Oelfken schnorkel.

schnorkels had either been fitted, or were being fitted, to the following U-boats:
Operational yards: St. Nazaire, *U264, U269, U575, U667*; Lorient, *U107, U530, U543, U547*; La Pallice, *U275, U953*; Brest, *U984*; Bordeaux, *U180, U195*; Toulon, *U642*.
Home yards: GW, *U235, U236, U237, U241, U1051, U1053, U1054*; DWK, *U490, U719, U743, U191*; there were also a few boats at other yards which had not submitted a report.

By the middle of June 1944, B&V had received a total of 14 schnorkel installations for VIIC boats, of which 6 had already been built into *U978, U998, U1019, U1020, U1021* and *U1022*, and a further 3 were intended for *U979, U1023* and *U1024*.

The schnorkel gradually gained ground. Increasingly, from the summer of 1944, boats fitted with the device reported successes, even from those sectors regarded by the British as safe from U-boats. But the next problem was the concealment of the schnorkel head from radar. The so-called 'ring' float, with its cylindrical surface, offered advantages in providing a shielding layer. Because of its simpler technicalities, it was intended that it replace the spherical float early in 1945; however, it suffered from being too inert in operation and was easily affected by wash. Only a few were fitted for operational trials, and it was hoped that a decided improvement would be obtained from the smaller, electro-pneumatic head-valve.

A big disadvantage of the existing schnorkel installations lay in the low schnorkelling speed of 5–6 knots. U-boats fitted with it spent most of their time outward and homeward bound, with only a short time in their operational zone. Obviously, the next stage of the development must be to increase schnorkelling speed. The basic operational demand that periscope observation be possible while using the schnorkel meant that it was necessary to ensure freedom from vibration of the periscope in higher speed ranges. To this end, the Oelfken schnorkel was developed. This contained, in an extended streamlined shape, a free tube through which the periscope could be raised when the extended schnorkel was locked in position. Only the head lens projected from the schnorkel's outer cover, and the periscope could not suffer any stronger vibration from motion through the water than the schnorkel. At the end of the war, two VIIC boats were apparently being converted at DWK for this type of schnorkel, which was also given an electro-pneumatic head-valve. It was calculated that this would enable a schnorkelling speed of approximately 10–11 knots to be reached.

NEW U-BOAT TYPES, 1943

Transport U-boats: Type XX and alternatives

U-boats had been used for transport purposes early on during the operation of Norway, and were in fact used to carry munitions and aircraft fuel from Wilhelmshaven and Kiel to Trondheim. The following deliveries were carried out up to the summer of 1940:

U26: first voyage 9 tons of 2cm ammunition, 7 tons hand-grenades, three 2cm anti-aircraft guns with accessories and the handing-over of her own MG C/30; second voyage 12.7cm and 3.7cm destroyer ammunition, aircraft bombs, aircraft fuel and lubricating oil.

U29: 5 tons of 2cm ammunition, 0.7m³ of distillate water, 1,300 phosphorus shells and the handing-over of her own 8.8cm gun.

U32: one 8.8cm anti-aircraft gun with steel base, and 706 shells, 20m³ aircraft fuel, 1,200kg of lubricating oil and a high-speed petrol-tank pump.

U43: first voyage 13 tons of infantry ammunition, 7 tons of mortar ammunition and 15 tons of 2cm ammunition; second voyage turbine components and generator for the destroyer *Paul Jacobi*.

U101: one 8.8cm anti-aircraft gun with accessories and 774 shells, eight 250kg bombs, 60m³ of aircraft fuel and 1,200kg of lubricating oil.

U122: one 8.8cm anti-aircraft gun with accessories and ammunition, aircraft bombs, 90m³ of aircraft fuel and lubricating oil.

UA: one 8.8cm anti-aircraft gun with accessories and 1,150 shells, sixteen 250kg bombs, 165m³ of aircraft fuel, 5 tons of lubricating oil for aircraft and 9 tons of engine oil for U-boats.

Additionally, during the Allied invasion of 1944, similar transport voyages were undertaken to bring supplies to the Atlantic bases, cut off from normal supply routes.

The first U-boat transport of supplies from the Far East to Europe was undertaken by the Japanese U-cruiser *I30* on her 'good-will' visit to Lorient on 5 August 1942. Up to that time, the only means for Germany to obtain important war materials such as rubber, tin, refined metals and quinine from the Far East was by surface blockade-runner, but it was obvious that it would become increasingly difficult for such vessels to make successful voyages. The decisive stimulus for the construction of special transport U-boats, however, had its origins elsewhere, and followed a discussion at Hitler's headquarters on 19 November 1942. The minute ran as follows:

'The Führer requires the construction of transport U-boats because, following the occupation of Iceland by the Americans, he has conceived the idea of a sudden invasion of Iceland and the consequent setting-up of an air-base there. The Chief of Naval War Staff suggests handing over this task to the Shipping Commissioner, as these boats should be built as commerce U-boats and could be used for commerce purposes (blockade-breakers). The Supreme Commander-in-Chief of the Navy agrees with this.'

There is no doubt, however, that the construction of special transport U-boats was regarded by the Supreme Naval Command principally for the supplying of materials from East Asia. The transport U-boats *Deutschland* and *Bremen* of the First World War had given Germany a good basis of knowledge for boats of this kind; it is, therefore, the more surprising that the German Navy took so long to show interest in transport U-boats during the Second World War. After the Italians had begun to use their operational submarines in growing numbers for transport purposes (supply-routes to North Africa) in 1940, special transport submarines were laid down by the Italians in the summer of 1942.

The first German design for a special transport U-boat, designated Type XIX, was being developed by the end of 1942. Of approximately 2,500 tons, she was to have received a new-style diesel installation, but, as this was not forthcoming, the project was abandoned in favour of a boat that could take the well-tried engine installation of the Type XIV. The project was designated Type XX, and the hull took its box-shaped cross-section from Type XB, which offered considerable capacity for

carrying rubber in external containers. For this large boat of 2,700 tons, eight outer containers were envisaged to take a total of approximately 820m³, which meant that with a stowing coefficient of 0.5 tons per m³ a load of approximately 400 tons of rubber was possible. There was additional dry storage capacity in the interior of the boat for approximately 220m³. It was proposed that on the loaded return passage the keel-compartment, which could be reached from the outer-loading compartments, be used to carry tin in ingots, or molybdenum and tungsten concentrate in pewter or tin cases. The use of the keel for stowage meant that the altered trimming moments occasioned by other cargoes could be compensated without need of dry-docking. The total load capacity on the return journey was calculated approximately as follows.

Raw rubber:	400 tons
Tin:	200 tons
Molybdenum and tungsten concentrate:	150 tons
Interior cargo (quinine, mica, oils):	50 tons
Total:	800 tons

The task of working out the constructional details was given to AG Weser, and the initial model towing tests were carried out in the earlier part of 1943. On 3 March, 15 of these large boats were ordered from DW in Hamburg-Finkenwerder, and 15 from Bremer Vulkan, Vegesack. The first boat was to be delivered in August 1944. From then on, a monthly total of 3 boats was to be delivered, the last by the middle of 1945. An essential condition was that these large, transport U-boats were to be additional to current U-boat production. The HAS announced that 2,810 more workers would be required.

As the rapid introduction of transport U-boats into operations was obviously not possible, Dönitz suggested in a Situation Discussion on 8 February 1943, in Hitler's Command Headquarters that, as a temporary bridging measure, the large Italian Atlantic U-boats (which were not particularly suitable for operational conditions anyway) be converted for use as transports for the Far East run. To make the most effective use of the

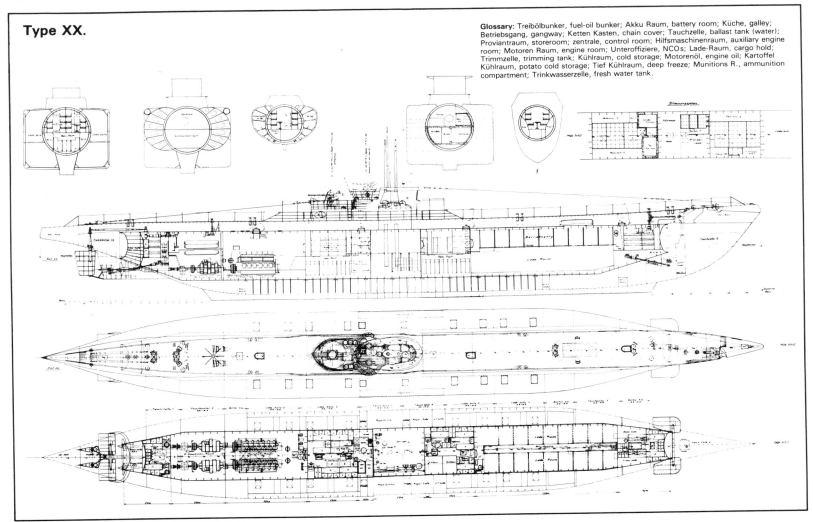

Type XX.

Glossary: Treibölbunker, fuel-oil bunker; Akku Raum, battery room; Küche, galley; Betriebsgang, gangway; Ketten Kasten, chain cover; Tauchzelle, ballast tank (water); Proviantraum, storeroom; zentrale, control room; Hilfsmaschinenraum, auxiliary engine room; Motoren Raum, engine room; Unteroffiziere, NCOs; Lade-Raum, cargo hold; Trimmzelle, trimming tank; Kühlraum, cold storage; Motorenöl, engine oil; Kartoffel Kühlraum, potato cold storage; Tief Kühlraum, deep freeze; Munitions R., ammunition compartment; Trinkwasserzelle, fresh water tank.

restricted payload of these boats, they should be used only on the Atlantic legs that Allied air power had rendered too dangerous for surface blockade-runners; for the Capetown-Madagascar leg, cargo could be transferred to normal surface ships. Hitler basically agreed with this suggestion and planned to talk to Mussolini in an effort to speed up the conversion.

On 13 February 1943, the conversion of VIIC U-boats to transport boats, with a range of 14,000 nautical miles at 8 knots, was discussed for comparative purposes. Two possibilities were contemplated: A, alterations only to the interior of the boat; and B, the building-on of a new, enlarged

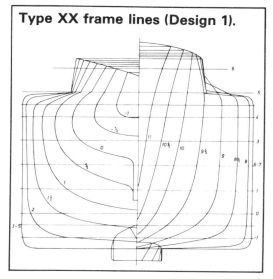

Type XX frame lines (Design 1).

outer ship. In the case of A, cargo compartments could be made available by removing the complete torpedo armament and part of the forward living quarters. Additionally, rubber and metals could be carried in the outer ship (water-tight forecastle and stern, ballast-keel). This would yield the following approximate cargo possibilities: 25 tons in the pressure hull, 35 tons in the outer ship (rubber) and 45 tons in the ballast-keel (metals), giving a total of 105 tons. By using the torpedo tanks, the fuel-oil supply was to be increased to 125 tons, but this was rather inadequate for the lengthy voyages being considered. A conversion building time of two or three months was calculated.

In the case of B, apart from the measures considered in A, the pressure-tight outer tanks were to be enlarged. This would mean that Diving Tank 3 in the pressure hull could be dispensed with, and an additional 100 tons of fuel-oil could be carried in the outer tanks, i.e., a total of 175 tons of fuel. This meant that the following approximate cargo possibilities were available: 75 tons in the pressure hull, 120 tons in the outer ship (rubber), 55 tons in the ballast-keel (metals), giving a total of 250 tons. Conversion B would have taken longer, and could not have been realized before the end of 1943. It was also recognized that the conversion of German offensive U-boats for use as transport

U-boats was only to be considered as a last resource.

In the meantime, an investigation had been made into the possibilities of converting the Italian Atlantic submarines: 3 large and 7 medium boats were available and, as they stood, each could carry 60 tons of internal cargo. If the diving bunkers were used, the load capacity would increase to 150 tons, but fuel-replenishment would be necessary in the South Atlantic on both outward and return passages. The total capacity for all 10 boats would amount to a maximum of only 1,500 tons. Approximately six weeks was estimated for the conversion. On 26 February 1943, Hitler turned down the idea, but the Supreme Naval Command persisted in their desire to use these boats for transport purposes. On 18 March, Dönitz was able to inform Hitler that the Italians had given permission for their U-boats lying in Bordeaux to be used as transports to the Far East, with the exception of the most modern boat, *Cagni*. However, this permission was purchased somewhat expensively — at the price of handing over to the Italians 10 VIIC boats (*U428–U430, U746–U750* and *U1161–U1162*). The Italian boats were given the cover-names *Aquila I* to *Aquila IX*. The conversion of the first boats was under the control of Kapitän zur See Grossi and was carried out very speedily, so that by May 1943, the first three were able to leave Bordeaux: they were *Aquila I* (ex-*Tazzoli*), *Aquila II* (ex-*Giuliani*) and *Aquila III* (ex-*Cappellini*). The German tanker *Burgenland* was intended for supply purposes. In June 1943, there followed *Aquila V* (ex-*Barbarigo*) and *Aquila VI* (ex-*Torelli*). However, only 3 boats completed the voyage, reaching Singapore in July and September 1943.

The attempt, in June 1943, to obtain the use of two special *Romolo* class transport submarines for the Far East was thwarted by Admiral Riccardi, Chief of the Italian Naval Staff, who wished to keep these modern submarines under his own command (even though, after the loss of North Africa, there was no longer any rôle for these boats in the Mediterranean). During the ensuing period, the Japanese sent 4 transport submarines (*I8, I34, I29* and *I52*) laden with raw materials to Europe and, of these *I8* and *I29* survived, to arrive at Lorient on 31 August, and at Bordeaux on 10 March 1944 respectively.

Two further *Aquila* boats, *Aquila IV* (ex-*Finzi*) and *Aquila IX* (ex-*Bagnolini*) were to make the next voyages to the Far East on 18 July 1943, but the fall of Mussolini and the resultant defection of the Italians delayed the whole *Aquila* programme. In Singapore, the three Italian boats were requisitioned by the Japanese, and only after prolonged negotiations could the German Naval Attaché succeed in having them released for transport undertakings by the German Navy. However, problems now arose in finding German submariners who could man these unfamiliar boats, and it was not until the beginning of 1944 that the first boat, *UIT24* (ex-*Cappellini*), sailed for home with a cargo of rubber, quinine and precious ores. As her tanker, *Brake*, failed to appear, however, the voyage had to be broken off and she returned to

Penang. After leaving Singapore on 14 February 1944, *UIT23* (ex-*Giuliani*) was sunk by a British submarine in the Malacca Straits. The last ex-Italian transport U-boat to leave Bordeaux, *UIT22* (ex-*Bagnolini*) was sunk by aircraft south of the Cape of Good Hope on 11 March 1944, and with this, the Supreme Naval Command abandoned the idea. The two surviving boats, *UIT24* (ex-*Cappellini*) and *UIT25* (ex-*Torelli*) were now to be used for supply and transport between the Japanese mainland and the harbours of Borneo and German bases in the Southern Hemisphere.

Consequently, combat U-boats returning from the Far East were now to be used to the full in carrying urgently-required raw materials. It was envisaged that a Type IXC could carry on its return voyage 115 tons of tin (of which 100 tons would be carried in the keel), 10 tons of molybdenum, 9 tons of tungsten, 10 tons of rubber, 0.5 tons of quinine, 0.2 tons of opium and 0.3 tons of other cargo, i.e., a total cargo of 145 tons. The larger Type IXD$_2$ was to carry 120 tons of tin, 15 tons of molybdenum, 80 tons of rubber, 1 ton of quinine and 0.2 tons of opium, a total of 216 tons. The rubber was carried in the free-flooding diving bunkers beneath the upper deck, and in the upper deck chambers; the tin was carried in ingots in the keel and in the interior of the boat; and the other precious metals were soldered into tin containers and stored in the bilges, the bow and stern compartments and in the empty torpedo tubes. The first to return with such a cargo was *U178* on 24 May 1944. In June 1944, *U188* followed. The next combat U-boats carrying raw materials were *U843, U861, U510* and *U532*, but they reached Europe only a short time before (or even after) the German capitulation.

In the autumn of 1943, it was decided to convert the large U-boats of Type IXD$_1$ (*U180* and *U195*), whose diesel plants had not given complete satisfaction, to transport U-boats. The removal of the torpedo armament and the reduction in propulsion to that in Type VIIC meant that a total storage capacity of 252 tons was made available. The conversion took place in Bordeaux from October 1943 to April 1944. Of the two boats, *U195* reached Batavia at the end of 1944, but *U180* was sunk by mines while outward bound in the Bay of Biscay on 22 August 1944. Additionally, two Type XB minelaying U-boats (*U219* and *U234*) and two torpedo-supply U-boats (*U1059* and *U1062*) were sent to Japan as auxiliary transports. However, only *U219* and *U1062* arrived safely. The two remaining VIIF U-boats (*U1060* and *U1061*) were used for transport duties in Norwegian waters.

Outside sources concerned themselves in 1943 in the planning of a transport U-boat. On 20 June 1943, Engineer Kohrs, a former colleague of Professor Flamm, showed the head of the HAS his design for a 4,000-ton 'U-ship' with a length of 93m and a beam of 11m, which would have a special pressure-hull construction. Just as in Flamm's U-cruiser projects, the pressure-hull cross-section was to be of a three-circle format, which would make possible a high underwater stability without ballast and, therefore, a greater laden weight. Kohrs wanted to avoid the drawbacks of Flamm's method (the complicated interior stiffening) by a

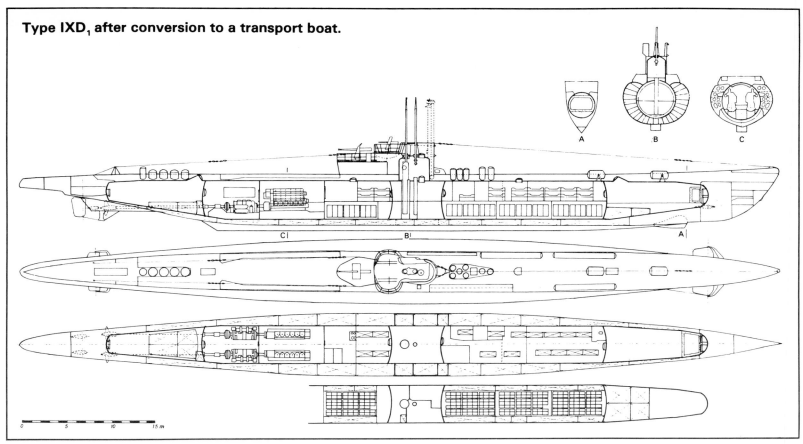

Type IXD₁ after conversion to a transport boat.

A B C

C B A

0 5 10 15 m

Kohrs' design for a 4,000-ton 'U-ship'.

0 5 10 15 20 m

Key: C, cargo; CQ, crew's quarters; CR, control room; D, diesel-engine room; E, electric engine room.

A B

A B

CQ

E D C C C C C C CQ

CR

CQ

different frame system: he envisaged longitudinal frames of double-T profile, which would be positioned between pressure hull and outer ship. Stiffened transverse bulkheads would be provided at regular distances apart to support the pressure from the longitudinal frames. This would play a special part in avoiding the dynamic concentration at the point of intersection of the pressure-hull circles. A further innovation was in the construction of the upper outer ship, where a pressure-hull cylinder was to take the water-pressure forces of the sectional circles underneath it. The idea was not pursued, however, and it is hard to judge the value of these suggestions.

In the early part of 1943, projects were also formulated for the construction of two towing-containers for U-boats, holding 150 tons and 450 tons respectively, intended principally for transporting fuel to North Africa. The unsophisticated construction was reminiscent of similar towing projects of the Japanese. After the loss of Tunisia, the project was continued as a research task. In October 1943, off Hela, towing tests with a 90-ton underwater towing-body showed the basic suitability for U-boat-towing. At the beginning of 1944, the Chief of Naval War Staff took up the idea of towing-bodies as they wished to use them in the Aegean. There were requests for the construction of similar containers for use off north Norway and East Asia. Two improved test units, one of 90 tons, and a 300-ton 'underwater lighter', were worked on at the Vulcan works at Stettin and tried out successfully in the summer of 1944. But this trial showed very considerable reduction in the range of the towing U-boat and, after acrimonious conflicts of opinion, and the placing of orders for a series of 50 underwater towing-bodies, the project was finally killed-off at the 26th Armament Discussion of 20 December 1944, the sources that required this item not being prepared to make available materials and labour at the expense of other projects. A different underwater towing-body, which would have transported and launched V-2 rockets, remained on the drawing-board.

Type XXI electro-boat.

Key: A, accumulator hatch; D, rubber dinghy; DT, diving tanks; E, electrics hatch; F, fuel-oil bunkers; T, torpedo hatch; V, ventilation hatch; WF, watertight forecastle; WS, watertight stern.

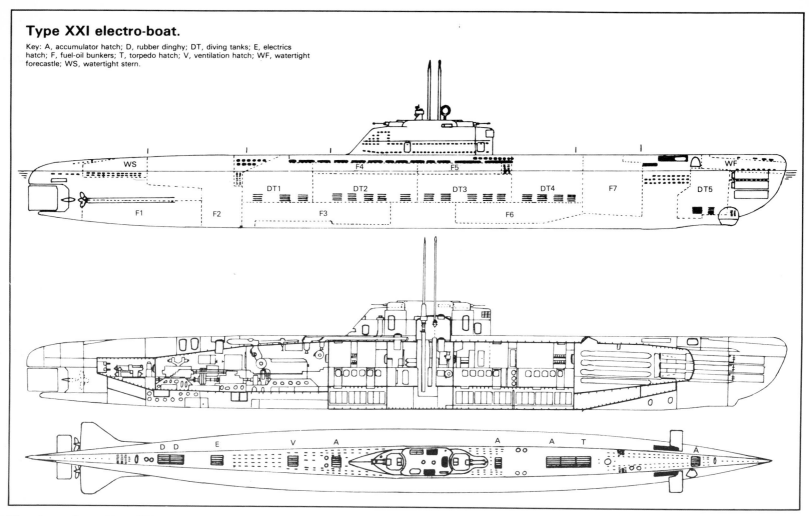

The electro-boat: Type XXI

After the final design of Type XVIII had been presented to 'K' Office, it became evident that, because of the extensive Walter-installation and large Aurol supply, the electric installation would have to be small. Consequently, once a boat's Aurol had been expended, its submerged performance would be poor. In March 1943, therefore, the Walter specialist, Heep, suggested that Bröking's reviewing officer, Naval Construction Director Oelfken, examine the possibility of using the very elegant shape of Type XVIII in an advantageous manner with conventional propulsion means. His investigations showed a possibility of trebling battery capacity over existing U-boats by enlarging the pressure hull downwards, to give an 8-shaped cross-section extending for approximately a third of the boats' length. This would give a significantly higher submerged speed and a greater submerged range. During a discussion in 'K' Office concerning Type XVIII, he stated: 'If we intend to build such a large boat and have so much space at our disposal, we can accomplish much more than hitherto by using conventional engine installations. Furthermore, if the submerged properties are considered to be more important than surface properties, then we shall naturally make use of conventional propulsion methods in ways different from those we have used in the past.'

When, in April 1943, it was acknowledged that conventional U-boats were unable to overcome the defensive measures of their opponents, Oelfken embarked on a rough plan for building the two-circle form, and discussed it with the Head of 'K' Office, in the presence of Schürer and Bröking. Admiral Fuchs thereupon gave permission for this rival to Type XVIII to be prepared to the stage where decisions could be made and, on 19 June 1943, it was placed before Grossadmiral Dönitz. He had certain reservations about the considerable bulk of this 'electro-boat' (the result of the proposed large battery capacity), but he accepted it as a replacement of Type IX and ordered that plans be worked-out immediately.

This new type, which had the outer shell of Walter's Type XVIII, was designated Type XXI.

Its most important innovation was the powerful electric installation which was to be built into the original turbine compartment of Type XVIII. The large gearing assembly remained more or less in the same place, but, instead of the turbine installation, two 2,500hp electric motors, two small motors for slow, silent running and two switchboards were to be accommodated. By the beginning of July 1943, the specifications for the new, powerful electric motors had been prepared, and they were to be built by SSW (Siemens Schuckertwerke AG) and AEG (Allgemeine Elektricitäts-Gesellschaft) in co-operation. By the end of July, tenders had been prepared showing the main measurements of the motors, including fan and radiator arrangements. The project was designated '2 GU 365/30' (cover-name 'Hertha', after a lady secretary at SSW). The propulsion unit was a ten-pole, separately-agitated shunt motor, with auxiliary stabilizing series windings, commutating pole windings and compensating windings. The usual tandem arrangement of two motors in one housing and two rotors on one shaft was retained. The commutator — the most important part of a direct-current motor — was appropriate for the severe requirements. The construction of the rotor had been developed by reference to fast-running railway engines. The commutator segments and the lug-throats were of copper, massively built, the lug-throats functioning as radial superchargers and contributing significantly to the cooling of the commutator. Each double-motor had a diameter of 1.3m, a length of approximately 3m (length of shaft, 3.26m), and a weight of 10.33 tons. The SSW and the AEG motors differed only in the pattern of the split conductors.

For the main switchboard, a method of construction previously planned for Type VIIC/42 was used: switchboards in the form of controller cylinders, which operated behind the winding-end face. However, in contrast to the design of Type VIIC/42, specially developed SSW switch elements with roller contacts were used. However, this arrangement required, in place of the simple cams, a link-motion with double cams. The electrical steering position in Type XXI, being at the winding-end face, with visibility in the direction of travel, could be kept small and was very well laid-out. Space-saving instruments and switches in connection with the cam-switching made possible the forced speed adjustments in the running-in times. Resistance to impact and shock was increased considerably, switch noise was reduced, and better access to the controls was provided. Now that the central passage was free, the complete switch assembly could be tested or repaired when the cowling had been removed.

The main switchboards of Type XXI were likewise designed as a combined operation by AEG and SSW, working from common drawings, models and castings, etc., and were mass-produced by both firms, at Berlin-Siemensstadt and Berlin-Treptow.

The motors for slow, silent running were developed by SSW, and were designated 'GW323/28'. They were eight-pole extraneously-agitated shunt motors, with auxiliary frequence winding and reverse poles. They attained a maximum of 83kW at 350rpm and 360 volts. Without gearing, they could drive the main shaft directly, by a system of twelve belts, and the boat could travel at speeds up to 6 knots with very little noise (except in the speed-range between 4.3 and 5 knots).

With regard to surface propulsion, the planners went back to a development that had previously been destined for Type VIIC/42, namely the supercharged six-cylinder MAN M6V 40/46. The lesser performance, compared with the 2,200hp nine-cylinder MAN M9V 40/46, was to be compensated by a BBC Büchi exhaust-gas turbo-supercharger. A maximum performance of 2,000hp at 522rpm from the engine and 12,240rpm from the supercharger were calculated. Because of the high-charging (90 per cent over effective pressure), a larger valve overlapping of 150° (compared to 130° in the nine-cylinder diesel) was necessary, which signified an increased counter-pressure sensitivity over the simultaneously-issuing exhaust gases. This was later to have disadvantageous effects for the schnorkel operation.

The armament and most of the boat's control systems were taken over from the plans of Type XVIII, or were adapted to suit the altered propulsion. Other installations, such as the SU echo-set, had been destined for Type VIIC/42. Also available was the outer-hull planning and the towing-test results for Type XVIII, which meant that the final design could be pushed through by AG Weser in the shortest possible time. With charged batteries, these new boats should be able to travel underwater at 18 knots for 1½ hours or 12–14 knots for 10 hours. At the economic speed of 6 knots, they should even manage 48 hours of silent travel. The estimated surface range exceeded that of the IXC boats, and made possible operations throughout the Atlantic without intermediate supply. That the maximum surface speed of 15.6 knots lay well below the speed achieved by existing operational boats was not regarded as too important. With the help of a quick-loading device, it was intended that up to eighteen torpedoes should be able to be fired within twenty minutes. The boat would be superior to all previous diesel-electric types. These factors offered the means of surmounting the U-boat crisis, with a new, operationally-effective boat of considerable submerged speed, which could be produced quickly. The Commander-in-Chief, U-Boats, intended, therefore, to use Type XXI, despite its size, for the convoy war in the North Atlantic, and decided in favour of a large series of them. This meant that the Walter Type XVIII U-boats quite simply no longer had any priority or special building capacity. On 29 June 1943, Dönitz wrote to Walter:

'Dear Herr Walter,
In line with the ideas stemming from you on the concept for a high-speed submarine, and following the development work achieved in collaboration between yourself and the Naval High Command in this sphere, through a design developed and planned by the Naval High Command, we have the possibility of developing a new U-boat type. This type, when fitted with engine installations as used

in conventional submarines, offers such remarkable qualities that I have ordered its immediate introduction.

'Apart from the indemnities which are due to you on account of existing arrangements, I express my special gratitude for the fact that through your ideas and spadework it has been found possible to achieve the development of an important new U-boat type. I hope further that in the autumn of this year, the anticipated first journeys that your boats will make will be successful, for I — as previously — lay great value on the development of Walter-boats with their high submerged speed with Walter-engine installations.

Yours sincerely, Dönitz.'

The coastal electro-boat: Type XXIII

During the design work on Type XXI, Naval Construction Director Oelfken came across Walter's new Type XXII coastal U-boat (page 177), which stimulated him to investigate whether it had any properties suitable for a coastal boat of similar shape, but with good submerged performance from conventional drive. It turned out that a considerable increase in displacement would be necessary, mainly because of the larger batteries and the heavy engine installation. A preliminary outline was proposed to Dönitz at the time of the presentation of Type XXI. Although he was much more interested in large boats, he accepted the idea of the small electro-boat and ordered planning to proceed. He required that the development work should include 7m torpedo tubes, and that the boat should be capable of being transported by rail for use in the Mediterranean and the Black Sea. These requirements strongly influenced the detailed planning of the design, which was carried out by Chief Naval Construction Adviser Grim.

The new coastal design, designated Type XXIII, showed only marginal similarities to Type XXII — its relative narrowness, single-shaft installation, knife-edge stern, bow torpedo arrangement and lack of anti-aircraft armament. It was very

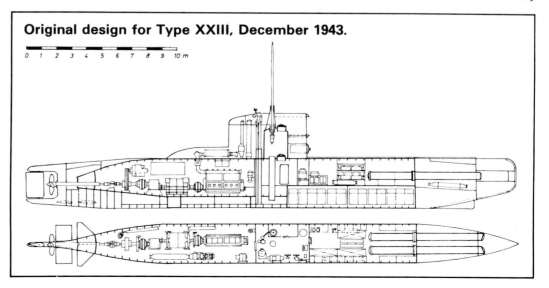

Original design for Type XXIII, December 1943.

0 1 2 3 4 5 6 7 8 9 10 m

different, however, in its increased length and displacement, comprehensive single-hull shape, almost symmetrical double-circle cross-section and, especially, in its conning tower with a higher bridge. Initially, it had been believed that the bow hydroplanes could be dispensed with, as in the smaller Walter U-boats. However, in the light of experience gleaned from the Walter boats *U792* and *U794*, first a rigid fin was fitted, and then bow hydroplanes were fitted to the forward section of the boat. The fin was retained as a rudder guard. In order to be transportable in four sections by rail, the after section was completely reshaped and the forward section was kept as short as possible, which prevented interior loading of torpedo tubes. The inclusion of a schnorkel was not decided upon until after the boat's shape had been determined. As there was no outer upper deck, the schnorkel had to be extensible, but it was strongly built and favourably sited, amidships abaft the periscope.

In contrast to the large electric U-boat, for which many innovations were planned, Type XXIII was kept very simple as regards installations and engines, and was to be assembled from well-tried components.

The six-cylinder diesel RS 348 made by MWM was envisaged for the engine. It had been developed in 1938 for the electrical generator in the battleships *Bismarck* and *Tirpitz*, and had been tested in U-boat operations as a diesel-generator in Type IXD$_2$. The GU 4463/8 electric motor was developed by AEG from the VIIC motor. In particular, the armature, field-disposition and sections from the Type VIIC were taken over, but the costly revolving yoke was replaced by a simpler construction. The yoke had feet screwed onto it and round bulges on which, when the feet were unscrewed, the housing could be rolled down and turned. The cover-name for this electric motor was 'Ursula'. Gearing enabled the relatively high-revving engines (maximum 850–1,000rpm) to be reduced to economic propeller revs. A smaller, lower-revving 25kW engine was envisaged for slow, silent running, and this, as in Type XXI, worked directly on the propeller shaft through a V-belt. BBC had developed a simplified switchboard, according to the principles as used in Type XXI. Access to this had to be from the passageway, because of lack of space.

On 30 July 1943, the project was ready for presentation. The boat was to be able to travel underwater at a maximum of 13 knots and have a submerged range of 106 nautical miles at 6 knots (i.e., almost four times that of Type IIC). The battery installation suggested was half the installation of Type IXC, i.e., 62 cells MAL 740, and in this, for the first time, double cells were to be used in order to achieve 240 volts. The projected surface range was rather smaller than in Type IIC, but, at 4,300 nautical miles at 6 knots, was adequate for the intended coastal operations. At the maximum surface speed of 10 knots, the schnorkel would be fully extended.

As no active submerged detection installation was planned for these small boats, torpedo firing would have to be carried out visually, at periscope depth or on the surface, so that conventional

piston-ejection tubes from current production could be used. The boat would have only a single 7.5m 'knee-bend' periscope, and a conning tower was necessary to give it a reasonable height. Unfortunately, this had the effect of increasing water resistance considerably in an otherwise very successful design.

Appropriate measuring tests were carried out in September 1943 at the Towing Test Institute in

Comparison between the silhouettes of Type XXII (shown shaded) and Type XXIII.

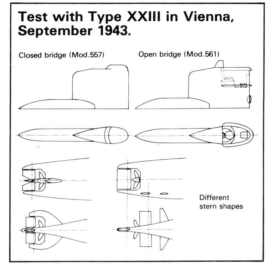

Test with Type XXIII in Vienna, September 1943.

Closed bridge (Mod.557)   Open bridge (Mod.561)

Different stern shapes

Vienna. With the original length of 32.48m, in submerged tests at 12.5 knots, a total resistance of 3,140kp was arrived at for the smooth hull with appendages and enclosed bridge. Of this total, 70 per cent (63.5 per cent frictional resistance) could be written down to smooth hull with vertical rudder; 23 per cent to the enclosed smooth bridge (8 per cent frictional resistance); and 7 per cent to fins and hydroplanes (2.5 per cent frictional resistance). In the final version (the boat made longer by approximately 2.2m, with an open bridge and flooding-slits), the total resistance rose by 40 per cent to approximately 4,400kp, of which 26.5 per cent could be written down to the open bridge, and approximately 13 per cent to the flooding slits and other apertures. Further towing tests were undertaken to establish the most favourable arrangement for the after hydroplanes, and these showed that the crossed rudder arrangement abaft the screw considerably increased the resistance and propulsion relationships. At 12 knots, the deep-set fins and rudders, which had yielded a very favourable total propulsion efficiency of 75.4 per

cent, came down to 62.2 per cent with the crossed rudder arrangement. A comparison with Type XXI showed that the boat's hull, without a bridge, gave roughly the same submerged C_w values as the almost unhampered shape of XXI. The better propulsion efficiency coefficient of the single-screw boat compensated, therefore, the shape resistance of the fuller stern. However, through the large resistance provided by the bridge, the C_w values of Type XXIII in its final version were no better than 145.

For comparative purposes only, theoretical calculations were made for an electric boat with the hull shape of Type XVIIB. This study was given the designation XVIIE. As a result of the more favourable submerged shape, half the VIIC battery installation provided a submerged range of 224 nautical miles at 4 knots, compared with 175 nautical miles at 4 knots in Type XXIII. With a 1,160hp electric motor, a maximum, submerged speed of 14.5 knots could be achieved. However, there was no prospect for an eventual realization of this electric motor; moreover, this design did not fulfil the conditions of transportability by rail, or of having 7m torpedo tubes; and it would have been considerably more expensive from the construction point of view. So Type XXIII remained the chosen boat.

THE FLEET CONSTRUCTION PROGRAMME OF 1943

Dönitz replaces Raeder

Following the failure of a German surface battle group against North Sea Convoy JW51B at the end of December 1942, Hitler in his initial agitation decided that the bulk of the large ships, the retention of which in his opinion could no longer be justified by their practical use, should be taken out of service and their artillery armament used on land. On 6 January 1943, he demanded that Raeder formulate an appropriate laying-up programme, and make proposals for an enlargement and acceleration of the U-boat programme. Raeder considered Hitler's decision to be an unjustified slight on the Navy and a personal insult to himself, and he offered his resignation, which Hitler accepted. As his successor, he suggested Admiral Carls or Admiral Dönitz; Hitler decided in favour of the latter, considering him to be a good representative for the young, keen, offensively-minded and successful U-boat arm. In him, he hoped to find a collaborator for the laying-up and scrapping of the large warships that he had ordered. A certain tragic element is to be found in the fact that Dönitz took over command of the Navy at a time when his own arm had reached its zenith, and was shortly to suffer its greatest reversal. So that the rupture would not be too evident to outsiders, Raeder suggested the date of 30 January 1943 — the tenth anniversary of the National Socialist seizure of power — for this change in the office of the Supreme Commander-in-Chief of the Navy.

In a memorandum dated 10 January 1943, on 'The Significance of the German Surface Forces in the Conduct of War of the Tripartite Powers' Raeder expressed himself positively opposed to Hitler's idea, pointing out the considerable drawbacks that would ensue from the lack of a surface fleet and the very small gain in items for other purposes that would accrue. With regard to the U-boat programme, the following would become available: at most, 50 officers from the crews of the large ships with knowledge of U-boat operations. During the period of time it would take for dismantling work (the amount of iron yielded would be 125,800 tons) and the setting-up of guns on land installations, the building of new U-boats would hardly increase. That large ships would no longer be required to be repaired would mean the saving of 800 workers and of 600 tons of materials each year, but this would enable only approximately 6 extra U-boats to be built each year. From the total amount of iron available from the dismantling, an additional 7 U-boats per month could be built, given the condition that a further 13,000—14,000 skilled workers were made available. The U-boat construction programme, set currently at 25 boats per month, could then (following the dismantling process, i.e., in 1½ years) become a theoretical 32 boats per month; however, in a further 18 months, it would fall once more to 25 boats per month.

In the discussions with Hitler that followed, Dönitz never showed approval for such a time-consuming and largely ineffectual method of providing materials for his U-boat programmes. Although he had earlier made representations as the Commander-in-Chief, U-Boats, to the effect that large ships should not continue to be produced or serviced at the expense of U-boat repairs, now as Supreme Head of the Navy, he supported the maintaining of offensive-readiness. Indeed, after some initial hesitance in this connection, he persuaded Hitler to allow larger units to operate in North Norway, and in this way effected in practical terms the lifting of the laying-up order. Hitler remained extremely sceptical about the success of these measures, but clearly did not want a difference of opinion with the new Chief of the Navy.

More steel, more U-boats

Dönitz also utilized the opportunity presented by his being in favour at this particular time, by using his direct contact with Hitler to achieve his hoped-for increase in U-boat production. As early as 8 February 1943, Dönitz obtained Hitler's signature to an exemption from call-up for workers engaged on U-boats and their weapons, and on surface vessels also used in U-boat operations, such exemption from military service being total and absolute. The next step was aimed at bringing about an increase in the extremely low steel quota of 119,795 tons monthly in the first quarter of 1943. Of this quantity, ship construction took 58,000 tons, gun armament 20,490 tons, torpedo armament 8,650 tons, and mines 9,490 tons; the balance, 23,165 tons, went to buildings, yard construction, bomb-damage repairs, etc. A memorandum from the Supreme Chief of the Navy, on 1 March 1943,

put the minimum quantity for naval requirements at 181,483 tons monthly. (Even with this amount, representing an increase of over 50 per cent on what the Navy had been receiving, the total quantity allocated to the Navy would be no more than 7.3 per cent of the country's total steel production.) On 6 March, Dönitz succeeded in obtaining Hitler's consent to a monthly increase of 45,000 tons from the second quarter of 1943.

On 14 March, he submitted a report to Hitler on the measures he planned to raise U-boat production to 30 boats per month. A complete new Fleet Construction Programme for 1943 was placed before Hitler for approval on 11 April 1943. In addition to the increase in U-boat production, a considerable strengthening of light surface forces was called for. The new U-boat programme was to be shown in Table 34. The additional requirement of iron for the increase in U-boats was stated by Dönitz as follows:

Required for U-boat construction
monthly: 4,500 tons
Required for the increase in
torpedo production: 1,500 tons
Monthly total   6,000 tons

For the comprehensive construction programme of light forces, Dönitz demanded additionally a monthly iron supply of 20,590 tons. At the same time, he presented a detailed memorandum in which he confirmed a total iron supply of 216,390 tons:

(a) Engine iron (monthly):
1. Shortage in the second quarter of 1943 for the completion of present undertakings (181,000—165,104 tons)   15,896 tons
2. For increasing U-boat production   4,500 tons
3. Armaments and increasing torpedo production
                                                1,500 tons
4. Increase in the new construction of light forces (20,600—7,000 tons already included in 1.)
                                               13,600 tons
5. Repair of additional U-boats and surface forces, yard requirements, service vessels, initial fitting-out, weapon repair   4,100 tons

Total additional engine iron   39,596 tons
Present allocation in the second quarter
                                              164,795 tons
New monthly allocation   204,390 tons
(b) Further quantity of construction iron:
                                               12,000 tons

'Hitler gave his approval to these representations and stated that the increase in U-boat planning must be accomplished if possible. The problem was where to get the iron. With his absolute authority, he could clearly command that the required quantities be made available, but they had to come from somewhere. He therefore ordered an immediate meeting with Speer, Röchling and Duisberg to discuss the raising of the programme from 2.6 to 4 million tons of steel monthly. It was clear to him that this demanded an immediate building of new installations (blast-furnaces, etc.) and an extension of existing works. Speer suggested the much speedier way of using steel works in occupied territories, chiefly Belgium and France. This made it possible in March 1944 to achieve the record amount for steel production of 3,173,000 tons, of which 2,674,000 tons were produced in German territories including the Saar, Lorraine and Luxembourg. The protection from deportation afforded to workers in occupied territories, however, seriously interfered with Sauckel's programme for supplying workers. The bottleneck in labour was the second obstacle to the realization of the Fleet Construction Programme of 1943. In a memorandum, Dönitz set out the requirements shown in Table 35. During the following weeks, the Main Committee for Ship Construction produced a new plan on the basis of 30 U-boats per month.

The heavy losses and meagre successes of May 1943 brought a renewed plea from Dönitz to Hitler to corroborate the urgency of his programme, despite existing crises elsewhere. Dönitz stated that, in fact, the U-boat campaign was foundering on the technical question of weaponry, but that the stepping-up of U-boat production would provide a

Table 34. The U-Boat Construction Programme of April 1943

1943 second half year	1944 first half year	second half year	1945 first half year	second half year
Increasing to 27 per month	27 per month*	27 plus 3 Type XX per month	27 plus 3 Type XX per month	30 per month

*Despite changeover to Type VIIC/42.

Table 35. Manpower needed for the Fleet Construction Programme of April 1943

Purpose for which used	Yards	Auxiliary yard industry[1]	Total
Existing (previous) shortage	13,000	14,000	27,000
In order to increase U-boats[2]			
New construction	3,000	1,000	
Repairs	8,000	2,000	14,000
In order to increase light naval forces[2]			
New construction	5,000	4,000	
Repairs	3,000	2,000	14,000
Total			55,000

[1] Plus weapons production, including torpedoes
[2] The labour forces were required in quotas by the end of 1944.

Yards	Actual delivery 1942	1943	1944	Target 1945	1946
Germaniawerft	18 VIIC +2 XB	19 VIIC +3 XB +2 WK202	22 VIIC +9 XVIIG	24 VIIC +3 XVIIG	24 VIIC —
Bremer Vulkan	21 VIIC	23 VIIC	15 VIIC +6 XX	11 VIIC +9 XX	26 VIIC
Flenderwerke	10 VIIC	14 VIIC	19 VIIC	22 VIIC	26 VIIC
Howaldt-Kiel	8 VIIC	11 VIIC	15 VIIC	18 VIIC	18 VIIC
Deutsche Werke Kiel	6 VIIC +5 XIV	12 VIIC +3 XIV	4 VIIC +7 XIV	12 XIV	12 XIV
Danziger Werft	12 VIIC	17 VIIC	25 VIIC	26 VIIC	26 VIIC
Schichau, Danzig	16 VIIC	25 VIIC	36 VIIC	36 VIIC	36 VIIC
Blohm & Voss	54 VIIC	60 VIIC +2 Wa201	54 VIIC +9 XVIIB	54 VIIC +3 XVIIB	56 VIIC
Flensburger SBG	7 VIIC	9 VIIC	9 VIIC	9 VIIC	9 VIIC
Nordseewerke	7 VIIC	10 VIIC	11 VIIC	12 VIIC	12 VIIC
Howaldt-Hamburg	9 VIIC	12 VIIC	15 VIIC	15 VIIC	15 VIIC
Stülcken	8 VIIC	10 VIIC	12 VIIC	12 VIIC	12 VIIC
KMW Wilhelmshaven	5 VIIC	9 VIIC	19 VIIC	26 VIIC	26 VIIC
Oderwerke, Stettin	—	1 VIIC	2 VIIC	1 VIIC	—
Stettiner Vulcan	—	1 VIIC	1 VIIC	—	—
Neptun Rostock	—	4 VIIC	9 VIIC	9 VIIC	9 VIIC
AG Weser	12 IXC +12 IXD	15 IXC +15 IXD	20 IXC +20 IXD	20 IXC +20 IXD	20 IXC +20 IXD
Seebeck	4 IXC	5 IXC	7 IXC	7 IXC	7 IXC
DW, Hamburg	23 IXC	25 IXC	18 IXC +7 XX	17 IXC +8 XX	25 IXC
Total No.:	239	307	373	374	379
Monthly average:	19.9	25.6	31.1	31.2	31.6

remedy of sorts. He wanted the planned increase to remain at 30 boats per month and believed even 'that the number of 30 U-boats is not sufficient as, in the last analysis, we need large numbers of U-boats to wage a successful defensive campaign in the Atlantic. I feel I am right in asking for the number of boats to be 40'. Hitler agreed, and without further ado, changed the prepared Führer Decree for the projected Fleet Construction Programme of 1943 to show delivery as 40 boats per month.

Neither the material aspects of the new programme nor the question of personnel were considered secure, and gave rise to grave concern. At a discussion with Hitler on 15 June 1943, Dönitz reported on the additional labour requirements for the increase in naval completions by the end of 1945 that Hitler had authorized, and made the requests shown in Table 37. He mentioned a shortage of 335,000 men, who would be needed during the next sixteen months to serve as crews in the new boats. He hoped to obtain these from 163,000 recruits, 140,000 from the Army and Luftwaffe and 32,000 internal transfers (replacement of personnel by female naval staff and prisoners-of-war). In the light of the current allocation of 30,000 men per year, however, these numbers were to be considered more as a hopeful expectation. Hitler reacted testily: 'I have not got these forces. It is essential that we strengthen anti-aircraft defences and night-fighters to protect German cities. It is essential to strengthen the Eastern Front. The Army needs whole divisions for the task of protecting Europe.' But Dönitz did not give up, and indicated the dangers to the entire conduct of the war if the U-boat campaign were terminated. Hitler acknowledged the truth of this, and declared that there was no question of stopping the U-boat campaign, but that, with regard to allocation of personnel, one had simply to get by in a hand-to-mouth manner and pay due heed to priorities. He would make no concrete promises, but confirmed his protection from call-up for those workers in naval production. He repeated that it was especially necessary that the increased construction programme be pushed through fully whatever the circumstances.

Distributions of steel to the Navy, however, continued to fall below the amount requested by Dönitz. Hitler's consent on 11 April to a further increase of 30,000 tons was reduced by the Armaments Minister to a one-off delivery. Speer had no mind for long-term delivery promises, preferring to make allocations on a day-to-day basis and according to priorities. Dönitz realized that he could not force his large Fleet Construction Programme through, alongside or in competition with the Armaments Minister, who controlled 83.3 per cent of the total industrial capacity. The overall production facilities of the Navy were too small to make good temporary shortages. No help was to be expected from Göring and Milch, who were involved in their own struggle to keep up the strength of the Luftwaffe. On 20 June 1943, Dönitz asked Speer to take over responsibility for naval armaments. This step was not lightly taken, and it received little support from Naval Command circles, who feared that they would no longer be masters in their own house. After examining naval requirements, Speer declared himself willing, provided that Hitler would allow partial cessation of civilian industrial production. The mobilization of hitherto-unused home reserves was a condition for the accomplishment of such an ambitious programme, as it was essential that neither the Army nor Luftwaffe programmes be adversely affected. Hitler consented and the programme was confirmed by official decree on 8 July 1943.

The OKM Construction Programme of July 1943

Following Hitler's signing of the Fleet Construction Programme of 1943, 'K' Office began immediately to work out a plan that would raise the present U-boat production to 40 boats per month. This plan was to provide the increased delivery numbers as soon as possible, but, on the other hand, also to take account of the new U-boat types. Type XXI boats were to be built in larger numbers because they were due to replace Type IX. On 6 July 1943, the following contracts for a total of 282 new U-boats were placed.

Walter U-boat Type XXII: Preliminary building and assembly yard Howaldt, Kiel (36 boats); additional construction yard Howaldt, Hamburg (36 boats).

Walter U-boat Type XVIIB: Preliminary building and assembly yard B&V (48 boats); additional construction yard Nordseewerke, Emden (12 boats).

Walter U-boat Type XVIIG: Friedrich Krupp; Germaniawerft; AG, Kiel (48 boats).

U-boat Type XXI: Preliminary building and assembly yard Deschimag, AG Weser (24 boats); additional construction yards: Deutsche Werft, Hamburg (24 boats); Danziger Werft (12 boats); Schichau, Danzig (18 boats); KMW, Wilhelmshaven (12 boats); Flenderwerke, Lübeck (12 boats).

It was estimated that if the highest priority stage (DE) were granted, the first 3 prototype boats of Type XXI could be ready from Deschimag in November 1944. Series production at the additional construction yards was calculated for March 1945.

Table 37. Planned manpower requirements, 15 June 1943

	Men required
1. Warship construction:	
Yards:	
New construction	
U-boats	25,300
Light naval forces	24,000
Repairs	
U-boats	8,000
Surface vessels	18,000
Supervisory staff	2,500
Auxiliary yard industry	40,000
Total	117,800
2. Weapons and equipment manufacture:	
Guns (without ammunition)	8,000
Torpedoes	8,500
Mines and mine-defence	850
Communications equipment	1,150
Nautical equipment	500
Other kinds of naval equipment	5,000
Total	24,000
Overall total for warships and equipment[1]	141,800
3. Construction undertakings	
Building workers	25,000

[1] Of these, at least 55,500 to be German skilled workers, of which 23,500 necessary to meet demands within 3 months, and 4,400 monthly from Oct 1943 to the end of 1945.

The maximum production of 15 boats monthly was to begin in August 1945. On the other hand, the small Walter U-boats were to be available in considerable numbers from the middle of 1944. There were to be, therefore, some changes in the present contracts. Where their production got in the way of the new boats, they were to be transferred to other yards or even deferred. The deliveries envisaged to the end of 1945 under this planning (without taking account of any necessary follow-on contracts) are shown in Table 38.

On 10 July 1943, in connection with the foregoing, a meeting took place at the Walter Works involving some fifty leading personalities from yards, armaments factories and industry to discuss armaments and, in particular, the realization of the new U-Boat Programme. The main point for discussion was the large contract for a total of 72 boats of the new Walter Type XXII. Dönitz wanted these for Mediterranean operations and they were to be transported via the Rhône. As had happened with the small IIB boats (page 142), it was intended to transport them on their sides. The first boat, *U1153*, was to be delivered by the Howaldtswerke, Kiel, in December 1943. (A production time of 120,000 hours per boat was calculated for ship and engine fitting.) The development of an ocean-going Walter U-boat was to continue despite the decision in favour of the new Type XXI. Following this conference, orders for 212 Walter-installations were placed, for delivery by the end of 1944. In previous years, Walter developments had proceeded with caution and delay — now, with the failure of conventional boats in the U-boat campaign, all inhibitions were put aside and the series production of a total of 204 Walter boats was to commence. When this decision was made, however, the test U-boats were still on the building slips.

Table 38 U-boat deliveries planned, July 1943

Yards	U-boat type	1943 Dec	1944 Jan	Feb	Mar	April	May	June	July	Aug	Sept	Oct	Nov	Dec	1945 Jan	Feb	Mar	April	May	June	July	Aug	Sept	Oct	Nov	Dec
Howaldt, Kiel	VIIC/41	1	1	1	1	1	—	1	—	1	—	1	—	1	—	1	—	1	—	1	—	1	—	1	—	1
	XXII	1	1	—	—	1	3	3	3	3	3	3	3	3	3	3	3	.	.	.	.	.	.	.	.	.
Howaldt, Hamburg	VIIC/41	1	1	1	1	1	1	—	1	—	1	—	1	—	1	—	1	—	1	—	1	—	1	—	1	—
	XXII	—	—	—	—	—	3	3	3	3	3	3	3	3	3	3	3	3	.	.	.	.	.	.	.	.
B&V, Hamburg	VIIC/41	5	4	4	4	4	4	4	4	4	2	2	2	2	2	2	2	3	3	3	.	.	.	.	.	.
	VIIC/42	—	—	—	—	—	—	—	—	—	2	2	2	2	2	2	2	2	4	4	4	4	4	4	4	4
	XVIIB	—	2	3	4	4	4	4	4	4	4	4	4	4	4	4	4	3	.	.	.	.	.	.	.	.
Nordseewerke, Emden	VIIC/41	1	1	1	1	1	1	1	—	1	—	1	—	1	—	1	—	1	—	1	—	1	—	—	—	—
	VIIC/42	—	—	—	—	—	—	—	—	—	—	—	—	—	—	—	—	—	—	—	—	—	—	—	1	—
	XVIIB	—	—	—	—	—	—	1	1	1	1	1	1	1	1	1	1	1	1	1	.	.	.	.	.	.
Germaniawerft, Kiel	VIIC/41	1	2	2	2	—	1	—	1	—	1	—	—	—	—	—	—	—	—	—	—	—	—	—	—	—
	VIIC/42	—	—	—	—	—	—	—	—	—	—	—	1	—	—	1	—	1	—	1	—	1	—	1	—	1
	XVIIG	—	—	—	—	4	4	5	4	4	5	4	4	5	4	4	5	4	4	.	.	.	.	.	.	.
	XB	1	—	—	—	—	—	—	—	—	—	—	—	—	—	—	—	—	—	—	—	—	—	—	—	—
Deschimag, Bremen	IXC	1	1	1	1	1	1	1	1	1	1	1	—	—	—	—	—	—	—	—	—	—	—	—	—	—
	IXD	1	1	1	1	1	1	1	1	1	1	1	1	—	—	—	—	—	—	—	—	—	—	—	—	—
	XXI	—	—	—	—	—	—	—	—	—	—	—	3	3	3	3	3	4	3	2	.	.	.	.	.	.
DW, Hamburg	IXC	2	2	2	2	2	2	2	2	2	2	2	2	2	2	2	—	—	—	—	—	—	—	—	—	—
	XX	—	—	—	—	—	—	—	—	—	1	2	2	2	2	2	1	1	1	1	.	.	.	.	.	.
	XXI	—	—	—	—	—	—	—	—	—	—	—	—	—	—	—	3	3	3	3	3	4	3	2	.	.
Schichau, Danzig	VIIC/41	3	3	3	3	3	3	3	3	3	3	3	—	—	—	—	—	—	—	—	—	—	—	—	—	—
	VIIC/42	—	—	—	—	—	—	—	—	—	—	—	3	3	3	3	3	3	3	3	.	.	.	.	.	.
	XXI	—	—	—	—	—	—	—	—	—	—	—	—	—	—	—	—	—	—	3	3	3	3	3	3	—
Danziger Werft	VIIC/41	1	1	1	2	1	1	2	1	1	1	1	2	2	2	2	2	2	.	.	.	.	.	.	.	.
	XXI	—	—	—	—	—	—	—	—	—	—	—	—	—	—	—	—	—	2	2	2	2	2	2	.	.
KMW, Wilhelmshaven	VIIC/41	1	1	1	1	1	2	2	2	2	—	—	—	—	—	—	—	—	—	—	—	—	—	—	—	—
	VIIC/42	—	—	—	—	—	—	—	—	—	2	2	2	2	2	2	—	—	—	—	—	—	—	—	—	—
	XXI	—	—	—	—	—	—	—	—	—	—	—	—	—	—	—	—	2	2	2	2	2	2	.	.	.
Flenderwerke	VIIC/41	1	1	1	1	2	2	2	2	2	2	2	2	—	—	—	—	—	—	—	—	—	—	—	—	—
	VIIC/42	—	—	—	—	—	—	—	—	—	—	—	—	1	1	2	2	2	2	2	.	.	.	.	.	.
	XXI	—	—	—	—	—	—	—	—	—	—	—	—	—	—	—	—	—	—	1	1	2	1	2	1	—
DWK, Kiel	VIIC	1	1	1	1	1	1	2	—	—	—	—	—	—	—	—	—	—	—	—	—	—	—	—	—	—
	XIV	—	—	—	—	—	—	1	1	—	1	1	1	1	1	1	1	.	.	.	.	.	.	.	.	.
	XVIII	—	—	—	—	—	—	—	—	—	—	—	—	—	—	—	1	1	.	.	.	.	.	.	.	.
Bremer Vulkan	VIIC/41	2	2	2	2	2	2	2	2	1	1	1	—	—	—	—	—	—	—	—	—	—	—	—	—	—
	XX	—	—	—	—	—	—	—	—	—	—	—	1	1	1	1	1	1	2	2	2	2	1	—	—	—
Seebeck, Wesermünde	IXC	1	—	1	—	1	—	—	1	—	—	1	—	1	—	1	—	1	—	1	—	1	—	1	—	1
H. C. Stülcken Sohn	VIIC/41	1	—	1	1	1	1	—	1	1	1	1	1	1	1	1	—	1	1	—	1	1	—	1	1	1
Flensburger, SBG	VIIC/41	1	1	—	1	1	1	—	1	1	1	—	1	1	1	—	1	1	—	1	1	—	—	1	1	—
Neptunwerft, Rostock	VIIC	1	1	—	1	1	—	1	1	—	1	1	—	1	1	—	1	1	—	.	.	.	.	.	.	.
	VIIC/41	—	—	—	—	—	—	—	—	—	—	—	—	—	—	—	—	—	—	1	1	—	1	1	1	.
Totals by type of boat	VIIC or VIIC/41	21	20	19	22	20	20	20	19	17	14	13	8	9	8	7	7	10	6	6	3	3	3	2	3	3
	VIIC/42	—	—	—	—	—	—	—	—	—	4	4	8	8	9	9	8	7	9	10	6	4	6	6	6	6
	IXC	4	3	3	4	3	3	4	3	3	4	3	2	3	2	2	1	—	—	1	—	—	1	—	—	1
	IXD	1	1	1	1	1	1	1	1	1	1	1	1	—	—	—	—	—	—	—	—	—	—	—	—	—
	XB	1	—	—	—	—	—	—	—	—	—	—	—	—	—	—	—	—	—	—	—	—	—	—	—	—
	XIV	—	—	—	—	—	—	1	1	—	1	1	1	1	1	1	1	.	.	.	.	.	.	.	.	.
	XX	—	—	—	—	—	—	—	—	—	1	2	3	3	3	3	2	2	3	3	2	2	1	—	—	—
	XXI	—	—	—	—	—	—	—	—	—	—	—	3	3	3	3	8	9	10	9	11	15	.	.	.	.
	XVIIB/G	—	2	3	4	8	8	9	9	9	10	9	9	10	9	9	10	8	.	.	.	.	.	.	.	.
	XXII	1	1	—	—	1	6	6	6	6	6	6	6	6	6	6	6	.	.	.	.	.	.	.	.	.
Overall totals		28	27	26	31	33	38	40	39	37	40	39	41	43	41	40	43	.	.	.	.	.	.	.	.	.

Note: A dot signifies 'unknown', a dash 'no delivery'.

8 THE CHANGE TO TYPE XXI AND XXIII CONSTRUCTION

THE PRODUCTION LINE SYSTEM

Otto Merker and sectional construction

The Supreme Naval Command's new U-boat Programme of 6 July 1943 highlighted the dilemma in which the Chief Office of Warship Construction found itself, as a result of the Chief of Naval War Staff's demand for new U-boats with a much higher submerged speed. In accordance with usual planning procedures, the large U-boats of Type XXI should have required a development and building time of at least 1½ years. It was understood, therefore, that the first 3 boats of this type would be ready in November 1944, and not until March 1945 would series production begin at appropriate yards. In the meantime, current U-boat construction would continue with small changes, but strengthened by an ambitious Walter Programme. It was hoped that small Walter-boats of Type XVII and XXII could be delivered quickly in order to meet, to some extent, the demands of the Chief of Naval War Staff. This large Walter Programme was, however, inseparable from certain conditions that had to be met, notably the allocation of special skilled workers, necessary materials and the production of an adequate supply of Aurol.

Dönitz, however, was principally interested only in the larger Type XXI, which he wanted to use in the Battle of the Atlantic. There was, at the time, no clear idea as to possible applications for the small Walter U-boats, apart from using Type XXII in the Mediterranean. The large boats, on the other hand, according to the existing Construction Programme, would not be ready for operational use before 1946 — in 2½–3 years. So long a delay as this seemed out of the question to Dönitz, who was conscious of the critical situation in the U-boat campaign. He made application, therefore, to Armaments Minister Speer for an alternative programme for the quickest possible construction of Type XXI.

During a conference with Hitler on 8 July 1943, Dönitz demanded that the construction of Type XXI be pushed forward with all available means. The firm decision must be taken for three-shift working round the clock. He also reiterated his personnel requirements and demanded an additional 262,000 men, especially technical staff, by the autumn of 1944 for the enlarged programme. Hitler, however, could only see his way — additional to the already planned measures for raising U-boat production — to providing 10,000 technicians, the class of 1925, for the Navy on an exchange basis.

Otto Merker.

Speer now authorized the new head of the Main Committee for Ship Construction, General Director Merker, of the Magirus-Werke in Ulm, to draw up a suitable plan. Otto Merker was experienced in the automobile industry, and was familiar with modern methods of series production. He was convinced that the relatively lengthy construction times in ship-building were a legacy of conventional, single-construction on the slips. At a meeting of the Sub-Committee for U-boats at the beginning of August 1943, he criticized current U-boat construction methods and suggested that U-boats be assembled from pre-fabricated sections, these to be put together like automobiles on an assembly line. If this process were used, the first Type XXI boat could be ready by 1 April 1944, and series production could begin immediately afterwards. This would mean that by the autumn of 1944, 30 U-boats per month could be delivered. It would be necessary, however, for constructional plans for Type XXI to be prepared by a new Central Construction Office by 1 December 1943, and for the entire U-boat industry to go over almost completely to the new process and the new type.

This plan suited admirably the wishes of the Supreme Commander-in-Chief of the Navy for the quickest possible operational availability of the new Type XXI boats. No objections were raised by the Head of Department K I U, Ministerial Director Schürer, against the intended section construction. It had been by no means an infrequent occurrence for U-boats to be built in sections, but this had been in the case of smaller boats, or when it had been intended that boats be transported for ultimate assembly elsewhere. Various attempts had been made between 1940 and 1942 to achieve series production of U-boats in this way, but the results had been disappointing because the problems of producing sufficiently precise section components had not been solved. The yards, therefore, tended to regard Merker's ideas with scepticism. An opinion of B&V on U-boat sectional construction stated:

'1. Section construction at one yard, i.e., construction of all kinds of sections with assembly carried out at the same yard. From a shipbuilding point of view, an exact tolerance of 2mm in section length is regarded as feasible. For diameter measurement, frames and internal items working to such exact dimensions will not be possible, as we shall not be able accurately to evaluate shrinkages due to existing tensions and stresses in constructional materials. This point is specially applicable to double-hulled boats, as in these it is absolutely essential to obtain complete and perfect accuracy in the pressure hull and also in the outer hull. The production of the battery compartments in their appropriate construction sections which are open on both sides will be especially time-consuming on account of the extreme accuracy that they require

— millimetres are of great importance here. All this precision work demands highly-skilled workers, and will involve the expenditure of an increased number of hours in many tasks even though improved equipment be made available for use. The manufacture of bulkhead gauges and of the numerous other items of equipment, which are mostly of considerable size, will make very severe claims on all yards in terms of expenditure of material and work-hours. The installation of necessary equipment will also involve a considerable expenditure in terms of time, which will make for further problems in getting the schedule under way.

'Pressure-testing of pressure hulls will no longer be possible. Pressure-testing with air, and finding leaks by means of soap will require many hours work, and is quite unsatisfactory especially in winter. Pressure-testing in a pressure-dock when the boat is complete would subsequently require considerably greater dismantling work to rectify faults that appear than would be necessary if normal pressure-testing were possible.

'The greatest difficulties are anticipated in the sphere of transportation. Each construction yard will have to have special carriages and lifting gear available in order that sections may be transported to the building-slips. Very few yards will be in the position of being able to remove sections weighing 70–130 tons and — even more difficult — get them to the building-slips. A case in point is provided by the fact that, in Hamburg, the non-availability of the 150-ton floating crane paralysed the whole U-boat construction and it would be essential for each yard to provide itself with new transport means suitable for the new purposes. It is only right and proper that we draw special attention to these problems. Most difficult from the transport point of view will be the bulky after-deck with its smooth, considerably overhanging outer components and heavy mountings. The fore-ship gives similar problems.

'It is completely out of the question to install in one section the propeller shaft in its stern tube, in another section, the electric motor and in a third, the diesel engines. Electric motors and diesel engines must at all costs remain unfixed, and only be finally installed and made secure after the welding together of various sections. This means, further, that everything that is connected to these engines cannot be given its final position while

sections are being constructed. That would mean, in the case of a diesel engine, almost all pipes and pipe-lines (exhaust pipes, cooling-water pipes, fuel-oil pipes, lubricating-oil pipes and compressed-air pipes). Then during the assembly time on the building-slips, the most appalling conditions would rule in these compartments because, in the very shortest space of time, engines would need to be set up and made secure while other essential work was taking place in other installations of such sections. All this would have to be carried out alongside the connection of mutually interdependent items with cables and tubes.

'It is, of course, anticipated that very great care will be taken in the planning, that connecting cables and tubes that have to run through sections will be kept to a minimum and that they will be so positioned and access so provided that assembly work is made simpler. But this will inevitably mean that these connections will require more space than they are given in present construction methods. We remain unconvinced that it is completely possible to build-in all cables in such a way that they may be so connected by cable connections and tubes that they can finally be secured to each other by simple screwing. One must certainly anticipate a certain amount of additional laying-work on pipes and cables following assembly.

'It is an important question whether the conning tower should be constructed in sectional form with the control room or added as a subsequent task. The second alternative would have many advantages with regard to the handling of the section and its transportation, but, on the other hand, the most important items of tubing are positioned in the upper deck around the conning tower, and these could only be put in place after erection of the conning tower, which would have marked effect on building-slip construction time. In methods of construction as used hitherto, the tests on auxiliary engines, hydroplanes, rudders, etc., were carried out one after the other. In the case of sectional construction, all this will have to be carried out in a short period of time and this will involve careful advance planning. The trial period in water following the slipway launch will be a longer one. Considerable difficulties will arise also in the installation and testing of tubing that runs from compartment to compartment. Two pressure tests will be necessary; once during the construction of

the section and again following completion of the boat. The first of these cannot be dispensed with, because all tubing will be so fitted that, if leaks occur, it will not be possible to rectify them.

To facilitate the work, two-shift working must be provided. As during the winter months a large part of working time would occur in the blackout period, special measures will be necessary for the welding together of sections on the building-slips. With existing construction methods involving considerably longer time for each boat at these building-slips, welding work could be so arranged that it could be carried out essentially during the day. However, with sectional construction, the time each boat spends on the building-slip is now so short that welding will have to take place during both shifts. Covering in the building slips is hardly practical as it would entail an enormous expenditure in corrugated iron or wood and would require many working hours.

'II. Section construction with two fabrication points for each kind of section with assembly at three assembly yards. In this method of construction, not only the difficulties enumerated under I. occur, but other weighty considerations become manifest. The solution of transport problems becomes even more difficult as there is not just the factor of transportation from production point of sections to the building-slips, but additional transportation between individual yards, including transportation by water. Apart from the organization of essential lifting gear for loading into lighters or ships and of cranes and like lifting apparatus for placing the sections on the building-slips, there is also the not inconsiderable claim for a sizeable amount of shipping space. Emphasis must also be laid on the possibilities of further difficulties posed by floating ice. The supply of sections to the individual yards can thereby be delayed by months. Under the old construction system, Blohm & Voss at the beginning of 1943 could not make any trials' trips with U-boats for a period of three months. Nevertheless, one boat was completed each week. That would now no longer be possible with barge-transportation of sections from other building points.

'In present building methods it is the case at available yards that their various workshops and trades are fully utilized. That is partly achieved by the fact that certain appropriate manufacturing processes are carried out at factories elsewhere. Such full use of capacity is desirable for use of works' installations. This would not, however, be the case if one adopted the proposed construction methods for boats involving only two fabrication points and three assembly centres. Many workshops and skilled labour teams would be inadequately used or no longer used. This would apply in the greatest extent to assembly yards. Restricting the assembly yards to three seems especially poor judgement. If one calculates a building-slip time of eight weeks, for each of the three assembly yards, 24 building-slip sites would be necessary. It would be far better to provide a larger number of assembly yards. In Hamburg, for example, one would wish to see two yards each with 12 building-slip sites in the interests of dispersal as a means of minimizing the effect of air attacks. As, with regard to expenditure on building-slip assembly installations, it is the number of building-slip sites that is paramount not the fact of their being situated in one place, nothing is saved by imposing a restriction of assembly yards to three. In the interests of using workshops to the full, it would be advisable for assembly yards in the immediate vicinity also to be involved in sectional construction.

'Consequently, Blohm & Voss make the following representations:
1. The old construction methods should remain fundamentally the same, but where possible to work in two shifts, and appropriate measures must be taken to meet this.
2. Greater reliance needs to be placed on the completion of component parts outside and a stronger concentration of completion of such parts at a few firms on behalf of all yards is recommended.
3. In consideration of the extraordinary expenditure on heavy and very heavy installations, lifting gear, special transport means, etc., and of what we have shown by our observations above to be in many respects a difficult constructional system, we maintain that an economy in work hours can only be achieved by long-term execution of the building programme and, even then, not in the proposed volume.'

However, in the meantime, the design for U-Boat Type XXIII was available and this was a simple, small 'Electro-boat' lending itself to quick building. Dönitz therefore directed, on 13 August, a basic changeover in U-boat construction to the two new Types XXI and XXIII. Details of his directive were:
1. The U-boat programme be reshaped around U-boats Type XXI and XXIII.
2. Type XXI for Atlantic use; XXIII for coastal or Mediterranean work.
3. XXI to take over tasks of present Types VII, IX, etc.; XXIII initially 120 boats; from March–April (1944) 20 per month.
4. Total U-boat production to remain at 40 per month; no production gaps to be tolerated through the changeover process; a split-up of the monthly quota into different types still to be established. 20 Type XXIII boats would equal (by provisional estimate) the expense of 5–6 large boats.

5. Type XVII (Walter) U-boats to continue to be built; 4+24=28; development of these also to continue.
6. Type XVIII (large Walter) U-boats: work to continue on both test boats.
7. Construction of Type VIIC/42 to be sacrificed in favour of Type XXI.

This meant effectively that the new large Walter programme for Types XVII and XXII had 'died'. And from this time, with very few exceptions, no U-boat of the old types was laid down. With a minimum building time of nine months, the existing programme (with certain deletions) ran until April 1944. From then on, deliveries decreased sharply. By telegram, dated 30 September 1943, various contracts dating back to 6 July 1943, as well as earlier contracts involving 162 boats of Type VIIC or VIIC/41; 174 boats of Type VIIC/42; 71 boats of Type IXC/40; 22 boats of Type IXD/42; and 18 Walter boats of Type XVIIB and XVIIG—all were suspended or cancelled. Only the Flensburger SBG, which was not involved in the programmes for Type XXI and XXIII, was to continue to build Type VIIC/41. The last keel-laying at this yard took place on 28 January 1944, and then it too was required to cease work on all older constructions.

The Ingenieurbüro Glückauf (IBG)

Following the subordination of Naval Armaments to the Ministry for Armament and War Production, various changes were necessary in the organization. A mutual decree by the Supreme Commander-in-Chief of the Navy and the Ministry of Armaments, dated 22 July 1943, announced the following new distribution of tasks and responsibilities:

'1. The working-out of sketches for new ship types will be continued by the Supreme Naval Command.
'2. The working-out of completed designs for new types and of changes in current types will be made by a Ship Construction Commission formed by the Minister for Armaments and Munitions. The head will be provided by the Navy, the 12 members will be chosen in equal numbers from Navy and industry. In addition to these, will be the Head of the HAS, the authorized Office Group Head of the Ministry for Armaments, the delegate for the Ship Construction and Naval Programme, and a member of the Imperial Commission for Merchantmen. To deal with certain specialized tasks; sub-commissions with a similar organizational structure will be formed.
'3. The Ship Construction Commission authorizes the Head Office for Warship Construction to carry out tests, calculations and design work.
'4. The Main Committee for Ship Construction will be reconstructed. It is placed under the Ministry for Armaments and takes over the detailed working-out of completed designs, and the allotment of contracts to the yards, by directing repair contracts, spare-part production and deliveries. It also looks after the fixing of quotas, the control of stock and machine tools, and the use of labour and the planning of necessary constructional undertakings. Allotment of contracts to the yards and the supply firms will take place in future only through the Main Committee or through the

Sections of Ministry for Armaments authorized to deal with such points.'

To cope with the numerous tasks of the Main Committee, Central Constructional Offices were set up. The office for U-boat construction was the Ingenieurbüro Glückauf (IBG) in Blankenburg/Halberstadt, which had taken over the task of the former Yard Construction Offices for new U-boat types. (In the interest of security from air attack, it was evacuated to a position in the Harz Mountains.) This meant that the new organization shown in the diagram existed for U-boat construction, while the following was the new distribution of tasks in U-boat construction:
1. Military requirements: Supreme Commander-in-Chief of the Navy (Chief of Naval War Staff).
2. Preliminary design: Head Office for Warship Construction (K).
3. Authorization: Supreme Commander-in-Chief of the Navy.
4. Finished design: Ship Construction Commission.
5. Overall construction: HAS/IBG.
6. Authorization for constructional drawings: Constructional supervision of the 'K' Office at the IBG.
7. Distribution of contracts: HAS.
8. Construction executions: Steel construction-establishments, yards, etc.
9. Procurement of components: HAS.
10. Construction overseeing: Steel construction, yards. Shipyards, naval construction-supervision.
11. Acceptance: U-Boat Acceptance Commission (UAK).

The constitution of the IBG followed in September 1943. At the head of operations was Naval Construction Director Oelfken, who also held a position in the Ship Construction Commission. He had direct control of naval supervision at the IBG, was the controlling authority for the total timetable, and was in charge of the lines of communication to the yards. The organization of the IBG in its details was as shown in the diagram. On 8 December 1943, the staff totalled 1,020; from September 1943 to March 1945, the average staff was 650. 25 per cent of the staff were female. The working day was twelve hours long with three Sundays worked monthly. Only two holidays per year were allowed, each of 6–8 days.

Initially, the various ordering agencies were concentrated in Halberstadt. When, however, the number of their tasks increased, they were decentralized early in 1944 to a number of yards and other centres. Details of groups working in this way were:
Pressure-tight hatches, doors and closures: Seebeck, Wesermünde.
Gearing and forged components: Deschimag, Bremen.
Propellers, shaft piping and schnorkels: Blohm & Voss.
Flexible and cast parts: Howaldtswerke, Hamburg.
Auxiliary engines and pumps: Howaldtswerke, Kiel.
Electric motors and fitting-out items: Germaniawerft, Kiel.
Rolled steel and profiles for upper works: DWK, Kiel.

The distribution of tasks and responsibilities between the Navy and the Ministry for Armaments

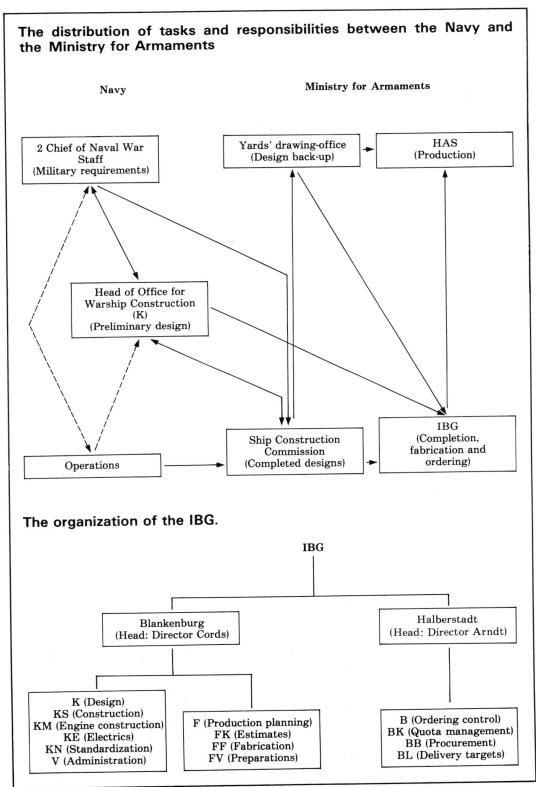

Navy

Ministry for Armaments

2 Chief of Naval War Staff (Military requirements)

Yards' drawing-office (Design back-up)

HAS (Production)

Head of Office for Warship Construction (K) (Preliminary design)

Operations

Ship Construction Commission (Completed designs)

IBG (Completion, fabrication and ordering)

The organization of the IBG.

IBG

Blankenburg (Head: Director Cords)

Halberstadt (Head: Director Arndt)

K (Design)
KS (Construction)
KM (Engine construction)
KE (Electrics)
KN (Standardization)
V (Administration)

F (Production planning)
FK (Estimates)
FF (Fabrication)
FV (Preparations)

B (Ordering control)
BK (Quota management)
BB (Procurement)
BL (Delivery targets)

Steel alloy and electrodes: Stülcken Sohn, Hamburg.
Special outer-ship fittings: Bremer Vulkan, Vegesack.
Screws and other standard parts, compressed-air leads and oil-pressure pipes and bottles: MBZA Central Procurement and Equipment Office of the Navy, Hildesheim.
Installations for assembly work: Danziger Werft AG, Danzig (later Halberstadt).
Walter-Drive installations: H. Walter KG, Kiel, in Oldesloe/Holstein.
U-Boat Type XXIII: Deutsche Werft, Hamburg.
Midget submarines: Germaniawerft, Kiel.
The quota section was moved to Cottbus, and later to Sangerhausen, while rolled steel for ships' hulls was distributed by the Stahlbau-U-Steuerung (Steel Construction Control, U-Boats) in Lünen/Westphalia.

Section construction for Type XXI

When the basic ideas of the sectional construction proposed by Merker had been explained at the beginning of August 1943, it was finally decided that Type XXI should be carried out in section construction according to the following plan:

Section 1: length 12.7m; weight approx. 65 tons (stern with stern compartment, steering installation and workshop).
Section 2: length 10m; weight approx. 130 tons (electric motor compartment).
Section 3: length 8.4m; weight approx. 140 tons (diesel engine compartment).
Section 4: length 5.3m; weight approx. 70 tons (crews' living quarters).
Section 5: length 7.6m; weight approx. 140 tons (control room and galley).
Section 6: length 12m; weight approx. 165 tons (forward living quarters).
Section 7: length 6.8m; weight approx. 92 tons (torpedo storage compartment).
Section 8: length 14m; weight approx. 110 tons (bow with torpedo tubes).
Section 9: length 14.1m (conning-tower superstructure).

Steel construction of these sections was to be completed as fully as possible at steel firms. This meant assembly of the pressure hull, the building-in of bulkheads, understructures and other items necessary to the production of the crude sections. Selection of these firms was made with regard to their being widely dispersed in the interior of the country, so that additional labour forces could be available for U-boat construction, and a further consideration was accessibility of such firms by waterways as it was intended that these large crude sections would be transported by ship. On the other hand, experience in ship construction was not required. The largest number of the selected steel firms were in western Germany, a small number in Silesia and Danzig, with the remainder in central Germany. Sections 1–8 were allocated as follows:
Section 1: Hannemann & Co., Lübeck; Norddeutscher Eisenbau, Sande near Wilhelmshaven; Gresse & Co., Wittenberg (Elbe); Strassburger Werft, Strassburg (Neudorf).
Section 2: Gutehoffnungshütte, Oberhausen-

Sterkrade; Seibert, Aschaffenburg; Dellschau, Berlin; Eilers, Hannover.

Section 3: MAN, Mainz-Gustavsburg; Krupp-Stahlbau, Hannover; Mittelstahl, Riesa; Gollnow, Stettin.

Section 4: Fries-Sohn, Frankfurt am Main; Hein, Lehmann & Co., Düsseldorf-Oberbilk; Kelle & Hildebrandt, Dresden; Gebr. Heyking, Danzig.

Section 5: Krupp-Stahlbau, Rheinhausen; Eggers & Co., Hamburg; H. J. Jucho, Audorf near Rendsburg; August Klönne, Danzig.

Section 6: MAN, Hamburg; Dortmunder Union, Gelsenkirchen; (Werk Orange); Demag, Bodenwerder; Krupp-Druckenmüller, Stettin.

Section 7: Schäfer, Ludwigshafen; Grohmann & Frosch, Wittenberg (Elbe); Uebigau, Dresden; Beuchelt & Co., Grünberg (Silesia).

Section 8: Hilgers AG, Rheinbrohl; GHH Rheinwerft, Walsum; Carl Später, Hamburg; Beuchelt & Co., Grünberg (Silesia).

This meant that almost 50 per cent of German steel production was involved. The chosen ironworks had to break off current armament undertakings not of the highest priority, and devote themselves completely to the new requirements. (As a case in point, the firm of Hilgers-AG had produced pioneer equipment, before having to take on the construction of crude sections.)

Ship and engine assembly of the crude sections was to follow in special section yards, each section being handled in at least two yards. For the final assembly, three large yards were envisaged. These had to be experienced in U-boat construction and had to be able to cope with modern series production. It was desirable that they should be in the vicinity of the section yards in order to keep risky sea transport to a minimum. The distribution was as follows:

Western Area:

Section 1: Howaldtswerke, Kiel.
Section 2: KMW-Wilhelmshaven.
Section 3: DW, Hamburg-Finkenwerder; Bremer Vulkan, Vegesack.
Section 4: Flenderwerke, Lübeck.
Section 5: Howaldtswerke, Hamburg; Bremer Vulkan, Vegesack.
Section 6: DW, Hamburg-Finkenwerder; Bremer Vulkan, Vegesack.

Assembly yards: Blohm & Voss, Hamburg; AG Weser, Bremen.

Section 7: Deschimag Werk Seebeck, Wesermünde.
Section 8: DWK, Kiel.
Section 9: Hitzler, Lauenburg (Elbe); Büsumer Schiffswerft; Sietas; Bremer Vulkan, Vegesack; Lübecker Maschinenbaugesellschaft.

Eastern Area:

Sections 1, 2, 3 and 8: Danziger Werft.
Sections 4 and 5: Schichau, Danzig.
Sections 6 and 7: Deutsche Werke Gotenhafen.

Assembly yard: Schichau, Danzig.

The selection of section yards was dictated by their capacity and by other important tasks to be carried out (e.g., the Hansa-Programme). The supply industry was also slotted into the new programme. The main engine installations that would decide delivery dates had to be developed in good time and then built by the manufacturers with all speed. The proposed diesel engines — MAN Type M6 V 40/46 KBB — were contracted to MAN, Klöckner-Humboldt-Deutz and Wumag, Görlitz. The new, large electric motors were to be built by SSW, AEG and BBC. The first contracts were sent to industry as early as August 1943, and the first steel requirements followed in September. Three weeks later, the necessary ship-construction steel was available thanks to the energetic intervention of Speer. The race against time began.

In the meanwhile, designing was going ahead at full speed at the IBG. At a delivery discussion on 25 September 1943, the following ship constructional planning was presented.

Materials disposition for pressure hulls, plates and frames — 22 Sept 1943
Dispatch of these to Düsseldorf — 4 Oct 1943
Delivery of pressure-hull materials for 30 U-boats — 10–15 Oct 1943
Completion of the main dimensions — 5 Oct 1943
Completion of drawings for the main frames — 9 Oct 1943
Winding-off the pressure-hull housing and the frames to the steelworks — 10 Oct 1943
Bending of frames and plates for the pressure hulls — 15 Oct–1 Nov 1943
Materials disposition for the outer ship — 23 Oct 1943
Completion of drawings for cast components and forged components of the hulls — 25 Oct 1943
Deschimag delivers templates for outer-ship plates — 25 Oct 1943
Final drawings of the pressure hull and for flanges and fittings from the construction office to the steel construction office — 1 Nov 1943
Commencement of crude section construction. (The crude sections for the first 10 boats to be delivered by the ship construction firms with under-structures, etc., but without flanges, consoles, etc.) — 1 Nov 1943
Drawings for the pressure bulkheads from the construction office to steel construction. (The first 10 bow and stern parts, including pressure bulkheads, to be constructed by the section yards) — 15 Nov 1943
Commencement of material deliveries for 20 outer-ship hulls. (Simultaneously, models and templates for these to the steel construction firms) — 25 Nov 1943
Last drawing for the outer hull from the design office to steel construction — 1 Dec 1943
Patterns for the pressure bulkheads ready for sending to the steel works — 1 Dec 1943
Completion of the first forward pressure bulkhead — 15 Dec 1943
Crude sections ready for transport — 1 Jan 1944
Commencement of section construction — 9 Jan 1944
Completion of the last drawings for the

armament, especially of the torpedo reloading installation — 15 Jan 1944
Delivery of the first conning-tower superstructure to the assembly yards — 1 Mar 1944
Completed section construction for the first boat — 5 Mar 1944
Beginning of complete assembly of the first boat — 15 Mar 1944
Delivery of the first complete boat — 15 Mar 1944

This planning, therefore, was not in line with Merker's promise to have the first boat ready for delivery in April 1944. He now demanded that delivery of the first boat be made on 30 April 1944. To achieve this, the other dates would have to be advanced. His programme of 20 August 1943, for Type XXI (officially published on 1 November 1943) envisaged the following deliveries in 1944.

April	3
May	9
June	18
July	27
August	33
September	33
October	35
November	37
December	38
Total 1944	233
1945 monthly	38

Of these, a maximum of 15 boats were to be delivered by B&V and 15 from AG Weser, as well as 8 boats from Schichau. In the meantime, however, the Type XXIII programme had been decided upon, and such a wide-ranging programme was simply not to be entertained, in spite of rationalization and the scraping the barrel for labour and material reserves. Correspondingly, the maximum delivery instalment for Type XXI had to be restricted to 33, of which 13 boats went to B&V, 12 to Weser and 8 to Schichau. On 6 November 1943, the first overall contracts for 170 boats of Type XXI were awarded. Written detailed contracts followed in the middle of December. By this time, it had been planned that at the end of 1944 the assembly side of AG Weser would be moved to Bremer Vulkan in the large 'Valentin' shelter. The envisaged delivery timetable for the entire western area is shown in Table 39.

On 8 December 1943, the IBG was able to announce the completion of design and fabrication drawings. (From September 1943 up to this date, a total of 18,400 constructional drawings had been prepared.) In the case of the first 3 boats, for which a maximum building time of three or four months from the commencement of section building had been estimated, the total development and construction time after the finished design was available amounted to approximately nine months. During this same period, preparations had to be made for their series production: various installations had to be set up for this completely new production method, together with building directives, assembly plans and so on.

In the planned production of 33 boats per month from October 1944, a total building time of approximately six months for each boat was anticipated. In this building time were included sixteen days for the rolling of metal and transport

	1944 Feb	Mar	April	May	June	July	Aug	Sept	Oct	Nov	Dec	1945 Jan	Feb	Mar	April
Sections for:															
AG Weser, Brémen	1	3	6	8	10	10	10	8	6	4	2	—	—	—	—
Bremer Vulkan/Valentin	—	—	—	—	—	—	2	4	6	8	10	12	12	12	12
Blohm & Voss, Hamburg	1	4	8	12	13	13	13	13	13	13	13	13	13	13	13
Total	2	7	14	20	23	23	25	25	25	25	25	25	25	25	25
U-boat deliveries:															
AG Weser, Bremen	—	—	1	3	6	8	10	10	10	8	6	4	2	—	—
Bremer Vulkan	—	—	—	—	—	—	—	2	4	6	8	10	12	12
Blohm & Voss	—	—	1	4	8	12	13	13	13	13	13	13	13	13	13
Total	—	—	2	7	14	20	23	23	25	25	25	25	25	25	25

to steel firms, forty days for the production of the empty crude sections, five days for the transport to section building centres, 50 days for fitting-out the various sections at the section yards, four days for transport to the assembly yards and, finally, 50 days for assembly work on each boat at the building slip. Following the slipway launch, six days were allocated for fitting-out work at the pier and in the dock. Finally, after five days' yard testing, each boat would be handed over to the Navy. As regards the series production of Type XXI, total work hours per boat from the manufacture of the steel construction items to the handing over was assessed at 257,800. However, the first boat at AG Weser, to which this calculation was supposed to apply, took 30 per cent more hours (this boat was supposedly U3009). A breakdown of work hours is shown in Table 40, and an analysis of assembly work hours at B&V is shown in Table 41.

The Supreme Naval Command did not expect any saving in financial terms or work hours in going over to section construction: what was wanted, above all, was a shorter period from beginning of construction to the first deliveries and a shorter overall construction time per boat. Nevertheless, the estimated cost per ton of ship's weight was 3,600 marks (i.e., 5.75 million marks for the complete boat) roughly the same as for Type VIIC. (Note, however, that the new type incorporated more costly installations and special items of equipment.) A comparison between the requirement in hours of U-boat Types VIIC, IXD$_2$ and XXI (likewise built in series) presents Type XXI in a very favourable light, as shown in Table 42. The comparison illustrates the relative similarity in expenditure of hours in single construction methods on the building slips, and makes plain the clear superiority of section construction, even in the initial building phase.

There was not much change in the greater constructional expenditure (including work preparations and contractual planning at the IBG) of 550,000 hours for Type XXI as against 270,000 hours in the roughly similar sized Type IXD$_2$, not very significant per boat when one takes into account the whole series. Approximately 40 per cent of this extra expenditure of 280,000 hours in Type XXI was necessitated by the construction of new engines and the considerably more comprehensive electrical installation, with 27,000 hours alone being required for the construction of a wooden model in 1:1 scale. This model was constructed to fulfil the following purposes:

1. To establish correct and completely accurate compatibility of all constructional items, including tubing of a diameter greater than 30mm. According to the constructional measures evolved hitherto, these tubes were to be supplied ready-bent by the tube-construction firms, and already fitted with flanges.
2. As a study for the building-in sequence of components.
3. Educational purposes for those firms involved in the construction.

It should be pointed out that in these quoted figures of work hours the wide-ranging, pre-building preparations carried out at the yards has not been included. According to Counsellor of State Rudolf Blohm, Blohm & Voss spent 820,000 work hours in preparation for assembly construction of Type XXI at a cost of 4,100,000 marks. Of the work hours, 475,000 were to be attributed alone to the construction of section sledges and supports.

Section construction for Type XXIII

On 30 July 1943, a preliminary discussion took place on the proposed preliminary sketch of Type XXIII, which was to be presented at Hitler's headquarters on 2 August. It was established that the boat would be assembled from four sections, all of which would be capable of being transported by rail; section 3, however, would be minus conning tower and superstructure. The lengths and steel-weights of the individual sections were as follows:

Section 1: 9.1m; 11.33 tons (stern with steering installation, silent creep-speed engine and gearing).
Section 2: 5.95m; 13.99 tons (main engines).
Section 3: 7.45m; 18.2 tons (control room and part of the forward living quarters).
Section 4: 9.98m; 16.5 tons (bow with torpedo tube installation).

The development and construction time for the first boat was estimated at seven months, and should, therefore, have been ready in February 1944. Then, from March 1944, 20 boats would follow monthly. The yards envisaged for constructional work were: Deutsche Werke AG, Kiel and Gotenhafen; the Howaldtwerke, Kiel and Hamburg; and Germaniawerft, Kiel.

On 5 August 1943, the Supreme Commander-in-Chief of the Navy decided that the small electro-boat should be built in large series alongside Type XXI, and be intended in the first instance for operations in the Mediterranean and the Black Sea. The working-out of the design and contractual

Table 40. Man-hours per Type XXI construction at AG Weser

	Estimate	Worked by 1944	Attainable target
Steel construction	60,000	80,000	64,000
Section construction			
Section 1	4,800	5,000	
Section 2	14,000	16,000	
Section 3	17,000	20,000	
Section 4	6,000	6,000	
Section 5	25,000	26,000	202,000
Section 6	20,000	24,000	
Section 7	9,000	8,500	
Section 8	7,000	6,000	
Total	102,800	111,500	
Assembly work	95,000	140,000	
Total work	257,800	332,500	226,000

Table 41. Man-hours per Type XXI assembly at Blohm & Voss

U-boat	Calculated	Actual
U2501	152,000	255,000
U2502	130,000	223,000
U2503	124,000	204,000
U2504	117,000	196,000
U2505	110,000	187,000
U2506	105,000	178,000
U2507	101,000	169,000
U2508	98,000	164,000
U2509	95,000	158,000
U2510	93,000	155,000
U2520	78,000	130,000
U2540	65,000	110,000

Table 42. Man-hours for Types VIIC, IXD$_2$ and XXI

	VIIC (autumn 1943)	IXD$_2$ (autumn 1943)	XXI (December 1944)	XXI (Final phase)
Steel construction	35,000	45,000	80,000	64,000
Yard	180,000	405,000	252,500	202,000
Total hours	215,000	450,000	332,500	266,000
Hours per ton weight	280	278	205	164

planning was to be carried out by the IBG, and a number of conferences took place, at which various questions were thrashed-out. For example, on 26 August 1943, problems concerning the completion of the proposed MWM RS 34 diesel engine were discussed. A subsequent conference, on 14 September 1943, dealt with the question of schnorkel design. As a folding schnorkel would have involved changes in the boat's shape, an extensible schnorkel produced by Heep-DWK was decided upon for Type XXIII, as it had been for Type XXI. A suggestion, made by Naval Construction Adviser Grim, to strengthen the pressure-hull skin of Type XXIII was rejected on the grounds of weight. The conning tower, however, was to be separated from the control room by a pressure-tight bulkhead.

In the meantime, it had been decided to hand over the complete Type XXIII construction to Deutsche Werft. With the sphere of operations of the North Sea and Atlantic coast in mind, the section construction and assembly would be carried out at the principal yard in Hamburg, Finkenwerder; those boats destined for operations in the Mediterranean and the Black Sea would be built by their foreign outlets in Toulon (Arsenal); Genoa (Ansaldo); Monfalcone near Trieste (Cantiere Riuniti); and Nikolayev. On 20 September 1943, DW was given a contract for a total of 140 of these small boats, of which 50 would be built at Hamburg-Finkenwerder, 30 each at Toulon and Genoa, and 15 each at Monfalcone and Nikolayev. As early as December, the yard at Odessa (at that time under Rumanian authority) was mentioned as suitable for Black Sea boats and, later, following reverses for the German Army in this region, the Linzer Schiffbauwerft was named. Deliveries required under the Ship Construction Programme of 6 December 1943 are shown in Table 43.

The timetable planning of the IBG for the middle of September 1943 envisaged the design and order sequence shown below:

Completion of arrangements for provision of materials (with small exceptions) 25 Sep 1943
Final ship's drawings to the steel construction office 15 Oct 1943
Completion of the last steel construction drawing and delivery of the materials for 6 boats to the steel construction firms, which were to deliver the crude sections in January 1944. (The first two boats to be built completely by DW) 1 Nov 1943
Delivery of the total amount of rolled steel for 120 boats to the steel construction firms to be completed by 15 Jan 1944. [Merker says, in connection with this, that the series is to be increased to 140 boats.] DW to deliver the cast models.
AEG promise to deliver the first main electric engine 15 Jan 1944

While, in the main, the crude sections were to be built at the steel firms that had already been chosen for the Type XXI programme, it was envisaged that the named yards would carry out both section construction and assembly. The transportation of crude sections to the yard could be carried out by rail, as the components were small. The long distance to the foreign yards did, however, make for certain difficulties. In the case of DW, Finkenwerder, the ship-building hangar on the Rüsch Canal, and another shipbuilding workshop were chosen for sectional construction. In a very short space of time, four sequence lines were built to facilitate the conversion of delivered crude sections to complete sections; the completed sections could then be taken from this spot by special vehicles directly to the building slips, where they would be welded together as a complete boat in eight weeks. This meant an elimination of all those difficulties that had occurred during the transportation of sections of Type XXI to the assembly yards.

On 18 May 1944, the Main Committee calculated a monthly requirement in hours for the overall programme of DW in Finkenwerder (approximately 8,000 employees) as shown in Table 44. However, for the first 10 boats of Type XXIII at Finkenwerder, a figure of about 90,000 work hours was stated. The building costs of the yard (without section construction) per boat are shown in Table 45.

Table 43. Deliveries of Type XXIII U-boats in 1944 under the Ship Construction Programme of 6 December 1943

	Feb	March	April	May	June	July	Aug	Sept	Oct	Nov	Dec	Total
Western Mediterranean	—	2	4	9	9	9	9	9	9	—	—	60
Adriatic	—	—	2	2	2	2	2	2	3	—	—	15
Black Sea	—	—	—	2	2	2	3	3	3	—	—	15
Foreign Yards Total	—	2	6	13	13	13	14	14	15	—	—	90
Hamburg-Finkenwerder	2	4	6	8	8	8	8	6	—	—	—	50
Total	2	6	12	21	21	21	22	20	15	—	—	140

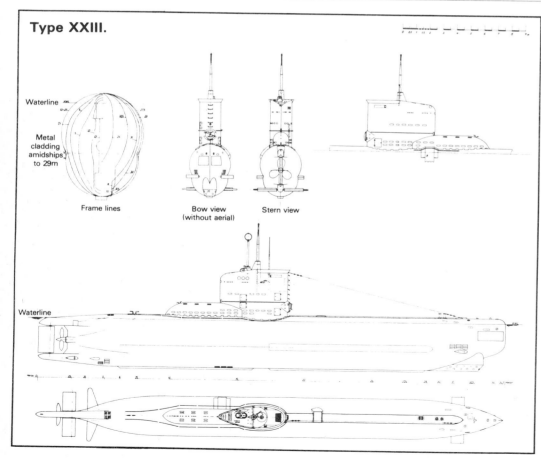

Type XXIII.

Waterline

Metal cladding amidships to 29m

Frame lines

Bow view (without aerial)

Stern view

Waterline

Table 44. Man-hours per month required at DW, Finkenwerder, 18 May 1944

Type XXIII[1]	400,000
Sections 3 and 6 of Type XXI	280,000
Hansa Programme	250,000
Repairs	170,000
Total	1,100,000

[1]50,000 man-hours per boat.

Table 45. Cost per Type XXIII boat at DW, Finkenwerder

	Marks
Boat construction:	
Materials	155,000
Man-hours (42,000 at 1.10 marks)	46,000
Total	201,000
Engine construction:	
Materials and engines	368,000
Man-hours (34,110 at 1.10 marks)	37,521
Total	405,521
Works expenses:[1]	155,000
Total cost per boat[2]	761,271

[1]85 per cent of the labour costs.
[2]Excluding cost of steel construction.

Opposite page, top: Series production of Section 2 for Type XXIII in a construction hall at DW Hamburg. **Below:** Bridge of a Type XXIII with partly welded-on flooding vents.

Type XXIII's at GW. **Above:** The floating crane manoeuvring a boat into position; note the altered bridge shape (the bulwark has been brought inwards), which was changed for test purposes. **Below:** *U2333* being launched on 16 November 1944. **Right:** *U4709* after launching, 1945.

As the threat of an Allied invasion grew, the importance of the small U-boats grew correspondingly. But production remained considerably behind planning and, above all, the foreign yards had not yet begun their deliveries; it was decided, therefore, at the beginning of July 1944 to include Germaniawerft, Kiel, in the Type XXIII programme, and to authorize further construction (185 boats by the end of 1945) on German territory. By now, the sheltering from air attack of the Type XXIII production centres had become an actuality. As there was only capacity at Hamburg for section construction of Type XXVI (page 235) and Type XXI, it was decided, in September 1944, to transfer Type XXIII construction from early 1945 completely to GW, and to carry out the complete section construction in box 2 of the 'Kilian' shelter. Assembly work could then be moved from the open building-slips at GW into the 'Konrad' shelter, once this had become available. The proposed monthly delivery quota for this protected U-boat construction was 10 boats.

The assembly sequence for Type XXI

The first constructional stage in hull manufacture took place in the steel works, where the requisite steel plates were rolled and cut, and pressure-hull rings and cast items were manufactured. All were then assembled into so-called crude sections. A departure was made from the usual method of constructing the pressure-hull rings: the plates were not rolled out along their length, but along their width, and were then connected to so-called discs. These discs were, in effect, very short pressure-hull rings, of a length equal to the distance between 2—4 frame spaces. They were then welded together with circular seams between them, to become section pressure-hull rings. The original reason for this disc method of construction was that flat discs were easier to transport. However, a contributory factor was that the steel plants selected for Type XXI did not have rollers sufficiently strong, or long enough, to bend the 26mm sheets over their longitudinal extensions. A drawback to the new method was the increased number of welded seams.

Initially, the permitted tolerance in the pressure-hull diameter was ± 2mm, but, because this limit could not be adhered to, soon after the start of the system changes were made to ± 2.5mm in the diameter and ± 5mm in the circumference. Furthermore, although the manufacturers adhered to these tolerances, temperature variations during fabrication of the pressure-hull rings led to even greater variations when assembly was later undertaken. In the steel construction industry, unlike the shipbuilding industry, exact detailed information was the rule. The IBG took note of this and formulated more precise building instructions and welding techniques.

The manufacture of section pressure-hulls, and the installation of understructures, decks, partitioning and tanks (i.e., the fabrication of so-called crude sections) followed next in sequence process. It was possible to accommodate only part of the lines in the building halls, and working in the open air presented many difficulties, especially with

The movement and assembly of sections for Type XXI. **Above:** The first Section 5 on a pontoon at HDW, Hamburg, shortly before transportation to the assembly yard B + V. **Below:** Installing a diesel engine in Section 3 of *U3001* at AG Weser in April 1944. **Opposite page:** Raising the stern section of *U3001*.

regard to welding. The welding-together of sections, and the welding-on of exterior frames was to have been carried out principally by 'Ellira' automatic machines, a process in which the sections were rotated in front of the machine. The welding seams were thoroughly checked and comprehensively 'x-rayed'. The first crude section, No. 1, made by the firm of Hannemann & Co., left the factory on 18 December 1943.

Further steel firms were earmarked for construction of the outer-hull casing, the so-called upper deck, the bulkheads and the subsidiary and supporting bulkheads. The outer-hull casings were given their outer skin, together with the appropriate frames and bulkheads. They were built to such a size that they could be transported by rail to the section yards, but the large, crude sections had to be carried by river boats.

In the section fitting-out yards, these crude sections were now put together into complete sections, and received all necessary installations and engines, with the exception of those parts that

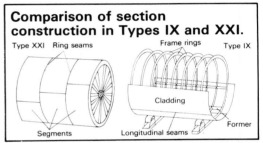

Comparison of section construction in Types IX and XXI.

Type XXI Ring seams   Frame rings   Type IX

Cladding

Segments   Longitudinal seams   Former

were either too heavy (diesel engines), or extended through two or more sections (main shafts). For these jobs, sequence-lines were set up in the large shipbuilding halls at the yards. At the Lübecker Flenderwerke, the 250m assembly-line functioned from the middle of December 1943. At other firms, the commencement of flow-assembly was delayed by air raids. Thus, the 350m assembly-line at the Howaldtswerke, Kiel, was not in operation until the middle of January; the line at DWK started at an even later date. Smaller sections rested on carriages that could be used to transport them from one construction point to the next, while the larger sections remained in one place. Yet here, too, identical workers were employed continuously at identical work processes. A good example of this stage of building is provided by a description of completion work on section 5 at the Hamburg Howaldtswerke:

'Crude sections and individual items delivered by the steel construction firms were taken, after some preliminary work in Hall VII, on pontoons into U-Boat Shelter 'Elbe II', where they were assembled and fitted-out to become complete sections, minus the conning tower and part of the upper deck. Part of the electrical cables that go through the length of the boat were cut to size in advance and ·coiled up at the section ends. The conning-tower deck and the periscope jack had been delivered in finished state, apart from the drilling for the after periscope, by a steel-moulding firm.

These items were screwed together in the workshops amd drilled as a single entity. The jack then had to be separated from the decks, so that decks and conning-tower housing could be better positioned for the welding process. Decks had to be fixed exactly vertical to the housing surfaces. It was not possible to drill holes after the welding of decks to the housing, as no machine tool large enough was available. The setting-up of the conning tower on its section took place beneath the large "hammer crane" at the Imperator Quay. The section had been transported from the shelter to this point by a special pontoon. Careful work then ensured that the approximately 12-ton conning tower was welded into place with millimetric-precision in both length and breadth, so that it was in equilibrium with the main ships' installations and in respect of the torpedo tubes. The first complete section was handed over to the appropriate assembly yard, B&V, on 28 March 1944.'

In accordance with an exact timetable, predetermined to a single day, sections complete to the last paint-brush stroke were delivered by sea to the assembly yards. When the sections arrived, diesel engines had still to be fitted in section 3 before assembly could begin. In order to utilize fully the large building-slips (and this had been carried out in the series construction of Types VIIC and IXC), on occasion two boats, one behind the other, and three boats abreast, could undergo assembly at each building-slip.

Single sections were now conveyed by single pontoons to the building-slips and, at B&V, using the floating crane 'Anton', set-up in the correct building sequence on sledges at the end of the line. Skids were then moved into the assembly position. The skids consisted of two runners and two transverse bearers, which could float, coupled together by hydraulic jacks. The transverse bearers remained underneath the boat for the entire building-slip time, leaving the slipway only on launching, and then together with the U-boat. Recesses in the transverse bearers permitted the accommodation of 50-ton presses for the alignment of sections according to their height. Lateral and longitudinal alignment was carried out by changes of position of the hydraulic jacks sliding on rails. Fine adjustment was ensured by small holes that had been bored in bulkheads, and in built-in auxiliary bearers, in certain, exactly-prescribed places. These had to match up exactly — when exact alignment had been achieved, one could observe through these holes, from both bow and stern, a light in the control room. Simultaneously, the diesel engines were connected in complete equilibrium with the shaft-housing of section 2, by means of adjustment pieces and small amounts of lateral movement. To assist in the assembly task, the complete boat had two main axes; these were the ship-architectural/weapon-technical main axis, which ran through section 5 (control room and conning tower), and the propulsion main axis, which ran through section 2. After alignment, the sections were put onto keel-supports beneath the transverse bearers side of the line and the hydraulic jacks were removed.

The sections were then welded together. Around the impact-edges of the pressure hull, the outer hull was left open to a width of 80cm, so that the welders could have entry to the pressure-hull sections. These were welded by four workers in a diametrical work process, a method necessary in order to maintain the aligned axis. Stresses could not be avoided. It usually took eight hours to complete seven welding seams in the pressure hull. In no circumstances could welding be interrupted, if 100 per cent perfect seam-welding was to be guaranteed. In connection with this, it was laid down that such work should not be suspended, even during air raids — special black-out blinds were designed, to enable welding to continue. The next stage was the building-in of the missing longitudinal braces of the inner and outer ship; and, finally, the outer ship was closed by the welding-in of the outer-casing belts. In order to establish whether any welding tears or weaknesses were present in the outer ship, exterior tanks and bunkers were placed under water pressure and hammered, which caused strongly over-stressed parts to tear open. Such parts were then cut out and welded afresh.

Now, in section 2, bushes were drilled into the shaft bossings from outside, and the main shafts were inserted and connected in line with the shaft-housings. Tubings and conduits between sections were connected, and any main cables running through them were also taken through; likewise, battery cells, periscopes, rod aerials and the schnorkel were installed in appropriate positions.

After application of a top coat of paint, boats were ready for launching. The only items still lacking were the gun armament, various minor items of apparatus and the inventory. In practice, however, many boats were given a slipway launch in a much less complete state of readiness. For launching, the rails were greased and the launching hydraulic jacks were brought into use. The boat was then wedged and, with the 50-ton presses in the recesses of the transverse bearers, pumped to a height sufficient to come free from the supports. To secure stability, trimming tanks, trimming bunkers

Above: The stern of *U3503* (Type XXI), after being lifted into the floating dock at Gothenburg, 1946. **Left:** Two views of *U2502* (Type XXI), after her delivery to Great Britain.

THE CHANGE TO TYPE XXI AND XXIII CONSTRUCTION 227

Type XXI's on the slips at Blohm and Voss. **Opposite page:** Two views of *U2501* before launching in May 1944. **Above, below and overleaf:** Boats lying abandoned after Germany's capitulation, May 1945. In the top photograph can be seen, from left to right, *U2561, U2563, U2555, U2556* and *U2557.* The photograph below shows in the foreground, from left to right, *U2564, U2562* and *U2560*; in the background are the five boats shown in the top photograph, but in reverse order. The photograph overleaf shows, top row, *U3502, U3048, U3504, U3506* and *U3060* and, front row, *U3501, U3049, U3055* and *U3057.*

and negative-buoyancy chambers were filled to approximately 60 tons, and a positive buoyancy tank of 124m³ was secured to the sharp stern. After launching, boats went for final fitting-out at the pier.

Only eight hours after a slipway launch, a building-slip could receive transported sections for the next boat.

Shelters for U-boat building

From the point of view of safety from air attack, the section construction of Type XXI did not mean any decentralization, but rather the opposite, for there was a growing concentration on relatively few fabrication points, all with increasing constructional facilities. The crude ships' components, which did not have great value, were produced in a well-decentralized manner, but section construction and subsequent assembly construction took place at only a few places. It is specially to be noted that sections 1, 2, 4, 7 and 8 for both the Western Area assembly yards, with a maximum output of 25 boats monthly, were constructed during that period at one section yard. For such centres, special protection from air attack had to be provided. The Luftwafte, it is true, provided additional anti-aircraft and fighter protection, but — and this is especially to be seen in the destructive attacks on Hamburg between 24 July and 3 August 1943 — the protection was inadequate. Only the covering over of workshops and of the large assembly yards with concrete seemed to promise truly effective protection.

The first U-boat shelter in home territory was ready in 1940. This was the 6-berth 'U-boat shelter' in Heligoland. It was proposed to convert the large construction dock in Wilhelmshaven to a shelter, with workshops, dock facilities and 18 berths, but, because of shortage of constructional steel and of workers, this project was postponed for a time, as were other proposed U-boat underground shelters in Kiel and Hamburg. On the French Atlantic coast, with the help of Organization Todt, U-boat shelter construction was started in the operational bases (Lorient, with 28 berths and a hauling-up slip; Brest, with 20 berths; St. Nazaire, with 21 berths). In Norway, the base at Bergen was provided with a shelter for 9 berths, and Trondheim a shelter with 8 berths. By the end of 1941, complete shelter for U-boats had been provided at Lorient and La Pallice; by the middle of 1942, for those at Brest and St. Nazaire and, at a rather later date, at Bordeaux.

At the beginning of 1941, work began in Hamburg for a shelter with, initially, 2 'boxes' at the Deutsche Werft in Finkenwerder. This first construction phase was completed in October 1941; the second phase began in the winter of 1941/42 and ended in October 1942. The complete construction now consisted of 4 'boxes', and was given the name 'Fink II'. A shelter with 2 'boxes' was erected at this same time near the Hamburg Howaldtswerke. This shelter was given the name 'Elbe II'. Initially, these shelters served the Hamburg yards, mainly for the fitting-out of their U-boats after launching. The proposed shelters for Wilhelmshaven and Kiel were postponed yet again, Wilhelmshaven's because of the transferring of a large part of its U-boat yard to Lorient, and Kiel's because of its reportedly good anti-aircraft defences. Not until the beginning of 1942 did construction begin in Kiel of a shelter with 2 'boxes', which was set up at the Kiel Howaldtswerke under the cover-name 'Kilian'. At this same time, a fifth compartment was added to 'Fink II'. On 22 December 1942, Raeder presented the following further construction plans:

New construction undertakings in home territories:
1. U-boat shelters for new U-boat construction yards (20 berths with 95,000 tons of steel).
2. 30 air-raid shelters for personnel (8,000 tons of steel).

Construction undertakings in French territory:
1. Roof strengthening of the present U-boat shelter (65 shelter berths with 52,000 tons of steel).
2. New construction of a further 45 U-boat shelter berths (each with 5,000 tons of steel, i.e., a total of 225,000 tons of steel).
3. Air-raid shelter for yard staff in western France (11,000 tons of steel necessary).

Among the planned new shelters in German territory were the large 'Valentin' shelter at Farge on the Weser, and a second shelter in Kiel, cover-name 'Konrad', which was set up over DWK Dock III in the construction harbour, and was given only one compartment. Further constructions were contemplated at Lorient and La Pallice, and a shelter with 20 berths was to be built in Marseilles. The Trondheim shelter was also to be enlarged. Following reverses in the U-boat campaign and the considerable losses of the summer of 1943, however, these extension constructions in foreign bases were no longer regarded as essential, and were not again contemplated. On the other hand, construction of shelters in home territories were held to be of priority.

A short time after the beginning of its planning in autumn 1943, the Main Committee decided that the large shelter project 'Valentin' should be an assembly bunker for Type XXI. In the contract placed with KMW, Wilhelmshaven, on 6 December 1943, it was anticipated that deliveries from the 'Valentin' bunker would begin in October 1944. The assembly shelter had external measurements of 450m by 100m. The concrete walls were to be 3–4.5m thick and the roof 7.3m thick, to afford protection against the heaviest (at that time) known bombs. In the interior, measuring 430m × 85.5m, there was room for 24 single sections (= 3 U-boats) and 13 complete boats in their varying stages of assembly. Flat-bottomed vessels of up to 3,000 tons were to ferry sections directly into the shelter along a connecting canal 7m deep. In the fitting-out basin they would then be loaded, by means of a large 200-ton crane, on to special carriages running on four sets of track. On the south side of the shelter, the sections could be unloaded by means of a second 200-ton crane.

The planned construction sequence was as follows. When the sections were in place, in the right sequence one behind the other on their assembly carriages, assembly construction could begin. During this, the boat on its building-slip carriage rolled along in 12 stages from station to station in the large assembly hall. In the first station, the 8 sections on the building-slip carriages were welded together. During further operations they were twice (stages 2 and 3) advanced forward by one boat's length. Between stages 3 and 4, the whole boat was shunted sideways to a parallel sequence route, on which the boat, after passing through stages 4 and 5, could be transported backwards by one boat's length each time. A similar operation was repeated once again. Above stations 10 and 11, two protected shelter superstructures were provided, containing in their roofs a 5-ton crane for the installation of periscopes, rod aerials and schnorkel. At the end of the line, stations 12 and 13 were positioned in a docking chamber. The 'launching' took place in station 12, by the flooding of the chamber to a point at which the boat floated free from the building-slip carriage. At station 13, a final inspection was carried out, and the boat then entered the fitting-out basin. The space available here sufficed for trimming and heeling tests. The completed boat then passed through the bomb-proof doors of the shelter into the outer basin and, from there, via the branch canal to the River Weser.

It was intended that here too, for the first time, large and very complicated ships would be assembled in consecutive stages in one hall (as in an automobile factory). Quite apart from the hoped-for protection against bomb damage afforded by the shelter, the advantages of this method of shipbuilding were beyond question, and would certainly lead to an abbreviation of the time spent by a vessel at the building-slip. A total of 30 days per boat was envisaged for assembly construction in the shelter — in other words, every 56 hours, one complete U-boat should be able to leave the shelter. It was intended to build nearby, as an addition, a large subterranean reserve store, which would be connected to the assembly bunker by tunnels. To aid in the accomplishment of this mammoth undertaking, a special construction bureau, with the designation 'U-Weser', was set up. The construction contract was principally entrusted to the firm of Wayss & Freitag, who already possessed considerable experience in erecting U-boat shelters. The construction advisers were the firm of Agatz & Bock.

When complete, in the autumn of 1944, the complex would be taken over by Bremer Vulkan, in Vegesack, and then AG Weser would carry out the section construction of the Vulkanwerft. Consequently, a shelter with the designation 'Hornisse' was planned for Bremen and finally, one further large shelter, with the cover-name 'Wenzel', was to be erected in Hamburg. However, in the early part of 1944, this was 'pie in the sky'. Of the available U-boat shelters at this time, only 'Elbe II' could be used for the construction of section 5 by the Hamburg Howaldtswerke, and a part of 'Fink II' could be used for sections 3 and 6 by DW. It was further envisaged that KMW, Wilhelmshaven, should move its sectional construction likewise into shelter 'Fink II'. Sequence-line working in the shelters took place on flat-bottomed boats. Construction work in wet shelters led to a whole host of problems, but these could be overcome.

In a report to Hitler on 4 May 1944, Dönitz bewailed the fact that the new U-boat construction was still very inadequately protected:

'Since on one site, 30–40 sections of the same kind are being built simultaneously, a single stick of bombs can disrupt at one fell swoop the production of 30–40 boats. A similar position exists with assembly; for example, in Hamburg at any one time, 30 boats lie next to each other for assembly purposes on the building-slips. Only a very small percentage of overall sectional construction is protected by concrete. Assembly in Hamburg and Danzig is completely unprotected; while an assembly shelter is being constructed for Bremen ['Valentin'] it will not be ready until early 1945. A similar undertaking for Hamburg ['Wenzel'] hangs fire in its initial stages (foundation work). Completion will be 1946 at the earliest.

'The Supreme Commander-in-Chief of the Navy has therefore discussed this question with Ministerial Director Dorsch, who now has charge of Home construction. He believes he can bring forward the date of the protection installations for Bremen ['Valentin'] — from early 1945 to autumn 1944 and, secondly, that he can have a dry-dock roofed over (in Bremen) to serve the purpose of protecting section construction ['Hornisse']. The Führer wants to discuss this question with Dorsch in the next few days and instruct him to accomplish erection of the protective buildings at all costs. The

Führer considers it essential to roof over further docks, and orders it to be established whether or not the fourth inlet to Wilhelmshaven can be roofed over and used for section construction.'

In consequence of this discussion, the 'Hornisse' shelter at AG Weser was given preferential treatment. It was now to deliver sections 2, 5 and 6, which hitherto had been constructed by the Vulkanwerft in Vegesack, to be worked on at 'Valentin'. A second shelter, designated 'Wespe' was to be erected for KMW, Wilhelmshaven. In accordance with U-boat planning as at 12 October 1944, 'Wespe', was from 1 September 1945 to be at the disposal of 'Valentin' for the remaining sections 1, 2, 4, 7 and 8. At a later date, building preparations began for this shelter.

A large dry dock near AG Weser was used for the erection of 'Hornisse'. The loss of repair facilities in the Atlantic shelters after the Allied invasion of Europe prompted the adoption of an alternative proposal for 'Hornisse', which had been meant for section construction only. The dock character was to be preserved, and the forward part of the shelter was to serve as a repair shelter with 4 wet and 4 dry berths at any given time. In the after part, section construction in 7 stages was to be carried out, and this was to involve sections 1, 2 and 3.

From September 1944, section construction was carried out in shelter conditions in the Kiel area. DWK moved its section 8 construction into the

completed 'Konrad' shelter; the Howaldtswerke Kiel used Box 1 of the 'Kilian' shelter for its section 1. Section construction for Type XXIII was to be moved into the second compartment. After the completion of Type XXI section construction in Kiel, the overall section and assembly construction for Type XXIII was to be carried out by GW in the 'Kilian' and 'Konrad' shelters. However, things did not progress as far as this. In October 1944, Dönitz stressed once more the provision of shelters as being the only effective measure against increasing air attacks on harbours. 'Large-scale shelter construction is most urgently required in the home harbours. The requirement is for 196 shelter berths in addition to those already prepared or those under construction.'

Shown below is a detailed plan of U-boat shelters available for U-boat repair and fitting-out and for training U-boats, either available or planned, as at 28 November 1944:

Completed shelters:
1. Nordsee III (Heligoland) 6 berths
2. Fink II (Hamburg-Finkenwerder) 10 berths
3. Elbe II (Hamburg-Tollerort) 4 berths
4. Kilian (Kiel-Dietrichsdorf) 8 berths
5. Bruno (Bergen) 9 berths
6. Dora I and II (Trondheim) 13 berths

}Type XXI

N.B. 2–4 currently involved in U-boat section construction, 6 being completed.

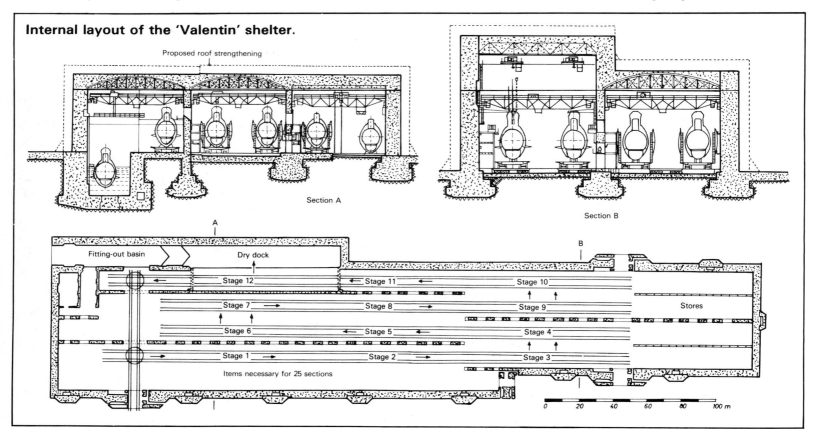

Internal layout of the 'Valentin' shelter.

Proposed roof strengthening

Section A

Section B

A

B

Fitting-out basin

Dry dock

Stage 12   Stage 11   Stage 10

Stage 7   Stage 8   Stage 9   Stores

Stage 6   Stage 5   Stage 4

Stage 1   Stage 2   Stage 3

Items necessary for 25 sections

0   20   40   60   80   100 m

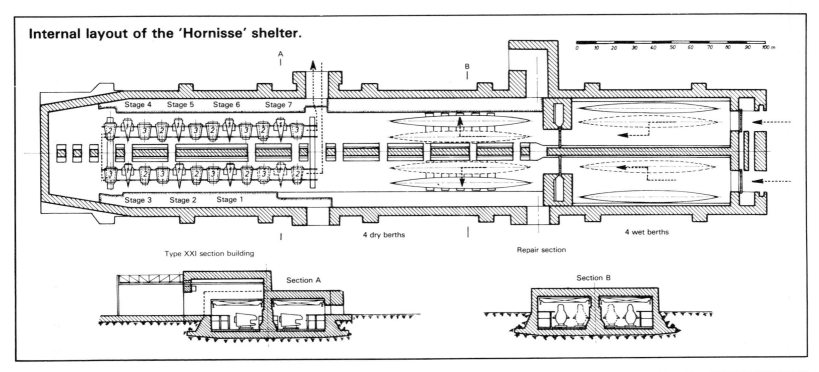

Internal layout of the 'Hornisse' shelter.

Stage 4   Stage 5   Stage 6   Stage 7

Stage 3   Stage 2   Stage 1

Type XXI section building

4 dry berths

Repair section

4 wet berths

Section A

Section B

The shell of the incomplete U-boat bunker 'Hornisse' at AG Weser in Bremen (photograph taken in 1977).

Planned shelters:

1. Elbe XVII (Hamburg-Tollerort) 12 berths
2. Wenzel (Wedel near Hamburg) 12 berths
3. Wespe (Wilhelmshaven) 16 berths
4. Valentin II (Farge near Vegesack) 14 berths   — Type XXI
5. Kaspar (Kiel) 11 berths
6. — (Rügen) 36 berths
7. — (Swinemünde) 24 berths
8. — (Gotenhafen) 24 berths   — Type XXI
9. Underground gallery construction in Bergen 12 berths
10. Underground gallery construction on Bornholm 12 berths

In Speer's opinion, however, the provision of shelters for fighter aircraft production was more important. He promised Dönitz that, when these had been completed early in 1945, he would then supply sizeable labour forces for additional U-boat shelters. Neither 'Valentin' nor 'Hornisse' were ever finished. Up to the time of the Russian occupation, U-boat construction in the Danzig area was completely unprotected. In the west, only a part of the section construction in the Hamburg and Kiel areas could be carried out in the wet shelters available there. Following the termination of section construction, these shelters were used for U-boat repairs from March 1945, with the exception of the 'Konrad' shelter. GW used this for the construction of the Midget U-boat type Seehund (page 288) until the end of the war.

U-BOAT DEVELOPMENT, AUTUMN 1943 TO EARLY 1944

New ideas for coastal boats: Types XXV and XXVIII

In July-August 1943, U-boat planning in the Walter Works was geared to the task of changing basic Type XVII into a small U-boat, appropriate for the new motto 'Submerged endurance is more important than submerged high speed', and able to compete with the small, electric U-boat Type XXIII. At initial discussions on 30 July 1943, a modified Type XVIIB, with only one small Walter-Turbine of 1,160hp was suggested; with an Aurol supply of 100 tons, it would have a submerged range of 660 nautical miles at 15.7 knots, or 3,200 nautical miles at 8 knots. By dispensing with the diesel engine, and using a 2,500hp turbine at a maximum submerged speed of 20 knots, a submerged range of 2,500 nautical miles at 8 knots, or 1,700 nautical miles at 8 knots plus 80 nautical miles at 20 knots would be possible.

Consideration was also being given in 'K' Office to the feasibility of having a 'pure' U-boat for coastal operations, but equipped with conventional propulsion. Type XXIII was used as the starting-point for this. By dispensing with the diesel installation, the volume could be reduced to 160m³. At the same time, by doubling the batteries of Type

XXIII, a submerged range almost three times as great could be achieved. The electric motor could remain small, at 160hp (silent, creep-speed motor of Type XXI), as there was the danger that a more powerful motor would exhaust the batteries too soon. As one would expect, the maximum submerged speed was only 9 knots. This project was designated Type XXV. It did not satisfy requirements, however, because in relation to its range (400 nautical miles at 6 knots) the boat was too big. This disadvantageous relation could only be rectified by some other method of propulsion. At that time, suitable remedies could be provided by the closed-cycle and the Walter-process. Especially suitable seemed to be the indirect process, tested from 1943 in the Walter Works, a process in which heating and turbine closed-cycle were separated, and which promised a significantly higher efficiency at low speeds than the direct process available at the time. In addition, the system was independent of depth. For such a propulsion method, 'K' Office projected, in the winter of 1943/44, a special U-boat of 200 tons displacement for Mediterranean use. It would have four bow torpedo tubes. As it was considered, at that time, that it would be sufficient for a 'pure' U-boat to have a submerged top speed of 10 knots, the turbine output could be limited to 250hp and a readily-available turbine could be used. The calculated submerged range of 2,000 nautical miles at 6 knots was considerable. In addition, to provide silent creep travel and for battery charging, a small electric motor was envisaged. The range on this installation was similarly sizeable — 250 nautical miles at 5 knots — which meant that the boat, running 144 nautical miles daily at 6 knots, could submerge for 14 days. This project, which was designated Type XXVIII, was initially postponed because the new engine had not been

developed sufficiently, and the realization that the indirect process could not be operationally-feasible in the near future, caused the project to be abandoned on 27 March 1944.

Side torpedo tubes: Types XXIV, XXIB and XXIC

Despite the use of a quick-loading installation in the new U-boat Type XXI, the number of torpedo tubes ready for firing at any one time was inadequate. Early in 1943, Project VIIC/43, eight torpedo tubes (six bow and two stern tubes) had been intended for the last stage of VIIC development; this demanded a large number of ready-to-fire torpedo tubes, rather than a large supply of reloads, better suited operational requirements that, in the face of growing defensive measures, saw few opportunities for a second attack. This demand went some way to meet the requirements of the shipbuilders, who considered it easier to construct tubes with ready-to-fire torpedoes, than to provide accessible space for reserves.

The Walter U-boats had dispensed with stern tubes — the turbine compartment being closed off by bulkheads would have made access tubes difficult, and the slim, streamlined, stern profile militated against their incorporation anyway. Type XXI, which had almost the same outline as Type XVIII, took over armament identical to the Walter boats, as a change would have involved comprehensive replanning and consequent lengthy delays. The possibility seemed to exist of increasing the number of torpedo tubes by inserting an intermediate section housing side tubes pointing obliquely aft. This arrangement was later given the designation 'Schneeorgel' (after Korvettenkapitän Schnee who, as Admiralty Staff Officer for Combat Against Allied Convoys, had represented the interests of the Chief of Naval War Staff in the new

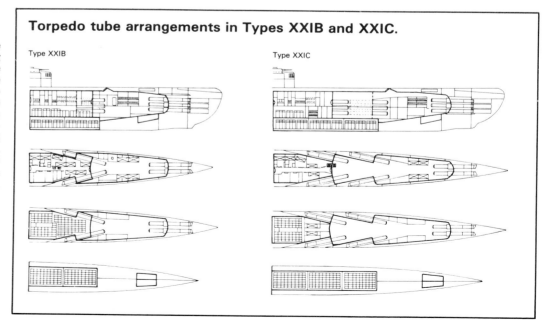

Torpedo tube arrangements in Types XXIB and XXIC.

Type XXIB

Type XXIC

Ship Construction Commission in requesting larger quantities of ready-to-fire torpedo tubes). From Type XVIII then, evolved the U-boat Type XXIV, which, in addition to six bow tubes would have either two triple or two quadruple side tubes. This meant that the surface displacement increased from 1,485 tons to approximately 1,800 tons. Discussion also took place of another version with twelve side tubes (2 × 2 × 3) and of approximately 1,900 tons displacement. As the Walter installation was to be retained, the maximum submerged speed dropped from the 24 knots of Type XVIII to 21 knots in Type XXIV.

The corresponding variations from Type XXI were given the designations XXIB (2 × 3 side tubes) and XXIC (2 × 2 × 3). In a discussion at the Ship Construction Commission on 19 November 1943, Type XXIB was seen as the successor to Type XXI. However, because of their considerable size, these boats were actually long-range, operational boats, which did not need a multiplicity of ready-to-fire torpedo tubes.

Walter Type XXVI

U-boat Type XXI was too large for the convoy campaign in the North Atlantic; it was also too costly and could not, therefore, be considered in the long term as a good replacement for Type VIIC. Following the decision to switch U-boat production to the new electro-boat Types XXI and XXIII, Walter Works had been thrust into the background with its projects for Types XVII, XVIII and XXII. They now saw a chance of re-emerging.

In September 1943, after the commitment to Type XXIII had been decided upon, an attempt was made, by enlarging Type XVII, to provide a new, more offensively-equipped U-boat, especially suitable for the convoy war in British waters. It would be small, manoeuvrable and as strongly armed as possible. In planning this, thought was also given to the various constructional ideas that had gone into Type XXII — for example, the simplified turbine installation with only one turbine and (something that had been proved in towing tests) good results obtained from the knife-edged stern and deep-set hydroplane. This new type was designated Type XVIIA. In the version dating from 12 October 1943, it was to have four bow and two triple side tubes for 7m torpedoes. The length of the boat was only 46.7m, so that, with a maximum beam of 4.9m, the length-to-beam ratio was 9.5:1. The displacement would be in the order of 500 tons.

As with Type XVII and XXII, no forward hydroplanes were envisaged. The boat would have as its turbine installation half the installation of Type XVIII. The diesel engine and the electric motor were to be approximately three times as powerful as in Type XVII. The bridge was similar to that in Type XVIIB. It was not intended that it should have anti-aircraft armament, but this was an indispensable military requirement of the Commander-in-Chief, U-Boats, for larger U-boats; in October 1943, 'K' Office projected a counter-design to the Walter Type XVIIA. This had affinities with Type XXI, a stronger torpedo armament (twelve torpedo tubes) and, notably, an

Type XVIIA with six side torpedo tubes (Project 477 A5 of 12 October 1943).

anti-aircraft armament (a bridge with conning tower and anti-aircraft guns as in Type XXI). This made the boat considerably larger, which in turn led to a corresponding increase in diesel and electrical installations. Additionally, for the purposes of reliability and for recharging while schnorkelling, a diesel generator was intended. In order to keep the displacement below 1,000 tons, initially — as with Type XXIII — interior loading of torpedo tubes was dispensed with. This project was designated Type XXVIA, and the drawings and design were to have been ready by the middle of November 1943.

Exterior loading of torpedo tubes would only be possible in dock. This was quite unacceptable for training operations and had serious drawbacks for operational purposes, because dock capacity was very limited. An alternative was a lengthening of the design by approximately 4m, which would bring the surface displacement to 1,050 tons. This made the new Type XXVIB design rather large, with a maximum submerged speed correspondingly lower at 21.5 knots.

Meanwhile, the U-boat designers at the firm of Hellmuth Walter KG, Dr. Karl Fischer and Engineer Ulrich Gabler, had worked out an improved Project XVIIA, and this was given the designation Type XXVIW. It differed from the project of 12 October 1943, principally by a lengthening of the midships section by approximately 7m, thus providing more space for essential detection installations and auxiliary engines. A corresponding increase in length was also made in the narrow control-room superstructure that enclosed the bridge and

extensible apparati. The maximum diameter was increased by approximately 40cm, which meant that the displacement was increased to 720 tons. In the final version, the surface displacement of Type XXVIW amounted to 841.6 tons, but this was still considerably under that of Type XXVIB. It was intended that the bow armament would be similar to that in Type VIIC, which made it possible to use the forward section of this type, thus avoiding the bottleneck in cast steel. The side-tube arrangement of Type XVIIA was retained, but differed from that used in Types XXVIA and B in that the tubes were situated internally, right up to their exit-flaps, which would make for easier pressure-hull construction. Nevertheless, the arrangement was not particularly satisfactory, as it meant that the bow compartment became very high, while the battery compartment underneath it became very low. As reserve torpedoes had been dispensed with, it was possible to house most of the crew in the bow compartment. The fittings of this compartment included sound-proofed, removable walls, part of which had to be removed during torpedo-tube loading. On the other hand, torpedo maintenance during training or on operations (withdrawing of torpedoes approximately 2.5m from the tubes) only required the lifting up of several bunks every 3—4 days. Installation planning was very successful in reducing crew discomfort to a minimum.

In order to achieve a streamlined, narrow bridge, it had been decided to do without a conning tower, and the shortage of cast steel also played its part in this decision. For the first time in German U-boats, a large boat was directed from the control room.

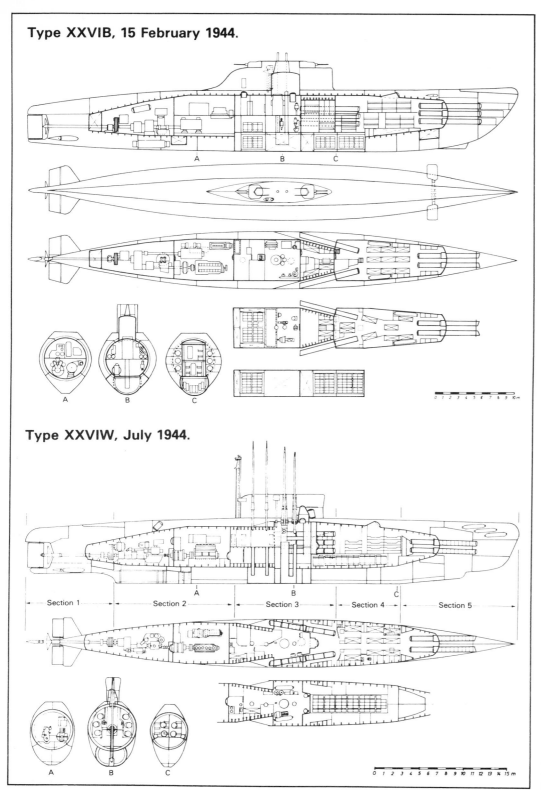

Type XXVIB, 15 February 1944.

A   B   C

A   B   C

0 1 2 3 4 5 6 7 8 9 10m

Type XXVIW, July 1944.

A   B   C

Section 1   Section 2   Section 3   Section 4   Section 5

A   B   C

0 1 2 3 4 5 6 7 8 9 10 11 12 13 14 15m

This step could be risked because 9m instead of 7.5m periscopes were now being used. The overall loss in periscope depth as compared to Type VII, was only 0.7m. This seemed acceptable, as the boat would be considerably shorter than the equal-sized Type VIIC boat, and it could therefore be assumed that the depth-keeping properties would be better than in earlier types. The passageway from bow compartment to engine compartment ran beneath the control room through the auxiliary engine compartment, so that the helmsman and hydroplane operators were no longer distracted by movement in the boat. This solution also permitted the commander's accommodation and detection and communications departments to be positioned in the immediate vicinity of the boat's control installations.

The submerged speed was to be as high as was technically possible, so that attacks would be feasible even at some future date when the expected fast convoys using 'Victory' ships would be travelling at approximately 17 knots. As the escort vessels of the time could use their detection devices up to a speed of approximately 18 knots, it would be essential that boats be able to travel faster than this in order to ensure their escape. It is of interest that a speed in excess of 18 knots was required; this was the previously hoped-for submerged top speed of Type XXI. Calculations for Type XXVIW foresaw a maximum submerged speed of 24–25 knots, which could be maintained for six hours, and this would surely be sufficient for quick approach to a convoy, effective attack and safe disengagement. In line with the Chief of Naval War Staff's views on the possibilities of successful surface attacks at night, the opinion was mooted that, although short, the boat would achieve a respectable 18 knots on the surface with its turbine. It was intended, therefore, to fit an optical aiming apparatus (UZO, or Uboot-Zieloptik, Column) on the bridge.

A smaller diesel engine was necessary, as the engine compartment was smaller than that in Types XXVIA and B. Two engines were considered: the 580hp MWM engine as used in Type XXIII, and the two-stroke T12 M133 diesel engine developed at the beginning of the war by Klöckner-Humboldt-Deutz. Developing 1,200hp, it had approximately the same length as the RS34. The Deutz engine had the advantage of a considerably higher performance, but the not inconsiderable disadvantage that there was no experience of the schnorkel used in conjunction with two-stroke engines, and the fact that series production had not yet begun. On the other hand, the MWM engine as used in Type XXIII had certain advantages: spare parts were available; technical staff were fully conversant with it; the engine was already being mass-produced; and it matched-up well with the electric motor of Type XXIII.

The proposed surface range of 11,000 nautical miles at 8 knots, or 15,000 nautical miles at 4 knots, was far in excess of the length of time a crew could be expected to exist comfortably at sea in this cramped boat, and was hardly called for by the tasks envisaged for the boat. However, it provided a very great safety margin and certainly measured

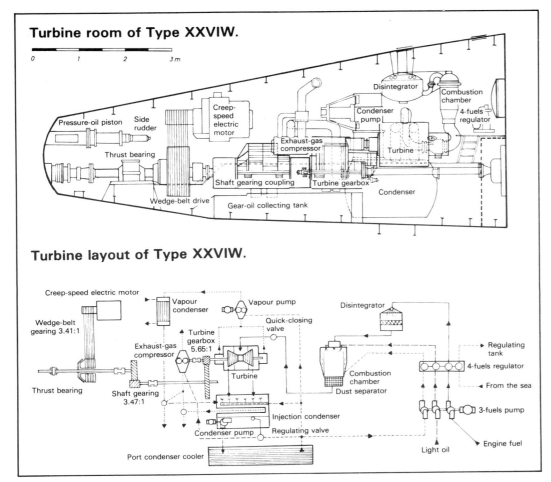

Turbine room of Type XXVIW.

0   1   2   3m

Turbine layout of Type XXVIW.

up to the demands of the Chief of Naval War Staff. The submerged range with the electrical installation was, at 2 knots, exactly the same as that of Type VIIC. At higher submerged speeds, however, the better submerged profile of the projected design was more efficient. It was intended that the electric, submerged top speed of 10.5 knots could be maintained for 1½ hours. The battery installation was similar to that in Type XXIII. As far as possible, engines, technical apparatus and installations intended for this design were ones that had already been well tested or were in series production for other U-boat types. It was intended to use the turbine installation developing 7,500hp that had been designed for Type XVIII and was in the course of construction. Only in cases where available items of equipment had not been used (e.g., the Lysholm compressor) was new equipment employed. By using the MWM engine, an installation similar in all essential parts to the engine and constructional components of Type XXIII could be used, which is why this engine was subsequently selected.

Everything had therefore been done in the planning stage to make the timetable and building time as short as possible for this new U-boat type.

As regards the turbines and gearing installation for the first boat, appropriate components, ordered and already in production for Type XVIII, were to be used (installations sufficient for five shafts, i.e., for five boats of Type XXVIW). Similarly, from the abandoned installations for Type XVII, approximately seven engines were available, which could be made ready in a very short time. It would therefore be perfectly possible, using available parts, to initiate a preliminary series of approximately 12 boats before the inception of series production, if only the work capacity of two yards could be made available. If an immediate start could be made with these boats (early 1944), completion of them could take place in the course of that year. There is no doubt, however, that this opinion was totally unrealistic — at this time, the design was far from finished.

In contrast to Project XVIIA, it was intended to equip Type XXVIW with forward retractable hydroplanes, a consequence of the poor results experienced with the Walter test boats *U792* and *U794*, which did not have forward hydroplanes. However, with Type XXVIW, the decision not to have anti-aircraft armament was adhered to. As it was feared that objections on this score would be

raised against the design, its presentation on 6 February 1944 (GKdo HWK B No. 313) contained a lengthy appendix in which the decision to dispense with anti-aircraft armament was justified. The disadvantages of such an armament for this boat were stated as follows:

'1. A streamlined arrangement of the anti-aircraft armament in turrets, as in Type XVIII or XXI, would mean in the case of Type XXVIW taking up the whole width of the upper decks and rendering impossible free passage from foreship to after ship.

'2. An anti-aircraft turret reduces the surface stability. The boat would need to be made wider in its flotational waterline.

'3. The crew would need to be augmented by the number of personnel manning the anti-aircraft armament (6 men); it would not be possible to accommodate them without increasing the length of the boat.

'4. Additional space would have to be provided for storage of ammunition, which once again would involve a lengthening of the boat.

'5. An anti-aircraft turret would increase profile-resistance in submerged travel. A further increase in resistance would take place through the greater displacement.

'6. To give the larger boat the required diesel and electric ranges, the fuel supply and the storage batteries would have to be increased.

'7. Stronger batteries would need a stronger electric motor and a stronger diesel engine to preserve identical short charging times.

'8. The installation of anti-aircraft defence would involve an increase in total displacement from 720 tons to approximately 1,150 tons (Type XXVIB). The speed of the larger boat, with anti-aircraft armament, may be calculated as follows:
The present bridge of Type XXVIW carries approximately 15 per cent of the total boat's resistance, the bridge as in Type XXI approximately 40 per cent. We can deduce for Type XXVIW the following distribution:

Bridge	990shp= 15%
Boat's hull	5,610shp= 85%
Total	6,600shp=100%

Propulsion performance for the 1,150-ton boat with anti-aircraft armament, to provide 25 knots:

Boat's hull 5,610 $(1,\frac{150}{720})$ ⅔	=7,620shp
Bridge (40%)	=3,050shp
Total	10,670shp

As only 6,600shp are available, however, we arrive at a boat's speed for the 1,150-ton boat with anti-aircraft towers as follows:
$$V=25^3\sqrt{\tfrac{6,600}{10,670}}=21.3 \text{ knots}$$

'9. Over and above all this, it must be assumed in the light of the war situation, that opportunities for surface operations will become fewer and fewer, especially in the intended sphere of operations, i.e., the Mediterranean and the North Atlantic.'

On 17 February 1944, an inter-office discussion was held concerning the new Walter Type XXVI: under consideration were the competing designs, XXVIB and XXVIW. On 22 February 1944, both versions were presented to Dönitz at his headquarters at Koralle near Bernau, together with two electro-boat versions of Type XXVI, in order that clarification could be made concerning a successor to Type XXI. The electro-boat designs had, in place of a Walter-installation, a strengthened electric installation with three half-batteries and the large Type XXI electric motor. Design $XXVIE_1$ (IBG-Oelfken) would have the side torpedo tubes, which took up much shipbuilding time, replaced by four stern tubes, which would be grouped around the boat's screw; Supreme Naval Command-design $XXVIE_2$ was related in shape and armament to Type XXVIB. However, both these designs from a performance point of view had little in common with either the Walter design or the electro-boat Type XXI. Dönitz consequently decided that Type XXVIE was inferior to Type XXI. 'The Walter U-boat of Type XXVI is to be considered as urgent and must be built as long as Aurol is available.' A choice between XXVIB with anti-aircraft armament, or XXVIW without it, would be made in eight days.

However, the decision was delayed longer than that. During the period of indecision, an acknowledgement was made of the failure to achieve satisfactory results by increasing the anti-aircraft armament of old U-boats. Quite apart from this, the schnorkel made it possible for boats to remain under the surface even when cruising. This meant that the question of anti-aircraft armament for a new U-boat type was by no means as significant as it had been in the autumn of 1943. On 28 March 1944, a final decision was made by the Supreme Commander-in-Chief of the Navy in favour of large series construction of Type XXVIW, dependent on K II U confirming the suitability for operational use of the new Walter-installation.

Appendix: Communication from Walter to Dönitz on the position with regard to Walter U-boats.

'To: The Commander-in-Chief of the Navy, Grossadmiral Dönitz,

Berlin

20th February 1944
W/Rö
Registered Letter
RM 1100-Secret Command
Headquarters Matter
B.No.498/44

Dear Grossadmiral,

In this letter I must refer to various problems of the situation regarding underwater high-speed boats.
1. The Aurol [H_2O_2] Position. Shortly, production will amount to approximately 20,000 tons per year. 3 large works are under construction, which, together with those currently in use, will supply by the end of 1945 a total amount of approximately 84,000 tons per year, if the works are finished according to programme. At the moment, supplies amount to approximately 10,000 tons. If the Navy were to demand for its needs from the end of 1945 a total production of 60,000 tons per year and indeed receives them, if one leaves out of reckoning other naval requirements (torpedoes, tests), then on 100 tons of Aurol per boat, 500 complete operations could be carried out in a year. In other words, according to my estimations, by roughly the end of

1945, 200 boats could be built and kept at this level by the building of an appropriate number of follow-up boats. However, this would almost certainly mean the restricting of activities of other sections of the armed forces and, in my opinion, a recommendation should be made that the OKM request the GB Chem to initiate the construction of a 100,000-ton works to be constructed by the end of 1946. This would mean that the construction programme could later be increased still further.
2. Military Value of a High Submerged Speed. As an argument for this extensive undertaking, I should like to stress once again that the detection battle can only be won by our boats possessing a high cruising speed. I am convinced that radar detection from the air can be nullified if we use the schnorkel and protect it from reflection in all radio wave ranges. And I am just as equally convinced that detection from ship to ship can only be nullified by higher submerged speeds. A completely black, noiseless U-boat is, to be sure, safe against most detection devices, but this means, from a tactical point of view, the boat is also somewhat immobile. The detection war, therefore, has to be fought on a different level, as has been done already with, for example, the schnorkel. The way to accomplish this is by high speed. Only a turbine installation can supply this, and the requirement for a relatively lengthy submerged cruising performance will only be fulfilled if one uses the right kind of fuel [Aurol]; not oxygen in gaseous or liquid form. I am therefore completely convinced that the path I am following is the correct one since I, now 10 years ago, for example tested practically the closed-cycle and abandoned it on the grounds of too great complexity and too little performance. The manufacture of the Aurol is certainly more difficult than that of oxygen. However, these difficulties do not have to be faced in the bases or on board ship, but in the interior of the country. Moreover, I am of the opinion that the goal set initially — that of constructing a 30-knot U-boat — can only be realized by continuing along the path we have initiated in a foreseeable period of time. I remain with friendly greetings
Yours truly, Walter.'

U-tanker alternatives

As the intended construction of 30 special transport U-boats of Type XX clashed with both the construction of Type XXIII at DW in Finkenwerder and the section construction of Type XXI at the Vegesack Shipyard, and since transport U-boats could not be dispensed with, a discussion took place at the Main Committee on 8 October 1943, at which it was resolved to move the construction of Type XX to GW in Kiel, which should additionally take over the Type XIV supply U-boat commissions from DWK, the construction of which had not been commenced. It was estimated that this alteration of contracts would involve a delay of only five weeks, provided GW did not have to take on the two large Walter U-boats of Type XVIII from DWK. But the necessity of taking on the urgent and difficult Type XVIII construction would inevitably mean a building delay of eight months from the first Type XX boat.

'K' Office was of the opinion that it could soon make a proposal for relieving GW of some of its work-load, occasioned by the desire of Department 2 of the Chief of Naval War Staff to retain Type XVIII by combining Types XIV and XX into a Type XXB. This would involve an attempt to come to terms with the danger from increased air observation in the Atlantic, by doubling the battery capacity and consequently the submerged range. If the displacement of Type XX were to be retained, additional batteries would have to be installed at the expense of the exterior loading facilities, or at the expense of interior loading space. The only alternative to these was a considerable increase in displacement, which was not at all desirable. These projects were worked on under the designation XXB and XXB2: the first of these would have an additional trough under the pressure hull to accommodate additional batteries; in the second, dry storage accommodation would have to be converted to serve as a battery compartment. Further design changes in Type XX made it possible for the outer tanks to be used when necessary, for the transport of fuel-oil or rubber, which would enable it to be used as a supply vessel.

A discussion that followed on 18 October 1943, between 'K' Office, the Armaments Offices and the Chief of Naval War Staff, decided that the combined Type XXB was not to be given serious consideration. Department 2 was foremost in rejecting it as a supply U-boat. Effectively then, a combination of Type XIV and XX had been thwarted. Apparently Type XIV had to be kept in being. In order to make it more suitable for the changed nature of operational requirements, on 8 November 1943, 'K' Office presented an enlarged version, XIVB, of 1,895m³ volume, and a length of 70.9m, which, with a battery loading time of 5.5 hours, would have a considerably increased submerged range of 90 nautical miles at 4 knots. As with Type XXB, this was to be achieved by an additional battery in a pressure-tight trough under the pressure hull. It was intended to alter the last 6 boats of Type XIV to be built in 1945 accordingly. On 19 November 1943, a final decision was taken to carry on building Types XIV and XX for the time being. On 14 December 1943, appropriate building contracts were awarded to GW for 11 DWK-boats of Type XIV, and for the proposed 30 boats of Type XX.

The increasingly difficult problem of which armaments to provide, and the preference given to the Type XXI construction meant, however, that further constructional delays occurred in these supply and transport U-boats. The first two Type XX boats were laid down at GW at the beginning of March 1944. Completion was calculated for 10 April 1945 and 22 May 1945. The last Type XX boats were to be delivered early in 1947. From March 1944, therefore, the Chief of Naval War Staff took up the suggestions of the 'K' Office that Type XX boats should be replaced as soon as possible by converting Type XXI boats for transport and supply purposes.

When it became clear in May 1944 that a further delay of three months would occur in the construction of Type XX, it was decided summarily, on 27 May 1944, to cancel the construction plan for Type XIV and XX boats. Only 3 Type XX boats, *U1701–U1703*, the delivery of which was anticipated now at the end of 1945, were to be constructed for the transportation of Aurol to Norway for Walter-boats. These were to carry 600 tons of Aurol and 100 tons of other supplies. Conversion of these boats was to be complete by 1 October 1944. A total of 400,000 work hours per boat was calculated. However, the worsening war situation meant that the construction made no headway.

During the discussion that took place on 8 November 1943 concerning the continued building of Type XIV, two alternatives to Type XIVB were suggested by the 'K' Office: a larger Project XXIC, developed from Type XXI, which would provide a supply U-boat by removing the comprehensive torpedo armament of eighteen torpedo tubes, and by reducing the batteries by a half; and of providing a U-tanker with a capacity equal to the Type XIV by enlarging the outer ship of a normal Type XXI and removing its torpedo armament. The second proposal concerned a type designated XXID. In this, the pressure hull, the propulsion unit and a large part of the installations of Type XXI would be retained. The following alterations, however, were required:
1. Removal of the torpedo armament and the fitting-out of the bow compartment with an enlarged workshop (and other items), which would not then be needed in the stern compartment.
2. Enlargement of the trimming tanks to be accomplished by dispensing with torpedo tanks.
3. Alteration to the compensating units.
4. A widening of the upper deck and installations necessary for transferring oil.
5. Additional accommodation for oil-transfer pumps, including necessary tubing in the auxiliary engine compartment. To accommodate these, the compressed-air bottles, stored there, to be moved elsewhere.
6. Enlargement of the refrigerated compartment to contain provisions intended for supplying.
7. A new anti-aircraft bridge in place of the Type XXI bridge, so that an adequate anti-aircraft armament would be available in the event of unexpected aircraft attacks during supply operations. 3.7cm guns would be carried in twin mountings on a raised platform forward and aft of the bridge, with two 2cm twin M38 provided on the bridge. Additionally, an open bridge was seen as necessary in the interests of manoeuvring when supplying.
8. The addition of a ballast keel.
9. The incorporation of a pressure-tight fuel bunker aft, in the interests of trimming compensation on the homeward passage, when conditions of loading might be unfavourable.

Later, this Project XXID received a modification in the light of changed operational demands. On 27 March 1944, the Supreme Commander-in-Chief of the Navy ordered that certain U-boat types should receive oil supplies only when submerged. This meant that the large anti-aircraft bridge was unnecessary. Furthermore, Type XXID was now to be ready as soon as possible in order to carry out

pressing underwater operations for which Type XIV was less suitable. This modified type, designated Type XXID2, was now to have the normal Type XXI bridge and two bow torpedo tubes positioned one above the other on the port side as defensive armament. The enlarged outer ship of Type XXID or XXID2 meant that it was not possible to use sections from the Type XXI series production. This involved a considerable constructional effort for a relatively small series — which was undesirable with the war situation as it was at that time. The goal was a supply U-boat based on Type XXI, with as few changes as possible in the normal constructional components of this type. The requirement that it should be able to carry the same amount of supplies as Type XIV had been dropped; clearly it was not going to be possible to achieve both of these. In order to provide adequate capacity without changing the outer ship of Type XXI, as had been proposed in the use of Type XXIC as a supply vessel, the battery system was reduced to three half-batteries. However, in this design XXI V, there was no escaping an altered deck, as the deck shape of Type XXI would made deck operations impossible even in light seas. Moreover, room had to be provided for connecting tubes and oil-transfer equipment, while towing hooks and hawse-holes were also necessary. However, there was no implementation of the construction of these projects, as the military situation of 1944 hardly permitted the idea of supplying at sea and the Type XXI boats, on account of their great range, were regarded as more or less indispensable. Closer working-out of the designs, therefore, was not proceeded with.

U-transport alternatives

Parallel with the design of U-tanker XXID, in the winter of 1943/44, consideration was given to the possibilities of providing a transport U-boat based on Type XXI. The tasks such a boat would carry out envisaged a vessel with the same overall pressure hull as Type XXI, but without torpedo armament, and with the same payload as Type XX. These conditions were not easily to be achieved, as the pressure hull of Type XXI was too heavy for a transport U-boat with these qualities, and it would also be necessary to have a large outer ship to accommodate the cargo. To cope with this weight, pressure-tight outer tanks would have to be provided. Additionally, the following significant modifications to the Type XXI design would be necessary:
1. The use of the bow compartment as a dry storage compartment with a large loading-hatch, as a replacement for the existing small torpedo hatch.
2. Enlargement of the trimming tanks, accomplished by dispensing with the torpedo tanks.
3. Changes to the compensating components.
4. An open anti-aircraft bridge as in Type XXID, because it was anticipated that a large part of a long journey to East Asia would be carried out on the surface.
5. Additional anchor installation.

This project was designated Type XXIE. Parallel with the modification of Type XXID, Type XXIE would be given the Type XXI bridge and the two

bow torpedo tubes to serve as defensive armament against U-boat hunters. The working-out of this version, Project XXIE2, took account also of the newly-changed requirements for carrying-qualities of Type XX, both in total capacity and in the composition of this capacity. As against Type XX, the rubber cargo was proportionately reduced, while other cargo items were correspondingly increased. The displacement of this large boat was 2,809 tons, which exceeded that of Type XX.

As had been remarked with Type XXID, the use of Type XXI sections was not possible because of the considerably changed outer ship, as long as the demand for the Type XX rubber cargo of 450 tons was retained. However, if the transport capacity were reduced, especially with regard to rubber, a solution was possible using the normal Type XXI outer ship; a version based on this was designated Type XXIT. To be sure, complete interchangeability of Type XXI sections for operational or transport U-boats could not be achieved completely, but one was getting nearer the goal and, in effect, a decision on the use of sections could be deferred to a later stage of construction. It was calculated that the decision as to whether a boat should be completed as an operational or as a cargo U-boat would have to be made seven months before delivery of the boat. The necessary transport compartment would be provided by dispensing with the following installations of Type XXI:
1. After part of crew compartment, port and starboard — Cargo Compartment I.
2. Lower battery compartment, midships and forward — Cargo Compartments II and III.
3. Upper battery compartment, forward — Cargo Compartment IV.
4. Torpedo tank, starboard — Cargo Compartment V.
5. Torpedo storage compartment (bow compartment) — Cargo Compartment VI.

The following loading suggestions were intended for a return journey.

A:	125	tons of rubber.
	12	tons of Molybdenum concentrate.
	67	tons of tin in ingots.
	67	tons of tungsten concentrate.
	4	tons general cargo.
	275	tons total
B:	153	tons of rubber (max. rubber load!).
	122	tons of tin, tungsten and Molybdenum concentrate.
	275	tons total

Both these suggestions envisaged using the ballast compartments beneath cargo compartments II, III and IV for storage of the tin on the return passage, while refined steel could be carried beneath them when outward bound. Finally, as an improvized measure, a Type XXI U-boat with normal batteries was planned, to be used for transport purposes and equipped to carry 95 tons of cargo in the interior of the boat and 65 tons of cargo in the keel.

In the autumn of 1944, a decision was to be made about the placing of contracts for appropriate transport U-boats, but this was deferred in view of the vicissitudes of the war. It was not, in fact subsequently taken.

9 CONSTRUCTION IN THE TWILIGHT OF DEFEAT

BOTTLENECKS, SHORTAGES AND AIR RAIDS

The Type XXI programme

The implementation of completely new production methods posed great problems for yards concerned with U-boat construction. Both the Navy and yard management feared that great difficulties would arise during the initial stages, and that section construction would lead to a lengthening of other aspects of construction. On 1 December 1943, the monthly report of Armament Command at Kiel stated: 'The impression exists generally that, in spite of series production which is now to unroll, the first months will throw up difficulties or a non-achievement of expected production figures. . . . A factory manufacturing accessories has already reported that, apart from drawings, materials are not so readily forthcoming.' In the case of the first boats, therefore, 'K' Office suggested that section yards be by-passed and the boats be regarded as prototypes to be built entirely by the assembly yards. But this was not to be: Merker carried through his plan, and an immediate start on section construction was made.

It soon became evident that, despite the very greatest efforts, the short delivery times could not be met. In addition to bottlenecks in the construction of accessories, and in other areas, delays occasioned by damage through air attack disrupted considerably the commencement of fabrication. In western Germany, DWK was especially affected. This yard was scheduled to complete the bow sections of the first two Type XXI boats by 20 February 1944, using the available pressure bulkheads of Type XVIII. Preparatory work, however, was interrupted when workshops were destroyed during an air raid on 13 December 1943, and further air raids on 4 and 5 January 1944 meant that section construction could not be started in January and February 1944. At an HAS meeting on 7 February, it was resolved that all section building, which was carried out in one place only for the entire western area, would take place in shelters, but DWK would be unable to move its section construction into a bunker before the autumn of 1944.

At the majority of the section yards, however, the cause of delays in production was the tardy arrival of crude sections and, to some extent, their inadequate construction. In a report from KMW, Wilhelmshaven, of 25 January 1944, the delayed section construction at this yard was discussed in these terms:

'Order-planning of the IBG in Halberstadt had set the following dates for delivery of the first sections for building component 2 at the yard:

No. 1 Eilers, Hannover   23.12.1943
No. 2 Gutehoffnungshütte   24.12.1943
No. 3 Seibert Aschaffenburg   27.12.1943

As it was not absolutely clear from previous instructions whether the quoted dates were despatch dates from steel construction or were to be regarded as delivery dates at the section yards, it was necessary at the yard to make certain changes in work planning in both ship construction halls in such a way that work on the sections could begin on 23.12.1943. By this date, the rearrangement of work tasks in ship construction Hall 3, where sectional construction was to start first, were so far advanced that building construction could have begun according to plan. However, the first crude sections from the firms of GHH Sterkrade and Seibert Aschaffenburg were not ready for despatch until 4.1 and 5.1, and then not in a state of completion. From the firm of Eilers Hannover, no construction component was ready for acceptance during January.

'In a letter dated 3.1.1944, the Building Planning Department of IBG at Blankenburg had informed the yard of changes to the upper deck, and the modification that this necessitated in the upper casings. This change meant that the delivery of the casings was delayed to the extent that casings for the first section did not arrive at the section yard at the same time as the rest of the section. Consequently it was necessary, in the case of the first sections, that completion of the interior had to be carried out before attachment of the casings.

'It can therefore be stated in the light of the difficulties and changes of plan that have been mentioned, that the originally determined delivery dates to the assembly yards (3 items in February, 7 items in March) will not be met, as IBG in Blankenburg has apportioned 9 weeks for the completion of section 2 and this has now been reduced to 8 weeks at the yard. Moreover, as the

extent of additional tasks existing at this time cannot be foreseen, delivery dates cannot be made for the time being; the overall construction planning that stems from the previously-notified work schedule issued by IBG Blankenburg is not a workable proposition, not only through changes of building that become necessary for various components, but equally through additional work that has to be carried out. Reference is made here only to problems existing with the pressure-test, when, on account of late receipt of casings, this has to be carried out after completion of the inner construction; if leaks are found, then possibly sizeable dismantling work becomes necessary.

'According to reports, it seems that, at the direction of IBG in Bremen, a container component ready for despatch from GHH Sterkrade to KMW Wilhelmshaven (according to the delivery note of 30 December 1943) was diverted to Danzig. At all events, no pressure hull has been received by us by 25.1.1944, only certain casing components from Seibert Aschaffenburg which came by rail. . . .

'A report will be made on delivery dates once parts have actually reached us, when the position with regard to construction can be ascertained. We also point out, in addition, that inspection of parts at steel construction firms has allowed differences of up to 35mm against those called for in drawings, but, originally, a ±2mm tolerance was allowed to the steel construction firms. The additional work will have to be carried out by the section yards, for the assembly yards B&V and Deschimag refuse to accept containers that exceed these tolerances.'

A similar picture was presented by DW in Hamburg-Finkenwerder:

'By 31.1.1944, DW had received only one each of the 7 crude sections III and 7 VI, one called for by the timetable: on 29.1.1944, one crude section III arrived from Gollnow from which various casings were missing, and one crude section VI on 11.1.1944 from the Dortmunder Union, which was incomplete in respect of casings, drilled parts and various other constructional components. On 31.1.1944, a further crude section VI arrived from the MAN Motorenwerk Hamburg, on which additional work had to be carried out because of unsatisfactory measurements. This additional work took the yard almost the whole month of February.

'The constructional planning called for the completion of 8 sections of III and 8 of VI for the month of April. But up to 1.3.1944 only one crude section III was delivered. By this date, and in total, only 5 crude sections had been received instead of the stipulated 26.'

Commencement of the series was also considerably hampered by the bomb damage sustained by MAN and SSW, the most important suppliers of main engines and motors, in February 1944. An HAS note dated 10 March stated:

'As a consequence of delays in completion of U-boat sections and interruptions caused by enemy action in the production of electric motors and diesel engines, the Navy will have to accept that only 63 U-boats of Type XXI will be ready for delivery by the end of August 1944. . . . Bombing has caused much damage to electric motors at SSW and this can only partly be made good by affiliated works in Nürnberg and Vienna. . . . Especially damaging was the attack on MAN; in this, 80 per cent of the test-beds were destroyed and 11 completed diesel engines so considerably damaged and burned that it will be necessary to dismantle them completely and overhaul them.'

By the end of March 1944, most of the sections for the first boats were ready at the various assembly yards, but sections 2 and 7 did not arrive at Deschimag until the beginning of April. Diesel engines for the first boats were not ready for despatch until 10 April, which meant that the maintaining of the April delivery was out of the question, and would not be achieved even for slipway launching. At Schichau of Danzig, sections for the first boat were delivered from outside sources on 20 March as planned, but with dummy items built in to replace fittings that were not yet available. Here, too, through late delivery of diesel engines, assembly work could not begin until the beginning of April — although, for prestige reasons, Schichau's first boat, *U3501*, was put into the water as early as 19 April 1944, one day before Hitler's birthday. However, the boat was by no means complete, and was not self-buoyant. Open parts of the hull were sealed with wooden closures, and it was necessary to tow the boat immediately into a floating dock. The consequence of this over-hasty launching was a lengthy time spent at a yard berth.

Right: Buoyancy tanks being installed in *U2501* after launching, May 1944.

U3501 was not delivered to the Navy until 11 July, and was not put into service until 29 July 1944. The first completed Type XXI boat was B&V's *U2501*, which was delivered on 15 June, and entered service on 28 June 1944!

The directors of the other two assembly yards, B&V and AG Weser, had refused to allow their first boats to be launched in such an incomplete condition merely in the interests of simulating a delivery date that simply could not be achieved. Thus were born the first, weighty, partly political differences between the yard directorates and Merker's HAS, which were to lead later to the introduction of Konteradmiral Karl Topp as Head of the Ship Construction Commission, whom Dönitz intended as 'moderator' to keep a balance between opposed opinions; he succeeded in calming ruffled feelings, but tensions remained. When series production got under way, delivery quotas began to climb, but remained well below the level called for in initial planning. In fact, delivery quotas never reached any of the planned levels, even when these were reduced from time to time.

Defects caused by the pressure of delivery dates showed themselves during the trials of the first boats, and delayed systematic testing and training. After commissioning, *U2501* had to go back to the yard for ten days at the beginning of July 1944 so that various faults could be rectified, all stemming from inadequate work on section 2 (entry of sea water into the lubrication system of the gearing and electric motors!). Furthermore, unsatisfactory work on the new and unfamiliar installations caused a series of breakdowns that delayed training procedures. It had not been taken into consideration that an electric motor running in reverse would drive the diesel engine in the same way, and the latter would then suck water in through the open exhaust-gas closures and through the submerged exhaust! Thus, in the case of three boats, the unrush of water into the cylinders severely damaged the propulsion unit.

Technical teething troubles further delayed the programme. In an attempt to achieve the utmost technical perfection in the design of the new boats, complicated measures were developed (a hydraulic

system for all control systems, movement of periscopes, anti-aircraft armament, and torpedo hatches) which could not be carried out with the building experience available, or which did not measure up to operational requirements. Moreover, not enough thought had gone into the disposition of various installations and auxiliary engines in terms of ducts, and various other items had been lacking in the wooden model, so that constructional decisions concerning the auxiliary engines had often been taken on inexact or even incorrect presumptions (for example, the layout of the almost inaccessible Junkers compressor).

In order to give the relatively small six-cylinder diesel engines as high a performance as possible, an especially powerful, supercharging system had been developed. Initial tests, however, showed that the supercharger did not provide any increase in performance during schnorkel travel. As surfaced performance was of secondary importance at this time, the supercharger was not installed in later boats, and valuable planning and construction work were thus wasted. Battery ventilators proved to be superfluous and, once again, were either dismantled or were no longer incorporated. It was found that the two compartment ventilators sufficed, and the exhaustion of battery air during schnorkel travelling could be accomplished via the diesels.

The schnorkel was not envisaged until after the designing of the Type XVIII had been completed. In order that the shape of the boat should not be altered, an extensible schnorkel was planned, the design of which turned out to be unsatisfactory. The chief disadvantages were inadequate watertightness, considerable noise from the compressed-air motor when the schnorkel was being extended, high resistance set up by the circular cross-section of the mast and considerable oscillations in the higher speed ranges. The requirement for a schnorkel speed of 10–12 knots could not be obtained with this type and, towards the end of the war, it was suggested that the schnorkel be of the hinged type (as in Type XXVIW), and be positioned at the after edge of the conning-tower superstructure, in place of the aftermost AA turret.

The bilge piping had too many bends, which allowed air pockets to form, and valves and suction heads were, to some extent, difficult to operate and were completely inaccessible. Operating the centrifugal pumps required a certain amount of skill: a closed pressure valve was opened until all air had been withdrawn, and was then opened further, but just enough so as not to break the filament of water. At first, operators restricted themselves to removing air pockets, but in later boats the bilge installation was redesigned in the light of experience.

The design had provided for the three port or starboard sectional batteries to be charged only in series. As the boat's main supply was fed at 120 volts, the auxiliary engines and other items that used electricity took their supply equally from the various sectional batteries. However, operational usage gave rise to the fear that by, say, above-average use of a bilge pump in dealing with an entry of water, one battery might be exhausted more quickly than the others. However, when batteries are connected in series, the charging of the weakest of them can only take place when the strongest battery is fully charged: this meant that a battery would stay only half-charged and could not be used effectively when the main engines were running. Despite representations to the BdU, the fear of delaying delivery schedules prevented any change. Not until AG Weser's first boat, *U3001*, had demonstrated this shortcoming in drastic degree at UAK, Kiel, was this latter body able to push through changes in this and other urgent matters.

Magnetic measurements showed that, when travelling at maximum speed, an extra magnetic field was set up by the boat through the battery lead to the main engines, which passed along one side of the boat and back along the other. The disposition of the lead had to be changed immediately, to minimize danger from magnetic mines. In order that a system of clear commands might be maintained in the event of a power failure, Type XXI had a built-in 'Telekin' (a wire connection running through tubing, similar to a Bowden cable). Many difficulties were experienced with this installation, because of the curvatures resulting from section construction.

The hydrogen filter did not function properly because, despite an air drying device, the dampness of air reduced the catalytic effect of the platinum-asbestos. This caused an explosion of oxy-hydrogen gas in *U3002*, during operational group training, when, after the failure of the battery ventilator, battery exhaust air, which was no longer being filtered, reached the battery turbo-ventilator. Gas would have accumulated here through weaknesses and been ignited by the commutator. Two further battery explosions were caused by over-filling the accumulator cells after full charging. During subsequent recharging, the battery gases could not be adequately ventilated because of their high acid content.

It was inevitable that such problems would occur, when, in order to meet delivery dates, no prototypes had been constructed, but the IBG was of the opinion that the first 6 boats from each yard would serve only as training boats, and that by the time that the seventh boat was commissioned most of the difficulties would have been surmounted. The Chief of Naval War Staff, on the other hand, regarded it as vital to have immediate delivery of operationally-sound boats of this new type. However, from the very beginning of the design planning, no opportunity had been taken to furnish the IBG with operationally-experienced engineers. Not until early 1944 were technical crews found for the first 3 boats. At the request of the Commander-in-Chief, U-Boats, Kapitänleutnant (Engineer) Fuchslocher went to Blankenburg as First Operational Officer. He arrived in Bremen on 7 February 1944, in order to prepare constructional instructions for *U3001*. As no overall plans were available at the yard or at KLA, he occupied himself initially in preparing at the IBG a serviceable description of Type XXI from the constructional drawings available there and

Right: Launching of a Type XXI at AG Weser.

Section assembly of Type XXIII's at DW, Hamburg, in June 1944. **Above:** A bow section being manoeuvred into position on the building-slips. **Left:** Assembly in progress on *U2324-U2326*.

through questioning the engineers who had worked on the design. Frequently, there was literally no-one available with the requisite knowledge — in the interests of secrecy, either background information or detailed instructions were missing. Many sections of the wooden model had items built-in without anyone knowing why or by whom! For example: compressed-air bottles, which required no attention, were positioned where they were easy to get at, while important auxiliary engines were sited where access was difficult.

In April 1944, Käpitanleutnant Fuchslocher spoke to the Commanding Admiral of U-Boats, von Friedeburg, and Konteradmiral (Engineer) Thedsen concerning the new U-boat type, and indicated technical problems that could be anticipated. However, because production was beginning and delivery dates had been fixed down to the day and hour, it was decided that no changes could be instigated until after the first boats had been handed over to UAK, Kiel.

The Type XXIII programme

While the first two sets of electric motors for Type XXIII were delivered by AEG, punctually in January 1944 despite bomb damage, in other areas of production, especially that of fittings and steel construction, delivery difficulties and bottlenecks made themselves felt. In an armament discussion of 26 January 1944, Merker acknowledged that a

delay of six weeks had to be expected in the timetable of the Type XXIII series construction. On 10 February, at a further conference, the delivery date for the first Type XXIII boat was set for the end of March 1944 — but, during an armament discussion on 23 February, it became clear that even this date would not be met, and that the delay would amount to eight weeks. The first boat from foreign yards would not be delivered before August 1944. A special bottleneck was caused by the schnorkel installation of Type XXIII, so that the eighteenth boat was the first to have the complete installation, and the earlier boats received their installations during the course of further work.

Meanwhile, weight checks revealed that the addition of various installations had rendered the boat too heavy and robbed her of her buoyancy. On 23 February 1944, it was decided to rectify this normally grave fault by the insertion of a 2.2m-long portion (section 3a or 'Oelfken-section'). Only section construction made possible such a change without further considerable delays. Through this lengthening of the boat, the narrow bow compartment was usefully enlarged and, beneath it, an additional storage compartment was acquired. A further enlargement by 1.3m would have been useful in the bow compartment to accommodate interior loading of the torpedo tubes, and two reserve torpedoes could have then been carried;

however, as this would have involved further design changes and, therefore, further delays, the suggestion was turned down by the Ship Construction Commission. The complicated exterior loading of tubes, accompanied by a necessary trimming of the boat, remained.

Assembly of the first Type XXIII boat, *U2321*, began at DW Hamburg-Finkenwerder on 10 March, and she was launched on 17 April. Like the first Type XXI boat launched at Danzig at the same time, *U2321* required a lengthy period of further work in dock, and clearly the launching dates were adhered to for prestige reasons rather than because the boats were structurally ready. *U2321* was not commissioned until 12 June 1944 (a week before the Allies had invaded France), but the delivered Type XXIII boats gave less trouble than their large Type XXI sisters.

The Type XXVI programme

When, on 28 March 1944, the Supreme C-in-C of the Navy decided in favour of the new Walter Type XXVIW, the problem was that of getting the new type into service as soon as possible, and it was thought that construction could be got off to a quick start by using as many components as possible from Types XVII and XVIII — which had been scrapped in the meantime — and components from current production jobs. However, rather excessive optimism was shown in this, because most of the corresponding installations in Type XVIII were only theoretical. While 'K' Office calculated that the first complete boat would be ready by the middle of 1945, representatives of the Armaments Ministry thought that February 1945 was a possible date.

During an armament discussion on 22 March 1944, the Navy stated its Aurol requirement for this programme: 2,000 tons per month immediately, 3,500 tons per month by the end of 1944 and 7,000 tons per month by the end of 1945, which would allow 70 operations, each using 100 tons of Aurol. At this time, 1kg of this fuel cost 2 marks, so that a single operation would cost 200,000 marks. The yearly output of the works at Bad Lauterberg amounted to only 12,000 tons, of which a sizeable portion had to be delivered to the Luftwaffe. An additional works in Rhumspringe near Bad Lauterberg would be able to deliver 25,000 tons per year, but this was still in the course of construction. As a further measure, two more works were planned in Heidebreck and Waldenberg in Upper Silesia, each of which was to produce yearly 30,000 tons of H_2O_2 based on the Antrachinon process, which had been developed by IG-Farben. However the suitability for U-boat purposes of fuel produced by this new process was doubtful. Indeed, it must be said that the entire supply system of Aurol for submarines was on a somewhat uncertain footing.

At a further conference on 5 April 1944, the Chief of Naval War Staff's demands regarding the new boat, now officially designated XXVI, were dealt with.

'The boat should have good speed on the surface and submerged, and be suitably equipped in equal measure for submerged day and surfaced night

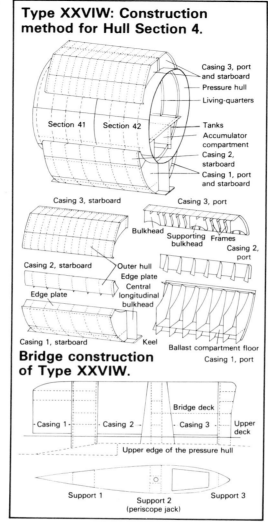

Type XXVIW: Construction method for Hull Section 4.

Section 41 / Section 42

Casing 3, port and starboard
Pressure hull
Living-quarters
Tanks
Accumulator compartment
Casing 2, starboard
Casing 1, port and starboard

Casing 3, starboard
Casing 3, port
Bulkhead Supporting bulkhead Frames
Casing 2, port
Casing 2, starboard
Outer hull
Edge plate
Central longitudinal bulkhead
Edge plate
Casing 1, starboard Keel
Ballast compartment floor
Casing 1, port

Bridge construction of Type XXVIW.

Bridge deck
Casing 1 Casing 2 Casing 3 Upper deck
Upper edge of the pressure hull
Support 1 Support 2 (periscope jack) Support 3

attacks. It should be as noiseless as possible in all speed ranges. It would be ideal if it could switch quickly from diesel to turbine. The battery for the schnorkel should be as quiet as possible. Electric motor slow silent running to exceed 3 knots, electric cruising submerged 6 knots and surface travel on diesels 12 knots. The bridge should have positions for a 4-man lookout and provision made for it to be covered at will by a 'cheese-dish cover'. It should be possible to carry out mine operations and submerged oil refuelling. The boat should be able to remain at sea for 8 weeks. Diving depth to correspond to that of Type XXI.'

At this conference, it was finally decided to use the MWM RS34S diesel engine of Type XXIII, and the gear arrangement of Type XVIII. The design and building preparations were to be handed over to IBG, and control of these aspects were given to Dr. Fischer of that body. From the very beginning, the working-out of construction details at IBG went hand-in-hand with construction planning, so that

the proposed series construction could be carried out as economically as possible. As with Type XXI, series production was to be carried out on three levels: crude section construction at the steel construction organizations; section construction at experienced U-boat yards; and, finally, assembly at a large yard commanding the necessary skills. The total production should be concentrated in the Danzig area and the Type XXI series construction was to be discontinued there. Schichau of Danzig was proposed for the assembly yard and received a contract for 100 Type XXVI U-boats on 26 May 1944. (Almost certainly, this decision was influenced by the fact that there was less danger from air attack in this part of the country.) On 3 May 1944, an initial production plan for Type XXVI, commencing March 1945, was issued:

March:	2
April:	—
May:	2
June:	4
July:	8
August:	10
September:	10
October:	10
November:	10
December:	10
Total 1945:	66

In Berlin on 17 May 1944, Speer, Dönitz, Merker and Waas discussed the new Type XXVI. It transpired that the equipment for the side torpedo tubes could not be delivered before January 1945, but HAS wanted delivery in November 1944 in order to facilitate the start of series production in May 1945. It was also required that steel construction commence in November 1944, and drawings would have to be ready at IBG as early as July 1944.

The IBG's initial work planning of 24 May 1944 envisaged eight weeks for steel construction, six weeks for the construction of sections and seven weeks per boat for assembly. According to planning, the prototype, *U4501*, was to be delivered on 15 March 1945. To accomplish this, steel firms should commence their work on 16 September 1944, construction of sections should begin on 10 December, and assembly should start on 25 January 1945. Meanwhile, production planning for the series was raised to 12 boats per month from September 1945, and this now gave a total of 74 boats for 1945. The achievement of these dates required principally that construction drawings be ready punctually, and these, for the first time in German ship construction, were being prepared according to the section page system used by steel construction in the interior of the country. (In this system, drawings depict not only the object being constructed, but also indicate clearly the steps necessary for its fabrication.) As a construction aid for the working-out of details, a full-scale model in wood was built at Blankenberg, equipped not only with engines and larger installations, but also with tubes and conduits. To help in this considerable undertaking, Schichau sent to the IBG various members of its staff who, as well as helping, could assimilate information on various constructional points.

During the following weeks, it became increasingly clear that only Blohm & Voss of Hamburg had the necessary experience to build the section containing the Walter-installation. On the debit side, though, there was the not inconsiderable transport problem posed by a long, risky sea voyage from Hamburg to Danzig. The fact that Schichau was less exposed to air attack lost some of its significance if one faced the fact that not a single boat could be assembled if delivery of sections were prevented. To concentrate the Type XXVI programme in the Hamburg area seemed the only sensible solution. Only B&V, with their experience of Type XXI, could be considered for assembly, and Type XXI construction was therefore to cease here in the summer of 1945. A further decisive point was that the Hamburg U-boat shelters 'Elbe II' and 'Fink II' would then be available for Type XXVI section work. In line with this, a plan was prepared for the Supreme Naval Command on 21 July 1944; details of the proposed construction of sections were as follows.

Section 1: Stern (approximately 10.5m, 42.4 tons); DW in Box 4 in 'Fink II'.
Section 2: Propulsion installation (13.55m, 174 tons); B&V in Box 3 in 'Fink II'.
Section 3: Control room and side torpedo tubes (11.65m, 184 tons); Howaldt of Hamburg in 'Elbe II'.
Section 4: Bow compartment (6.8m, 66 tons); KMW, Wilhelmshaven, in Box 2 in 'Fink II'.
Section 5: Bow with bow torpedo tubes (approximately 13.7m, 60 tons); DW in Box 5 in 'Fink II'.

The requirement for raw steel amounted to 462.4 tons per boat, i.e., 46,240 tons for the complete series. Steel construction for the first four boats was to be carried out by the section yards. This would enable the steel construction time for the first 4 boats to be shortened and, despite certain delays that were already apparent in the preparation of design drawings, as well as longer time taken by steel production firms in their preparation planning, the March delivery date for the first boat could be kept, as well as the delivery date of 14 July 1944 for the first 4 boats. For the series to follow, steel construction was planned among the following firms: Nordd. Eisenbau, Sande Wilhelmshaven; Heyking Danzig; Beuchelt & Co., Grünberg/Silesia; Stahlbau Eggers, Hamburg, and MAN, Mainz-Gustavsburg. For these firms, the maximum steel construction time per crude section amounted to twelve weeks. To this figure could be added a four-week period for transportation and other requirements. The commencement of steel construction for the first series boat, U4505, was scheduled for 17 December 1944; commencement of sections for this boat could be achieved by 8 April 1945, and assembly work could begin on 20 May 1945. The provisional delivery date for U4505 was 8 July 1945.

Although written permission for the transferring of assembly work from Schichau to B&V was not given by the Supreme Naval Command until 28 September 1944, appropriate preliminary work was being done at B&V as early as the end of July, and members of the staff were sent to Blankenburg to familiarize themselves with drawings and assist in the final design. They criticized the arrangement of tubing in the model, pointing out that it was suitable only for single construction methods as used hitherto. B&V therefore suggested that, for the series construction, where tubing was to be built-in, valves should be collected together into groups, and be assembled with their appropriate tubing at the workshop stage. It was suggested, in the interests of simplification, that the sections be joined together from casing plates with flat, longitudinal welds, instead of using the curved-piece section construction of Type XXI, which involved circular seams. In a pressure hull with a length of approximately 40m there would be sections and, therefore, pressure-hull lengths of more than 8m, which would have to be split-up into 2–3 portions.

Similarly, improvements were planned in the design and construction of the outer hull, as compared with the casing-construction of Type XXI. In Type XXVI, the outer ship no longer completely enclosed the pressure hull. For this reason — and because the boat was smaller that Type XXI — when the sections of the outer ship were ready (four large and two small casings), they could be welded in a simple way to the pressure hull. To assist this, the transverse bulkheads had already been built-in with the casings, and an adequate space between outer shell and pressure hull permitted efficient welding.

In this Type XXVI, the designing of the schnorkel went hand-in-hand with the designing of the boat, so that both aspects of construction could be made compatible. The result was a streamlined, sheathed, folding schnorkel, positioned at the after edge of the bridge superstructure to avoid the disadvantages of the Type XXI schnorkel (sealings for lips, considerable noise when extended, high resistance). As soon as the design details had been completed orders were immediately distributed. In contrast to what had taken place with Type XXI, blanket orders were no longer issued by Central Procurement Planning (ZBP) in Halberstadt, but only by those ordering bodies that received ordering details directly from the Constructional Department at Blankenburg. ZBP, as the authoritative service body, had only organizational and distributive functions. To deal with the Walter-installation, a special ordering body was set up by Walter's firm in Bad Oldesloe/Holstein. The delivery dates for the constructional drawings could not be adhered to. On 19 August 1944, a new disposition of section yards was made:
Section 4: DW, Hamburg-Finkenwerder.
Section 5: Construction of the fore-ship (steel construction) KMW (Kriegsmarinewerft), Wilhelmshaven; section construction in 'Fink II' (outside department of KMW, Hamburg). At a discussion between B&V and the IBG on 26 August 1944, clarification was achieved concerning constructional details of the first 4 boats, which, with the exception of certain bearing components, were now to be built at B&V. This meant that preparations for the commencement of the series could be carried out more efficiently. The highest priority designation (DE) was obtained for the first 3 boats. Agreement was reached that the first prototype, U4501, must be ready before commencement of section construction of the first series boats. However, B&V calculated a total construction time of approximately seven months for U4501 in contrast with the IBG's initial planning, which had estimated 4⅔ months, which meant that the first boat would not be delivered until 8 May 1945. This delay stemmed from Production Planning, who estimated too low a number of work hours (a total number of hours per boat of only 145,200, instead of 180,000 as B&V had estimated). It was further established that to reach a monthly delivery quota of 12 items, one box of the Finkenwerder shelter was insufficient for the construction of section 2. On 8 September 1944, therefore, a new construction plan was drawn up, which both lengthened the total building time to 6½ months for the first boat, and set the commencement of construction at an earlier date, so that, overall, the March delivery date for the first boat could just about be retained. Details of this planning are shown in Table 47.

Table 46. Schedule for the first 4 Type XXVIW boats, 14 July 1944

	U4501	U4502	U4503	U4504
Commencement of steel construction	5 November 1944	26 November 1944	21 January 1945	4 February 1945
Commencement of construction in section yards	24 December 1944			
Commencement of construction at assembly yard	4 February 1945			
Delivery	25 March 1945	15 April 1945	10 June 1945	24 June 1945

Table 47. Revised schedule for the first 4 Type XXVIW boats, 8 September 1944

	U4501	U4502	U4503	U4504	U4505
Commencement of steel construction	17 Sept 1944	8 Oct 1944	3 Dec 1944	16 Dec 1944	24 Nov 1944
Commencement of section construction	1 Dec 1944	21 Dec 1944	15 Feb 1945	28 Feb 1945	15 March 1945
Commencement of assembly construction	4 Feb 1945	25 Feb 1945	22 April 1945	5 May 1945	20 May 1945
Delivery	31 March 1945	22 April 1945	17 June 1945	30 June 1945	15 July 1945

Allied air raids

The first RAF raid directed specifically against a U-boat yard had taken place on 18 May 1940. Blohm & Voss was the target, and the raid was not particularly successful. Sporadic night raids were subsequently made against various harbours, with Wilhelmshaven featuring frequently as a target. The first real damage sustained was to *U593* on 13 March 1941, when 49 aircraft bombed B&V. Two heavier raids by 44 and 36 aircraft on 7 and 8 April 1941 caused short-term disruption at Kiel. On 8 May 1941, Bomber Command launched the heaviest attack to date on Germany, with 359 aircraft. The main targets were Hamburg and Bremen, but U-boat production suffered no damage. Not until Kiel was attacked, on 24 February 1942, was U-boat production affected: at DWK, *U466* and *U474* were hit, which delayed delivery of the former by about eight days. A further raid on Kiel, on 12 March 1942, caused additional delivery delays at GW, involving 4 Type VIIF boats, *U1059–U1062*, *U791* (V300) and all VIIC boats from *U247*.

Sir Arthur 'Bomber' Harris had now been appointed Head of Bomber Command. His goal was the systematic destruction of German cities by nightly saturation raids, using incendiary and high-explosive bombs, and the first such raids were carried out against the cities of Lübeck (28/29 March 1942) and Rostock (24 and 25 April 1942). 1,000-bomber raids followed against Cologne (30 May 1942) and Bremen (25 June 1942). The immediate effect was the laying waste of residential areas and the destruction of cultural monuments — only incidentally were industrial installations destroyed, and the amount of such destruction bore no relation to the effort expended. U-boat production was little affected by these attacks. The tempo of these air raids slowed down towards the end of 1942; official RAF records show that the 1,000-bomber raids were suspended because of high losses and lack of effective result. In order to achieve the spectacularly high number of bombers for these operations, insufficiently trained formations had had to be used.

During the second half of 1942, the only yard to receive any severe damage was the Flensburg Schiffbau-Gesellschaft. Of three attacks carried out on this yard, the daylight raid of 2 July 1942 by 5 Mosquitoes at low level is especially noteworthy, in that sections of *U361* and *U366* were damaged. However, both boats were in an early stage of construction and their completion date was not affected. In a later attack on the Flensburger SBG on 27 October 1942, *U364* and *U368* suffered damage by bomb splinters. Apart from ports with yards, the RAF also included delivery firms for U-boat construction among their targets: on 17 April 1942, 8 aircraft made a precision attack on the MAN works in Augsburg, but damage was slight and production was hardly affected. In 1942, RAF Bomber Command flew approximately 7,000 aircraft sorties against U-boat yards and supply industries (approximately 20 per cent of total operations) and dropped approximately 11,000 tons of bombs. No appreciable effect on U-boat production was caused.

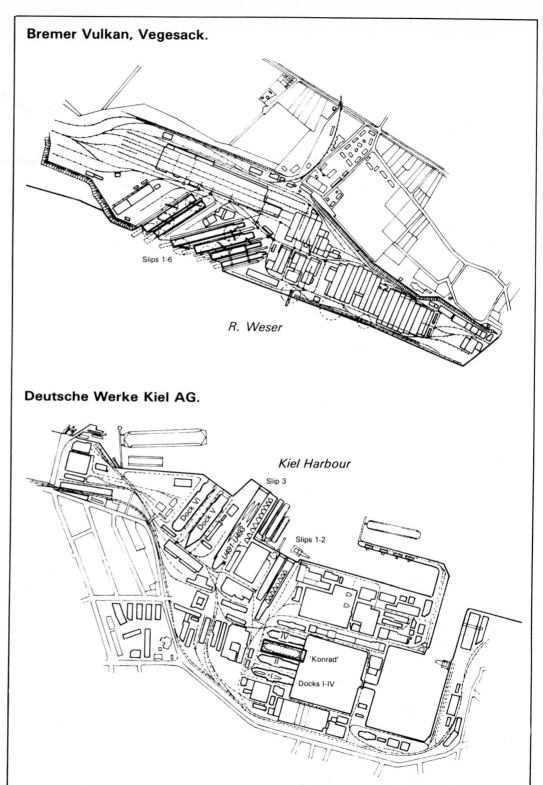

Bremer Vulkan, Vegesack.

Slips 1-6

R. Weser

Deutsche Werke Kiel AG.

Kiel Harbour

Slip 3

Dock VI

Dock V

Slips 1-2

U491 U483

'Konrad'

Docks I-IV

Not until the United States Eighth Air Force entered the fray on 17 August 1942 did the picture change. While the British, with their nightly saturation bombing, concentrated on areas with a central aiming-point, the Americans concentrated on more risky, but more exact, daylight attacks. At the beginning of 1943, the two air forces collaborated in an endeavour to eliminate U-boat bases in France and U-boat production in Germany. On 14 January 1943, heavy joint attacks were carried out against U-boat bases on the French Atlantic coast. The French targets were indeed knocked out, but the large U-boat shelters suffered very little damage and no U-boat was hit. In the period up to and including May 1943, 3,568 aircraft sorties were flown and 9,133 tons of high-explosive and incendiaries were dropped. The first daylight raid by the Eighth Air Force, using 58 B-17 bombers, took place on 27 January 1943 against Wilhelmshaven. Simultaneously, smaller attacks were launched against Vegesack and Emden. The first large raid by the Eighth Air Force against a U-boat yard was on 18 May 1943 against Bremer Vulkan in Vegesack, when 73 B-17s and 24 B-24s dropped 268 tons of explosive and achieved 76 hits. However, relatively slight damage was caused to building-slip installations. Of 18 boats lying at them, only two, *U287* and *U295*, were severely damaged. However, this daylight raid caused severe casualties — 108 dead and 103 wounded. Loss of production amounted to one month, but delivery of *U287* was, in fact, delayed by three months. It is a matter for some surprise that this yard was not attacked again until the autumn of 1943, when the only damage was an oil tank that was set on fire. Until the end of the war, U-boat production at this yard suffered no further damage from air attack.

The next severe raid by the Eighth Air Force employed 126 bombers, which dropped 250 tons of bombs on Kiel on 14 May 1943. GW suffered the most damage. Bomb hits on the conning tower of *U1061* and on the adjacent *U1062* caused damage. A lifting installation was damaged and sunk with *U236* and *U237*. *U235* was hit in the forepart of the ship. Bombs struck the foreship of *U234* on Building Slip VII, and the newly-built *U1051* at Building Slip V. Finally, the staging around *U244* was set on fire by exploding anti-aircraft ammunition, but the boat was not burned out.

In all, to the end of May 1943, the Eighth Air Force flew 3,414 sorties, dropping 9,745 tons of high-explosive and incendiary bombs on German ports.

The British meanwhile concentrated their energies on the destruction of Hamburg. On the nights of 24, 27 and 29 July 1943, the RAF attacked Hamburg with 700 aircraft, dropping approximately 6,900 tons of bombs. This caused a fire-storm that destroyed the larger part of the inner town. The Eighth Air Force supported this attack by daylight raids on the yards of Hamburg, Kiel and Wilhelmshaven on 25 and 26 July 1943. However, a subsequent night attack on Hamburg by the RAF on 2 August 1943, using 425 bombers, was less successful. It must be pointed out that, despite all these efforts, these attacks caused

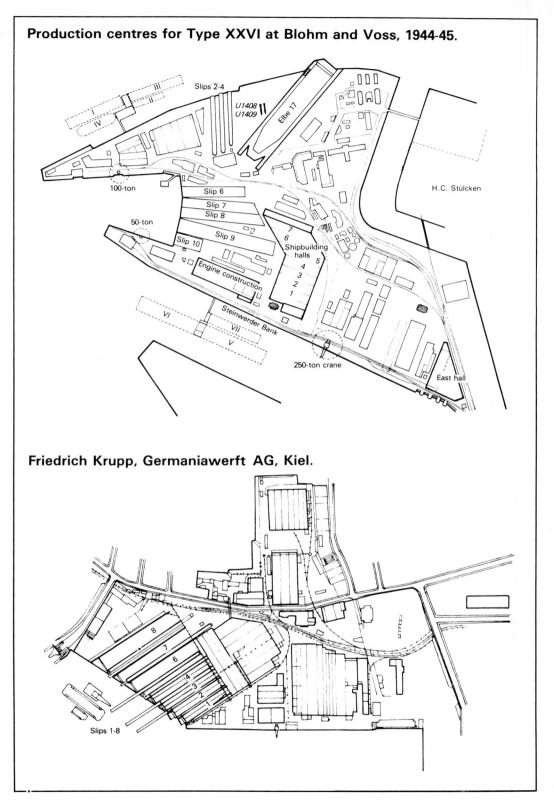

Production centres for Type XXVI at Blohm and Voss, 1944-45.

Friedrich Krupp, Germaniawerft AG, Kiel.

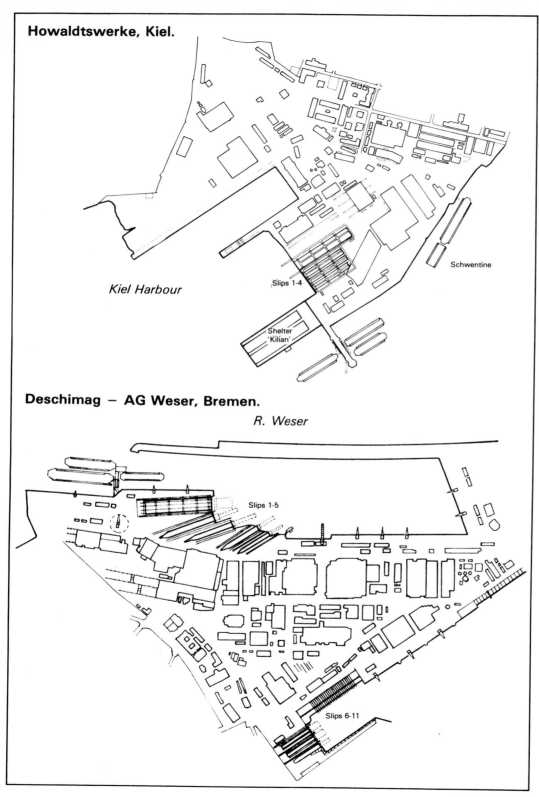

Howaldtswerke, Kiel.

Kiel Harbour

Slips 1-4

Shelter 'Kilian'

Schwentine

Deschimag — AG Weser, Bremen.

R. Weser

Slips 1-5

Slips 6-11

little damage to the port of Hamburg, and even less to the U-boat yards. B&V had 38 U-boats lying at building slips, of which only *U1011* and *U1012* and the two Walter-boats *U792* and *U793* were damaged. One of the Walter-boats was overturned by high-explosive blast, while the other was displaced from its blocks. Additionally, *U996* was sunk in the yard basin. At Kiel, *U395* was badly damaged at the Howaldtswerke. The greatest disruption experienced by U-boat construction in the weeks that followed was caused by the absence of Hamburg yard workers, some of whom had been bombed-out and others killed. In this way, B&V alone suffered the loss of 20—25 boats. After these catastrophic raids, the delivery rate of 5 boats in four weeks fell to 1 boat every fourteen days and later to 1 every twelve days. However, in the light of the crisis in the U-boat campaign at that time and a decision to switch to new types, the practical effects were small.

The Eighth Air Force sustained heavy losses in their attacks on industrial targets in southern Germany. On 13 December 1943, 349 aircraft again attacked Kiel by day. DWK was the most severely affected, and *U485* and *U486* were damaged. *U288* sustained a small amount of incendiary damage and *U345* was hit aft. Most significant was the wide-ranging destruction of workshops, which caused considerable delays in the deliveries of the last two boats, *U492* and *U493*, and caused special delays in the initial section construction. At the same time, important supply industries such as AEG and SSW in Berlin, AFA in Hagen and MAN in Augsburg were suffering damage through nightly, large-scale RAF attacks.

On 1 October 1943, 236 RAF bombers attacked Hagen, with the object of paralysing the most important production centre for U-boat batteries. Apart from four high-explosive bombs, only incendiaries were dropped on the closely-spaced buildings of the works complex. Approximately 35 per cent of the vital buildings were destroyed, most importantly the rubber factory, woodworking sections, installation section and plate preparation section. Repair work was set in hand immediately, through Organization Todt, and was carried out so systematically that production could recommence after only a few weeks. The major part of the damage was made good in approximately six months. Some time previously, the initial stages of increased production of the new Type XXI had been transferred to sister firms in Hannover, Vienna and Posen, to ensure that production of this new boat would proceed efficiently.

Nor was the attack on the Berlin SSW Dynamo Works on 15 February 1944 able to halt production, but only delay it. Five steel construction firms with mobile cranes, including the Dortmunder Union, were immediately given the task of rebuilding work at this, the main supplier of electric motors for the new U-boat Type XXI. The Navy supplied two companies and technical personnel to help in clearing work and repair of machine tools. Approximately two-thirds of the production halls and test beds had been destroyed, and the power supply was paralysed. Nevertheless, two weeks later, machine tools for stamping-out metal were at work in the

Howaldtswerke AG Hamburg.

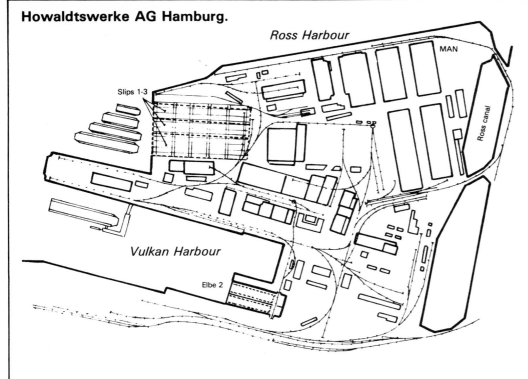

Ross Harbour

MAN

Slips 1-3

Ross Canal

Vulkan Harbour

Elbe 2

Deutsche Werft (Hamburg, Finkenwerder), 1944.

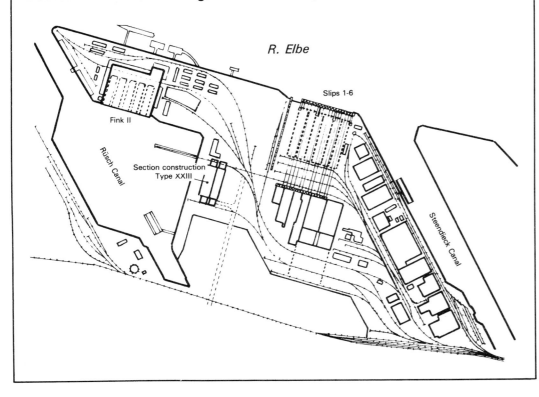

R. Elbe

Slips 1-6

Fink II

Rüsch Canal

Section construction
Type XXIII

Steendieck Canal

open air under temporary roofing, and replacement stands had been set up for the destroyed test beds. All obstacles had been overcome by July 1944. No further destruction occurred at the Dynamo Works during subsequent raids on Berlin, but, during a period of twelve months, 200 air raid warnings caused a loss in work time of, on the average 1½ hours — with a production force of approximately 500 workers, that represented in this area alone a total time loss of approximately 150,000 hours per year.

The night attack by 528 aircraft of the RAF on 25 February 1944 against MAN at Augsburg had a similar effect. It is quite astonishing that these destructive, saturation bombings of towns did not have more far-reaching effects on the industrial firms that suffered damage. In connection with this, Dönitz explained to Hitler on 19 August 1943:

'I am convinced that in a material sense the air attacks on our armament programme will have very little damaging effect. I have observed how in the engine hangars of yards in Hamburg, engines standing on the very edge of craters caused by direct hits penetrating the hangars are completely undamaged, as the bomb effects seem to have no sideways power but to be dispersed in an upward direction. The iron construction of these buildings with glass roofs seems to work in our favour in these cases, as the roofs disintegrate immediately and no shock waves are caused. I believe, therefore, that ship construction, carried out as it is on the coast in the west, will survive despite air attacks and, indeed, it is necessary that it should do so.'

During 1943, the Eighth Air Force dropped a total of 20,362 tons of bombs on U-boat installations and production centres — i.e., 41.8 per cent of their total bombing. During the first eight months, these remained their main targets, but with the lessening of the U-boat menace in the summer of 1943, the weight of Allied air attacks was turned towards other targets. Now, only 16 per cent of bombs dropped by the Eighth Air Force were directed against U-boat yards and bases. During the first quarter of 1944, this dropped to 4.4 per cent of the total bombing, i.e., down to 3,509 tons. It is possible that, with the change-over to section construction, empty building slips at many yards gave an outward impression that U-boat production was declining. Bombing was subsequently distributed over the entire country, and this chiefly affected the supply industries, so that section construction and assembly construction for the new U-boat programme of 1944, which was being carried out in a centralized manner at a few yards, was relatively free from attack, save for a few incidental attacks — notably in July — on Kiel, Hamburg and Bremen.

On 23 July 1944, DWK especially suffered damage in Kiel. Section construction was delayed as a result of destruction of the engine-building workshops. More serious were the direct hits on the power plant, in Docks 7 and 9, and on the last available 150-ton floating crane. At the Howaldtswerke, *U239* and *U1164* were damaged, and delivery delays were caused to the Seehund prototypes. On 26 July, to the west of Möltenort near Kiel, the new Type XXIII boat, *U2323*, hit an aerial mine and sank. On 28 July 1944, the RAF attacked Hamburg and Bremen with 305 bombers. During this raid, at B&V in Hamburg, the bow of *U2503* was damaged by a delayed-action bomb. In Bremen, *U872*, *U890* and *U3009* were hit, and *U872* sank. The large, 100-ton floating crane was out of action until 8 September 1944.

In July and August, the Eighth Air Force concentrated on the U-boat base at Toulon, and almost all U-boats lying there were destroyed. On 6 August 1944, the port at Hamburg was once again their target, and sections 2 and 3 of *U2505* were so badly damaged that they had to be replaced. Subsequent attacks by the RAF and the Eighth Air Force against different ports did not cause actual U-boat losses, but work was constantly interrupted by air-raid warnings and miscellaneous destruction, especially of electricity supply lines to workshops. It was not until 4 November 1944 that further U-boats (5) were damaged by the Eighth Air Force during a raid on fuel storage installations and oil refineries in Hamburg harbour. The night-raid on the harbour by 345 aircraft occurred on 21 November, when *U2529* was hit while in dock, and *U2532*, on a slip at B&V.

The total expenditure in terms of time needed to rectify bomb damage, to the Type XXI programme in the autumn of 1943 amounted to 300,000 hours per month (=1.25 per cent of total work time), but it climbed in 1944 to an average of 2,200,000 hours per month (=7 per cent of the total work time). During the same period, time lost through air raids amounted to approximately 10 per cent. In relation to the overall war situation, these figures were acceptable. Meanwhile, from aerial photographs and reports from agents, the Allies had become aware of the threat posed by the new U-boats, and these would be their targets for air attack at the end of 1944. From then until the end of the war, efforts were concentrated on the destruction of the U-boat yards, against which 138 attacks were directed. Additionally, four saturation raids were made on the most important supply industries.

The first of these took place on 31 December 1944 when 72 aircraft from the Eighth Air Force attacked B&V. Although most of the bombs fell in the south-eastern sector of the yard area (on the East Hall and the Steinwerder Bank) the extensive damage considerably delayed section construction of the first Type XXVI Walter-boats. Of the Type XXI boats fitting out at the Steinwerder Bank, *U2532*, *U2530* and *U2537* were sunk; section 7 of *U2515* was hit and *U2547* and *U2556* suffered lesser damage on the building slips.

On 17 January 1945, this yard was attacked again by the Eighth Air Force, with 71 aircraft. Hits were scored by 132 high-explosive bombs over the entire yard area. Building Slip 9 alone received eight direct hits. Now, for the first time, a large number of boats lying at building slips were damaged: in particular, *U2557* was badly damaged by hits in the control room, *U2551* suffered moderate damage, while *U2542*, *U2544*, *U2545*, *U2546*, *U2547*, *U2548*, *U2550*, *U2555* and *U2556* suffered slight damage. Dock III, occupied by *U2515*, was sunk. *U2515*, which had been earmarked for the replacement of two sections damaged by

bomb hits on 31 December 1944, had been cut apart for this operation and was now capsized in sections. Dock V disintegrated. The east section, with *U2530*, which had recently been raised, was sunk. Also sunk were the salvage ships, *Hiev* and *Griep*, which were engaged in lifting *U2532*. Finally, *U2523* was sunk, while *U2541* and *U2534* were damaged. This attack also caused further delays to the first Type XXVI boat, *U4501*. Section construction could now not begin before the middle of March, which meant that delivery would not be possible before the middle of July 1945 at the very earliest. During February 1945, B&V were spared further attacks and most of the damaged boats were able to be repaired. Only the sunken *U2523* had to be completely written off. The Eighth Air Force now concentrated on central Germany, apparently in support of the Russian offensive.

Precision attacks on AG Weser in Bremen began on 17 February 1945. As had happened in 1943 against various steel works in the Ruhr, the RAF attacked the Weser yard using only 3–6 long-range Mosquitoes, achieving relatively great damage and a considerable loss in production. On 17 February, *U3042*, at Building Slip 1, suffered damage to the stern by a near-miss from a 254kg bomb, and this blocked-in *U3043*, lying behind it. More serious, during a raid on 22 February, was hit by a 2,032kg bomb on Building Slip 5 between the fore-ships of *U3052* and *U3048*. The bomb exploded approximately 4.5m above the ground, twisted the bow sections and forced *U3052* from its launching slip, blocking-in *U3053*, which was lying behind them. In a discussion on 23 February 1945, Dönitz drew Hitler's attention to this problem. The appropriate minute stated:

'The report of the renewed boomerang air attacks on the Deschimag U-boat construction yard in Bremen leads the Supreme C-in-C of the Navy to make the following points:

'As the [artificial] fog is totally ineffective at the considerable heights that these attacks are carried out — 9–11,000m — and as the anti-aircraft defence is of limited use, defensive measures must take place using jamming transmissions and night-fighters. The Supreme Commander of the Luftwaffe is arranging that two jamming transmitters be set up as speedily as possible in the area to the west of Bremen. They will be functional in approximately 8 days. The employment of fighters to hunt Mosquitoes during night attacks in the Bremen area seems urgently necessary. . . .'

On 24 February 1945, 195 bombers of the Eighth Air Force made a daylight attack on Deschimag, and *U3007*, which had just been cleared for final fitting-out, was sunk at the quay. Further damage was caused to a 100-ton and a 25-ton floating crane, and to the crane installation on the fitting-out quay.

On 25 and 27 February, and on 4 March 1945, further boomerang attacks were made by Mosquitoes, the most severe result of which was the sinking of Floating Dock V by near misses. On 11 March, the Eighth Air Force attacked Deschimag once again, with 403 aircraft, dropping 861 tons of bombs. A 254kg bomb tore through the outer hull of *U3060* and detonated beneath the boat,

Effects of air raids on employment at B + V, Hamburg, during the summer of 1943

Figures from USSBS report

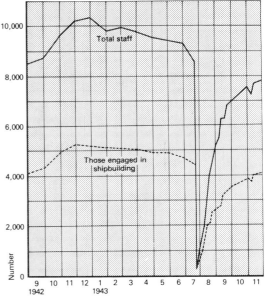

blocking-in *U3061* which was lying behind it. The impact of three bombs caused considerable damage to 4 boats on the building slips, and prevented or considerably delayed the slipway launch of 4 others. An additional consequence was, of course, that these building slip berths were not available for the boats that were scheduled to follow. The non-availability of Dock V was to have a considerable effect on new construction and maintenance work.

The last big attack by the Eighth Air Force on Deschimag took place on 30 March 1945, when 433 aircraft dropped 830 tons of bombs. No further damage was caused to the building slips, but 8 boats were lost in the fitting-out basin: *U72*, *U329*, *U430*, *U870*, *U884*, *U886* and the two new boats, *U3045* and *U3046*. A simultaneous attack was made on Wilhelmshaven, in which 916 tons of bombs were dropped. *U96*, *U429* and *U3508* were sunk, and the electricity power-station was badly damaged: since pumps could not be used because of the breakdown of the power supply, the docks began to overfill. In order that *U3008* could be kept floating in the dock, the open floor valves of the bilge installation had to be wedged tight in a makeshift manner. Then temporary cables were connected from *U3008* to the power-station. By using the boat's electrical installation, an emergency supply of current was made available until the power-station was functioning again.

On 11 March 1945, the Eighth Air Force began again to attack the harbour of Hamburg. A total of 466 aircraft dropped 983 tons of bombs on the area occupied by the Rhenania oil refineries. Severe damage was caused around the large 250-ton hammer-head crane at B&V, and the crane itself

Deployment of labour at DWK, 1944

Figures from USSBS report

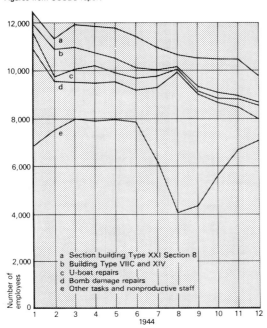

a Section building Type XXI Section 8
b Building Type VIIC and XIV
c U-boat repairs
d Bomb damage repairs
e Other tasks and nonproductive staff

Number of employees

1944

Deployment of labour at AG Weser

Figures from USSBS report

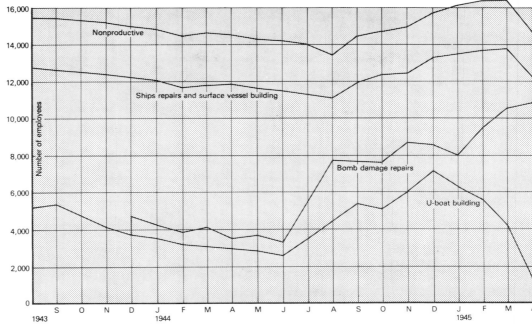

Number of employees

Nonproductive

Ships repairs and surface vessel building

Bomb damage repairs

U-boat building

1943   1944   1945

---

was destroyed by direct hits. At Building Slip 6, *U2549* and *U2550* were damaged and five high-explosive bombs fell on the unoccupied Building Slip 7. The next large attacks were carried out by the RAF, and were directed against the whole of Hamburg. On 31 March, 454 bombers dropped 2,217 tons of bombs; on 8 April, 414 aircraft dropped 1,481 tons of bombs; finally, on 9 April 1945, 424 aircraft dropped 1,571 tons of bombs. These attacks destroyed a large number of U-boats, as well as causing much destruction at B&V, Howaldt-Hamburg and, for the first time, DW, Finkenwerder. The attack of 31 March 1945 caused the greatest damage at DW, Finkenwerder: large fires in U-boat construction installation with destruction of the ship construction hangar for the Type XXIII section construction; two U-boat docks and a U-boat lifting installation sunk; *U350*, *U348* and *U1167* capsized and sunk; *U1131*, in its lifting installation, capsized; *U2340* sunk with its lifting installation. But the attack of 8 April was especially severe for B&V and Howaldt. A first report from B&V to the Armaments Inspectorate, Hamburg, stated laconically: 'At least 250 high-explosive bombs, 20 unexploded bombs, no deaths, two slightly wounded. Several boats [*U982*, *U2509*, *U2514* and *U2516*], Salvage Vessel 2 and Dock I sunk, other items severely damaged (e.g., salvage

ship *Ausdauer*). No victualling possibilities!' Howaldt-Hamburg suffered 52 direct hits, including hits on the stern of *U3502*, on Dock V, which held *U3512* and *U2519*, Salvage Vessel 5 and Dock II.

On 9 April, a precision attack by the RAF with 17 Lancasters on the large Finkenwerder shelter brought an end to attacks on U-boat installations in the Hamburg area. During this raid, two 10-ton 'Grand Slam' bombs and 15 5.5-ton 'Tallboy' bombs were dropped. Six of the latter penetrated the 3–3.5m-thick shelter covering of reinforced concrete; another exploded approximately 30m from the west wall of the shelter and twisted it. In all, Boxes 1, 2 and 5 were damaged in this raid. In Box 5, a lifting installation with 2 U-boats (*U677* and *U747*) was capsized.

Kiel provided the third focal-point of the Allied air offensive against U-boat yards in the early part of 1945. The Eighth Air Force made the first attack on 11 March, with 340 aircraft. No U-boats were hit. In their next attacks on 3 and 4 April, *U1221* at Howaldtswerke, Kiel and *U2542* and *U3505* at the Hindenburg Shore were sunk, and *U2516* was damaged at DWK. On 4 April, *U3003* was sunk by direct hits. These attacks, by approximately 700 aircraft, were the heaviest to date on the harbour of Kiel. The yard installations of GW and DWK were also hit. During the Führer Situation Discussion of 4 April 1945, Dönitz stated in connection with this (extract from a minute): 'The air attacks on Kiel on the 3rd and 4th April have given the Supreme C-in-C of the Navy proof that our opponents achieve better bombing results when they get a direct view of their target than when cloud cover is provided by use of the 'Rotterdam' Equipment.

This serves to confirm once again the continued value in providing smokescreens for objects to be protected.'

Two further severe attacks by the RAF on the nights of 9 and 13 April 1945, with 359 and 467 aircraft, set the seal on the destruction of DWK. During the raid on 9 April, *U2516* and *U1227* in Dock I were badly damaged by bomb hits, and *U1131* and *U3512* were sunk. At GW, a Type XXIII U-boat, *U4708*, was destroyed, three days before its commissioning. The final attacks made by the RAF on Kiel and Bremen were carried out in conjunction with the occupation of these cities by British troops; they were not aimed at U-boat production which had already come to a standstill.

Although much devastation had been caused in the yards, an overall look at the situation shows that, even in the early part of 1945, Allied air attacks could not actually prevent U-boat construction. The Type XXI section construction, especially, suffered little damage. From the fact that both the sensitive centres for this section construction, namely the unprotected production of sections 4 in Lübeck and of 3, 5, 6 and 9 in Vegesack were not attacked at all, one can conclude that details of new U-boat production were not known to the Allies, and that the lack of U-boats on the building slips at both these yards had clearly conveyed a misleading impression. The majority of boats lying at the building slips at the time of the capitulation were either undamaged or only slightly damaged. Frequently, damaged boats blocked-in other undamaged boats behind them, which meant that for some time these latter could not be used. The most crippling damage occurred to floating docks and floating cranes. The sinking of a large

Deployment of labour at Blohm and Voss, Hamburg, early in 1945

Figures from USSBS report

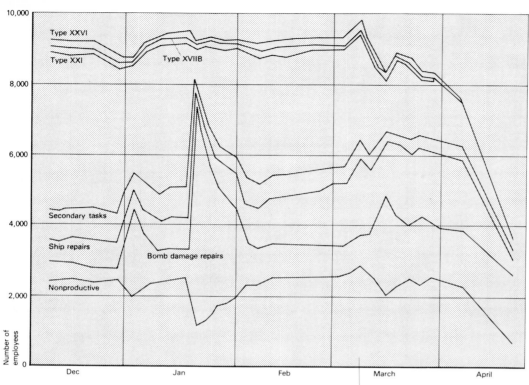

number of U-boats in harbours must be seen in the light of the fact that the harbours were considerably overcrowded and suffered obstructions during the latter stages of the war.

With regard to air attacks against the supply industries during the latter part of the war, only the attack on Hagen on the night of 2 December 1944 was particularly significant. Here, 43 high-explosive bombs and several hundred incendiaries fell on the yard complex of AFA, and destroyed approximately 50 per cent of the buildings. Especially badly hit were the lead works and the production shops for steel batteries. The track systems were completely destroyed, and shunting operations could not be carried out for several weeks. Following improvized repairs to the damaged buildings, the lead works was able to start restricted production again at the beginning of February 1945. However, the general transport position had become so acute that hardly any batteries produced by AFA-Hagen could reach the yards. Alongside the destruction of the railway network, the bombing of the Ruhr waterways had far-reaching effects on U-boat construction in the Bremen and Hamburg areas, and caused considerable delivery delays.

In the autumn of 1945, when interrogated about the effects of Allied air attacks on U-boat construction, the former Head of the Ship Construction Commission, Vizeadmiral Topp, stated:

'No stoppage of production was brought about by Allied air attacks until almost the end of the war. Germany succeeded in keeping the production of new U-boat construction at a considerable level until the beginning of 1945. From the beginning of 1945, it would have been very possible from the production point of view to recommence the U-boat campaign with the new, possibly very effective Types XXI and XXIII (and later on, also XXVI) . . . Destruction at U-boat yards and in the supply industry certainly caused a noticeable diminution of production, but never an effective cessation of production. That this was so is due to U-boat production, including section production from May 1945, being carried out in the whole western area in bomb-proof shelters. Serious stoppages in U-boat production occurred only when the yards in Danzig were no longer available — through the Russian advance, and, in Hamburg, through the British advance. New U-boat construction in Bremen had been suspended, however, following the 'boomerang' bombing of Deschimag as early as March 1945, i.e., prior to the occupation of Bremen. . . . A greater concentration of bomb attacks on bottleneck supplies for U-boat construction (batteries, periscopes, part-sections and sections that were only produced in one particular place) and, above all, on the single production centre for hydrogen peroxide in Lauterberg (Type XXVI) would have been more effective in shortening the U-boat campaign than

the scattered attacks on the larger cities and their neighbourhoods and on the overall armaments industry.'

It must, however be doubted whether, from the production point of view, the early part of 1945 could have seen a full-scale resumption of the U-boat campaign. Furthermore, the Navy's supplies of diesel fuel, which had remained at about the minimum-necessary level of 100,000 tons since the middle of 1941, had become inadequate following the loss of Rumanian and Hungarian oilfields and the destruction of the Hydrierwerke. Topp was also certainly over-optimistic concerning the prospects for undisturbed U-boat production from May 1945.

On 27 March 1945, a special British formation of 17 Lancasters attacked the almost completed 'Valentin' assembly shelter. Thirteen 'Grand Slam' (10-ton) and 4 'Tallboy' (5.5-ton) bombs were dropped. Two 10-ton bombs struck the still un-reinforced 4.5m covering and the tremendous explosion caused it to collapse over Assembly Stations 5 and 8. Although the major part of the explosion dispersed upwards, the destrucion of roofs occasioned a considerable interruption in production, because the system had only a single-track rail-launching system. While this shelter, with its proposed reinforced roof of 7m thickness, would have been immune against 10-ton bombs, the section shelters, with much thinner coverings, could not have withstood these bombs, as was shown in the bombing of 'Fink II' on 9 April 1945. Neither were roof reinforcements an absolute remedy in the long run, as was proved when a near-miss caved-in the west wall of 'Fink II'. Furthermore, the bomb hits in front of 'Elbe II' on 8 April 1945, in which the anti-splinter aprons were shattered and the interior workshop walls forced inwards, clearly show that if further such attacks had been carried out, the shelters, with their concentration of production methods, could easily have become traps. Only the thwarting of precision attacks by fighter defence and jamming transmissions could have allowed U-boat production in shelters to continue successfully in 1945.

THE FINAL PROGRAMMES, 1944–45

The Construction Programme of 1 June 1944

The two new focal points of concentration — the Walter Type XXVI and the Seehund midget U-boats (page 287) — required a reallocation of armament capacity, and due account had to be taken of the long-term plans for series production of Type XXI and XXIII. The new programme, as set out by the Armaments Minister on 1 June 1944, called for deliveries as shown in Table 48. To this had to be added a rapidly-growing Seehund production from September 1944, which was supposed to deliver 80 boats per month by December 1944 and, following the commencement of production at Ulm in the early part of 1945, would reach approximately 100 boats per month. The overall programme now amounted to 580 Type

XXI, 260 Type XXIII, 100 Type XXVI plus 1,000 Seehund. To cope with this, steel construction would have to supply monthly from the middle of 1944:

22 sets of crude sections Type XXI = 17,300 tons or 2 million man hours.
10 sets of crude sections Type XXIII = 900 tons or 0.2 million man hours.
Total: 18,200 tons or 2.2 million man hours.

By the end of 1944, 257 sets of crude sections for Type XXI and 95 sets for Type XXIII were to be ready. The fact that steel deliveries reached record proportions in August 1944 shows that the steel construction industry realized what was expected of it, even if, during the initial phases, many crude sections were incomplete. The shipbuilding industry was unable to emulate this.

The comprehensive foreign building programme for Type XXIII was frequently revised and progressively reduced in the light of changing circumstances. After Nikolayev and Odessa had been retaken by the Red Army early in 1944, the contract for Type XXIII was transferred to Linz Schiffbauwerft on 1 May 1944. But, just two months later, Linz was rejected on the grounds that it would take so long to produce boats there that there would be little chance of using them for operations in the Black Sea. At the same time, the delivery quota for Type XXIII boats for use in the Mediterranean was considerably reduced. While it was still intended, on 1 May 1944, to liquidate the whole programme by March 1945, and have only a follow-up programme of 3 boats per month from DW in Hamburg-Finkenwerder and 2 boats per month at each of the other yards, just eight weeks later only a considerably restricted construction was envisaged at foreign yards, namely 18 boats in Toulon, 18 in Genoa and only 7 in Monfalcone. If necessary, further construction with complete sections sent from Germany could then follow.

By the beginning of July 1944, German steel construction firms had sent sections for a total of eight boats to Italy, but these were found to be incomplete on arrival at the yards. Certain missing components and the sections for a further 8 boats were to have been produced in Italy. In May 1944, construction for the first boats began in Genoa and Monfalcone, but it cannot be established that any assembly took place at these yards and, at the beginning of July, it was decided to dispense with

Monfalcone. When the Allies invaded France, Toulon became untenable, and the contract which had been allocated to Toulon was transferred to DW at Hamburg-Finkenwerder on 7 July 1944.

After it had been decided not to continue building transport and supply U-boats, GW, Kiel, was involved in Type XXIII construction: GW and DW, Hamburg-Finkenwerder, were now to bear the weight of the entire Type XXIII programme, following the loss of almost all foreign yards. So that GW could embark on production at the earliest possible moment, in addition to the contract for the 48 U-boats U4701–U4748, they were given the assembly construction of boats U2332 and U2333, the sections for which had already been produced at DW. GW was to deliver both these boats by August 1944, with series production following from October 1944, and a monthly delivery of 5 boats from each yard.

On 12 July 1944, Merker appointed Johann Köhnenkamp, Director of the Stülcken Sohn yard of Hamburg as 'Supreme Authority for the XXIII Programme', because 'the urgency of the new construction programme Type XXIII' demanded extraordinary measures for its handling.

With regard to Type XXI, the principal task now was to achieve the planned objectives without further delays and to complete the changeover to construction in shelters. While delays had been caused by bottlenecks in supplies during the initial building phase, now once again — and in increasing measure — the delays resulted from a lack of skilled workers at the yards, and the intended call-up of workers classed as dispensable (special call-up) hung over industrial firms like the sword of Damocles. Thus, the plan of 1 June 1944 was not to be fulfilled, and delivery dates had to be put off time and time again. At the Nineteenth Armament Discussion on 7 September 1944, the programme shown in Table 49 was laid down. It was to run from 7 September 1944.

While the production planning of the IBG now had to formulate afresh delivery plans for various supplies and disposition plans for section construction in the U-boat shelters, Merker, on 13 September 1944, held a meeting of directors of those yards involved in the U-boat programmes, both to co-ordinate matters and to stress their obligation to fulfil the new programme. At this meeting he stated:

'Every couple of weeks the programme crumbles a little more. In spite of the many views to the contrary, the HAS is of the opinion that the output figures could be considerably higher if all bodies involved put their full energies and their full enthusiasm into the stated programme. In effect, the yards have blamed poor production on lack of supplies. That means partly by the bottleneck in electric motors, partly by incomplete delivery of components, which have to be built-in later than the timetable had envisaged. In the steel construction firms there may be a bottleneck suddenly in fore-parts of the ships. This bottleneck is quickly settled.

'At the beginning of production, the bottleneck in the work force was not too decisive a factor. It began to have an effect when the programme called for an increase in numbers. It must therefore not be left out of our reckoning that, as the programme increases in tempo and with production experience growing, a considerable decline in work hours will follow. . . . It can be shown that the present shortage of workers, adduced by certain yards as the reason for the non-fulfilment of their programme, is principally to be attributed to inadequate preparation of the practical construction preliminaries. Correct planning suitable for the tasks in hand, construction preliminaries, and the adoption of practical measures etc., can bring about the saving of many productive work hours. It is unthinkable theoretically to formulate constructional preliminaries for a programme that is thwarted in its practical realization by such happenings and has to suffer variations and immediate modifications. With energy and with positive organizational thinking, production can be increased significantly. Poor production would have been significantly better if correct application of organizational principles had been made and all potential realized and, likewise for the future, to ensure that the programme delivery promises are kept to, the yards must increase their output considerably.'

A discussion followed, at which the various yards stated their positions:

1. KMW, Wilhelmshaven:
'KMW, Wilhelmshaven, draws attention to the interrupted and irregular delivery of steel containers, which has meant the loss recently of 3 whole days production. KMW also levels the

Table 48. The Ministerial Construction Programme of 1 June 1944

	1944 April	May	June	July	Aug	Sept	Oct	Nov	Dec	1945 Jan	Feb	March	April	May	June	July	Aug	Sept	Oct	Nov	Dec
Type XXI	—	2	5	9	18	26	29	33	33	30	28	22	22	22	22	22	22	22	22	22	22
Type XXIII	—	3	5	8	12	15	18	18	18	17	16	10	10	10	10	10	10	10	10	10	10
Type XXVI	—	—	—	—	—	—	—	—	—	—	—	2	—	2	4	8	10	12	12	12	12

Table 49. Revised construction programme of 7 September 1944

	1944 May	June	July	Aug	Sept	Oct	Nov	Dec	1945 Jan	Feb	March	April	May	June	July	Aug	Sept	Oct	Nov	Dec
Type XXI	—	1	7	5	14	28	32	33	33	30	28	22	22	22	22	22	22	22	22	22
Type XXIII	—	2	4	6	9	9	11	15	15	14	10	10	10	10	10	10	10	10	10	10
Type XXVI	—	—	—	—	—	—	—	—	—	—	1	1	—	2	3	8	10	12	12	12

criticism that, a short time ago, 6 completed sections were not collected. In August, KMW lost 2 whole days work through air-raid alarm. KMW is to deliver 21 sections by the end of September, and achieve its production target in the following month. Merker reproaches KMW with the fact that they have not yet moved into the shelter in Hamburg. KMW argues that they are faced with the alternative either of delivering the required sections or of moving into the shelter. Becker points out that, by the end of September, 22 rather than 21 sections are to be delivered, as one section that was not delivered in August will be added. KMW indicates delivery bottlenecks in: friction clutches, shaft brakes, air filters, 8 electric motors, 5 control panels, electric motor fans, etc. KMW asserts that only 40 per cent of fittings are available for assembly purposes, and that of 500 soldiers promised, only 150 have been supplied by this date. The previously stated shortage of welders will be made good by the middle and end of October. KMW agrees that 22 sections instead of 21 will be delivered by the end of September. Use will be made of Kemper to resolve transport problems.'

2. Seebeck, Wesermünde:
'Seebeck states that keeping to programme dates in the face of lack of welders of Grade 1 and Grade 2 proficiencies makes for difficulties. Seebeck will be able to deliver only 18 in September instead of 24, 20 in October instead of 24, 23 in November instead of 26, and 26 in December. Seebeck blames this non-achievement of quota on the shortage of 20 welders, but for whom the set target could have been achieved. Schmelter has received the request from Saur to look into the question of welders together with an appointed commission, and to remedy this. Merker and Saur order that the programme of 7 September be carried out.'

3. Bremer Vulkan, Bremen-Vegesack:
'Kabellac states that he has currently 394 welders, of whom 16 are required for plastering work, leaving 378 welders for section construction. These would suffice if he did not have to take on additional work, and he is 70 welders short for such work. Kabellac has appointed personnel to be trained as welders as follows: 8 in April, 29 in May, 64 in June, 96 in July. Currently, 112 men are being trained in 3 shifts. Nevertheless, it will be November before sufficient welders are available to maintain the programme. Kabellac cites shortage of oxygen as an additional bottleneck.'

4. Deschimag, Bremen:
'Target: 38 boats by the end of the year and 7 boats by the end of August. Only 4 have been delivered. Damage by air attack has been cited as the reason for reduced delivery. The programme of 5 in September, 9 in October, 11 in November, 12 in December could not be realized owing to shortages among the labour force. The allocated concentration camp inmates were completely unsuitable for assembly work. Changes in the interior operational organization could not be carried out so quickly because Deschimag, Bremen, was involved in important engine construction as well as in shipbuilding. Merker makes the comparison between Deschimag and B&V with regard to their number of workers and finds that B&V, although it

has 1,000 fewer workers, achieves 51 boats, that is to say over a dozen boats more than Deschimag. Professor Bauer points to poor black-out conditions and premature stoppages for air-raid alerts. Saur has established that the programme imposed by Merker on Deschimag is too stringent.'

5. Deutsche Werft, Hamburg:
'Dr. Scholz has still not received the programme of 7 September in respect of sections 3 and 6, and quotes delivery dates that are incompatible with the target. Saur and Merker have decided that decisions will be made tomorrow concerning September and October targets, but that from October the programme of 7 September must be adhered to.'

6. Blohm & Voss, Hamburg:
'Walter Blohm states an assembly time of 64 days instead of the planned 56 days, and justifies this extra time by the poor state of finish in sections that have been supplied. B&V will deliver 7 boats instead of 8 in September, 8 instead of 9 in October. By 13 September 3 boats less than the quota will have been hauled up the slipway. In addition to this, a further 3½ boats will not be able to be hauled up according to timetable on account of non-delivery of sections, thus making a total shortage in the planned quota of 6½ boats. There is a special shortage of section 2 from KMW, Wilhelmshaven; blockade by mines prevented their delivery and, when delivered, they were in a poor state of completion. Blohm also points to a compulsory curtailment of lighting [power cuts during the night shift], which has lost the production of approximately 1,000 men. The condition of sections that arrive are as bad as they were formerly. At present, only approximately 56 per cent of fittings are in position and only 38 per cent of tubing. Blohm states that the expenditure in work hours for subsequent incorporation of tubing is something like 2½ times that of such work done at the section yards. Saur uses this as proof of the immense advantage of the section method of construction. Saur also states that the question of supplies shortages is being cleared-up by a thorough investigation and subsequent settlement of the shortages by a commission with participation by the Armaments Delivery Offices, and that he expects a report within a fortnight to settle this bottleneck in a definite way. Saur states further that the night shift at B&V can be retained by intervention with the Air Raid Protection authorities responsible for lighting restrictions.'

'7. Howaldtswerke, Hamburg:
'The programme of 15 in September, 16 in October, November and December will not be achieved by the Howaldtswerke, Hamburg, because approximately 50 per cent of the supplies will not arrive punctually and it will therefore not be possible to carry out the sequence working as planned. Howaldtswerke asserts that 26,500 work hours are currently having to be expended per section instead of the 24,000 hours set out in the planned sequence working, that they themselves are having to improvise a sizeable portion of the missing supplies and that they are short of 60 coppersmiths for these tasks. The Howaldtswerke is additionally concerned over the fact that, during air attacks,

working time in the shelter cannot be used to the full because the shelter has to serve at this time as a personnel shelter, and the work timetable is consequently hampered. Schmauterer from the Armaments Staff has been required by Saur to investigate this problem and to rectify this particular prevention of production. Merker blames the poor practical work preparations and inadequate pre-planning of the work timetable. Howaldtswerke points out that blame for poor organization should really be levelled at the missing supplies. Furthermore, they themselves had expended 131,000 hours in an effort to resolve supply bottlenecks. Attempts, however, would still be made to keep to the programme.'

8. Howaldtswerke, Kiel:
'Section 1: a target of 20 for September, 25 for October, 26 each for November and December. November and December would be achieved, but not September and October on account of the effects of heavy air-raid damage. Dealing with unexploded bombs alone has accounted for 10 days. Workshops are up to 60 per cent burned out. At the moment, there is no railway line connection to the works. 50 per cent of work area is without a roof; out of 37 electric trucks, only 2 are in use; out of 36 hangar cranes, only 9 are in use. During September, only 8 of section 1 were delivered instead of 20. Becker states that this will suffice because initial work can be done in other quarters. Saur and Merker have ordered that the October target of 25 must be kept. Saur has requested, as Liaison Officer for the Supreme C-in-C of the Navy, that soldiers be made available for the purpose of clearing débris from the Howaldtswerke, Kiel. Up to now, the Navy has made available as a vanguard only 130 men. Many times this number are necessary.'

9. Deutsche Werke, Kiel:
'The programme of 7 September will be adhered to with the exception of September, when only 17 instead of 20 will be delivered. The missing 3 will be delivered 3 days later. The 60-ton crane has been out of use for 16 days. This has meant that 10 fore-ships could not take their place punctually in the sequence lines as planned. Only 20 out of 250 red dockets have been cleared to date.'

10. Lübecker Flender-Werke:
'Flender-Werke will deliver fewer sections than required by the following quantities: 4 in September, 5 in October, and one section each in November and December. Bunte cites shortages of oxygen and in the work force as the reasons. The shortage of oxygen has been made good. Through the intervention of Dr. Wolf, 40 bottles per day will be delivered by DW, Hamburg. Saur decrees that the stipulation of 7 September is to be kept.'

11. Deutsche Werke, Gotenhafen:
'DW, Gotenhafen, states the target for sections 6 and 7 will be met by the required date.'

12. Danziger Werft:
'The Danziger Werft says its programme is on time.'

13. Schichau, Danzig:
'Schichau, Danzig says its programme is up to schedule as regards sections. As regards assembly, it will achieve 4 instead of 5 in September, 8 instead of 9 in November and December. Saur orders the

achievement of target for November and December.'

14. Deutsche Werft, Hamburg (Type XXIII):
'Scholz asserts that he is not familiar with the new target of 7 September. Saur commands the intervention of Dr. Wolf and yard delegates to investigate and adopt the strongest measures.'

15. Germaniawerft, Kiel (Type XXIII):
'Germaniawerft will deliver monthly from October 1/3/6, and attributes non-achievement of target to the considerable delays caused by air-raid alarms. Schmauterer is to investigate air-raid alarms also in Lübeck.

'Saur demands that all yards inform Schmelter within 3 × 24 hours in all details how many women can be used in building work by the application of the strongest measures. When the yards make this declaration, the possibility of providing accommodation is to be stated. Desch is immediately to introduce acceptance engineers into the section construction yards to receive deliveries of sections.'

Following a reappraisal of the state of shelter construction, and the delay of four weeks to the commencement of the Type XXVI programme because of late completion of drawings, the construction plan at the beginning of October 1944 was as shown in Table 50. Assembly work on Type XXI at Deschimag was to cease with the 82nd boat, and be replaced by Type XXI section construction in May 1945. The 18 boats that remained from the contracts dated 6 November 1943 and 6 May 1944 were transferred to Bremer Vulkan in the 'Valentin' shelter. Assembly work was to cease at B&V with the 108th boat in July 1945, so that series construction of Type XXVI could commence. Of the remaining 154 boats of B&V's contracts, Bremer Vulkan would receive 101 and Schichau, Danzig, 53 boats. On 27 September 1944, these transfers were given to both yards as new contracts, which meant that they were now committed to delivering 195 boats; however, 11 boats were cancelled at Schichau, which left only 184 boats under contract. Type XXI section construction for Bremer Vulkan ('Valentin') was to follow from February 1945 in the 'Hornisse' shelter (sections 3, 5 and 6) of Deschimag, and from June 1945 in the 'Wespe' shelter (sections 1, 2, 4, 7 and 8) of KMW, Wilhelmshaven.

The following construction centres were now envisaged for Type XXVI section construction.
Section 1: KMW, Wilhelmshaven in 'Fink II', Box 3, with steel construction supplied by Stülcken.
Section 2: B&V in 'Fink II', Box 4 and 5.
Section 3 and bridge superstructure: Howaldt-Hamburg in 'Elbe II'.
Sections 4 and 5: DW in Hamburg-Finkenwerder (4 unprotected, 5 in 'Fink II', Box 2).

Initially, assembly work would then take place in an unprotected condition at B&V. Building Slip 7 was intended for the first 3 series boats; Building Slip 6 for the next 3. However, the first 4 boats were to be built completely by B&V and, in detail, sections 1, 4 and 5 in Engine Factory II and the large sections 2 and 3 in the yard's east hall. Assembly work would then take place on large work-pontoons beneath the hammer-head crane.

Type XXIII assembly work at DW in Hamburg-Finkenwerder was to cease after the 67th boat in March 1945. This would allow commencement of Type XXVI section construction in the Finkenwerder shelter. Type XXIII section construction and assembly work only then would be carried out in the Kiel area by GW in the 'Kilian' and 'Konrad' shelters. The contractor for the first 140 boats was still DW; for the subsequent 120 boats.

The main stumbling-block was still the bottleneck in labour. In order to reduce the amount that ship construction lagged behind steel construction the latter — under the slogan 'Helping Hand' — was ordered to lend welders and fitters to ship construction from 15 October 1944. This loan was intended to last only until 20 December 1944, but it was extended, in part, to 31 January 1945. The impending special call-up (SE-Aktionen) of those born up to 1906 was to be countered by an increased use of female labour. With regard to existing difficulties, the minutes of a meeting of the Naval Armaments Staff on 11 October 1944 stated among other points:

'B&V is currently experiencing considerable difficulties in hauling sections to the slipway on account of mining operations. In connection with this, HAS should try to procure more steamships for carrying sections. The Reich's Sea Commission for Merchant Service has given approval for one steamship. In addition, two Finnish lighters can be used.

'Welders — Additional Measures at Steel Construction.

'Merker: HAS calculates that steel construction has worked 400,000 hours fewer on ring-sections than were laid down. Even now, on the average, 400 work hours per ring-section are being lost. Therefore, if steel construction now remedies this it must make good the hours that it has already lost.

'Desch: Steel construction cannot make better deliveries as it has a shortage of many supplies.

'Merker: The 400,000 hours that have been saved have now to be made good by the yards; that means 1,000 men — 2 months. That is a fact which has to be noted against steel construction.

'Use of Women:

'Merker: 11,000 currently in the yards, with yards requiring an additional 8,000. That is to say 14 per cent of personnel. According to available reports, the percentage of women including those requested but not yet actually employed are: Neptun 28.6 per cent, Howaldt-Hamburg 10.1 per cent, Seebeck 7.8 per cent, B&V 7 per cent, Kiel Area 15—20 per cent, KMW 16.5 per cent, DW 9.3 per cent, Deschimag 12.6 per cent, Eastern Area 20 per cent. Merker is of the opinion that, on the average, the yards should use 20 per cent.

Dr. Schmitz (Neptun): But the use of a large number of women makes for many difficulties. Women complain about the lack of clothing and footwear. There are additionally severe problems with open-air working, as there is no assembly hangar at Neptun.

'Merker: Hamburg and Bremen have especially large percentages of those born in 1906. They will therefore have to take on in good time especially large numbers of women and concentration-camp inmates. One must anticipate the call-up of all men from 1906 and later with the exception of a few key skills.

'Desch requests a decree by 15.11. that welders born in 1906 and later will be replaced by new trainees. Merker is releasing personnel from later years from the construction offices.'

At a subsequent Naval Armaments Meeting on 25 October 1944, Saur stated with regard to this problem:

'Ship construction must take a unified attitude in this. At the moment there are still 26,000 men born in 1906 and later in the yards. A breakdown in production by their call-up is unthinkable. During the First World War, the iron-producing industry employed 17 per cent of women; today 25 per cent. Yards should use not just 20 per cent but 40 per cent of women, even in repair work. . . . Russian women should be used not simply in subsidiary work, but in the main aspects of work.

Table 50. Revised construction programme of October 1944

	1944 to Sept	Oct	Nov	Dec	1945 Jan	Feb	March	April	May	June	July	Aug	Sept	Oct	Nov	Dec
Type XXI:																
Deschimag 'Valentin'	8	5	9	12	12	12	12	9	3	—	—	—	—	—	—	—
B&V	—	—	—	—	—	—	—	3	9	12	12	14	14	14	14	14
Schichau	12	9	9	15	12	11	11	9	8	6	6	—	—	—	—	—
Total	26	21	27	36	31	31	31	29	28	26	26	22	22	22	22	22
Type XXVI:																
B&V	—	—	—	—	—	—	—	1	1	—	2	4	8	10	12	12
Type XXIII:																
DW	17	7	10	9	8	8	8	—	—	—	—	—	—	—	—	—
GW	—	1	3	7	7	7	7	7	10	10	10	10	10	10	10	10
Total	17	8	13	16	15	15	15	7	10	10	10	10	10	10	10	10

Distribution of labour at naval shipyards in 1944.

Distribution of man hours for U-boat construction in 1944.

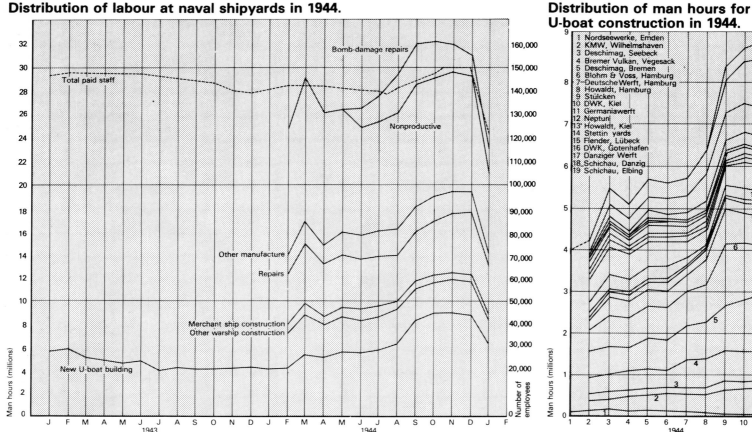

Table 51. Revised programme, 18 October 1944

	1944 to Sept	Oct	Nov	Dec	1945 Jan	Feb	March	April	May	June	July	Aug	Sept	Oct	Nov	Dec
Type XXI:	26	18	26	32	33	33	33	33	26	26	26	22	22	22	22	22
Type XXVI:	—	—	—	—	—	—	—	1	1	—	—	2	4	8	10	12
Type XXIII:	17	7	12	14	14	14	12	10	10	10	10	10	10	10	10	10

Table 52. The New Construction Plan, end October 1944

Type	Construction yard	1944 Oct	Nov	Dec	1945 Jan	Feb	March	April	May	June	July	Aug	Sept	Oct	Nov	Dec
VIIC/41	Flensburger, SBG	—	2	1	1	1	1	1	1	1	—	—	—	—	—	—
	Other yards	—	2	2	—	—	—	—	—	—	—	—	—	—	—	—
IXD/42	AG Weser	—	—	—	1	1	—	—	—	—	—	—	—	—	—	—
XVIIB	B&V	—	—	1	2	2	—	—	—	—	—	—	—	—	—	—
XVIIK	GW	—	—	—	—	—	—	—	—	—	1	—	—	—	—	—
XX	GW	—	—	—	—	—	—	—	—	—	—	—	—	—	1	1	1
XXI	B&V	9	5	12	12	12	12	.	.	.	.	.	.	.	.	.
	AG Weser	5	7	9	11	12	12	.	.	.	.	.	.	.	.	.
	Schichau, Danzig	3	7	8	8	8	8	.	.	.	.	.	.	.	.	.
	Bremer Vulkan	—	—	—	—	—	—	.	.	.	.	.	.	.	.	.
XXIII	DW	5	12	9	8	8	8	—	—	.	.	.	.	.	.	.
	GW	1	2	5	6	6	7	10	10	10	10	10	10	10	10	10
XXVI	B&V	—	—	—	—	—	—	1	1	—	—	2	4	8	10	12
127 (Seehund)	GW	17	25	25	25	24	23	6	—	—	—	—	—	—	—	—
	Schichau, Elbing	17	37	45	45	45	45	45	45	45	45	45	45	45	45	45
	Klöckner, Ulm	—	3	10	10	11	12	29	35	35	35	35	35	35	35	35

Note. A dot signifies 'unknown', a dash 'no delivery'.

'Saur orders that, within a fortnight, the Labour Unit of the Armaments Staff should set 40,000 women to work in the yards.' This was not implemented, however; Dönitz obtained permission from Hitler on 31 October 1944 to exempt yard personnel from the special call-up and all further draftings.

The pressure of delivery dates for the new construction programme had meanwhile had the effect of increasingly pushing repair work into the background. In the short term, the repair organization had to supply urgently needed tonnage for the numerous operational and transport undertakings, particularly in the Baltic. Concerning this, Saur stated on 25 October:

'*Repairs:* Repair work is a special concern of the Navy's and, according to a direction of Speer's, is one step above new constructions. One notices psychological inhibitions in all places, but repair work must be given preference.

'He draws comparisons with locomotive construction and tank construction and demands that HAS make a basic research into the repair question. Efforts must be made to use once again the smallest yards and repair undertakings that are still capable of such work.

'He demands comradeship and mutual support along the single chosen way.

'He will take to task any firms that oppose the goal.

'Every opportunity must be taken with all possible resources to protect work from air attack. . . .'

But, even with such threatening words further delivery delays were not to be avoided. As early as 18 October, therefore, a new plan had to be issued in which the shortages to December 1944 would be made good by a greater production at the beginning of 1945. The start of series construction of Type XXVI had to be delayed by a further month.

The yard delegates regarded the scheduled deliveries of Type XXI for November and December 1944 as impossible, because insufficient sections could be brought to the ways. As was usually the case, this excuse was not immediately recognized by Merker and Desch, who invariably believed that they could rectify an insufficiency of material items by organizational methods. The new construction plan of the end of October 1944 did, however, take account of some part of the reduced production expected for Type XXI. It was not clear whether, and how, the quantities could have been made good in the following months. A decision regarding production of Type XXI from April 1945 was, therefore, postponed.

In order to do something about the constant delays occasioned by the delivery of incomplete or inadequately-built sections, Merker authorized engineers in the assembly yards, by circular letter on 14 November 1944, to refuse acceptance of incomplete sections. In the interpretation of this decree, a section was considered to be complete when it could be shown that all the items sent by a section yard contained all necessary fittings. To assist in the assessment, therefore, the Procurement Department of HAS sent a fortnightly list of bottlenecks to various yards. enumerating those

components that could not be delivered punctually to section yards. If items were refused on grounds of incomplete fittings, this had to be reported immediately to the delegate responsible for the section yard and to the Special Committee for U-Boats, together with an estimate of work necessary for rectification and the extent of the delay that this would cause. The amount of work involved was calculated by the appointed engineer in the section yard. The Special Committee for U-Boats then decided the final hauling-up date at the assembly yard. If, as a result of sections being refused, blame could be apportioned to a section yard, Merker reserved the right to take special measures 'for such blame must be considered as damaging to our waging of war'.

which had been heavily bombed, was rendered adequate for the purpose by a drastic curtailment of all necessary transportation. The password for preferential consignments was 'Tanks'; consignments with the password 'Navy' had secondary priority. While most of the yards had supplies of materials because of the considerable delays in deliveries, the first noticeable effects were severe shortages of coal and power. A minute from a meeting of the Navy Armaments Staff on 27 October 1944 stated: 'The supply of coal at Seebeck is sufficient only until 31.10. Working will now have to be restricted to an 8-hour day'. And on 1 November 1944, it was noted:

'As the situation in the Ruhr has now become critical by the loss of 70 per cent of production,

---

The revised organization of the armament and equipment branches of the Navy, November 1944

Supreme C-in-C of the Navy (Dönitz)   Reichsminister for Armament and Ammunition (Speer)

Chief of Navy Armament (Backenköhler)   Armaments staff (Saur)

Head Office for Warship Construction (K) (Ruge) —— Ship Construction Commission (Topp) —— Main Committee for Ship Construction (HAS) (Merker)

Section shipbuilding and mechanical engineering (Heimberg)   Committees for U-boats (Oelfken): motor torpedo-boats, torpedo-boats, minesweepers and landing-craft   Special committee for U-boats (Sperling) Committees for minesweepers, torpedo-boats, wooden boats and merchantmen

K I U (Aschmoneit) ——

K II U (Oelfken)   Construction inspectorate

Central construction offices U-boats: Ingenieurbüro Glückauf (IBG) (Fischer) Minesweepers: Ingenieurbüro East, Königsberg Landing-craft: Ingenieurburo West, Walsum

---

In November 1944, in connection with more wide-ranging personnel changes in the Supreme Naval Command, a new organizational chain of command was set up in Armament and Equipment branches of the Navy.

'The Restricted Immediate Programme'
On 11 September 1944, the United States First Army reached the border of Germany, north of Trier, but German resistance now began to increase. The tenacious defence of the mouth of the Scheldt and of the Aachen area thwarted Allied plans for a quick occupation of western Germany. Continuation of the war effort was unthinkable while this direct threat was posed to the Ruhr, and a counter-offensive into Belgium was planned as a method of easing it. In order to take part in this important battle, battered and weary armoured divisions had to be reorganized and supplied with ammunition and fuel, and all the resources of the Ruhr were to be geared to a powerful armament effort to aid this undertaking. The railway network,

construction workers and other skilled workers will be drafted in large numbers into the Ruhr. The very continuation of current production undertakings and the alleviation of bomb damage is therefore seriously being placed in jeopardy. The non-arrival of steel items from the Ruhr makes a basic change of programme necessary. Herr Desch is preparing a new, essentially smaller programme. A 45-hour week has now been introduced at Deschimag. There will be no working on Saturday and Sunday. The tramway system in Bremen is not working from today through lack of electricity. All yards report difficulties in procuring of wagons.'

However, during the next months, thanks to foggy weather, the assembly yards managed to achieve something like their targets for the first time. In December 1944, 28 Type XXI, 6 Type XXIII and one each of Type VIIC/41 and XVIIB were delivered. This made a total of 36 U-boats or 47,981 tons of U-boat tonnage (excluding midget boats), i.e., more than three times the monthly average between autumn 1941 and summer 1944.

However, it was evident to Merker that this high rate of delivery could not be maintained. It had resulted from a large armament effort in the summer, contained some overspill from the poor delivery situation of November and, in the meantime, the position had changed, especially with regard to steel supplies. It was therefore decided that a new plan ('Restricted Immediate Programme') should be drawn up, based almost solely on items already available from steel construction. According to this, it should be possible to build a total of 350 Type XXI and 135 Type XXIII boats by the autumn of 1945. In reports made at the beginning of January 1945 by the Main Committees for Ship Construction, Steel Construction and Electro-Technology to the Industrial Control Section of the Technical Office, the conditions necessary for this new plan were evaluated and a picture was drawn of the state of production at that time:

'The extent of the ship construction programme is really decided by the bottlenecks in steel construction. In order to fulfil the ship construction programme authorized by Hitler in 1943, including the Hansa programme, a monthly delivery of 55,000 tons of steel are necessary, of which 46,000 tons are ships' plates. However, the average amount of steel delivered up to September 1944 was only 39,000 tons. In October, 31,000 tons were delivered. In November, as the result of almost no shipments from the Ruhr, a mere 11,000 tons. Consequently, in December 1944 an immediate programme was decided upon which should permit the delivery of 350 boats of Type XXI and 135 boats of Type XXIII by July/August 1945. For Type XXI, steel construction received by 31 December 1944, 225,000 tons from the rolling mills and 7,000 tons by HAS allocation, making a total of 232,000 tons of steel. Steel construction despatched 2,000 tons of this amount to the yards for outer hulls and pressure hulls for crude sections I and VIII constructed at the yards. This meant they retained 230,000 tons. Production up to 31 December 1944 was reported by Steel Construction as:
Crude Section I: 153 constructed and 31 incomplete, i.e., total 184 each of 37 tons=6,808 tons.
Pressure Hull II: total 231 each of 59 tons=13,629 tons.
Pressure Hull III: total 230 each of 69 tons=15,870 tons.
Pressure Hull IV: total 254 each of 48 tons=12,192 tons.
Pressure Hull V: total 231 each of 86 tons=19,866 tons.
Pressure Hull VI: total 213 each of 96 tons=20,488 tons.
Pressure Hull VII: total 245 each of 43 tons=10,535 tons.
Crude Section VIII: 133 constructed, 50 incomplete, i.e., total 183 each of 50 tons=9,150 tons.
Total steel used in construction: 108,538 tons.
Additionally, the following outer hulls were supplied for crude sections:
Part II: 266 each of 24 tons=5,424 tons.
Part III: 227 each of 20 tons=4,500 tons.

Part IV: 238 each of 11 tons=2,618 tons.
Part V: 224 each of 29 tons=6,496 tons.
Part VI: 248 each of 21 tons=5,208 tons.
Part VII: 246 each of 17 tons=4,182 tons.
Total: 28,468 tons.
This gives a total amount of 137,006 tons. The portion supplied by the steel construction firms up to 31 December 1944 amounted, however, to 146,000 tons because as a result of different bases of calculation, the total weight of steel was approximately 7 per cent higher than the quoted amounts. Of the rest of the material, amounting to approximately 83,400 tons, a further 3,400 tons was delivered to the yards. This left 80,000 tons. However, for a further 100 sets of crude sections, an additional 95,000 tons would be necessary, that is to say 15,000 tons more than we calculate is available without taking into account amounts lost by enemy action. In the estimation of the Main Committee for Steel Construction, 17,000 tons must be provided additionally for the immediate programme for Type XXI and 1,200 tons for Type XXIII.

'Thus the Immediate Programme could be secured by the production of a further 18,200 tons of steel by the end of January. The vicissitudes of steel deliveries for U-boat Programmes XXI and XXIII leaves, however, little hope that this quantity of steel will be forthcoming:

1944	Planned tons	Delivered tons	Discrepancy tons
August	15,000	15,000	—
Sept	15,000	12,000	3,000
Oct	15,000	7,000	8,000
Nov	15,000	5,000	10,000
Dec	15,000	2,000	13,000

In order that at least the crude sections can be delivered for which a considerable quantity of accessories is already available, it has been necessary to move the production of rolled steel from the steel works in the Rhineland and the Ruhr to central Germany, as it is very likely that, in the coming weeks or perhaps months the western rolling mills will not be available.

'It had been planned to commence crude section construction of Type XXVI in January 1945. However, as there are not even materials for the Type XXI and XXIII Immediate Programme, there is, at the moment, no prospect for the Type XXVI series construction.

'While, due to the shortage of materials, there is less pressure on steel construction, the continuation of the 'Helping Hand' activity at the yards is evening matters up. A large number of workers is also occupied with Ruhr relief, with improving output of the armaments industry there and with repair work occasioned by bombing. Remaining work capacity has been funnelled off into various programmes (e.g., anti-aircraft). However, firms can only work even in these ways when materials and acetylene are available. The bottleneck in acetylene has occurred through bombing of the Knappsackwerke, which supplied the whole Rhine/Ruhr district. An additional bottleneck is that of electrode production. The Westfälische Union in Hamm supplies over 50 per cent of electrodes for the U-boat programme and

this body, too, has been hit several times recently by bombs.

'In contrast, this delivery of the main electric motors and switchboards is in line with HAS requirements. Individual delivery problems are compensated for by existing delays at the yards. In the field of electrical items, the main problem at the moment is in the production of batteries. Air attacks have meant that the main suppliers for Type XXI have suffered the following losses:
AFA, Hagen: 6 sets (bomb damage).
AFA, Hannover: 7 sets (power shortage).
AFA, Vienna-Floridsdorf: 2 sets (bomb damage).
Total: 15 sets, i.e., 50 per cent of the monthly target.
To these must be added the hoped-for production of 3 sets from AFA Posen. The significance of these figures is that in January no more than 20 sets will be available; in February, at the most, 23 sets of batteries for Type XXI. This means that only approximately two-thirds of the planned U-boat production will be possible. Extraordinary measures will have to be taken in the matter of battery production if a catastrophe in U-boat production is to be avoided.'

Questioned by the Allies after the war, Vizeadmiral Karl Topp stated:
'The sole bottleneck that really mattered in U-boat production and which had the effect of preventing yards from fully accomplishing their monthly U-boat deliveries was that of batteries. This shortage . . . came about because (a) The Armaments Ministry, after its assumption of responsibility for naval armaments in 1943, did not carry out the Navy's intention to set up in good time additional battery factories in Vienna and Bohemia, or initiated their construction too late. Thus, when production facilities at Hagen were destroyed and Hannover was unusable through paralysing of power-stations in west Germany, Vienna [Liesing] had not yet commenced production. No preparations were in force for additional production undertakings to rectify matters. (b) At this same point in time, the battery factory in Posen was lost through the Russian advance.'

And further, in the Main Committees' memorandum:
'The situation with regard to transport is catastrophically bad. The large U-boat sections can only be transported by water. The different breaks in the canal system has hit ship construction especially hard. In November, bombing of the Dortmund-Ems Canal held up approximately 80 crude sections. As far as possible cargoes have had to by-pass the points where damage has occurred by road, and, from Münster to Meppen by the coastal canal, which has not received as much damage as the more heavily used Dortmund-Ems Canal. As the railway system in the present state of affairs cannot nearly cope with requirements, a large portion of important deliveries have to be made by lorry [wood-gas propulsion]. However, not enough lorries are available.

'The very large number of ships requiring repair following air attacks in ports or through mine damage has meant that an enormous increase in the labour force is necessary and this requirement has been aggravated by the fact that, the speedy evacuation of Holland has caused 170 ships needing attention and repair to be collected in German ports from Dutch ones.

'Following the Führer's decree that yard workers should be protected from call-up, the Navy had the temporary use of over 11,000 soldiers and additionally prisoners-of-war and Dutch workers, and the situation at the moment is rather better. However, the need to take over the more urgent ship repairs means an interruption and post-ponement of new construction. U-boat repairs are to be given especially the highest priority. Initiated by Dönitz, a special action is to commence whereby the number of repair workers for January will increase from 27,000 to over 40,000. This can only be achieved if at least 4,400 men engaged on new construction are handed over to U-boat repairs.

'The severe power crisis occasioned by the non-arrival of coal supplies reached its climax at the end of December 1944. However, since then, efforts made by the Navy, by the Armaments Staff and by the Coal Authorities have reduced the seriousness of the situation somewhat. The position with regard to power supplies is now that, apart from smaller and medium shipyards, they are more or less reasonable.'

Despite the abysmal state of the armaments industry, preparations went ahead for the commencement of construction of the new Walter-boats. On 8 December 1944, a new timetable was necessary for the start of Type XXVI at B&V. Director Süchting suggested 20 February 1945 as the commencing date for section construction for the first prototype, U4501. In particular, he justified the two months' postponement by outstanding deliveries (e.g., gearing to be supplied by Krupp), the fact that steel construction was four weeks in arrears by delayed delivery of constructional drawings from the IBG, and bomb damage caused on 4 and 21 November 1944. An additional reason was the shortage of personnel. Up to then, only 100 men had been approved by the Labour Authority for Type XXVI. Some of these reasons (bomb damage) were not accepted by the Special Committee for U-Boats, and the commencement of section construction was set for 1 February 1945. No precise date was set for the series production that would follow, because of the confused situation in the Ruhr.

For the first boat, an internal decision suggested commencement of assembly on 5 April and delivery on 4 June 1945. Only the first two boats counted as prototypes and these were to be built as a matter of urgency. It was now decided that sections 1 and 4 should be constructed in Engine Factory II (M-II) with sections 2, 3 and 5 constructed on a concrete strip on the west side of the East Hangar, which was to be ready in January 1945. However, on 31 December 1944, an air raid on B&V thwarted this intention. Especially badly damaged was the East Hangar, by several direct hits, with trains and track systems destroyed. Of necessity, the assembly of section portions was interrupted by the need for clearing-up and urgent repair work. It was to recommence on 15 January 1945 and, in fact,

crude section 2 was to be built at Elbe 17 Dock, alongside the Type XVIIB small Walter U-boats being constructed there. As the middle portion of crude section 3 was at this time in the East Hangar and could not be brought out because of destruction of train and track systems, it was obvious that assembly of this crude section would have to take place in the East Hangar if much time were not to be lost. Consequently, at least one crane and the track would have to be made good once again. A new date for the commencement of section construction was set for 18 February 1945.

With regard to U-boat Type XXIII, the following new decisions were taken on 11 January 1945.

'1. U-boat Programme

	DW	GW	Total
To 31 December 1944	33	2	35
January 1945	11	4	15
February 1945	6	5	11
March 1945	2	5	7
April 1945	2(4)	5	7(9)
May 1945	—	5	5
June 1945	—	7	7
From July 1945	—	10	10
Total to the end of 1945:	54	93	147

2. The section yard for all sections, apart from section 4, is — from the fifteenth GW boat (U4713) — DW until March 1945, when DWK in Kiel can take over sections 3 and 4 as long as punctual delivery of crude sections can be made. In order to benefit the production of Seehund and the 'Alberich' covering (from April 1945, 6 boats per month) at GW, the latter will transfer a number of its crude sections to the smoothly-functioning sequence construction at DW. Steel construction section portions being brought back from Italy will be taken first to DW, Hamburg. From there, all crude sections 3, 3a, and 4 will be taken to DWK.'

Not until 26 January 1945 was the Restricted Immediate Programme authorized as Reichs State Secret No. 82. With the title 'Completion Programme for Type XXI, XXIII and XXVI', the new total delivery was determined as: 336 Type XXI, 140 Type XXIII and 20 Type XXVI. Any boats that had been placed in contract over and above these were not to proceed; in the case of Type XXI, only from the 401st; Type XXIII, from the 171st and Type XXVI, from the 25th boat.

However, the new Russian offensive, which led to the loss of the Upper Silesian area and of the yards in the Danzig area, made nonsense of this programme even as it was being formulated. Only top-priority armament undertakings 'of an importance crucial to the war' could bring about such an 'emergency programme'. The repair programme was the most important one in the Naval Sector that could be accorded this treatment.

The terminal phase

On 22 January 1945, the HAS prepared a list of probable losses to be expected in the shipbuilding industry as a result of the Russian offensive in Prussia. The loss of these yards meant the following production losses.

30 per cent of Type XXI U-boat production.
60–70 per cent of Seehund production.
50 per cent of minesweeper production.
100 per cent of torpedo-boat production.
20 per cent of MTB production.
33 per cent of repair capacity.

The well-timed transfer of skilled workers, however, meant that some repairs could be carried out at yards in western Germany. As had already happened, with the evacuation of Holland, whenever possible, all ships awaiting repair, and vessels launched but not yet complete were towed to ports in western Germany. Among these were the incomplete Type XXI boats U3526–U3534 from Danzig, and perhaps U3535–U3537 which had been lowered into the water. When the Russians entered Schichau, Danzig, only U3538–U3542 were on the slips. (Swedish photographs show two captured Type XXI in Danzig being towed by the Russians to Kronstadt.) Additionally, the Russians acquired a further eight sections 1, twelve sections 2, fourteen sections 3, fourteen sections 4, twelve sections 5, ten sections 6, ten sections 7 and eight sections 8. But certain valuable supplies had been transported in the steamship Celebes to Hamburg, where they arrived at the beginning of March 1945.

The available yards in western Germany were now to carry out only important tasks that could be completed quickly — principally repairs. But they would complete, from the new construction programme, those U-boats whose construction time

Table 53. Estimated capacity loss expected upon Russian advance, 22 January 1945

Yard	Type of construction	Personnel: Repairs	Total
1. Lindenau, Memel (later Pillau)	Older minesweepers and M43 Sections	few	400
2. Schichau, Königsberg	Minesweepers M43 (4 per month) and M43 sections	2,400	9,200
3. Maureb, Pillau	—	425	500
4. Schichau, Elbing	Torpedo-boats (1 per month) and Seehunds (55 per month)	600	6,400
5. Schichau, Danzig.	U-boats Type XXI (8 per month) and sections IV and V	300	8,300
6. Danziger Werft.	Sections I, II, III, VIII for U-boat Type XXI	2,500	9,200
7. Deutsche Werke, Gotenhafen	Sections VI & VII for U-boat Type XXI	2,200	6,400
8. Danziger Waggonfabrik	Motor torpedo-boats	—	1,300
9. KMA, Gotenhafen	—	600	1,500
Total		9,000	43,200
Percentage of total Naval Armaments		33%	28%

was short. On 26 January 1945, Speer told Hitler that 170 Type XXI and 70 Type XXIII boats, from the new construction programme, should now be included in the emergency programme, which now had absolute priority over all other urgency stages and was to be prosecuted energetically. Sections for these boats were already available or were being constructed. By the end of January 1945, 95 Type XXI were ready and a further 60 were on the slips; sections for a further 15 were in position on the sequence assembly lines of the section yards. In the case of Type XXIII, the corresponding numbers were 50, 11 and 9. By 1 April 1945, 70 Type XXIII and 125 Type XXI boats were to be delivered. If the overall U-boat programme could no longer be protected against call-up, at least the completion of boats lying on the slips of B&V, AG Weser, Schichau, Danzig, DW and GW should be within the framework of the repair programme.

Above all, the repair programme was to secure capacity for the increasingly important transport tasks in the Baltic and to Norway. It was also intended that the majority of training U-boats which, with the virtual cessation of training, had been tied up in ports, should be converted or equipped for operational use. At this juncture, the German U-boat arm totalled 416 boats, including 272 school and training boats, but only 144 operational U-boats! On 6 February 1945, a telex from Merker to B&V expressed the absolute priority accorded to the repair programme:

'By command of the Führer, the sphere of ship repair is to be included completely in the emergency programme of the Reichs Minister for Armament. This means that repairs, including the supply of essential items and spare parts, is to be carried out with an unconditional priority over all other armament programmes not part of the Emergency Programme.

'To aid this task the Armament Commissions will guarantee production supplies such as coal, power and transport space. As it is unlikely that power supplies will be available in sufficient quantity for the New Construction Programme, repair work is to be carried out with the use of all possible work forces at the expense of new construction — with the exception of certain U-boat programmes described in the separate letter; such repair work must certainly be carried out in 2 shifts and, if possible, in 3 shifts.

'I have to expect that in the light of the seriousness of the situation, the works directors will do their utmost to carry out this requirement and that in the next weeks the Navy and the Reichs

Table 54. The Emergency Programme of 10 February 1945

'I. TYPE XXI PROGRAMME
'1. Section Construction:

		Target for Emergency Programme	Available as at 10 Feb 1945	Balance
Section I	Howaldt-Kiel	150	144	6
Section II	KMW, Wilhelmshaven	150	137	13
Section III	Bremer Vulkan	70	68	2
	DW-Hamburg	80	66	14
Section IV	Flender Werke	150	157	—
Section V	Bremer Vulkan	65	61	4
	Howaldt-Hamburg	86	74	12
Section VI	Bremer Vulkan	88	78	10
	DW-Hamburg	64	57	7
Section VII	Seebeck	150	141	9
Section VIII	DWK	150	150	—

'Steel construction items for deliveries still outstanding are guaranteed apart from 1–2 crude sections III and VI at DW, Hamburg.
'Section yards have been instructed that all available supplies surplus to those required by the Emergency Programme are to be placed at the disposal of assembly yards for use in new constructions, repairs and remaining work on U-boats.
'2. Assembly Construction: Slippings-up in the western area as per the Emergency Programme

	Target	Available as at 10 Feb 1945
Deschimag	65	57
B&V	75	59
Total	140	116

'A further 18 complete sets of sections are available for additional slippings-up as at 10.2.45. The remaining 30 boats will be delivered by Schichau, Danzig.
'3. Boat Deliveries by 10 Feb 1945:

	AG Weser	B&V	Schichau	Total
(a) Boats at the yards before operational use.[1]	—	3[2]	—	3
(b) Boats in operational training groups.	7	9	11	27
(c) Boats delivered to KLA.[3]	1	2	1	4
(d) Boats at UAK-testing.	12	9	9	30
(e) Boats commissioned prior to UAK-testing.	9	7	2	18
(f) Delivered boats (still at the yard).	6	5	2	13
(g) Delivered, very heavily damaged boats.	—	5[4]	—	5
	35	40	25	100

[1] Reported for remaining work: U3007, U2502, U2506, U3504, U3508.
[2] U2503, U2511, U2519.
[3] U2501, U2504, U3001, U3501.
[4] U2508 (Accident), U2515 (Mine), U2530 (Aerial bomb), U2532 (Aerial bomb).

'II. TYPE XXIII PROGRAMME
'1. Programme at 10 Feb 1945:

			1945			
	By 1 Feb	Feb	March	April	May	Total
DW-Hamburg	41	7[1]	1	—	—	49
GW	7	5[2]	4	4[3]	5[3]	25
	48	12	5	4	5	74

[1] The February boats, three of them being retrospective to January, were not completed because of shortage of batteries.
[2] Among these two 'Alberich' boats.
[3] From April, all boats have 'Alberich'.
2. Section Construction:
DW is to deliver the sections for the 14th–21st and for the 25th GW boat. The 74 new construction boats (4 more than originally called for in the Emergency Programme) are guaranteed their steel construction items. Over and above these, the following crude sections are available:

Section	I	II	III	IV
No. of items	8	2	—	6

'3. Boat deliveries by 10 Oct 1945:

	DW	GW	Total
(a) Boats ready for operations.	1	—	1
(b) Boats at the yards before operational use.	6[2]	—	6
(c) Boats in operational group training.	10	1	11
(d) Boats delivered to KLA.	1[4]	—	1
(e) Boats at UAK trials.	13	1	14
(f) Boats commissioned prior to UAK testing.	7	5	12
(g) Delivered boats (still at the yard).	1	—	1
(h) Delivered, very badly damaged boats.	3[5]	—	3
	42	7	49

[1] U2324.
[2] U2321, U2322, U2325, U2326, U2328, U2329.
[3] Reported for remaining work: U2335, U2336, U2340.
[4] U2327.
[5] U2323 (Mine), U2331 (Accident), U2342 (Mine).'

Sea Commission for Merchant Service will have more shipping space at their disposal. I regard it as your duty, by personal model and unflagging enthusiasm, to make sure that the yards carry out the above request with full zeal. Above all, I bid you to try to achieve the use of as many workers as possible in 3 shifts. A single ship made ready in the next weeks is worth far more than 3 ships in the coming months.

'I anticipate that any problems that you cannot solve by your own powers will be reported either to the Special Committee for Repairs or to me personally.'

Details of U-boats to be constructed under the Emergency Programme were announced on 10 February 1945, as shown in Table 54. However, even this U-boat Emergency Programme was not to be realized. In addition to catastrophic happenings in eastern Germany, the new Allied bombing offensive was exacting an increasing toll from assembly yards, deliveries and traffic installations. With regard to this, a minute of the 30th Armaments Discusssion on 26 February 1945 stated:

'Delivery of batteries: from 28.1.–17.2.45, 7⅔ sets of batteries were produced for Type XXI, and of these on 23.2., 1⅔ were still in Hannover and 1⅓ in Hagen. In the same period, 5 sets of batteries were produced for Type XXIII and, of these, one set is still in Hannover and one in Hagen. At the yards there are increasing problems through the shortage of coal, gas and electricity. Similarly there are difficulties with battery accessories, especially with those for Type XXIII. (20 complete sets of these were left behind in Posen!) Difficulties with coal and power are present also at delivery firms in Ilmenau and Conti Hannover. Director Merker states that the delivery plan for batteries formulated at the 29th Armaments Discussion cannot be achieved.

'New construction of U-boat Type XXI: in February, provisionally 14; however, only 8 have been produced up to now. Delivery in March, provisionally 9; if batteries can be made available from KLA [construction-training] boats, a further 3 are possible. The idea of fitting boats with two-thirds of the batteries was turned down by the Supreme Commander in Chief of the Navy.

'Type XXIII: in February 7; 5 delivered up to now. Further deliveries depend on supply of batteries. Schnorkel problems at GW. The first 'Alberich' boats delivered by GW [U4709]. Suggestion: the 'Valentin' shelter to be used for 'Alberich' covering. GW to continue with its provision of a covered-over building for 'Alberich' covering. 'Alberich' materials are guaranteed for 54 Type XXIII boats. The request that VIIC boats be covered with 'Alberich' means that each VIIC will require a similar amount to 2½ Type XXIII boats.

'Type XXVI: the first 4 boats of Type XXVI are included in the Emergency Programme. Further ones will not be constructed. The Navy, however, will try and obtain a complete clarification between Dönitz and Speer as to their further construction.

'The last two XVIIB boats at B&V will not have a completion date, as specialists are urgently required for repair of operational boats.

'General: because of the boomerang air attacks [see below] on Deschimag, the boats there that are capable of floating should be taken to smaller yards and ship workshops for further construction. Increased fighter protection is necessary.'

Following the conclusion of work on Type XXVI, the Design Department at IBG had prepared some further design details for other projects, especially midgets, but such work ceased in Blankenburg at the end of February 1945. Dr. Fischer was appointed Special Commissioner for the Weser area, charged with the task of accelerating the preparation of available U-boats for operational use. He arrived in Bremen at a time when the almost-daily precision attacks by British long-range Mosquito squadrons (German code-name 'Boomerang') were threatening to paralyse work at AG Weser, and when the unavailability of the docks meant a parlous situation for the completion of boats that had been launched from the slipway. Dr. Fischer ordered, therefore, that the boats in a floating condition (those to U3041) leave Bremen by 5 March 1945. It was envisaged that dock work should now be carried out at Wilhelmshaven and in the large dock at Wesermünde. From then on, new construction boats were to be launched from the slipway in such condition that they did not subsequently need to be docked.

Table 55. U-boat fitting-out in Weser area, 13 March 1945

	Type XXI	Type IX	Type VII	Type II
Wilhelmshaven	6	—	6	9
Bremen	—	2	4	—
Wesermünde	—	5	3	—
Vegesack	—	—	2	4
Total	6	7	15	13

On 13 March 1945, distribution of U-boat fitting-out in the Weser area was as shown in Table 55. Its excellent dock facilities meant that Wilhelmshaven was now to be the focal-point of U-boat fitting-out, but the severe shortage of labour prevented its immediate use to full capacity. Dr. Fischer ordered, therefore, that this deficiency be made good by the new construction sector of AG Weser. Additionally, he proposed that personnel be allocated from yards in eastern Germany, and that those workers occupied in the 'Fink II' shelter at Hamburg be returned to KMW, Wilhelmshaven. However, instead of the requested workers from eastern yards being made available, management staff were sent from Schichau who wished to take over part of the yard. This prompted Dr. Fischer to write to Merker on 13 March 1945: 'What is necessary to cope with U-boat repairs in Wilhelmshaven are qualified skilled workers, certainly not management staff who neither know the area nor the method of operations.' On 21 March 1945, Merker sent the following telex to Dönitz: 'An evacuation order for the Danzig yards has still not been received even though yards are under artillery fire. Gauleiter Forster is requested to have an evacuation order issued after which special yard personnel can be removed together with hand-tools and special tools. I request further that instruction

be given to the Sea Transport Chief that shipping space be made available for this transport undertaking. I request that the same be carried out at Stettin by Gauleiter Schwede-Koburg with GW, Kiel, as the reception point.'

The next naval armaments discussion, on 14 March 1945, indicated a further worsening of the battery situation, as deliveries from the works at Hagen were no longer to be counted upon in view of rail transport difficulties. It was decided, therefore, that 50 sets of battery-maintenance equipment for Type XXI and other urgently required material should be collected from Hagen by lorry. In order to increase production at AFA-Hannover, additional skilled labour would be necessary, and these could perhaps be transferred from Hagen. Finally, Vienna-Floridsdorf was also ruled out because of transportation difficulties. Following stronger pressure and forced by the turn of events, the Supreme C-in-C of the Navy had at last agreed that two-thirds of the normal battery installation could be used in the Type XXI new-construction U-boats. This meant that only the five installations that could be delivered in March would be used to equip approximately seven boats. Batteries from the KLA boats could be used for the boats scheduled for April, and each KLA boat could then be given, in exchange, two-section batteries from VIIC U-boats no longer in commission, so that they could remain usable for training purposes.

The distribution of deliveries between B&V and Deschimag had changed in the light of the delivery situation. An HAS decision of 12 March 1945 stated that B&V should now provide only 67 boats and Deschimag 73 boats. Type XXIII production depended also on battery availability. Only five sets of batteries arrived at the yards in February and five sets in March. In order to remedy the battery crisis, it was suggested that batteries be manufactured in the 'Valentin' shelter. But this shelter was already intended for 'Alberich' covering, and was claimed by Deschimag for U-boat repair work. Schwarzenbach, near Hof, was also intended for use as an emergency centre for battery construction, and it was decided to direct all efforts to a speedy production of batteries there. When production slowed almost to a standstill on the last two Type XVIIB Walter-boats at B&V, the Admiral, U-Boats, raised an objection, but to no avail. Likewise the request made by the Supreme C-in-C of the Navy for continued construction of Type XXVI in excess of the 4 boats 'if sufficient Aurol is available' was pointless.

On 24 March 1945, in 'Reich Secret Matter No. 138', the Supreme Naval Command authorized cancellation of any U-boat construction that had not yet commenced. This meant that in the Type XXI Programme, only 82 boats remained at B&V, 108 boats at Deschimag and 166 boats at 'Valentin' Bremer Vulkan, i.e., a total of 356 boats. No cancellations were announced for Danzig, but it was calculated that only 30 boats would be delivered from this source. With regard to Type XXIII, 56 boats remained in contract at DW and 114 boats at GW, a total of 170 boats. This was many more than the Emergency Programme called for and, for the time being, the discrepancy was regarded as a quantity on which work had been suspended. On the other hand, of Type XXVI, almost the entire contract, with the exception of the 4 prototype boats that were to be built wholly at B&V, was cancelled.

These official cancellations corresponded more or less to the resolutions that Merker had made on 23 February 1945, during a discussion with the Head of the Main Committee for Electro-Technology, Director Lüschen: no U-boats were to be built over and above those contained in the Emergency Programme. Work on all boats from Nos. 171—336 of Type XXI were to be stopped, with Nos. 171—236 earmarked for use in providing available materials in case of renewed production at any time. All boats from Nos. 337 were to be cancelled. In the case of Type XXIII, the cancellation was from No. 141, with work stopped on Nos. 71—140, materials from these being retained. Finally, all Type XXVI boats with the exception of the first 4 were likewise cancelled.

The increasing tempo of air attacks in March and at the beginning of April virtually halted new production, and work continued only on boats that were almost complete. The last Type XXI, U3051, left the slipway at AG Weser on 20 April 1945 (seven days before the British occupation); and at Kiel, the last Type XXIII, U4714, at a date as late as 26 April. With great tenacity, attempts were made to the last to prepare at least a few boats of the new type for operational use. Over and over again, crews that had already been trained, or commanders with special operational experience had to change boats because the boat destined for them had been destroyed while finishing work was being carried out. As a specimen outline of the great difficulties that constantly delayed the operational use of Type XXI in the final phases of the war, despite the relatively large number that had been delivered, here is the laconic report of Kapitänleutnant Fritz Kallipke:

'2.2.45 After the conclusion of operational group training, U2516 leaves Hela in a westerly direction.

4.2.45 Arrive Travemünde. The following boats are already there: U2506 (von Schroeter), U2519 (Cremer), U3007 (Manseck) and U2502 (Mannesmann). [U2511 (Schnee) with special powers, had used his judgement to cut short the training timetable and was already lying at a yard berth in Hamburg. This boat, as the first Type XXI, left Kiel for Norway on 16.3.1945. The four boats already lying in Travemünde were likewise urgently required for operations and were therefore to proceed to their yards, without torpedo-firing training, for remaining work to be completed. At the yards, during air attacks, U3007 was sunk, U2519 damaged and the commander of U2502 was killed by bomb splinters.] U2516 [on the other hand] was ordered to remain in Travemünde to await the training flotilla for torpedo firing which, in the meantime, had been transferred from Gotenhafen to Travemünde. It was to be the first Type XXI boat to undergo this aspect of training. This meant that U2516 lost 10 days.

14.2.45 Commencement of torpedo-firing training in the Travemünde Bight at a depth of 23 metres.

21.2.45 End of firing training. Against the wishes of the commander, the boat had to stay once more in Travemünde for depth-charge tests on 23.2.45.

24.2.45 Arrive at the Kiel base.

26.2.45 Hand over weapons to the arsenal.

27.2.45 Shift berth to DWK.

29.2.45 Yard discussion concerning remaining work.

4.4.45 16.30 hours, in effect two days before completion of remaining work, during an air attack on Kiel, hit by bombs beneath starboard bunker Ia. 8 square metres hole caused. Sluice-door damaged. Repairs not being carried out.

9.4.45 20.15 hours, during air attack on the yard area, hit by 1,000lb bomb through the pressure hull, and explosion in the engine compartment. Port diesel shattered. Blast disintegrates the complete wood installations right through to the fore-ship. Two men on watch killed, the third rescued alive. A further hit outside on the bow torpedo hatch starboard.

10.4.45 Report to Admiral Thedsen. Boat is to be withdrawn from service. As the crew of U2516 is the first one for Type XXI that has completed its training according to plan, by personal command of Admiral von Friedeburg, a second boat, U2529, which at the moment is in Kiel in its UAK period, is procured.

15.4.45 Take over U2529. Necessary conversions are carried out to the torpedo installation and equipment for a 5 months undertaking. To this end, the following items are taken on: 196 tons of fuel, 22 tons of supplies, 20 torpedoes of the newest type.

26.4.45 Following the conclusion of a final trimming test, the estimated time of departure of 20.30 hours had to be delayed in consequence of an air attack.

27.4.45 06.00 hours, leave for Norway.

28.4.45 After joining escort, enter Kattegatt. After the reef of Zeeland, dive to avoid detection and travel underwater to Anholt. On surfacing part company with escort. Surface travel: Anholt-Läsö. After reaching a depth of 40 metres, submerge again to 40-metres line in Oslo Fjord.

29.4.45 13.00 hours, arrive Horten.

1.5.45 Propeller repairs necessary (straightening of 6 deformed propeller tips); carried out in a remote fjord the other side of Horten with the boat just floating, flooded apart from diving tank 1. Engineers lend help with a pontoon and welding equipment. Repair job carried out by our crew.

2.5.45 Travel submerged to Kristiansand.

3.5.45 Build-in strengthenings in the shaft bosses, Frame 10.6, and effect strengthening in the torpedo hatch, based on Schnee's experiences. The parts were fabricated at the Howaldt shipyard in Kiel. The yard, however, was not in a position to work on them mechanically any longer, but such work was possible at the base at Kristiansand.

5.5.45 17.15 hours. Discussion with escort concerning sailing on a hostile mission fixed for 21.00 hours.
19.00 hours, sailing agreed. Boat is required to moor by warp to a buoy and prepare itself for immediate sailing for an operation to the south. The crew now has to keep out of touch with shore installations.

8.5.45 Boat receives command to carry out a deep diving test in which 220 metres is reached. 20.15 hours, boat passes the Lighthouse of Oksöy. Its signalling position carries the Norwegian flag. Germany has capitulated, and this is the first intimation of it that the boat has.'

Of those Type XXI U-boats transferred to Norwegian waters, only U2511 was used operationally. By the time it met a larger British warship formation on 4 May 1945, U-boats had already been ordered not to carry out attacks. Likewise, a second U-boat of this type, which had left Wilhelmshaven only on 3 May 1945, U3008, with Manseck's crew, fell in with a large British unit in the Skagerrak, but, in view of the impending capitulation, did not carry out an attack.

Of Type XXIII on the other hand, from February 1945, seven boats were used operationally and carried out several operational voyages from the bases of Kristiansand and Stavanger along the east coast of Britain and in the Thames Estuary. Without loss, they sank at least five cargo ships, and severely damaged another, a considerable achievement for these small boats, each of which carried only two torpedoes.

On 27 April, Bremen was occupied by British troops; Vegesack was occupied on 30 April and Hamburg on 3 May. Following the lifting of Hitler's 'scorched earth' order, the yard installations still available were not destroyed. A large number of available ships and harbour vessels were scuttled prior to the actual occupation (Operation 'Regenbogen'), including all U-boats in service. Despite much destruction, the yards were still functioning. When the war ended, 14 Type XXI U-boats, in different stages of assembly, were at the building slips of B&V. Only one of these (U2550) was seriously damaged. At Deschimag, however, there were as many as 16 boats, including 4 rather more badly damaged (U3042, U3048, U3052 and U3060). There was, additionally, a very large quantity of fully-equipped sections, either at the section yards or at various collecting points (e.g. the Veersmann Quay at Hamburg).

Survey of programmes and actual deliveries of Type XXI

Table 56. Type XXI programmes to December 1944

	Merker's Programme, 1 Nov 1943	HAS Programme, 26 Jan 1944	Armaments Meeting, 22 Mar 1944	Armaments Meeting, 3 May 1944	Armaments Meeting, 15 May 1944	Ministerial Programme, 1 June 1944	HAS Programme, 21 July 1944	HAS Programme, 7 Sept 1944	Planning, 5 Oct 1944	Armaments Meeting, 18 Oct 1944	Armaments Meeting, 15 Nov 1944
1944:											
April	3	3	—	—	—	—	—	—	—	—	—
May	9	9	3	3	3	2	—	—	—	—	—
June	18	19	9	5	7	5	1	1	1	1	1
July	27	27	18	8	10	9	7	7	7	7	7
August	33	31	30	12	21	18	13	5	5	5	5
September	33	31	30	15	30	26	22	14	13	13	13
October	35	31	28	20	30	29	30	28	21	18	17
November	37	29	28	20	30	33	34	32	27	26	17
December	38	27	27	18	30	33	36	33	36	32	32
Total	233	207	173	140	161	155	143	120	110	102	92
1945											
January	38	.	.	20	.	30	.	33	31	33	
February	38	.	.	20	.	28	.	30	31	33	
March	38	.	.	20	.	22	.	28	31	33	
April	.	.	.	1[1]	.	22	.	22	29	33	
May	.	.	.	.	.	22	.	22	28	26	
June	.	.	.	.	.	22	.	22	26	26	
July	.	.	.	.	.	22	.	22	26	26	
August	.	.	.	.	.	22	.	22	22	22	
September	.	.	.	.	.	22	.	22	22	22	
October	.	.	.	.	.	22	.	22	22	22	
November	.	.	.	.	.	22	.	22	22	22	
December	.	.	.	.	.	22	.	22	22	22	

[1] Hereafter changing to Type XXVI.
Note. A dot signifies 'unknown', a dash 'no delivery'.

Table 57. Type XXI deliveries achieved.

Yard	1944: June	July	Aug	Sept	Oct	Nov	Dec	Total	1945: Jan	Feb	Mar	April	Total
B&V	1	2	3	6	9	3	10	34	4	6	2	1	47
Deschimag		2	2	4	5	2	11	26	7	8	2		43
Schichau		2	1	2	4	4	7	20	5			4	29
Total	1	6	6	12	18	9	28	80	16	14	8	1	119

Table 58. Orders for Type XXI diesel engines

	1st order	2nd order	3rd order	4th order	Total
MAN	87	55	84	13	239
Moha	17	20	30	31	98
Deutz	40	23	36	16	115
Wumag	45	32	48	21	146
Total	189	130	198	81	598

Table 59. Type XXI section deliveries

	3[1]	5[1]	6[1]	9[1]	5[2]	8[3]
1944:						
March	1	1	1	1	1	2
April	1	1	1	1	1	4
May	3	3	3	3	4	6
June	3	3	3	3	3	13
July	5	4	4	4	6	9
August	6	4	5	5	8	15
September	8	8	12	9	7	17
October	9	8	14	10	11	28
November	9	9	11	9	7	27
December	10	8	11	10	12	13
Total:	65	49	65	55	60	134
1945:						
January	10	10	11	9	5	13
February	7	5	6	1	4	4
March	1	1	2	—	1	—
Total	73	65	84	65	70	151

(Section number)

[1] From Bremer Vulkan, Vegesack.
[2] From Howaldt, Hamburg.
[3] From DWK.

Table 60. Deliveries of diesel engines for Type XXI from MAN-Augsburg

	Projected	Completed
1944:		
March	16	2
April	16	4
May	16	20
June	16	28
July	16	26
August	16	12
September	20	20
October	20	20
November	20	26
December	20	21
Total	176	179
1945:		
January	20	24
February	20	21
March	13	—
April	10	—
Total	239	224

Note: more than 400 engines (over 200 sets) were delivered by the end of the war.

Table 61. Electric motors for Type XXI

	SSW	AEG	BBC	Total
Orders:				
1st order	57	13	20	90
2nd order	116	36	48	200
3rd order	197	73	20	290
Total	370	122	88	580
Deliveries:				
To 30 Sept 1944	74	30	6	110
To end of war	252	160	.	.

Note: a monthly average of 20 electric motors was to be supplied by SSW Dynamowerke and 18 by AEG, Berlin. The first motors arrived from SSW in March 1944, and from AEG in June 1944.
A dot signifies 'unknown'.

10 U-BOAT DEVELOPMENT AT THE END OF THE WAR

NEW BOATS ON TRIALS

The Walter-boats

On 28 September 1943, the first Walter boat, *U792*, entered the water at B&V and, on 7 October, *U794* followed at GW. Between 15 October and 9 November, initially only with *U792*, comprehensive surface tests of the lateral rudder installation were carried out by the yard. These showed that the divided lateral rudder was considerably under-dimensioned: only after increasing the area of the rudder surfaces several times, finally by 62 per cent, could a surface turning circle diameter of

300m be achieved at a speed of 8 knots with full rudder. Subsequently in Hela, both the spade rudders were replaced by a single lateral rudder positioned in the propeller wash. This arrangement provided a submerged turning circle diameter of 180m at a speed of 4.8 knots with full rudder. On 11 November 1943, the initial surface acceptance trip was carried out, after which *U792* was commissioned on 16 November.

During submerged trials using the electric motor, it was evident in both boats that the lack of forward hydroplanes showed to considerable disadvantage at slower speeds. The first submerged runs by *U792*

on 17 and 19 November and by *U794* on 20 and 22 November, showed that, when submerged, the boats could only be controlled at fast speeds (5 knots). At slower speeds, changes of depth could not be made by use of the hydroplanes. The boats certainly became down at the head with hydroplanes inclined downwards, but the effect of this was nullified by positive buoyancy. A corresponding effect appeared when the hydroplanes were inclined upwards, when the boats became stern heavy. At even slower speeds, and with very precise controlling of the boats, it was possible once again to achieve changes of depth by

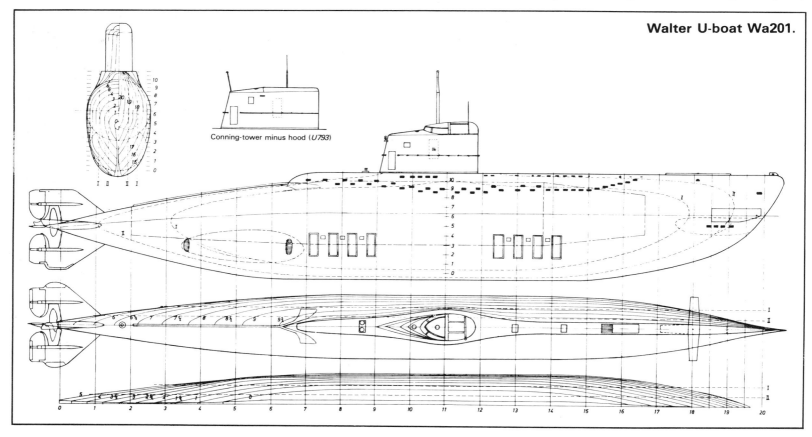

Walter U-boat Wa201.

Conning-tower minus hood (*U793*)

'parallel steering': — slow ascent with hydroplanes inclined downwards, or slow descent with hydroplanes inclined upwards. On 22 November 1943, the following measures were suggested as a remedy:

1. Reducing the size of the fins in order to bring about a reduction of the considerable hydrodynamic stability.

2. Reduction of the weight-stability to the smallest permissible measure by re-stowing ballast.

3. Installation in the fore-ship of a turnable fin that could be swung out, providing a reduction in the dynamic stability at slow speeds.

However, on 26 November 1943, the UAK decided: 'In order that, at all costs, tests of the Walter-installation shall not be delayed, both boats are to proceed in their present condition to Hela. It is suggested that depth-controlling tests be carried out by the UAK Branch Department at Danzig on one of the boats with fixed fins on the fore-ship, as long as this can be done without any hindrance to the Walter trials.' On 1 December 1943, U792 and U794 reached the testing unit for Walter-boats in Hela. Initially, further trials were carried out to test diesel and electric drives in the interests of investigating the steering capabilities. On 16 December, U794 and, on 17 and 19 December, U792 made several submerged measured-mile runs, with a fixed fin, 3.40m long, secured to the fore-ship. After the results of wind tunnel tests at the LFA, it had been expected that U792 would show better depth-controlling properties than U794, given the same conditions. However, at the very start of depth-controlling, it was noticeable that U792 had greater stability with less control than U794. Equipped with a fin, the lowest speeds for normal, acceptable controlling was 2.7 knots for U794 and 3.6 knots for U792. Above all, in these tests the weight-stability of U792 was still larger; even when it was reduced, the depth-controlling properties of U792 remained unsatisfactory. Sudden trimming and weight changes, such as occur when, for example, a torpedo is fired, just could not be compensated dynamically.

Even at higher speeds, U792 did not come up to expectations as regards directing force supplied by the hydroplanes: at 13 knots, it amounted to only 56 per cent of the LFA measuring value, and the counter-turning moment of the bridge was twice as big as had been planned. The measured propeller revolutions at 300rpm at 13 knots were higher than

had been expected, which was attributed to more favourable resistance properties than had been manifest in model tests at the HSVA. In surface travel, too, the boat's resistance proved to be smaller than had originally been calculated, and this was verified after measurements of fuel consumed during the trip to Hela.

At 75 seconds, the diving time of U792 was quite lengthy, certainly in the light of opinions concerning submarines at that time. During a diving test on 11 January 1944, at 1-ton negative buoyancy, the following results were obtained: 15 seconds flooding time for diving tanks; after 19

U792 (Wa201) in Kaiser Wilhelm Canal, November 1943.

seconds, upper deck beneath the surface; after 42 seconds, upper edge of bridge beneath the surface. Apparently, during diving, the boat was in a position of suspension from its bridge superstructure.

The first trials voyage with a Walter-installation was made by U792 on 21 December 1943, after a test scheduled for 20 December had been abandoned when the quantity-regulating mechanism had not functioned (quantities of four different substances: Aurol, fuel, feed-water and compensation water). The installation was tried out for ten minutes on the surface, and twelve minutes submerged. But the effect of this was that steam made its way through the labyrinth of turbines into

the turbine compartment and, next day, the first loggings were made with the Walter-installation. On 19 December, however, trials had to be halted because of poor Aurol concentration.

On 6 January 1944, the necessary new Aurol arrived at Hela, and was supplied to U792. After a closed-cycle test at the pier, the boat sailed on 8 January, to carry out a test of the Walter-system under travelling conditions. After unsuccessful attempts to ignite the system, the boat had to be put back to port. The combustion-chamber cover was buckled and torn. After the repair, as there was still no ignition, the ignition valve unit was

removed and exchanged for that from U794 (which was not ready for trials because of turbine damage). On 10 January, a further attempt was made, using the Walter-installation. During this trip, considerable temperature fluctuations occurred in the combustion chamber, caused by the jamming of a turbulence disc in the feed-water meter. Nevertheless, a submerged run was attempted with the Walter-installation. High combustion-chamber temperature caused the insulation jacket of the dust separator to ignite, but it extinguished itself from lack of oxygen in the partitioned-off compartment. Exhaust gas traces were observed in the water by an escort ship. When in use, but not ignited, the Walter-installation caused a clearly

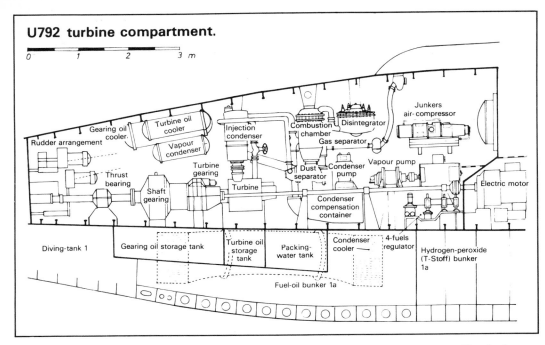

U792 turbine compartment.

0 1 2 3 m

Rudder arrangement
Gearing oil cooler
Turbine oil cooler
Vapour condenser
Injection condenser
Combustion chamber
Gas separator
Disintegrator
Junkers air-compressor
Thrust bearing
Shaft gearing
Turbine gearing
Turbine
Dust separator
Condenser pump
Vapour pump
Electric motor
Condenser compensation container
Diving-tank 1
Gearing oil storage tank
Turbine oil storage tank
Packing-water tank
Condenser cooler
4-fuels regulator
Hydrogen-peroxide (T-Stoff) bunker 1a
Fuel-oil bunker 1a

wanted to use *U792* in preference, as he considered this boat the more reliable, but this would have meant that Aurol would have to be transferred and Dönitz did not want to waste time on this. Apart from an initial failure of the regulator, the trial run of *U794* went smoothly, however. Heller took the boat through all speed ranges, and carried out appropriate alarm manoeuvres. He repeatedly switched from electric drive to Walter-drive. Dönitz and his entourage (Admiral von Friedeburg, Admiral Backenköhler, Admiral Thedsen, and Konteradmiral Godt) were most enthusiastic. This must have been the only occasion when five

visible light-green trail in the water, which, when the installation was ignited, immediately disappeared.

The difficulties experienced with the quantity-regulating system, which almost certainly had not been developed to a point of functional reliability, as well as the above-mentioned temperature variations in the steam mixture strained the turbines considerably. Further breakdowns were caused by the unsatisfactory piston-rod collar tightness of the turbines, and the unsatisfactory lack of pressure caused by over-pressure in the closed water tank. This meant that vapour was not sucked into the stuffing boxes, but entered the turbine compartment where this oxygen-enriched steam caused damage to the insulations of the field windings of the electric motors of the various auxiliary engines. After this had caused a total breakdown of the vapour-pump motor on 11 January, *U792* was taken into dock for an overhaul on 16 January. However, the problems were not solved. The vapour pump worked badly, with over-pressure in the packing-water tank causing the same effects. There were additional ignition problems caused by a leak in the ignition valve unit, which was difficult to rectify. On 22 January, when warping, a collision with the jetty occurred and this caused slight damage to the fore-ship. The boat was docked once again on 26 January for an intended exchange of turbines, and the opportunity was taken to improvise repairs to the damaged fore-ship. The hydroplanes were also enlarged, and the divided rudder blades were replaced by a single rudder blade of a larger surface area. Dismantling the vapour pump showed that the cellular blades of this water-ring pump had been damaged by pieces that had broken off. On 19 February 1944, *U792* was ready to sail once more. The new turbines were

first run without closed water. The feed-water packing of the turbine stuffing boxes had shown itself to be relatively ineffectual; if it were not used, the closed-water installation could be simplified. Above all, the electrically-driven packing-water pump, which was liable to break down, could be dispensed with. In its place, a simple hand pump was used to empty and fill the closed-water gravity tank.

On 20 February, for the first time, the Walter installation ran for 50 minutes underwater without interruption. However, difficulties involving the regulator and ignition valve occurred in subsequent runs. During measured-mile runs and progressive-speed runs with the bridge partly covered by two flaps and without a guard rail, an average Cw value of 203.5 was obtained, which was well above the value obtained in model tests. At a lower speed (5.39 knots) this value was reduced to 198.5 because of the more difficult depth-controlling previously described, which meant that the rudder had to be hard over. In all these tests, performance was measured by the Maihak-torsion indicator. The performance of the electric motor was also evaluated. In order to establish the towed performance of the boat, on the surface and submerged, a test was carried out by a Type IXD$_2$ boat towing *U792*, without her propeller. But no absolute conclusions were drawn from these tests.

As the water regulator kept breaking down when the Walter system was in use, it was often operated by hand. On 31 March 1944, the installation ran perfectly in *U792*, apart from a sticking exhaust valve. The first teething troubles had been overcome.

At the end of March 1944, Dönitz visited the test unit at Hela and took part in a trial in *U794*. The test commander, Kapitänleutnant (Engineer) Heller

admirals sailed together in one U-boat. On leaving, Dönitz declared: 'With more courage and confidence in the Supreme Naval Command, we could have had this boat 1–2 years earlier.'

On 4 April 1944, *U792* carried out an endurance test underwater for 125 minutes, making several speed tests on the Hela Mile. The highest speed measured was 20.63 knots at 475rpm. It was difficult to determine the exact speeds of submerged measured-mile tests because below the surface, it was difficult to carry out exact plotting of the boat. It was possible to measure exact speeds only by induction when electric cables were crossed,

giving confirmation of values obtained by speedometer. The lack of audible detection and of audible propeller noise in the Walter-boats was observed later by the Nexö monitoring service on Bornholm with *U793*: at higher turbine speeds, instead of propeller noise only an indistinct 'heavy breathing' type noise was distinguished, which did not allow positive audible detection. It was found that much of the noise was absorbed by the carbon-dioxide emission from the stern of the boat.

When the *U792*'s starboard turbine became unusable, the port turbine only was used from the middle of May onwards and, at the end of that

month, the installation was due for a complete overhaul. Between 19 February and 21 May 1944, the turbine installation had been subjected to 16 combustion operation hours, of which almost 11 hours had been underwater. *U792* was taken into dock and the complete steam-producing installation with its various auxiliary engines, items of apparatus and tube ducts were dismantled, and the turbines were sent for overhaul to the BKC-Turbine Factory, Dresden. Two new turbines were delivered

Below: Walter U-boat *U795* laid up at GW in February 1945. In the foreground is a Type XXIII boat.

U793 (Wa201), the second Walter-boat to be built by Blohm and Voss, April 1944.

to replace them, but these could not be built-in immediately because of different-sized understructures and tube connections. The inner components of the combustion chamber and dust remover showed considerable damage, which was attributed to the frequent breakdowns of the regulator. The question of expediency in overhaul work was considerably influenced by the shortage of labour at B&V. Various tasks that should really have been carried out by B&V had to be performed by the firm of Walter KG, or by the U-boat test unit. The shortage of coppersmiths was specially onerous, and rebuilding work was also made more difficult by the shortage of berths. All of this combined to delay the boat's being ready for use again until 12 August 1944.

Meanwhile, in April 1944, U793 and U795 had been commissioned, with only one turbine each. Of the two, U793 proved to be considerably more reliable than her predecessors. After the first three trials of 25, 26 and 29 May had been accompanied by the usual troubles (regulator not working, starter winding of the vapour-pump motor burned out), this boat then functioned without any particular breakdown until the conclusion of the trials on 4 July 1944. UAK trials of U793 followed on 20 June, after a depth test on 15 June in 55m of water (345rpm, steam consumption 15.8 tons per hour) and a submerged endurance test (331 minutes) on 17 June 1944. These provided a maximum speed of 20.3 knots at 425rpm. U793 was then handed over to Training Command and, by 22 August 1944, its Walter-installation had achieved a total combustion operation time of 46 hours 37 minutes.

The first voyages made by U792 in August 1944 with the new turbines were once again marked by various failures, not, however, with the quantity-regulator, but mainly as a result of unsatisfactory assembly conditions in Hela — partial burning of the dust remover; Stoeckicht shaft gearing seized up; Aurol supply line leaky; combustion-chamber cover unsatisfactory; and, finally, entry of sea water in bag group 4 on 14 September. This meant that the boat had to return to dock where bag groups for hydrogen peroxide, numbers 1, 2 and 4, were changed.

On 28 September, U792 was ready for sea. During the following days, certain tests were carried out on behalf of Walter KG without incident. UAK acceptance tests for this boat with the Walter installation began on 2 October 1944. Initially, measured-mile (measured distance of 2 nautical miles) tests were carried out, the speeds of which were exactly computed by inductive measurement with the aid of an electric coil. After speeds had been calculated in this way, loggings were carried out exactly. These showed that, at 14.40 hours, the maximum attained measured-mile speed of 24.784 knots was achieved at 527rpm. However, during this high revving, the ambient temperature in the gearing climbed to over 100°C: the gear oil became so hot that its colouring matter separated and completely blocked the oil filters. Most of the oil flowed into the bilges by foaming up over the oil smoke catchers. The gear sump was refilled and, on 3 October, surface measured-miles were run to establish the surface speed limit of the Walter-drive. All that could be achieved (and then only for a short time) was 13.14 knots at 395rpm, as it had not been established how fuel-oil and Aurol would behave with high consumption and with low water pressure. However, the limit of revolutions before unintentional diving of the boat would take place was obviously very little above 400rpm. As the disintegration temperature of larger concentrations of H_2O_2 was less than 300°C, it was decided on 4 October to replace the stone lining of the disintegrator, which had already withstood a total concentration of 40 tons.

Following testing of the Walter-installation in progressive speed stages, UAK measured-mile testing began again on 7 October. At different speed stages, speed, number of revolutions and performance were measured. The highest submerged speed travelled was 21.575 knots at 470rpm and 2.720shp corresponding to Cw=186.3.

On 10 October, U792 carried out a lengthier trial, describing a submerged square. For approximately four hours, the installation was driven with, on the average, 435rpm. When the H_2O_2 was almost totally consumed, the number of revolutions was reduced to 336rpm and this was maintained for just about half an hour before Aurol was completely consumed. The total duration of the run amounted to 4 hours 25 minutes; H_2O_2 consumption 28.96m³; diving depth 18 metres; under-pressure in the boat 260mb. Further trials (H_2O_2 consumption measurements at depths of 18m, 30m, and 50m, turning circle measurements and crash-diving tests with the electric motor and deep-diving to 70m) followed on 11 October. On the 12th, certain malfunctions occurred in which pressure in the turbine compartment climbed to 0.25 atmospheric overload, and a small fire occurred in the Ju-compressor. This was caused by diesel oil escaping and being ignited by the H_2O_2 injector. The H_2O_2 was present at that place because of a leak in the valve through which H_2O_2 was taken on board. After thorough ventilating of the turbine compartment, the Walter installation could be run once again. On 17 October, because of destroyed insulation (supposedly a consequence of the pressure rise on 12 October) an electric motor in the turbine compartment was once again burned out. On this occasion it was the motor of No. 1 condenser pump. There was also a short circuit in the vapour-pump motor. As no replacement was available, the fault was not easily to be rectified, so these particular parts were borrowed from GW boat U795 as a short-term measure.

On 27 October 1944, U792, after a submerged cruise of one hour without fault being found in her Walter-installation, was handed over to the Training Unit. By this time, the total running time of U792's installation amounted to 41 hours 21 minutes, of which 28 hours 45 minutes had taken place underwater.

UAK trails had shown that in U792, the stress-limit of the installation for sustained running was 440rpm or 19.7 knots, much below the required 26 knots. This was not the fault of the turbine installation, but resulted from the high temperatures of the lubricating oil and bearings in the gear system. The GW boats had 23 per cent larger cooling surfaces in the gear-oil cooling system, and the temperatures here were considerably lower; however, this boat, on account of her greater resistance, could not achieve the higher speeds either.

In the autumn of 1944, U794 was subjected to depth-charge tests, and a number of faults became apparent. The most serious was that the disintegrator functioned imperfectly, apparently because the particles in the disintegrator were no longer in their correct position. Faults also appeared in the combustion chamber. However, Walter KG hoped that these various faults could be rectified by the time the first Type XXVI boat was ready for commissioning. No faults of any importance were apparent in the Aurol storage: the method of storing H_2O_2 in plastic bags had been well-tested in a test-bunker long before completion of the first Walter U-boat, and it had been found that this storage method was proof against explosions, and was as effective with full as with empty bags.

To sum up, it can be stated that the Walter-drive showed its value during tests despite numerous initial difficulties. Almost all breakdowns had identical causes — principally, the unproved quantity regulator and the poor design of the electric motors. Other faults could be attributed to inadequate yard work. It is noteworthy that, during these breakdowns, the installation showed itself to be robust and safe, in that the effects of breakdown were local and did not lead to mishaps involving loss of life. The various faults were able to be rectified in a relatively short time and with little trouble, so that the second B&V boat, U793, ran almost faultlessly. Design shortcomings — as for example the under-dimensioned steering installation and the gear-oil installation in the B&V boats, or the ill-chosen rudder shape of the GW boats (factors which considerably inhibited performances of these boats) — were nothing to do with the Walter-installation, and reflected, rather, the difficulties inextricably bound up with the development of new U-boat types with many untried innovations (as was also experienced in Type XXI).

Type XXI

The material for the pressure hull of the Type XXI U-boat was St 52 KM alloyed with aluminium. The armour material intended originally for Type VIIC/42 had also been discussed initially, but this was not available in any quantity and required a longer delivery time. The upper pressure hull had a maximum thickness of 26mm amidships, decreasing in thickness to 18mm forward and aft. The double-hull shape meant that, for the large part, outer frames (240mm × 11mm flat bulb frames, 80cm apart) could be used. Only the conical pressure-hull rings in the bow and the stern were given interior frames. This would provide adequate strength for a designed diving depth of 135m, i.e., 2.5 times as safe as the calculated destruction depth of 330m and 1.5 times as safe as the test diving depth of approximately 200m (60 per cent of the destruction diving depth).

However, only the upper part could accurately be considered as a circular pressure hull for appropriate calculations to be made. The lower part could not be considered in the same light because, on the one hand, the frames from the upper part overlapped considerably and, second, this lower part had floor timbers. The lower part had therefore to be designed without the benefit of exact basic calculations, and its strength would have to be tried out retrospectively. A pressure test of a model at GW showed that the lower part of the pressure-hull was approximately 10 per cent weaker than the upper part. This meant a destruction depth of 300m, a test diving depth of 180m and a designed diving depth of 120m. It was intended that these values should be established before the boats were made operational. With Chief Naval Construction Adviser Diestelmeier in charge, the first Type XXI, *U2511*, left Kiel for Horten on 16 March 1945 to carry out her first deep diving trial. The IBG had been informed that, in order to accommodate a shaft-brake at pressure-hull Frame 10.4, two interior frame rings had been cut away by 20mm, but, inadvertently, this had not been reported to the Design Department. With calculations appropriate to rectification of the cut-away profile being incomplete, the test diving depth for *U2511* was restricted to 160m until the frame-strengthening, ordered by the Supreme Naval Command, was completed. This depth was achieved at the first deep diving test in Oslo Fjord at the end of March. The most important result established was that measured tensions at the unsupported torpedo hatch were much greater than the calculated values. At 160m depth, these exceeded the yield limit, reaching values up to 4,000kg/cm^2.

Immediately after the Easter holidays, work was carried out in the State Yard of Horten, when, with very great difficulties for the fitters, the cut-away pressure-hull Frame 10.4 was strengthened without removing its electric motors, and a transverse support was incorporated in the torpedo hatch.

A second deep diving test took place off Kristiansand at the beginning of April 1945, when, deformation measurements in the region of the cut-away Frame 10.4 and tension measurements in the area of the strengthened torpedo hatch were calculated. This time, no limit had been set on the diving depth; the decision was left to the discretion of the Test Controller. When a depth of 160m had been passed, a cracking noise, increasing with depth, was heard from the after battery trough, and was interpreted by the Test Controller, in the light of model tests, as signifying the imminence of dent formation. This test was therefore abandoned at 170m. Deformation around the cutaway frame was slight at this depth (only approx. 1.5mm decrease in the cross-section), but tensions around the torpedo hatch, despite the added support, were so high that it was considered necessary to use two supports. The Test Controller then returned to Kiel and initiated work on corresponding torpedo-hatch strengthening in the boats lying there. After thorough discussion, the cracking noises were attributed to plastic deformation of outer-ship components, caused by the elastic pressure-hull

deformation, and were not thought to be dangerous.

Dönitz showed displeasure that no greater depth had been attempted. Consequently, on 14 April 1945, the KIU Head, Ministerial Counsellor Aschmoneit, left Kiel in *U2506*, bound for Horten, to superintend personally the next deep diving test. This took place on 26 April, with built-in hatch support beams and a strengthened pressure-hull Frame 10.4. Apart from a loud noise at 160m, from the collapse of the GBT (acoustic buoy) secured on deck, nothing particular occurred down to 220m. The shape change remained minimal, tensions measured in the vicinity of the strengthened torpedo hatch were insignificant, and the deformation noises were normal. At 220m a 'pressure-tight' rubber dinghy container imploded with a loud noise and the test was broken off.

A further deep diving test was carried out with *U2529* just before the capitulation on 8 May 1945. The Test Controller on this occasion was Naval Construction Adviser Grim. When 140m had been passed, slight frame deformation was discovered at one interior frame beneath the conning tower. At 190m, implosions of the rubber dinghy containers on deck occurred. At 210m, the diving test was discontinued because of the colossal din caused by imploding containers. After surfacing, it was established that the implosions had not endangered the boat, and a further diving test was carried out, this time to 220m, when nothing untoward occurred. It is known that, during a diving test off southern Norway at the beginning of May, *U3008* touched the bottom at 170m.

On 21 November 1944, during a measured-mile run on the surface, using both diesel engines and superchargers (supercharger pressure 0.44 atmospheric overload) *U3005* attained a speed of 15.23 knots at 486rpm of the engine shaft, and a total fuel consumption of 640kg per hour. When operating on diesels only, the electric motors and gearing and associated pumps were being driven at all times, which corresponded to a constant performance loss of 7 per cent. This meant that the mechanical diesel efficiency was only 88 per cent. A deliberate decision had been made to do without a clutch for disconnecting the electric motors during diesel operation, as it was assumed that the large batteries would never be fully charged and that charging would be constantly taking place during diesel operation. However, the mechanical performance loss could be reduced, and 95 per cent efficiency obtained, if the electric motors were allowed to turn over electrically, without supplying any propulsion to the propellers. This would mean that, supercharged, 2 × 1,900hp could be delivered to the shaft (15.7 knots). The flattened part of the performance-curve in the 15–18 knots range could only be used with electrical supplement because of the relatively small diesel power. On 15 December 1944, with electrical supplement (drawing from the batteries each side 1,347A=6 hours current), *U3507* reached a maximum surface speed of 18.08 knots at 544rpm of the engine shaft, and 0.4 atmospheric overload supercharger pressure. The corresponding performance on the boat's shaft amounted to 2 × 2,380hp.

It had originally been intended that charging should also take place during schnorkel travel, but the danger existed that, with considerable valve overlapping, the engine might come to a standstill through reversal of the charging pressure caused by strong counter-pressure. In order to prevent this, a second cam arrangement was provided on the control shaft (schnorkel adjustment), which reduced the amount of valve overlapping. The diesel performance then went back to 1,400hp at 470rpm, and the supercharger ran at only 10,000rpm instead of 12,240; on the other hand, the counter-pressure sensitivity was decreased, as were the unpleasant effects it had caused.

On 21 October 1944, during schnorkel travel, *U3503*, using both diesel engines and supercharger (supercharger pressure 0.35 atmospheres overload and 7,500rpm supercharger revolutions) attained a speed of 10.4 knots at 395rpm on the engine shaft, with a total fuel consumption of 412kg per hour. With battery charging carried out (starboard engine charging only, 625A and port engine drive) a maximum of 5.6 knots was obtained. In operational use, it turned out that this schnorkel performance could also be achieved without supercharging. As pure surface performance was no longer of paramount importance for this type of boat in 1944–45, there was no particular gain in using a supercharger during schnorkel travel, and it was therefore omitted from later boats. The effect of this was that the maximum surface performance went down from 2 × 2,000hp (=2 × 1,760hp on the shaft, corresponding to 15.4 knots) to 2 × 1,400hp (=2 × 1,230hp on the shaft, corresponding to 14.6 knots). The maximum schnorkel performance was now 2 × 1,200hp (=2 × 1,060hp on the shaft, corresponding to 10.9 knots). However, in practice, due to oscillations in the periscope and schnorkel, 6 knots was hardly ever exceeded in schnorkel travel.

The test bed results for the large main motors had shown a maximum 1,800kW performance at 5,500A current-intake, and engine revolutions of 1,675rpm. With fully-charged batteries, this performance could be maintained for one hour. Normal boat practice, however, was that each double motor would attain only 1,650kW for 20 minutes, or 1,550kW (=2,100hp) for 50 minutes, because batteries, even when fully charged, did not hold their intended 360 volts charge at maximum performance. A test in *U3506* showed that with batteries carrying a charge of 361 volts and a constant discharge of 2 × 5,540 Amps, the charge in the electric motors not supplying power was 350 volts, and when supplying power, only 336 volts. After thirty minutes, the charge was down to 332 volts, after fifty minutes, discharge was down to 305 volts. After that it went down very rapidly.

In a submerged measured-mile run on 8 November 1944, at a diving depth of 20m, *U3506* (in her original version) achieved a speed of 15.93 knots at 316rpm. This was 2 knots below the theoretically-calculated value. It corresponded to a Navy Constant of $C_W=149$

Since Type XXI was conceived originally as a diving-boat, it was necessary that the diving time be as short as possible. Consequently, numerous flooding and ventilation openings had been made in

Left: The conning-tower fairing of *U2502.*

the outer ship, but these considerably increased resistance. Towing tests established that the figures obtainable with a smooth hull would be decreased by 17—19 per cent by a vented hull. Tests in which the flooding slits were made smaller or welded up showed that the slits increased resistance by approximately 28 per cent, which, from a performance point of view, represented a consumption of approximately 850shp at top speed. Although the total cross-section area of the flooding slits and other openings were radically reduced (flooding slits reduced to 20—30mm width; openings in the bridge covering closed; upper-deck gratings covered with sheet metal; complete openings left only in the water-tight fore-ship and in a row of lower flooding slits in the bridge bulwarks; ventilation holes and small slits in the upper deck) the diving time increased by only approximately 10 seconds to a maximum of 30 seconds, and the decrease in resistance was reduced by only 5 per cent. So a compromise was agreed. The final version envisaged a flooding slit proportion of 1.98 per cent of the total surfaces, which increased resistance by 15 per cent, and allowed a diving time of 25 seconds. With the drastic, two-thirds' reduction in the flooding slit surfaces, *U3507*, on 21 November 1944, attained 17.2 knots (Cw=197) at 3,100kW (2 × 2,100hp). Using the originally intended power of 3,500kW, this version would have been capable of 18 knots. In the final version (reduction of flooding-slit surface by one-third), on 30 November 1944, *U3507* achieved 16.8 knots for 20 minutes, and 16.5 knots for one hour (Cw=175).

The shape of the conning-tower fairing was decided by the necessity to accommodate anti-aircraft turrets, the echo-ranging installation and various items of extensible apparatus. Although the anti-aircraft turrets were faired neatly into the streamlined conning tower, they still caused an increase in resistance of 7 per cent. On the other hand, the open, surface control position let into the bridge roofing had very little such effect. Tests carried out with *U3001* (a bridge with just such a cut-into structure) and *U3507* (a fully-enclosed bridge) showed that the fully-enclosed bridge had a speed advantage over the normal bridge of only 0.15 knots. When wind protection screens were raised, there was a speed loss of 0.35 knots and, in the cut-into bridge, a loss of 0.45 knots. The maximum surface speed with electric motors was higher than the maximum submerged speed, amounting in *U3506* (final version) to 16.93 knots at 5,994A, and in *U3005* (with covered flooding slits) to 17.94 knots at 5,798A current intake per engine. This result showed clearly that the boat's hull had been well designed for good surface performance. Tests of the silent creep-speed engines showed that the expected results were indeed attained. In a submerged measured-mile run, *U3506*, using these silent engines, achieved a maximum of 6.1 knots at 123rpm.

The diving time (20 seconds) of the first boats at maximum speed was very short; even in the final version (25 seconds) they were lower than in Type VIIC. The best diving time was achieved when the after hydroplane, after 13 seconds, was moved from the 15° angle to its former position, so that the stern did not 'stick' to the surface. However, the speed of descent decreased rapidly. If the boat was to be brought quickly to considerable depth, the rudder would have to be set at 25° until the requisite depth was achieved.

In diving at top speed, the negative buoyancy tank, which in all previous U-boats had been essential for the diving operation, had only minimal effect (shortening of the diving time by a mere 5 seconds). The boat was so well designed that, when the negative buoyancy tanks were empty, by an increase in dynamic forces (increase in speed), the diving process was considerably accelerated. On the other hand, with flooded negative buoyancy tanks, even when the boat was motionless, one could almost achieve the minimum diving time. When diving from rest or at the lower speed ranges, negative buoyancy tanks did indeed enable a reduction to be made in diving time, but this requirement was of lesser importance, so that it was possible to dispense with the negative buoyancy tanks. When submerged, the boat reacted with sensitivity to adjustments of the hydroplanes. In the higher speed ranges (over 6 knots) the boat could be controlled by the after hydroplanes alone (adjustment ± 5° for ± 0.2m stability). Use of the forward hydroplanes was more of a hindrance than a help.

As designed, the 8m-wide fins were over-dimensioned: after towing tests, they were reduced to 6.4m, thus providing less resistance. Later, 5.5m-wide fins were to be tried out on the completed boat, and these would certainly have been adequate, as the fin width of *Wilhelm Bauer* (ex-*U2540*) was to show.

Less favourable was the effect of the Type XXI lateral rudders. The boat's slim shape and the lack of rudder effect (the lateral rudder, except at extreme rudder angle, lay outside the propeller wash) made the turning circle very large; in submerged travel, with the most favourable conditions (rudder hard over=25°) and with outer screw alone (at about 11 knots) it was approximately 365m. With both screws and at top speed, it was approximately 420m; at 6 knots, it was approximately 450m. In surface travel, a turning circle of 800—1,000m resulted, which was almost twice as large as in previous boats of the same size, and made for difficulties in surface manoeuvring. The propeller shafts, inclined very slightly outwards, had an effect that was not expected at that time; when turning, it was necessary to let the inner propeller run more quickly than the outer, so that as small a turning circle as possible be achieved.

Type XXIII

U-boat Type XXIII had a pressure hull of shipbuilding steel St 52 KM, with a maximum thickness of 11.5mm. Rigidity was provided by 140 × 7mm flat-bulb interior frames at distances of 450—550mm. This design was to reach a designed diving depth of 100m (2.5 times safety), a test diving depth of 150m and a destruction diving depth of 250m. As in Type XXI, however, the basic calculations concerning the double-circle shape were conjectural, so that only a diving test could establish the final safety factor. On 24 January 1945, the first test was made under the control of Naval Construction Adviser Grim with *U2324* off the coast of Norway. A depth of 150m was reached quite uneventfully, and apparently the assumed diving depths were wholly attainable. Not until 6 December 1946, when *U2326* (with a French crew aboard) sank off Toulon, did doubts arise concerning the estimated strength. Exact calculations by the Lübeck Engineering Office subsequently confirmed these doubts — the assumed diving depths were too large. The serviceable diving depth for *Hai* (ex-*U2365*) and *Hecht* (ex-*U2367*) was only 80m.

U-boat Type XXIII was designed principally for submerged performance; even the propeller was designed with submerged travel in mind. From approximately 9 knots on the surface, over-flooding of the forward deck caused a considerable increase in the boat's resistance. Above 9.5 knots, the surface power requirement became so high that each increase in power, above the normal diesel full power of 575hp (=405kW on the shaft) had no effect, and no increase in speed was possible over approximately 10 knots. The theoretically-possible maximum load on the diesels of 630hp at 880rpm (=445kW on the shaft) only brought about an increase in speed of 0.1 knots.

While there was no over-flooding of the deck forward of the bridge, the wave resistance stayed relatively small (up to approximately 6–7 knots); in fact, the surface resistance was less than the submerged resistance at this same speed. In this speed range, with the same power, a higher speed was reached above water. The cause lay mainly in the considerable resistance of the bridge. The schnorkel results were especially favourable. The high bridge made it possible for the fixed length of schnorkel and periscope to be relatively large (2m) and the free part to be extremely small, which meant that in all speed ranges there was no oscillation. As the resistance figures at top speed underwater were considerably superior to those on the surface, the maximum schnorkel speed was greater than the surface speed. (Measured value of *U2321* in its final version: 10.75 knots at 380kW on the shaft.) Full diesel performance could be achieved during schnorkel travel, the schnorkel cross-section being relatively large and the underpressure (38mb) and the exhaust-gas counter-pressure (0.35 atmospheres overload) supplied by the generously proportioned engine (without loading) were endurable. This boat was the first to achieve a relatively high operational schnorkel endurance.

The test bed results for the electric motor had shown a maximum 427kW (=580hp) at 240 volts, 1,960A current intake and 850rpm. This result was also obtained with practical tests at sea. Through friction losses in the gearing and shafting, 95.5 per cent, or 408kW, was delivered to the screw. During diesel operation, the electric motor, when not connected for charging, acted as a performance balancer, which guaranteed a uniform running of the diesels even in a swell. It was noted in Type

U2321 (Type XXIII) being positioned at Slip 8, GW, for an overhaul. Note the upper part of the bridge, which had been rounded off for submerged test runs.

XXIII, as in Type XXI, that a reduction of the flooding slits and a removal of all inessential appendages brought about an increase in the submerged top speed. Originally, to help achieve an extremely short diving time, many flooding apertures and ventilation openings had been provided, especially in the conning-tower superstructure.

In her original version, with an upper-deck gangway and a forward fin, *U2321* reached an underwater speed of 11.2 knots at 405kW on the shaft; after a 70 per cent reduction of the flooding slits on the bridge and the sound-proofing fairing, 11.6 knots at 410kW on the shaft. The highest submerged speed was achieved after further reduction of the flooding slits at diving cell 3 (each by 3 flooding slits aft), removal of the 'upper deck' and all fins; 12.58 knots at 415kW on the shaft. In her final condition (flooding slits reduced by approximately 30 per cent, 'upper deck' removed, minus the forward fins) *U2330*, on 29 October 1944, achieved 12.25 knots at 390kW on the shaft and, on 1 November 1944, 12.5 knots at 415kW, both underwater. The appropriate Navy Constants were $C_W=146$ and $C_W=148$. At a depth of 20m on silent

creep engine drive, *U2321* achieved 4.8 knots at a maximum 28kW on the shaft. The submerged range was greatest at 2.5 knots and amounted to 215 nautical miles. At this speed, the propeller noise was almost undetectable. At the beginning of 1945, tests were made in *U4703* and *U4705* to fit thickened propellers (with 20mm and 30mm bulges) which would cause considerably less propeller noise in the higher speed ranges. The loss of speed caused by this thickening was negligible (0.3 knots at top speed). It was decided to introduce the 20mm bulge in all Type XXIII boats.

Being an almost 'pure' submerged vessel, Type XXIII did not have negative buoyancy tanks. When diving from a position of rest without any enforced trim down by the head, it took only 21 seconds for the final component, the high bridge, to become submerged. With the aid of the deep-set, forward hydroplane when diving in motion, the boat quickly came down steeply at the head, which produced a strong, dynamic negative buoyancy, enabling complete submergence of the boat after approximately 14 seconds. In this case, too, the last part of the boat to be covered by water was the upper edge of the bridge. The considerable reduction in the flooding slits did not increase this extremely short dynamic diving value, but it later turned out that the fins forward of the hydroplanes lengthened dynamic diving by approximately 1 second.

The very high descending speed made it imperative, when deep dives were being undertaken in motion, to make a timely adjustment of the hydroplanes so that the permitted diving depth should not be exceeded. The low reserve displacement of 10.5 per cent meant that the boat would sink extremely quickly in the event of water entering, as was amply demonstrated by accidents with *Hai* (ex-*U2365*), described on page 312, and *U2331*, which sank with all hands on 10 October 1944, during surface travel off Hela. After the boat had been raised, a reconstruction of events showed that, before the accident, *U2331* had been travelling in reverse, with forward hydroplanes set at 0° and after hydroplanes at 4° upwards. The dive must have taken place so suddenly that no one could escape. Tests with *U2330* established that, with diving cells flooded in advance and when reversing, the danger existed of an unintended dive. With diving cell 1 flooded to 25 per cent, and forward and after hydroplanes inclined 10° upwards, after 50 seconds' reverse top speed, a trim down by the head of 18° was already apparent.

The boat was very easy to control underwater. The submerged turning circle was small and almost independent of speed. At 10° rudder inclination, it amounted to approximately 350m diameter; with full rudder, as little as 150m. Steering was also good on the surface. In *U2321*, at a speed of 10 knots the lateral rudder could be brought right across from one position to the opposite one in 14 seconds. During UAK tests, *U2330*, on the surface at 4 knots with 10° rudder inclination, had a turning circle diameter of approximately 830m; at top speed of 10

knots it was approximately 570m. With full rudder, the corresponding values were 280m and 250m. In other words, Type XXIII was also very manoeuvrable on the surface.

UNFINISHED PROJECTS

Electro-boat Projects XXIX to XXXI

With the preliminary sketch for the new Walter Type XXVI, two electro-boat projects were presented on 22 February 1944 for the purposes of comparison; instead of a Walter-installation these would have a large electric installation. Dönitz turned them down, however, on the grounds that their performance would have been much inferior to the already-available Type XXI. (See also page 240.) As the situation in 1944 favoured the use of a smaller and more simple U-boat than the large Type XXI, for operations against convoys around Britain and in the North Atlantic, consideration was given once more to an electro-boat with a single-shaft installation, and of the same size as Type VIIC. A further contributory factor was that there was scepticism concerning a prompt entry into operations of a large number of Walter-boats — especially on the grounds that insufficient Aurol was available.

Design XXVIE₁ presented by Naval Construction Director Oelfken on 22 February 1944, already embodied most of the points that prompted such considerations. Also making use of other suggestions from departments outside the U-Boat Departments of the Supreme Naval Command, he invited the Chief of Naval War Staff early in 1944 to have 'K' Office produce a design for a medium-sized electro-boat of 800—900 tons (not above 1,000 tons), which would have half the engine installation of Type XXI. What was to be planned,

therefore, was a small, manoeuvrable, ocean-going boat for operations between the North Cape and Gibraltar, i.e., not a real 'Atlantic' boat. This requirement was made in the light of judgements formed on those VIIC boats equipped with schnorkels. The required range was set at approximately 7,000 nautical miles at 10 knots.

There was an additional requirement for a rather larger boat with twice the range, which was to replace Type XXI for long-range operations, even though it would have only half the engine installation. A decisive factor in this was the bottleneck in engines for Type XXI at that time.

An important design condition was that use should be made of already-available and tested engines and building components — which was not at all the way to set about achieving the hoped-for optimum results, but which promised a quick realization. The largest possible number (at least eight) of ready-to-fire torpedo tubes should be installed in such a way that the requirements for a simple design, simple to build, should not be impaired.

During the summer of 1944, in response to these demands, a number of designs from inside and outside 'K' Office was produced. The Office designs all featured a new bow torpedo-tube arrangement, the result of work carried out under the control of the new Head of K I U, Ministerial Counsellor Aschmoneit. The forward section of the pressure hull was constructed in an 8-shaped section, which housed four torpedo tubes in each of its upper and lower parts. This meant that the bow compartment could be divided into two storeys and could be used to much better effect than in Type XXVI. Of these designs, those with a surface range of approximately 7,000 nautical miles at 10 knots were given the designation XXIX. The projects based on Type XXI, having ranges of approximately 15,000 nautical miles at 10 knots, were designated XXX and XXXI.

The presentation of Office Designs XXIXA–D, XXXA and XXXB, XXXI, and IBG Designs XXIXG was made at an Office discussion on 29 August 1944. After close deliberation on XXIXA–D, which differed from each other mainly in size and, therefore, in their electric motive capacities, the most appropriate type was judged to be XXIXB, with regard to the relationship between outlay and performance. The charging time of nine hours was too high, and the maximum submerged speed of 15.4 knots was inadequate, but only a small increase in size to this design, putting in a more powerful diesel engine, and an increase in the number of cells per battery would rectify these weaknesses. This new design was given the designation XXIXB2. For tactical operations when submerged, this type, although only half the size and with half the engine installation of Type XXI, had almost the same performance. (But whether, in practice, the designed surface speed of 16.6 knots could really have been achieved must be doubted in the light of experience with Type XXI.)

Projects XXIXF, G and H, designed by the IBG, were aimed especially at adequate noise-suppression during schnorkel travel and at high schnorkel speeds. In all of them, the diesel

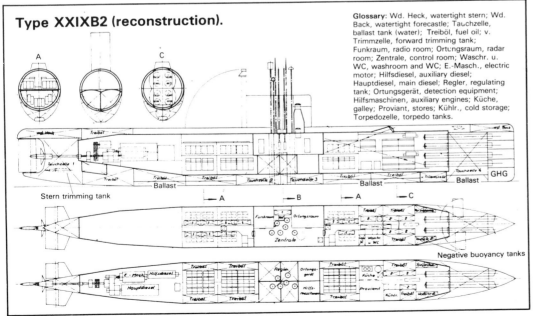

Type XXIXB2 (reconstruction).

Glossary: Wd. Heck, watertight stern; Wd. Back, watertight forecastle; Tauchzelle, ballast tank (water); Treiböl, fuel oil; v. Trimmzelle, forward trimming tank; Funkraum, radio room; Ortungsraum, radar room; Zentrale, control room; Waschr. u. WC, washroom and WC; E.-Masch., electric motor; Hilfsdiesel, auxiliary diesel; Hauptdiesel, main diesel; Regler, regulating tank; Ortungsgerät, detection equipment; Hilfsmaschinen, auxiliary engines; Küche, galley; Proviant, stores; Kühlr., cold storage; Torpedozelle, torpedo tanks.

installation consisted of two MWM RS34 diesel engines. The performance of the electric motors corresponded to the maximum battery voltage. The smallest design, XXIXH, had only two batteries, XXIXF had three, and XXIXG had four. These three designs differed from the Office designs in their torpedo installation. The IBG had not formulated any new ideas concerning this, but retained the available XXI and XXVI installations. Unusual features for XXIXG and H were a schnorkel periscope for high schnorkel speed, and a special 'anti-detection' boat shape (K-shape).

Of the designs intended to produce a successor to Type XXI for longer operations, Type XXXI was judged the best. In Type XXXA, four side tubes had been planned in addition to the eight bow torpedo tubes, as in design XXIXD, so that an appropriate number of torpedoes could be carried for longer operations. Although the provision of a large number of reload torpedoes would have been useful for a long-range U-boat, this was not considered, as it would have meant, willy-nilly, going back to a costly design on the lines of Type XXI. Type XXXA had a single-circle pressure hull, except for the sections in the vicinity of the torpedo tubes. The intended submerged speed for this project, 15.6 knots, was not considered satisfactory, and the armament, with only twelve torpedoes, did not measure up to what was expected in a long-range U-boat. These factors led to Project XXXB, in which the side tubes were dispensed with and, in their place, eight reserve torpedoes were carried in the lower deck bow compartment. In place of the living quarters which were originally in that space, an intermediate section was to be inserted abaft the bow compartment, which was to contain only crews' quarters. Even with this addition, the length and displacement would still be less than that of Type XXXA, because of the removal of the side torpedo tubes. The submerged speed was increased to 15.8 knots, but still remained distinctly below the hoped-for speed of approximately 16.5 knots.

Real improvements were only to be attained when insistence on the simplest possible hull construction was abandoned. A further increase in submerged speed could only come about, using the same power, by effecting a reduction in the frictional resistance, i.e., of the surface and form resistance. Only a very squat shape would serve the purpose. An increase in the pressure hull cross-section was not wanted, for it would need great steel strength and therefore involve production problems, so the symmetrical two-circle shape was therefore chosen. The considerable increase in height that this brought about made possible the installation of several decks (four amidships) and a relatively low positioning of the extensible items of equipment, with correspondingly low resistance. Above the engine compartments there was also sufficient room for a stern torpedo compartment with four torpedo tubes. This meant, therefore, that a total of twelve torpedo tubes was available with an additional twelve reserve torpedoes. Also, at 16.4 knots, the submerged speed corresponded to the requirements for a successor to Type XXI and, with only three-quarters of the displacement, half

the production expenditure as regards the propulsion unit and two-thirds of the production outlay in terms of batteries (which constituted a similar bottleneck problem). On the other hand, in the field of armament there was a doubling of ready-to-fire tubes and a 20 per cent increase in the number of torpedoes carried. This design was designated Type XXXI. With all these favourable properties, the project had one real disadvantage, and that was its considerable draught, 7m. Its realization, therefore, would involve a large number of constructional measures in the ports, which would mean that advantages in the saving of work time as compared to Type XXI would be devalued by additional work in other directions.

Schnorkel Project 'Tümmler'

In the light of favourable reports on schnorkel performance in Types VIIC and IXC in the summer of 1944, the U-Boat Delegate in the Construction Commission, Korvettenkapitän (Engineer) Hans Müller had arrived at the following conclusions:

'1. The introduction of the schnorkel to combat detection by the enemy was a correct basic step.

'2. However, boats are too slow when schnorkelling. When using the schnorkel, one is not really in a position to out-distance, to attack or to disengage.

'3. U-boat losses are especially hard to bear in that, when they occur, many highly-trained individuals, much material and much skilled building capacity are lost at one blow.'

He went on to state the following construction requirements:

'1. It is essential that maximum diesel performance be attainable while schnorkelling.

'2. As, even with the fullest application of defensive means, losses will still occur, boats must be made as small, simple and easily manned as possible, so that the least possible outlay is made with regard to personnel and materials in the shortest possible building time.'

The project for a coastal U-boat, worked out according to these ideas, was given the descriptive name 'Tümmler' ('Porpoise'), as it could proceed dynamically from surface travel to schnorkel travel (and vice versa). As the exhaust gases were fed into a special, high-positioned diving tank (exhaust gas tank), a small amount of residual bouyancy was present during schnorkel travel. The hull of this 200-ton boat was completely streamlined, and designed without an upper deck. The armament envisaged consisted of four bow torpedo tubes (no reserve torpedoes) with a fire-control system identical to that of Type XXIII. The propulsion unit consisted of a 2,000hp MAN diesel (Type XXI) to provide a maximum schnorkel speed of 17 knots, and a small 60hp Büssing diesel generator (the Seehund propulsion installation), which would serve to charge the small battery (the size of twenty torpedo troughs) and provide almost noiseless schnorkel travel of 5–6 knots. Electric propulsion was by the creep-speed motor of Type XXIII, which took its current from the battery during submerged travel. The electrical installation was, therefore, quite small, a big point in its favour in view of the battery bottleneck. It possessed the advantage that, during

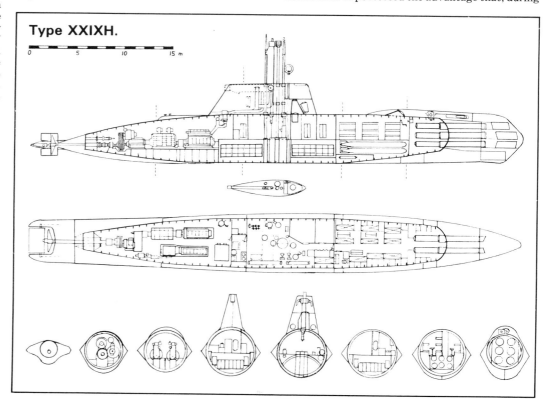

Type XXIXH.

Type XXXA.

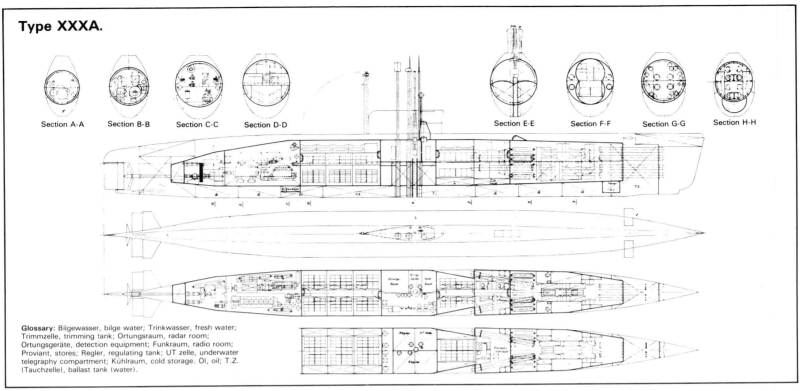

Section A-A Section B-B Section C-C Section D-D Section E-E Section F-F Section G-G Section H-H

Glossary: Bilgewasser, bilge water; Trinkwasser, fresh water; Trimmzelle, trimming tank; Ortungsraum, radar room; Ortungsgeräte, detection equipment; Funkraum, radio room; Proviant, stores; Regler, regulating tank; UT zelle, underwater telegraphy compartment; Kühlraum, cold storage. Öl, oil; T.Z. (Tauchzelle), ballast tank (water).

Type XXXI (reconstruction).

Glossary: Wd. Heck, watertight stern; Wd. Back, watertight forecastle; Trimmzelle, trimming tank; Treiböl, fuel oil; Torpedozelle, torpedo tank; Stauraum, stowage; Küche, galley; Waschr u. WC, washroom and WC; Prov., stores; Funkraum, radio room; Horchraum, listening room; Zentrale, control room; Horchgeräte, listening equipment; Trinkw., fresh water; Kdt., commander; Mot. öl, engine oil; Hilfsmaschinen, auxiliary engine; Off., officers; Regler, regulating tank. T.Z. (Tauchzelle), ballast tank (water).

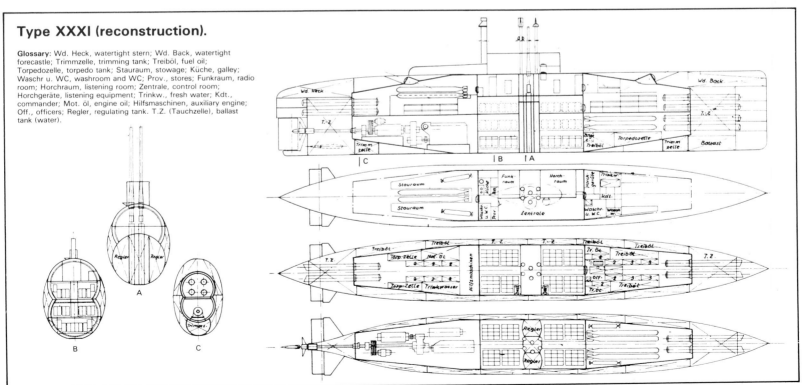

schnorkel travel, the battery was constantly being charged. The disadvantage was that the submerged range was small when, for any reason, schnorkel travel was not possible. However, it was believed in 1944, following successful use of it by U-boats in the Channel, that the schnorkel was difficult to detect, and that escape opportunities were, therefore, good, especially when a high schnorkel speed was also available. High schnorkel speeds demanded principally a strong streamlined, sheathed schnorkel, and this sheathing would incorporate — as a special feature — a schnorkel lookout beside the periscope.

A crew of only six men was envisaged. One or two men, from a combined rudder and control position, would be able to supervise the propulsion and steering. Additionally, when travelling, the commander would be at the periscope or in the 'schnorkel look-out', one man would be listening (i.e., monitoring) and, when attacks were being carried out, one extra man would be in charge of torpedo firing. The engine compartment was shut off by bulkheads, and would not normally need to be entered during schnorkel travel, which meant that the crew could avoid pressure variations caused by closing of the schnorkel head. At the beginning of 1945, the HSVA carried out towing and propulsion tests on a 1:8 model of this type, but no building contract was ever awarded. It seems very doubtful, in view of the extremely tight enemy air observation over the proposed operational areas, that a pure schnorkel boat on the lines of the 'Tümmler' could have reasonably justified itself. It is arguable whether further development would have gone over straight away to a closed-cycle drive.

Closed-cycle projects: Type XXIXK
The favourable outcome of test-bed trials of the MB501 C closed-cycle installation for the GW test boat *U798* (page 187) gave rise to expectations that, in a relatively short time, it would be possible to have available for trials operationally-suitable closed-cycle installations for larger U-boats, and 'K' Office, therefore, included this method of propulsion in its considerations for a follow-up boat for Type XXI. It seemed that even in strongly patrolled waters, in which schnorkel travel would be very restricted, the closed-cycle drive would enable boats to achieve positions from which attacks might be made while completely submerged. In comparison with the Walter-drive, the considerable range at submerged endurance-travel in the medium speed ranges was seen as an advantage, and even more advantageous was the use of the very much cheaper and more readily available pure oxygen.

Early in 1944, therefore, various studies were undertaken to establish what properties would accrue from incorporating a closed-cycle diesel installation in the available Walter Types XVIIB and XXVI. However, the retention of the shape of these boats yielded unsatisfactory results, in that it was not possible to store a sufficient quantity of gaseous oxygen. A comparable investigation was therefore carried out in August 1944 with four different designs, all of them based on the shape of

Type XXIXB, and which had been designated XXIXK1–K4. However, the relatively large volume of oxygen gas carried in bottles and the considerable weight of the bottles necessitated a rather large displacement — which, on the other hand, in the case of Types XXIXK1, K2 and K4, worked in favour of a stronger armament (eighteen torpedoes!). Sketches for Types XXIXK1–K3, together with modified Type XXIXB2, were presented on 14 September 1944.

Types XXIXK1 and K2 differed in size and performance. Type XXIXK1 had two six-cylinder diesel engines, each of 1,000hp (probably RS34S with high supercharging); for Type XXIXK2, four of these were proposed. Design XXIXK4 corresponded to Type XXIXK2, except that it would use two twelve-cylinder diesel engines (probably RS12 V26/34a, with high supercharging) instead of the four six-cylinder engines. Weight saved in this way should enable a greater oxygen supply to be carried. It was additionally proposed to carry part of the oxygen in liquid form, which would enable a considerable increase in the submerged range to be achieved.

Type XXIXK3 took a different turning. It was proposed that this type be given the high submerged speed of a Walter-boat by installing a closed-cycle drive, but it turned out that this could not be attained, even by comprehensive restriction of armament and crew's quarters. Nevertheless, the result was quite considerable. With four MB501C diesel engines, the boat could achieve in closed-cycle when submerged a maximum of 21.5 knots. Once again, to achieve a satisfactory submerged range, part of the oxygen was to be stored in liquid form.

Post-war studies of this design (Type 126K) by Oelfken and others showed that a somewhat shorter boat, fitted with three MB501C diesel engines could have achieved a maximum submerged speed of 20 knots. This project anticipated using only oxygen gas storage, in order not to be restricted to the closed-cycle range when making an endurance voyage. The daily evaporation of approximately 5 per cent of the liquid oxygen supply would otherwise have necessitated the constant use of some part of the oxygen supply, even if there were no pressing need for closed-cycle travel, or the use of a special installation to convert evaporated oxygen back to liquid. Furthermore, despite its incontestable advantages, the large number of high-performance diesel engines, part of which would be used only for peak speed, but would be merely ballast for the greater part of operations, put Type XXIXK3 in a problematic light in view of the situation as it was in 1944. A judgment given by Ministerial Counsellor Aschmoneit shortly after the war, named Type XXIXK2 or K4 as the most likely of these versions to have been considered worthy of realization.

A more feasible possibility of achieving Type XXVI's submerged performance in an 'oxygen boat' was that of feeding a Walter-turbine installation with pure oxygen instead of Aurol (see page 282). Further improvement of the closed-cycle drive in U-boats could only be achieved by having an oxygen-producing installation on board, so

investigations were also made into the properties a U-boat would need in order to carry such an installation. The closed-cycle range was to be limited only by the amount of fuel-oil carried.

In Project XXIXKS, just as in Type XXIXK4, two 2,000hp diesel engines served as propulsion. Work on this project, however, showed that it was not feasible to incorporate an oxygen-producing installation in a boat of this size (approximately 1,000 tons). The size and weight of such equipment would necessitate a large boat of 1,500–2,000 tons displacement, with a pressure-hull height of at least 5.5m.

Type XXXIII
After some thought it became apparent that reconstructing Type XXIII to have a closed-cycle drive, with oxygen gas stored in bottles, would be completely unsatisfactory: only liquid oxygen could provide the desired large submerged range. Certainly, in the case of Atlantic U-boats requiring a large surface range, the constant evaporation of liquid oxygen would have been a big problem, restricting considerably the closed-cycle operational time; but this drawback was not too serious in the case of coastal U-boats. With the idea of matching the length of operations with the evaporation time of the liquid oxygen, Type XXXIII was formulated. It could be assumed with reasonable accuracy that the whole oxygen supply would have evaporated after the operational period of 30 days. Logically then, after 20 days at sea, during which there had been constant consumption of oxygen, despite its tendency to evaporate the supply available for the attacking run would still be in excess of that needed for the actual attack. With pure submerged travel, the boat could subsequently close on its target from a greater distance, as an electro-boat might do.

The range of operations was expected to be approximately 1,500 nautical miles. Calculations showed that, assuming twelve hours of schnorkel cruising, complete emptying of the batteries, and daily closed-cycle operation consumption of oxygen, decreasing through evaporation, a day's run of 152 nautical miles could be achieved. Thus, ten days would be necessary to reach the intended area of operations, and ten days could then be spent in this zone if the return trip were to be carried out in the same way as when outward bound. Closed-cycle speed during the outward and return voyages would be as low as possible without causing sooting-up of the engine; this would keep consumption of oxygen as low as possible. Three knots was anticipated for the electric motor performance, this being a speed at which depth-control would be good and the electric motor (creep-motor Type XXI) would be reliable. The electric range should be 52 nautical miles at 3 knots. This method of travel would yield a maximum range of 4,600 nautical miles, and a smaller battery could be fitted than in other U-boats of the same size.

The boat would have a displacement of 360 tons. The pressure hull could be given a very stable shape, as the simple storage of the oxygen tank together with its insulation and the compensating tanks meant that adequate weight was available.

This made possible a considerable diving depth of 180m (designed diving depth 2.5 times the safety margin).

In order to provide a good shape for the oxygen tank so as to curb expenditure on insulation, the whole pressure hull cross-section was to be used to accommodate it, and passage between control room and bow compartment would have to be made through a flat conning tower. Equipment including periscope and communications apparatus was to be as in Type XXIII, but the armament would consist of four bow torpedo tubes (plus two reserve torpedoes).

The project was placed before the then Head of 'K' Office, Admiral Fuchs, but there was no Office discussion. It was then shown to the Chief of Second Naval War Staff, Konteradmiral Godt, who criticized the low submerged top speed of 11.5 knots. An altered design, XXXIIIB, was discussed, which would be given a submerged speed increased by 2 knots, to be achieved by fitting a diesel engine with twice the performance. Because more space was needed to store a greater quantity of oxygen, the displacement climbed to approximately 450 tons, and this did not please 'K' Office. Only subsequently was it shown to the new 'K' Head, Vizeadmiral Ruge.

Type XXXIV

Apart from Type XXXIII, during the winter of 1944/45, another closed-cycle U-boat with a high submerged speed, intended for coastal operations, was projected. The stimulus for this was not that of military requirements. The starting-point was a technical, theoretical one — to establish, through this project, the extreme limits in submerged speed for the closed-cycle in a smaller U-boat. A large range was therefore not considered. The boat was to be as simple to build as possible, and to have a short building time.

With a surface water displacement of 90 tons, the project bordered on the small U-boat size. Having a schnorkel range of 1,200 nautical miles at 11 knots, operational endurance would be one week, which was considered adequate for use in the North Sea and the English Channel. The choice of the boat's shape and size was dictated by a desire to use the MB501C diesel engine, which had already been tested in closed-cycle. The hull was to be designed in four sections bolted to each other for simple assembly and maintenance; the separating-joints would be directly abaft the diesel engine and on both sides of the oxygen tank. Rubber would provide tightness for the sections. A similar, simple sub-division had already been used successfully in midget U-boats (page 284). The frame distance was to be small, at 300mm, so that small frame heights could be achieved. The 8.5mm pressure-hull skin was suitable for a designed diving depth of 100m. As torpedo tubes would have involved a considerable increase in displacement, the suggested torpedo armament was of a freely-flooding nature, but, to avoid too great a resistance from the two torpedoes, they were positioned in the upper deck in departure boxes or on rails. When they were to be fired, the upper deck would be opened by a hinged flap; the torpedoes would be released from their fastening and the torpedo propulsion unit would be set in motion. As the negative-buoyancy compensation, amounting to 300kg in a normal torpedo, was not easily achieved with such a small boat, torpedoes without negative buoyancy were to be used. Their smaller range was acceptable because this boat had a high submerged speed and was very manoeuvrable.

A three-man crew was intended: helmsman, engineer and an observer. The entire engine installation could be operated from a control position forward of the engine compartment bulkhead. As the height of the hull did not permit of a sufficiently long periscope and as it was considered inadvisable to fit a high periscope jack, because of resistance, a folding periscope was planned.

With closed-cycle use, the boat was to achieve a maximum submerged speed of 22 knots; with schnorkel use, bearing in mind oscillations of

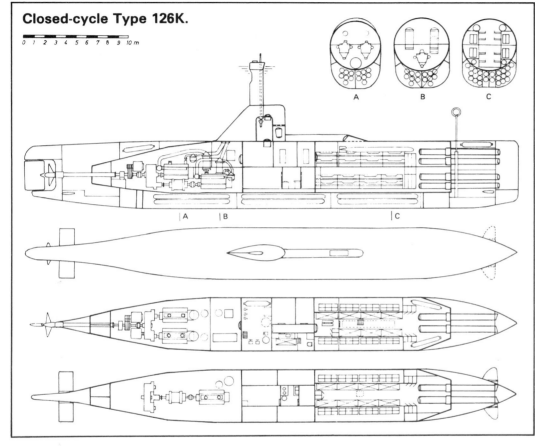

Closed-cycle Type 126K.

0 1 2 3 4 5 6 7 8 9 10m

A B C

|A |B |C

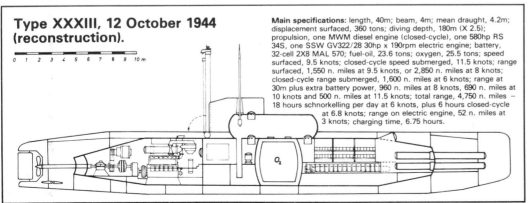

Type XXXIII, 12 October 1944 (reconstruction).

0 1 2 3 4 5 6 7 8 9 10m

Main specifications: length, 40m; beam, 4m; mean draught, 4.2m; displacement surfaced, 360 tons; diving depth, 180m (X 2.5); propulsion, one MWM diesel engine (closed-cycle), one 580hp RS 34S, one SSW GV322/28 30hp x 190rpm electric engine; battery, 32-cell 2X8 MAL 570; fuel-oil, 23.6 tons; oxygen, 25.5 tons; speed surfaced, 9.5 knots; closed-cycle speed submerged, 11.5 knots; range surfaced, 1,550 n. miles at 9.5 knots, or 2,850 n. miles at 8 knots; closed-cycle range submerged, 1,600 n. miles at 6 knots; range at 30m plus extra battery power, 960 n. miles at 8 knots, 690 n. miles at 10 knots and 500 n. miles at 11.5 knots; total range, 4,750 n. miles — 18 hours schnorkelling per day at 6 knots, plus 6 hours closed-cycle at 6.8 knots; range on electric engine, 52 n. miles at 3 knots; charging time, 6.75 hours.

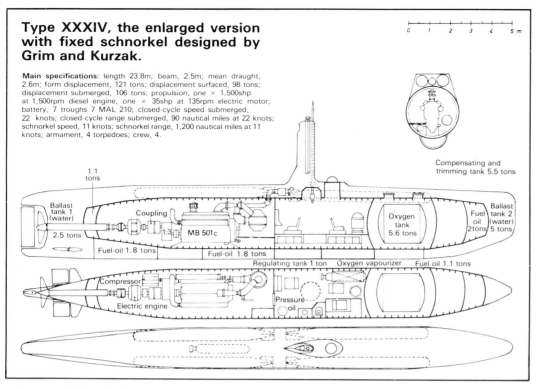

Type XXXIV, the enlarged version with fixed schnorkel designed by Grim and Kurzak.

Main specifications: length 23.8m; beam, 2.5m; mean draught, 2.6m; form displacement, 121 tons; displacement surfaced, 98 tons; displacement submerged, 106 tons; propulsion, one × 1,500shp at 1,500rpm diesel engine, one × 35shp at 135rpm electric motor; battery, 7 troughs 7 MAL 210; closed-cycle speed submerged, 22 knots; closed-cycle range submerged, 90 nautical miles at 22 knots; schnorkel speed, 11 knots; schnorkel range, 1,200 nautical miles at 11 knots; armament, 4 torpedoes; crew, 4.

1.1 tons

Ballast tank 1 (water) 2.5 tons

Coupling

Fuel-oil 1.8 tons

MB 501c 1:3

Fuel-oil 1.8 tons

Regulating tank 1 ton   Oxygen vapourizer   Fuel oil 1.1 tons

Oxygen tank 5.6 tons

Fuel oil 2tons   Ballast tank 2 (water) 5 tons

Compensating and trimming tank 5.5 tons

Compressor

Electric engine

Pressure oil

periscope and schnorkel-mast, and the considerable surface influence of depth-keeping, 11 knots; with the electric motor (Seehund-EM), 6 knots. As Project XXXIV, it only got so far as being presented to the Head of 'K' Office: it was the last coastal U-boat project to be formulated before the war ended.

Oxygen-fed turbine boats: Types XXXV and XXXVI

If insistence were made on a speed higher than 22 knots, this could only be achieved by using a turbine for propulsion. Towards the end of the war, attempts were made to establish if and how the Walter-installation could be used with pure oxygen. Basically this seemed quite possible, and two designs were formulated for comparative purposes. They were designated Type XXXV and XXXVI, and were the last U-boat designs formulated by the Navy. They did not reach the stage of being presented to the Supreme C-in-C.

Type XXXV took as its starting-point work done on the Project Series XXIX: eight bow torpedo tubes and a structurally simple construction without side tubes. The arrangement in which batteries were placed near the living quarters against the pressure-hull wall was a new departure. As it was intended to achieve the performance of the Walter Type XXVI, for reasons of weight, oxygen gas storage was excluded: the 60 tons of oxygen that would need to be carried would, at 400 atmospheres, require more than 90 steel bottles, each containing 1.25m³, with a total weight of 207 tons. On the other hand, the use of liquid oxygen

meant inevitably that the range of Walter-turbine use would depend on the length of the operation. It was desired that the boat, on entry into operations, should have the same turbine range as Type XXVI, and an operational zone approximately 2,000 nautical miles from base was assumed. Duration of operations was estimated as six weeks, of which two would be spent outward bound, two homeward bound and two weeks in the operational zone. These requirements were not wholly met in the design calculations. The increased space requirement for storage of the oxygen bottles beneath the pressure hull, the oxygen tank in the interior of the boat, and the larger engine installation necessitated a displacement larger than that of Type XXVI.

Consequently, a more powerful diesel engine than that of Type XXVI would be needed. The intention was to use the twelve-cylinder RS12 V26/34a V-engine by MWM, which would provide, when supercharged, 2,000hp at 850rpm. This engine was already intended for Walter U-boat Types XVIII and XXIV, and probably for the closed-cycle Type XXIXK4 boat. It was not intended to use both the BBC superchargers in the diesel destined for Type XXXV, because it was considered, in the light of experience with Type XXI, that they would not bring about any increase in performance during schnorkel travel. The diesel range was to be 7,000 nautical miles at 10 knots. A total of 65 tons of oxygen was proposed, in order that the submerged range of Type XXVI, 160 nautical miles at 24 knots, might be achieved; of this amount, 25 tons would be carried in gas form in bottles, and 40 tons in a tank. The length of the boat was 50m and

the pressure hull diameter was 5.3m. The compartment distribution from aft forwards was as follows: turbine compartment, electric motor and diesel compartment, control room (including auxiliary-engine compartment), oxygen tank with passageway to the starboard side (passage-way with a circular cross-section), bow compartment (subdivided into two decks, each deck having living quarters and four torpedo tubes). As in Type XXVI — apart from the commander's cabin abaft the control room — all the crew were accommodated in the bow compartment. Also located in this area were an additional four reserve torpedoes, the galley, the WC and provisioning.

As the situation in 1944–45 made it almost impossible to carry out completely new U-boat development, especially in terms of production, an attempt was made to redesign Type XXVI, already in production, to use oxygen as a propulsion fuel. To this end, components from Type XXVI were to be used as far as possible. This led to Project XXXVI. The most simple way was to store oxygen bottles in those compartments in the outer ship intended for Aurol bunkers. For reasons of weight and trimming, only 16 large bottles, containing a total of 10 tons of oxygen gas at 400 atmospheres could be accommodated, but this quantity would only suffice to provide one-fifth of the turbine range of Type XXVI. This solution, then, was completely impracticable. It was intended, therefore, to fit an additional interior bunker containing liquid oxygen in Type XXXVI. To accommodate this, a 5m section was to be inserted between diesel compartment and control room. The upper part of this bunker was to be taken up completely by the oxygen tank. The portion of the outer ship beneath this was to be made into a pressure-tight trough, which would serve as a corridor from control room to diesel compartment, and would accommodate the oxygen compensating tanks. Through this enlargement, the displacement was now approximately 1,000 tons, while the turbine range was somewhat below that of Type XXXV.

The proposed use of the Walter installation with pure oxygen in U-boat Projects XXXV and XXXVI, to provide a performance identical to that of Type XXVI, necessitated a number of design changes in the installation of this latter boat. The combustion chamber developed for Aurol operation could not simply be used for oxygen operation. Aurol splits up into steam and oxygen in the disintegrator and, having the same properties as air, is taken into the combustion chamber where combustion temperature is kept at controllable limits. If this were to be achieved with pure oxygen, it was necessary that, before contact with the fuel-oil, the oxygen be so mixed up with steam that the resulting mixture would have an oxygen content of 15–30 per cent. In practical terms, this meant that all the water that was to be added had to be mixed as steam with the oxygen prior to combustion. This necessitated the use of a conventional water-pipe boiler, which, unlike the Aurol installation, demanded much cleaner feed water. The extra compartment space that this required was hardly to be found in the small turbine compartment of Type XXVI. A better possibility seemed to be the use of a cooled combustion chamber with water injection, but this would have required a complete design and testing of a new part of a turbine installation.

Unlike the Aurol operation, in the oxygen operation it is essential that in the regulating installations, apart from three liquids (fuel-oil, additional water and compensating water), there be an additional 1—2 gaseous substances (oxygen and, eventually, the steam mixture for the oxygen) kept in a constant, exact weight relationship with each other. But the volumes of gases are dependent on pressure and temperature and, therefore, these elements must be kept constant at all times if one is to achieve a particular relationship of quantities by simple volume regulation. This brings in a further technical problem: that of considerable temperature fluctuations when running at lower power, and resulting from the constantly-changing oxygen container pressure. The proportion of steam in the operating mixture is 6 per cent smaller when using pure oxygen than when using Aurol, with a corresponding increase in the amounts of gas (carbon dioxide and remaining oxygen). Therefore, a larger quantity of gas is expelled outside the boat, which means that a compressor with a 35 per cent larger capacity is required. Weight compensation in the oxygen operation must be on a much larger scale than in the Aurol operation, as the quantity of consumed oxygen cannot be replaced directly by sea water, as is done with Aurol or with fuel, but must be compensated to the full level above the regulating tank. It therefore needs to be approximately twice as large as in Aurol operation. Furthermore, the supply of fuel-oil in turbine operation with supplied oxygen is higher than with Aurol usage in terms of tons per hour of steam consumption. However, no problem was presented because there was a considerable reserve displacement caused by storing oxygen in bottles.

The idea of using the Walter-turbine installation with pure oxygen was certainly a way out of the Aurol shortage. Over and above this, there was the factor of overwhelmingly lower production costs and simpler production methods of pure oxygen (in 1944 1 hp/hr with Aurol cost something like 20 times as much as 1 hp/hr with oxygen!). Apart from this, the use of pure oxygen offered no advantages, but should rather be considered as a poor solution, especially in the light of oxygen storage and with regard to the production of operating steam.

Postscript: German influence in the post-war era

After the capitulation, although a great deal had been destroyed, the British and the Americans acquired much background material concerning U-boat development, especially from B&V and GW. By order, secret microfilm (such as, for example, the Walter test reports) was handed over. From official documentation the War Diaries of the Chief of Naval War Staff were handed over to the British, but the major part of the Constructional Office records had been lost by voluntary destruction. Additional captures made by the victors were the new Type XXI and XXIII U-boats in Norway, and raised Walter-boats that had been scuttled in Cuxhaven without great damage having been caused to them.

Until 1946 the U-boat construction departments of the German Supreme Command were not dissolved, but worked with reduced staff for the British occupation forces reconstructing projects for which no background material was available, and collecting reports concerning developments in weaponry and detection techniques, engine and constructional development.

France, which, like the Soviet Union, was treated in niggardly fashion in the matter of distribution of U-boat prizes, showed similar considerable interest in the most recent German U-boat development. She supported the formation of an Engineering Office in her occupational zone, and here German developments and tests carried out in the U-boat sector were evaluated. During 1947—49, reports totalling several thousands of pages were compiled for the French Navy, concerning basic and particular points resulting from U-boat development during the Second World War. Parts of these reports were subsequently communicated to Sweden. The Soviet Union, apart from the few U-boats handed over by the British in 1947 (most of the surrendered U-boats had been sunk in the North Atlantic by the British as early as the winter of 1945/46) acquired the sections still lying in Danzig together with the unfinished Type XXI boats. It is not considered likely that they acquired much in the way of useful design material.

The first acknowledgement of German and Japanese development was manifested by the United States with her 'fleet' submarines, equipped with schnorkels, and the gradual turning towards electric submarines, i.e., to submarines with a larger battery capacity, stronger electric motors and an outer hull shape more conducive to a high top speed — the so-called 'Guppy' submarine ('Guppy'=Greater Underwater Propulsion Power). The first new submarines to be built to specifications based on Type XXI were six 1,600-ton boats of the *Tang* class, which entered service in 1951—52, and which had a submerged speed of 17 knots. The construction of these had been preceded by large-scale tests carried out with two of the surrendered Type XXI, *U2513* and *U3008*.

The U.S.A. did not stop at this stage of development, but made further constructional strides, both in hull shape ('tear-drop') and in the matter of propulsion. Here, too, German patent origins can be proved. The midget U-boat Delphin and a 36m-long high-speed submarine project, which were being investigated at the HSVA in April 1944, at the request of the Research Institute of the Reichs Post Office, had the tear-drop shape of the later American atomic submarines; and the first design for an atomic submarine, by the American Dr. Abelson in 1946, used the German Type XXVI design, but fitted with a sodium-graphite reactor in place of a Walter installation. The Americans were not particularly successful with the Walter-drive. True, they had received the captured Walter boat *U1406* from the British, together with duplicate copies of acquired Walter reports, but they did not have the help of the German specialists, who, from personal experience, could have assisted in the testing of these completely unfamiliar installations.

In contrast, the Royal Navy showed a greater interest in the Walter-drive, particularly in the well advanced and finished U-boat design Type XXVI. During a British Commission interrogation on 22 June 1945 (Commander Hall, Lieutenant-Commander Welbourn), Naval Construction Director Dr. Fischer was asked whether it would be possible to build a series of 10 Type XXVI boats at B&V. The minutes of the interrogation state at this point:

'In view of the lack of background material and in the light of ignorance of existing conditions at the yard and at delivery firms, no commitments could be made with certainty. Construction Director Dr. Fischer thinks that it should be possible to complete two boats within 6—12 months using turbines available in the British Occupation Zone. The opinion of the British was that there was very great interest in such an undertaking from the technical point of view, but that higher authorities, on the grounds of political expediency, would first have to be consulted before approval could be given. The opinion of Construction Director Dr. Fischer was that it would be advisable to set up an Engineering Office in the event that such work would be recommended.'

However, the authorities had other ideas, and ordered the complete dismantling and demolition of B&V. The British were to take fully ten years to build, with their own resources, two Walter test-submarines of the same size and engine installation as Type XXVI, *Explorer* and *Excalibur*, but before this, they carried out comprehensive tests with the overhauled Type XVIIB prize U-boat, *Meteorite* (ex-*U1407*), in which they had the assistance of one of Walter's colleagues, Heinz Ullrich, as chief test engineer. In addition, from the beginning of 1946 until 1949, Hellmuth Walter (accompanied by five of his staff) worked as constructional adviser for Vickers-Armstrong in Barrow-in-Furness, on the construction of Walter-installations.

Meanwhile, the Soviet Union built up a large, conventional submarine fleet, using her *W* class, based on Type XXI, as the backbone. The Soviet Navy preferred well-tried and tested methods and components rather than revolutionary innovations to achieve series production of a reliable submarine. Only slowly did they turn to the design of faster submerged boats with streamlined outer hulls. France, too, based the design of her first post-war submarine type, the *Narval* class, very much on Type XXI, but changed the 8-shaped pressure hull to a circular cross-section.

It can be stated, with certain reservations, that many recently developed submarines of conventional propulsion are continued developments of the German designs and projects for electro-boats, even if — particularly during the 1950s — development has progressed far beyond what the Germans had achieved when the war ended. For the Walter and closed-cycle drives there was no future in post-war, large submarine construction, however, as interest in them was effectively ended by the introduction of atomic propulsion.

11 SMALL AND MIDGET U-BOATS

REALIZED MIDGET U-BOATS

Designs for small and midget U-boats had been rejected by the German Navy, while available boats, especially Type VIIC, proved successful and so long as the main tactical objective was the attacking of convoys. The antipathy of the Navy towards very small U-boats was of very long standing, going back to the origins of German submarine construction. There had been no lack of suggestions as to their employment, and it had been proposed that small or midget submarines be used as single units and for hunting in packs from 'mother' ships. A noted champion of the small U-boat concept was Dr. Heinrich Dräger, the owner of Dräger-Werke, Lübeck. In a memorandum dated 1 October 1941, he presented a series of designs for small U-boats of between 70 and 120 tons, with diesel-electric and diesel-closed-cycle drive:

'1. To build the required number of units, present warship construction methods must be abandoned. Instead of building a complete boat, from keel laying to launch, at one particular building slip on the coast, we must adopt the production methods of aircraft, of tanks and of locomotives. The sizes of boats and designs must be adopted for mass-production by these methods.

'2. The construction of larger boats must be sub-divided (cell-construction). It is necessary that the cells lend themselves to transportation by rail, by road, by waterway, etc., so that pressure-hull construction and time-consuming interior assembly can be carried out in those places where, at any time, spare industrial capacity, both in terms of personnel and construction installations are available in areas as safe as possible from air attack.

'3. One estimates the following production times:
Pressure-hull construction
and cells: 14—20 working days.
Interior assembly of cells: 30 working days.
Welding together of cells
and the remaining
completion tasks: 30 working days.
Including an additional period for transportation, Sundays, etc., we arrive at a period of 6 months from heat-forming to slipway launch, given uninterrupted working. After things have been in progress for some time, some reduction of this time will probably be possible.

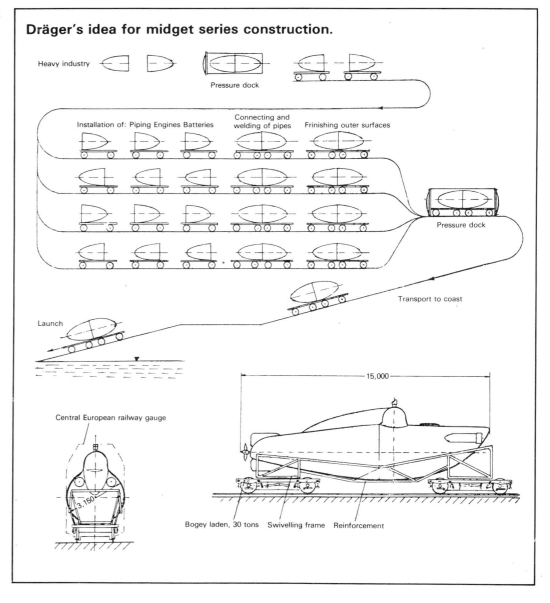

Dräger's idea for midget series construction.

Heavy industry

Pressure dock

Installation of: Piping Engines Batteries

Connecting and welding of pipes

Frinishing outer surfaces

Pressure dock

Transport to coast

Launch

Central European railway gauge

3,150

15,000

Bogey laden, 30 tons   Swivelling frame   Reinforcement

'4. It is essential to try and achieve as accurate a uniformity of various components in manufacture as possible, so that repair and yard times can be a half of the usual times, through the quick and simple interchangeability of components.'

Thus, in 1941, he anticipated Merker's ideas on the section construction of U-boats. Dr. Dräger went on to suggest the construction of midget U-boats of only 23 to 25 tons, which could be carried to their operational zone by surface vessels, or be used by auxiliary cruisers or aircraft carriers for their own protection. Finally, for the two most important aspects of operation, he regarded the development of special 100-ton U-boats as feasible, and for them to be built in very large numbers for the following purposes.

'1. A U-boat for surface night attacks, with a good surface shape and a submerged propulsion as is in general present use (night-hunter type of submersible motor torpedo-boat). Required: 300 of these.

'2. A U-boat for submerged attacks, shaped like a torpedo and, if possible, a new type of submerged propulsion to provide a high submerged speed. Required: 150 of these.'

In fact, test vessels for both types did exist at that time, but Dr. Dräger knew nothing about them because of the secrecy surrounding them. These were: 1. The so-called Engelmann High-Speed Boat of 256 tons (page 120) which, in its originally planned form, could not dive, and which was unstable at higher speeds, but which, with its low surface silhouette (half-submersible boat) and its strong diesel concentration, came very near to Dräger's conception, and 2. The Walter test boat V80, which did, in fact, measure up to requirements with regard to a high submerged speed and great manoeuvrability, but which would not be suitable for operations of this kind, because of its very noticeable wake of bubbles. However, Dräger's ideas did not elicit any support from the Navy, or other ship-construction circles and, on 22 January 1942, he received a final rejection for his U-boat suggestions from Counsellor of State Rudolf Blohm:

'Even if the small U-boat can be brought to the point of fulfilling technical requirements, we cannot regard it as adequate for operational purposes because, carrying only 2 torpedoes, it has a minimal armament and because, in adverse weather conditions, heavy seas do not allow small vessels to be used adequately in operations. Furthermore, the radius of operation, in the light of the increasing distances over which we are having to wage war, is insufficient. Concerning an increase in launching of Types being currently constructed, capacity is totally dependent on personnel and materials. As regards materials in providing power and fuel supplies, bottlenecks in such areas as non-ferrous metals are highly significant.'

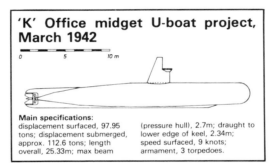

'K' Office midget U-boat project, March 1942

Main specifications:
displacement surfaced, 97.95 tons; displacement submerged, approx. 112.6 tons; length overall, 25.33m; max beam (pressure hull), 2.7m; draught to lower edge of keel, 2.34m; speed surfaced, 9 knots; armament, 3 torpedoes.

A small U-boat design was worked out in 'K' Office at the beginning of 1942, with a length of 25.33m and a displacement of 97.95 tons, but it did not get beyond the project stage. One assumes that it had its origins in the impression caused by the exaggerated reports of Japanese midget U-boat successes during the attack on Pearl Harbor on 7 December 1941, and would have had, as they did, a torpedo-shaped hull. Three torpedo tubes would have been fitted in the bow.

Midget U-boats Hecht and Seehund (Type XXVII)
Not until the autumn of 1943 was there a change of opinion regarding the possible successful application of midget U-boats. On 23 September 1943, the British 30-ton boats *X6* and *X7*, succeeded in placing detonation charges under the battleship *Tirpitz*, damaging her and putting her out of action for at least six months.

Subsequently, 'K' Office worked out a design for a German two-man U-boat designated Type XXVIIA Hecht ('Pike'), which, like the British prototype, would attach limpet mines to ships lying in otherwise safe anchorages. It was to be considerably smaller, however, and, in contrast to the *X* class would reach its target purely by submerged travel. Naturally the radius of action was very restricted, and the boat would have to be carried to the vicinity of the target by surface transport. In order to trim the floating boat, and as it was anticipated that the boat would have to break through nets, adjustable weights on spindles were provided in place of hydroplanes. This method, which harks back to Bauer's *Brandtaucher* (page 10), proved to be completely unsuitable because in conditions of considerable inclination these weights could not be moved by hand quickly enough for them to be effective. Hecht, therefore, was given forward hydroplanes, with stabilizing fins aft, an improvized measure that did not make for particularly good depth keeping. With only submerged travel in mind, no diving tanks were provided. The residual buoyancy of approximately 200 litres necessary before the crew entered the boat was, in submerged travel, destroyed by the flooding of the compensating tanks. The propulsion unit consisted of a 12hp AEG torpedo engine, whose revolutions were reduced by a V-belt drive. The battery consisted of five 17T torpedo troughs, the plates of which were replaced by stronger ones, so that the battery would have a greater capacity and a longer life in conditions of low discharge. The designation of this altered battery was 8 MAL 210. The largest installation was a gyroscopic compass with a transformer, for it was believed that this was indispensable for pure submerged travel.

When design work had been completed, the Chief of Naval War Staff made an additional demand that this midget U-boat be able to carry torpedoes, so that it could be used against moving targets in the immediate coastal vicinity. As the volume of the boat was only 9.47 tons, only torpedoes without negative buoyancy could be used, and these, lacking a battery trough, had a restricted range. Hecht therefore had the choice of a mine or a torpedo under its keel as armament. If she were being used for torpedo carrying, a battery head with a further three battery troughs could be installed: in practice, however her range of 69 nautical miles at 4 knots was too small for this type of operation.

On 18 January 1944, Dönitz discussed with Hitler the plan for building 50 midget U-boats of this type. Hitler regarded it as good judgement to develop

Type XXVII, Hecht.

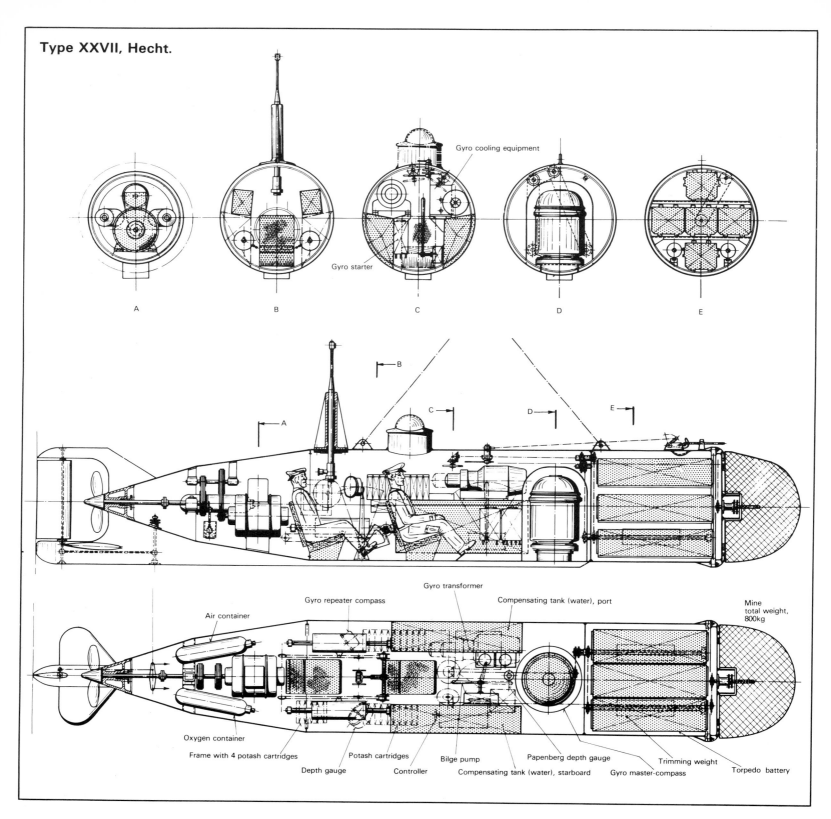

Gyro cooling equipment

Gyro starter

A   B   C   D   E

Gyro transformer

Gyro repeater compass

Compensating tank (water), port

Air container

Mine total weight, 800kg

Oxygen container

Frame with 4 potash cartridges

Potash cartridges

Bilge pump

Papenberg depth gauge

Depth gauge

Controller

Compensating tank (water), starboard

Gyro master-compass

Trimming weight

Torpedo battery

this type for both mine and torpedo use and, on 9 March 1944, GW was given a contract for a prototype and, on 28 March, a contract for a series of 52 boats. In April, it was decided to carry on building the Type XXVII midget U-boats in large numbers.

Meanwhile 'K' Office had produced numerous designs under the Type designation XXVIIB, which would have an increased range (a true U-boat propulsion installation with diesel and electric motors) and a heavier armament (two torpedoes). An initial design for which the HSVA carried out shape research in June 1944, strongly resembled Hecht. However, a fore-ship for surface travel had been added to the torpedo-shaped hull, and the keel had been enlarged to receive battery troughs. Saddle tanks were arranged close to the midships section. All this meant that the surface displacement, without torpedoes, rose to 12.95 tons. A small 22hp diesel was provided for surface travel, and it was estimated that this would provide a speed of 5.5 knots on the surface and 6.9 knots submerged.

At about this time, the Supreme Naval Command's representative for closed-cycle development at GW, Chief Naval Construction Adviser Kurzak, stimulated by the successful closed-cycle testing at FKFS of the two OM59/1 vehicle engines (each of 55hp maximum performance), set about designing a midget U-boat that could use this propulsion unit. It was evident that the closed-cycle drive in these small boats would have to be much more efficient, a sentiment that Dr. Drääger had uttered as early as 1941.

Chief Naval Construction Adviser Kurzak's first design, involving a closed-cycle drive was 'Small U-Boat K', which had very little in common with Hecht. The boat's hull was suitable for surface travel and had diving cells arranged on the sides, which partly enclosed the torpedoes and replaced the torpedo attachments. This had the effect of reducing somewhat the considerable submerged resistance of the underslung torpedoes. The propulsion engine planned was the ship's-boat 95hp diesel engine MWM-GS 145S, produced in large

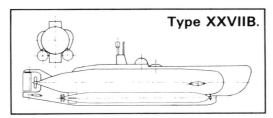

Type XXVIIB.

numbers by Süddeutschen Bremsen AG, Munich, and used by the naval spare-parts organization. It was expected in closed-cycle operation that this engine would supply a submerged top speed of 11—12 knots and a range of 70 nautical miles and, for long-range travel at a speed of 7 knots, a range of 150 nautical miles. Oxygen was to be stored in a large pressure bottle containing 1,250 litres in the keel, and 4 accumulator troughs 8 MAL 210 were to be accommodated in the fore-ship. The boat was to have a length of 11.74m and a submerged displacement of 13.8 tons.

The complete design for 'Small U-Boat K' was ready on 21 May 1944, and was discussed at a Supreme Naval Command meeting chaired by the Commander of the Midget Weapons Units, Vizeadmiral Heye. Chief Naval Construction Adviser Kurzak was requested to plan a closed-cycle installation appropriate to such a boat.

The shape of his design was to exert a considerable influence on the final version of the small U-boat Type XXVIIB intended as the successor to Hecht. Designated XXVIIB5 Seehund ('Seal'), later Type 127, a completely finished midget U-boat evolved under the direction of Naval Construction Adviser Grim, with a relatively powerful diesel-electric installation (60hp Büssing lorry diesel and 25hp AEG electric motor), which had all the essential installations of a larger diving boat. Without exterior bunkers, the surface range amounted to 270 nautical miles at 7.7 knots and, with exterior bunkers, as much as 500 nautical miles at 7.7 knots, but this would have been rather much for the crew in such a cramped boat. The battery capacity of 8 troughs of 7 MAL 210 (better capacity than the 8 MAL 210!) made possible a submerged voyage of 63 nautical miles at 3 knots or 19 nautical miles at 6 knots. The submerged properties of speed and range were not good, and this was evident from the towing tests at the HSVA in July 1944. Without torpedoes in submerged travel, a Cw value of 73 was measured; with torpedoes, it was only 59. From its very conception, Seehund was rather more of a 'semi-submersible' with a very low surface silhouette and superior diving qualities.

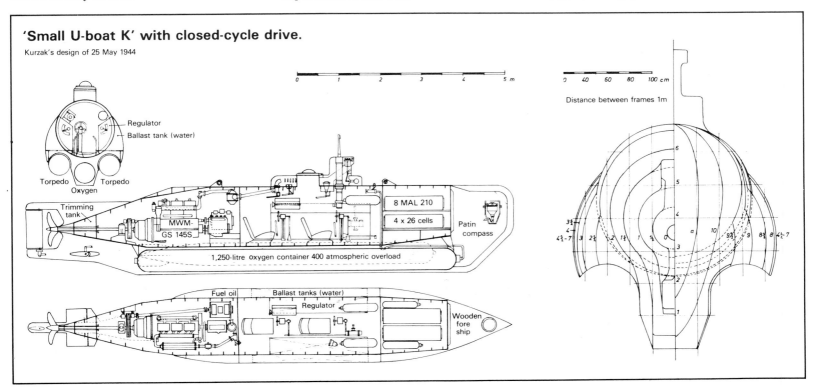

'Small U-boat K' with closed-cycle drive.

Kurzak's design of 25 May 1944

0   1   2   3   4   5 m

0 40 60 80 100 cm

Distance between frames 1m

Regulator
Ballast tank (water)

Torpedo Oxygen Torpedo

Trimming tank

MWM-GS 145S

8 MAL 210

4 x 26 cells

Patin compass

1,250-litre oxygen container 400 atmospheric overload

Fuel oil

Ballast tanks (water)

Regulator

Wooden fore ship

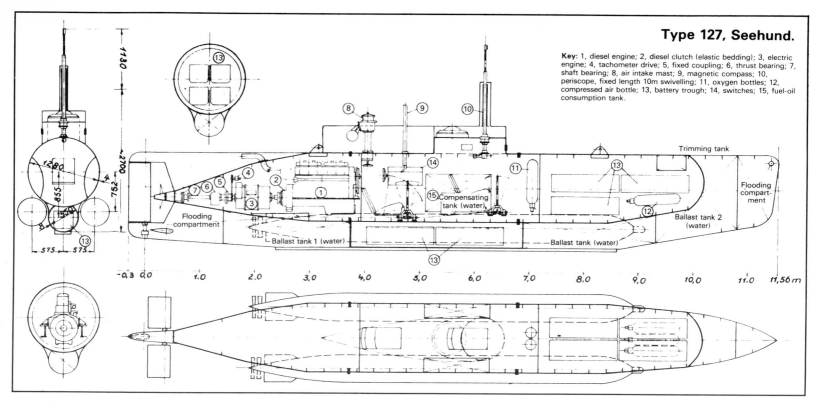

Type 127, Seehund.

Key: 1, diesel engine; 2, diesel clutch (elastic bedding); 3, electric engine; 4, tachometer drive; 5, fixed coupling; 6, thrust bearing; 7, shaft bearing; 8, air intake mast; 9, magnetic compass; 10, periscope, fixed length 10m swivelling; 11, oxygen bottles; 12, compressed air bottle; 13, battery trough; 14, switches; 15, fuel-oil consumption tank.

Initially, a profile-rudder was intended for the lateral rudder, but the turning circle was unsatisfactory. An improvement was subsequently expected by using a Kort nozzle rudder, but this was not realized. Finally, a two-surface rudder on one axle ('box rudder') was tried out, and this did improve the turning circle, but was liable to flutter.

The detailed planning of the 11.865m boat, which had a displacement of 12.3 tons, was handed over to the IBG, with Naval Construction Director Dr. Fischer in charge, and Howaldt-Kiel received a contract for 3 prototypes on 30 July 1944. Series construction would subsequently be carried out at GW; Schichau, Elbing; Klöckner-Humboldt-Deutz, Ulm, and at CRD-Monfalcone. Most of the contracts and U-boat numbers had been awarded by April 1944, even before the design of Seehund was completely ready.

The Ministerial Programme of June 1944 (page 255) planned a total of 1,000 Type XXVII midget U-boats, of which Elbing was to supply 45 and GW 25 boats per month. Initially, it was intended to manage without other production centres. When GW took over the complete Type XXIII construction, it would then cease to take part in the Seehund programme, and production of these would then begin in southern Germany. At the beginning of January 1945, the delivery plan for Seehund was as shown in Table 62.

When Schichau, Elbing, was no longer available, it was decided, on 30 January 1945, to accelerate the commencement of construction of Seehund at Klöckner-Humboldt-Deutz in Ulm, and at the firm of W. Schenk in Hall, using Elbing personnel, and to raise production to 50 boats per month by July 1945 as shown in Table 63.

At the same time, GW was to continue to deliver. The total programme was reduced to 600 boats in the Emergency Programme (page 262). As the 'Konrad' shelter in Kiel was now required neither for Type XXI nor for Type XXIII, it could be used additionally by GW for Seehund construction.

Table 62. Delivery programme for Seehund, January 1945

1945	Schichau, Elbing	GW, Kiel	Southern Germany
January	55	25	—
February	55	25	3
March	55	30	5
April	55	30	10
May	55	25	20
June	55	—	30
July	55	—	35

Table 63. Revised Seehund construction programme, 30 January 1945 (excluding GW)

1945	Ulm	Hall
January	—	—
February	5	—
March	10	—
April	10	5
May	10	15
June	10	25
July	10	40

Sequence production was carried on there from the middle of March, while production at Ulm, which was not very accessible from a transport point of view, was stopped and construction at Hall did not begin. The main difficulty that developed in the latter stages of the war, and was to affect even the Seehund programme, was the bottleneck in accumulators. Thus, in March 1945, instead of 60 Seehund batteries, only 40 could be provided.

The total of Hecht and Seehund delivered is shown in Table 64. 3 Seehund were produced at Howaldt-Kiel, 136 at Schichau, Elbing, and the remainder at GW. The Hecht boats saw service only as training vessels; the Seehunds were put into service from January 1945, operating from Ijmuiden in the Netherlands.

Table 64. Hecht and Seehund: actual deliveries

	Hecht	Seehund
1944:		
May	2	—
June	1	—
July	7	—
August	43	—
September	—	3
October	—	35
November	—	61
December	—	70
1945		
January	—	35
February	—	27
March	—	46
April	—	8

Above: A Seehund with saddle tanks to accommodate extra fuel. **Below:** Series production of Seehund type midget submarines in the 'Konrad' bunker at DWK, May 1945.

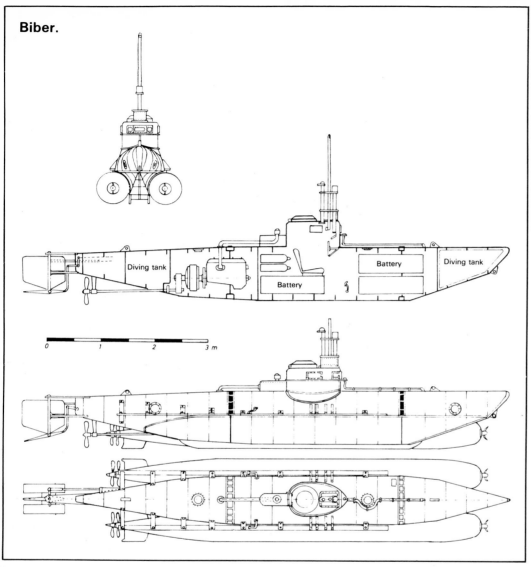

Biber.

Battery

Diving tank

Battery

Diving tank

0   1   2   3 m

One-man boats: Biber, Neger, Marder and Molch

The smallest U-boat in the German Navy was the Biber ('Beaver') type, developed by Lübeck Flenderwerke, at the instigation of Korvetten-kapitän Bartels. Once again, a British midget submarine provided the lead: on 22 November 1943, during an attack on Bergen, a British midget of the Welmancraft type was captured. Without its mine charge, this vessel had a length of 5.13m and weighed 2.075 tons; it had only electric drive, and trimming was effected by a movable weight. Its range was 30 nautical miles at 3 knots.

Initial negotiations concerning Biber began on 4 February 1944 at Flenderwerke. By 15 March, the first 'Bunte boat' (after Director Bunte of Lübeck Flenderwerke), the so-called 'Adam', was ready. It was very different, as regards bow and observer-

bubble, from the mass-produced boats that followed, and had the following specifications:
Length: 7m.
Beam: 0.96m.
Draught: 0.96m.
Displacement: 3 tons.
Surface: 7 knots/13h=91 nautical miles.
Submerged: 6 knots/2¼h.
Diving depth: 25m.
During the acceptance trials in the River Trave on 29 May 1944, the boat created a very good impression. To the fears expressed by the Head of 'K' Office concerning the use of a petrol engine in this midget U-boat, Director Bunte and representatives of the Marinegruppenkommando Nord/Flottenkommando in Kiel said that they had no objections to petrol engines, which had the considerable advantage that an almost unlimited

quantity could be supplied and were, furthermore, almost noiseless. Consequently, an immediate series of 24 was ordered from Flenderwerke, to be delivered by 31 May 1944. Additional contracts were placed with Klöckner-Humboldt-Deutz and with other firms.

Without armament, the mass-produced boats of the Biber type had a displacement of 3.645 tons, a length of 9.035m and a pressure-hull diameter of 0.96m. The surface propulsion was provided by a 32hp Opel-Blitz Otto engine. The danger from poisoning or explosion by using an Otto petrol engine was the weakest part of this design, but no suitable diesel engine was available in large quantities, and there was certainly pressing need for the early entry into operations of a vessel of this kind — more suitable than Hecht for coastal operations in view of the impending invasion. With approximately 225 litres of petrol, the surface range was 100 nautical miles at 6.5 knots. For submerged travel, three torpedo battery troughs Type 13 T 210, and a 13hp electric torpedo motor were provided, giving the boat a submerged range of 8.6 nautical miles at 5.3 knots plus 8 nautical miles at 2.5 knots. The armament consisted of two suspended torpedoes without negative buoyancy, which were carried in curved indentations in the hull.

The pressure hull was formed from 3mm sheet steel, and was intended to have a permissible diving depth of 20m. Efforts to produce a pressure-hull shape with a small displacement and a small transportation weight were not conducive to strength. Compensating and trimming tanks had been dispensed with. Before beginning a voyage, solid ballast had to be stowed. During travel, weight and trimming changes could only be compensated dynamically or by partial flooding of the diving tanks. This represented a considerable headache for the boat's controller who, on this account, was very much stretched during rapidly-changing manoeuvres, especially when diving. The restricted proportions meant that periscope observation could be provided only in a forward direction. As the boat could not be kept at periscope depth, because of her rather primitive design, attack would be carried out only when surfaced.

Delivery of Bibers in 1944 was as follows:

May:	3
June:	6
July:	19
August:	50
September:	117
October:	73
November:	56
December:	—
Total:	324

The first Biber flotilla was prepared so quickly that an operation was carried out on 29–30 August 1944, against the Allied invasion fleet, but without success. All the boats returned, but had to be destroyed next day when their operational base at Fécamp was evacuated. During further operations from Den Helder, in the winter of 1944/45, these 'fair weather boats' suffered considerable losses without achieving any success worth mentioning.

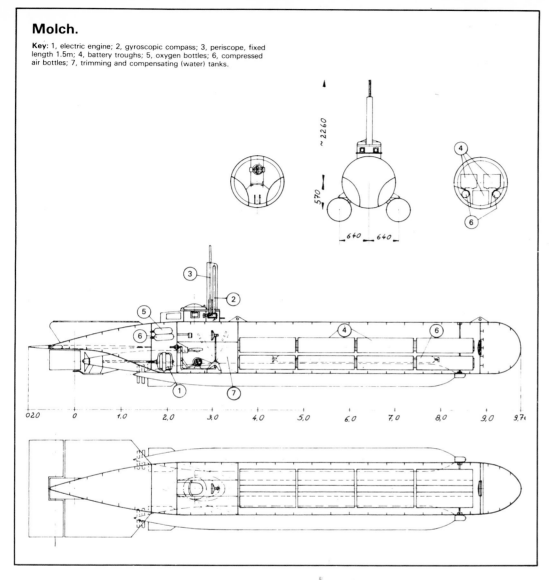

Molch.

Key: 1, electric engine; 2, gyroscopic compass; 3, periscope, fixed length 1.5m; 4, battery troughs; 5, oxygen bottles; 6, compressed air bottles; 7, trimming and compensating (water) tanks.

The TVA-Eckernförde also provided stimuli for the development of submersible small formation units. As early as 21 December 1943, Naval Construction Adviser Richard Mohr, during a discussion concerning anti-invasion measures, had suggested that an inexpensive torpedo-carrier could be acquired by using a manned torpedo, which — used in great numbers against an unsuspecting enemy — must achieve success. This equipment was later given the designation Neger in association with the name of its enthusiastic progenitor (a German pun on the name Mohr, which means, in English, Moor). It was developed very quickly, and was ready in time for the Allied landing at Anzio. The operation, however, was carried out over-hastily in an improvized manner, and brought no success; on the contrary, it led to the Allies' capturing a Neger, which meant that the element of surprise was lost. Searching for the domes of Neger and Biber craft was a favourite sport for both enemy fighters and motor torpedo-boats.

A further development of Neger was the rather longer Marder which had a small diving tank and could, therefore, submerge for a short time. Approximately 500 of these were constructed for harbour and coastal defence. Consideration was also given, for a time, to the construction of a manned 'Dackel' torpedo (T III d) designated Hai ('Shark'), but only a test vessel was built. As Neger, Marder and Hai must really be considered as weapons rather than submarines, no further space will be devoted to them.

Only midget U-boats, travelling mainly underwater, could approach an invasion fleet without being discovered and without suffering considerable losses. With this in mind, the TVA evolved the midget U-boat Thomas II, later called Molch ('Salamander'), an all-electric one-man U-boat, which had similar propulsion to Hecht, but which, from the beginning, was planned as a torpedo-carrier for two torpedoes without negative buoyancy. As with all TVA developments, it was designed to use as many available torpedo parts as possible, with simple production a main objective. The complete vessel resembled a rather enlarged torpedo, and contained 12 battery troughs Type 13 T 210 in the fore-ship.

Midget U-boat Type Molch, camouflaged.

The after part of the vessel contained simply the after part of an electric torpedo for propulsion; but, because of its lower speed, the stabilizing fins and hydroplanes were given larger dimensions. The high battery weight made the displacement considerably greater than that of Biber, and this amounted (without torpedoes) to 8.4 tons. The total range was lower than Biber's, but the submerged range of 50 nautical miles at 3.3 knots, plus 50 nautical miles at 5 knots, was considerably greater. However, the submerged operational capabilities were impaired by the restricted periscope observation (approximately 30° to each side) and by the lack of underwater detection installations. As with Seehund and Biber, instead of the complicated gyroscopic compass installation as fitted in Hecht, a simple magnetic compass, on a mast outside the hull, could be observed from the interior. Only a few test boats were fitted additionally with an automatic course-keeping mechanism and a listening device. The ballast tanks represented a combination of diving, compensating and trimming tanks, which had to be adjusted exactly prior to each voyage.

The first appearance of a test vessel on 19 March 1944 gave the impression, in comparison with Biber, of a still incomplete and inadequate design. An attempt at diving was unsuccessful in that the boat, with her long fore-ship, could not be made to submerge. The first acceptable boat was not shown until 12 June 1944 in Eckernförde. The series construction immediately put in hand was as follows:

June 1944:	3
July 1944:	38
August 1944:	125
September 1944:	110
October 1944:	57
November 1944:	—
December 1944:	28
January 1945:	32
February 1945:	—
Total:	393

Production was carried out mainly at Deschimag-AG Weser of Bremen. While these boats had a considerable displacement, their specifications were kept simple so that a large number might be completed in the shortest possible time.

The Molchs were used from the autumn of 1944 against Allied supply lines off Anzio and, from the beginning of 1945, off the coast of Holland. As with Biber, losses bore no relationship to their meagre successes. In the case of Molch, the essential reasons lay in inadequate training, technical shortcomings and, once again, the fact that the boat's controller had far too many tasks to complete.

Biber and Molch were regarded as intermediate solutions, designed and built as a short-term improvization. The only possible success was based upon the element of surprise, but this was not achieved, as the very first operation was a disaster, inadequately prepared as they were and with all circumstances against them. It was not until Seehund had been produced that the Germans had a midget U-boat with some chance of offensive success.

PROJECTED DESIGNS

Alongside the more or less improvized projects for quickly-built midget U-boats, certain projects with considerable potential for operationally-sound vessels were being developed in the early part of 1944. Prototypes of certain designs were manufactured and these had considerable qualities. Series production was no longer possible after the Supreme Naval Command, at the beginning of 1945, had ordered a cessation of all projects not already contained in the current programme; however, the multiplicity of bodies engaged in midget U-boat development, and the independent position of the Admiral for Midget Weapons ensured that design work went on in great measure until the very end of the war.

Type XXXII

With the designation Type XXXII, a midget U-boat of approximately 20 tons displacement was developed during the autumn of 1944; it was similar to Hecht, but, from the very beginning, was designed for torpedo operations. Seehund, despite all its merits, was a conventional submarine designed to operate mainly on the surface, and a disadvantageous factor was that its torpedo arrangement beneath the hull meant that loading was only possible in dock or on land. In contrast to this, the Supreme Naval Command's Design XXXII placed both torpedoes above the hull, so that loading in water was possible and the boat, even when armed, could rest on the bottom when the current was against her. She was to have a conning tower so that periscope depth could be greater while using the same periscope length, and the conning-tower height was such that the commander could stand at the periscope. A 25hp Seehund motor was intended for electric propulsion. She was to have an endurance at sea of approximately four days, and was intended to operate in the Channel.

Seeteufel

Apart from Molch, other designs for midget units were being developed at the TVA early in 1944. The most advanced of these was certainly the Seeteufel of Engineer Alois Lödige which was developed and built in four months by its designer and a few colleagues at TVA-North, and was ready for testing as early as July 1944. The considerable difficulties experienced in putting even the small one-man double torpedo of the Neger type into the water stimulated the designer to create an amphibious midget U-boat with a tracked arrangement for motion on land. In March 1944, the TVA had invested in the towing canal of the HSVA a one-man U-boat design with tracks for land travel; this was designated Sonderfahrzeug (special vessel). It had a length of 9.825m and a submerged displacement of 16 tons without armament. The two torpedoes were to be carried next to the tracks. Although this design enclosed the commander's lookout position in a streamlined fashion, the vessel had a considerable submerged resistance, and had easily the greatest friction value of all researched midget U-boats.

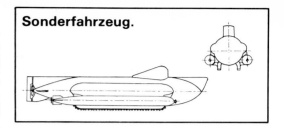

Sonderfahrzeug.

As built, the test vessel had a two-man crew and was correspondingly larger than the other types (35 tons displacement, length 14.2m, beam 2m). Propulsion was provided by an 80hp petrol engine, which could be switched to drive either the caterpillar tracks or the propeller for surface and schnorkel travel. For submerged travel, the boat had the Seehund 25hp electric motor, which would give a submerged speed of 8 knots despite the numerous appendages. The petrol engine was installed in the bow compartment beneath the fixed schnorkel mask. Immediately aft of this was the control room, then the batteries (electric torpedo troughs) and the petrol tank. The electric motor was situated in the stern. Apart from conducting air, the schnorkel mast contained the periscope, a rod aerial and the magnetic compass with lighting transmission. All controls for the rudder and after hydroplanes (forward, the boat had only one fixed stabilizing fin) were grouped together in a control column placed forward of the driver's seat beneath the Plexiglass dome. Control of this rather fat boat was apparently very good. When submerged, the commander directed the vessel from his position at the periscope, which, however, was rather poorly supplied with light. The greatest diving depth achieved by the test boat was 21m. A special flooding device enabled Seeteufel, unlike all other midget U-boats, to fire even the normal 7m torpedoes with negative buoyancy without running the risk of breaking surface after firing.

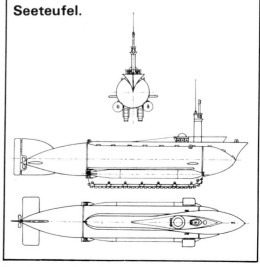

Seeteufel.

Opposite page: Seeteufel at the TVA, Eckernförde.

Tests on *Seeteufel* were carried out by Test Command 456 of the Midget Weapons Units in conjunction with TVA-North. These showed that, on land, the petrol engine was too weak and the caterpillar tracks too narrow for the heavy vehicle. In water, the design proved satisfactory. Vizeadmiral Heye (Admiral for Midget Weapons) contacted the automobile firm of Carl Borgward to determine the possibilities of mass-production and, in October 1944, *Seeteufel* was demonstrated to Borgward and Director Kynast in Eckernförde. Finally, Borgward was authorized to prepare series construction of an improved *Seeteufel* which would have a 250hp diesel engine in place of the petrol engine, and wider tracks; three such prototypes were to be produced. But the Supreme Naval Command's decision regarding limitations on the construction of midget units put an end to the project. Following the conclusion of tests in Eckernförde, the TVA Test Boat was taken to the 'Blaukoppel' Depot of the Midget Weapons Unit at Lübeck, where it was destroyed at the end of the war.

Closed-cycle Seehund

On 4 May 1944, Chief Naval Construction Adviser Kurzak reported that the use of liquid oxygen instead of gas might be possible in midget U-boats with closed-cycle drive, and might furnish considerable saving in volume and weight. On 12 June 1944, appropriate tests were carried out by K II. These confirmed the basic feasibility of such an application in midget U-boats, especially as such boats would be carrying out operations of short duration.

Kurzak then projected a closed-cycle midget U-boat to carry liquid oxygen. This design was similar in shape to 'Small U-Boat K' (page 285), but with slightly enlarged dimensions. However, the diesel engine selected was the Daimler-Benz OM67/4 of 100hp at 2,000rpm, this being very similar in the matter of consumption to the OM59/1, which meant that available test results could be transferred to the newer engine with consequent quicker development of the closed-cycle installation. The engine installation was to be mounted on a common frame, which could be introduced into the stern section and secured by a few screws to give easy access. To muffle the noise, the complete frame was given an elastic bedding, using four rubber buffers at the edges of the frame, and the vibrations were so finely adjusted that the engine ran smoothly. It was hoped especially that, at low revolutions, noise from the hull could be so reduced that ultimately the silent creep-speed installation could be dispensed with, the propulsion installation then becoming extremely simple and light. As an interim measure, while awaiting the maximum achievable noise-damping to be established, it was intended to use an electric, silent creep-speed plant for the lower speed ranges. This was to be a fast-running electric motor with V-belt drive, which was the installation with the shortest possible dimension. If the Seehund electric motor had been used, a lengthening of 55cm would have been necessary.

If liquid oxygen were to be used, the greatest possible care would have to be taken to avoid gas problems during the intervals between operating. For this reason, the oxygen container was to be made pressure-tight to 6 atmospheres overload operating pressure, and 9 atmospheres overload test pressure. The normal operating pressure of liquid oxygen was 1 atmosphere over pressure. Through the possibility of an increase in pressure from 1 to 6 atmospheres overload (the escape pressure of the safety valve), if the insulation were carried out efficiently, escaping of gas could be prevented for approximately two days. With each use of a quantity of oxygen, the pressure would sink of its own accord to 1 atmosphere overload, and would be kept at this level when the engine was operating by a regulator that controlled the flow of liquid oxygen to the evaporator.

Heat necessary for the evaporation process and for heating the liquid oxygen was taken from sea water and introduced through an exterior maze of tubes. With a full oxygen supply of 650kg, a submerged closed-cycle range of 69 nautical miles at 11.5 knots or 150 nautical miles at 7.25 knots was calculated. The project for these midget U-boats was given the designation Type XXVIIK, and was made available to the Supreme Naval Command on 10 August 1944.

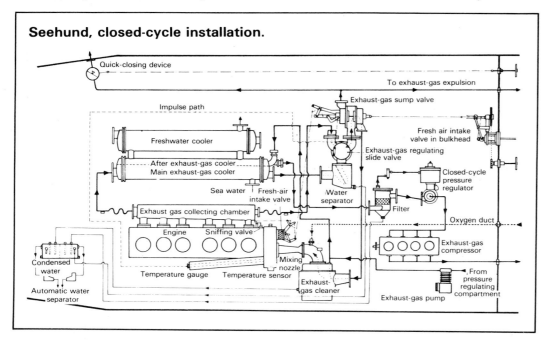

Seehund, closed-cycle installation.

Quick-closing device
To exhaust-gas expulsion
Impulse path
Exhaust-gas sump valve
Freshwater cooler
Fresh air intake valve in bulkhead
After exhaust-gas cooler
Main exhaust-gas cooler
Exhaust-gas regulating slide valve
Sea water Fresh-air intake valve
Water separator
Closed-cycle pressure regulator
Exhaust gas collecting chamber
Filter
Oxygen duct
Engine Sniffing valve
Exhaust-gas compressor
Condensed water
Mixing nozzle
Temperature gauge Temperature sensor
From pressure regulating compartment
Automatic water separator
Exhaust-gas cleaner
Exhaust-gas pump

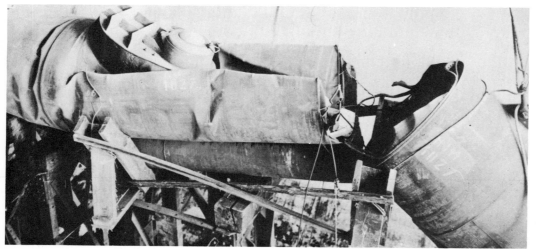

Left: A GW-built Seehund (Construction Number 1027) after a pressure test at the beginning of 1945. **Right:** Büssing-NAG LDG closed-cycle installation for Seehund, 1945.

In order to have an early testing of the closed-cycle installation under working conditions in a midget U-boat, Chief Naval Construction Adviser Kurzak suggested, on 8 September 1944, building some closed-cycle test boats by making use of Seehund hulls and components already in production. Lengthening Seehund by 1,800mm (incorporation of an intermediate section between control room and rear section) would afford sufficient room for the larger installation. Kurzak did not consider construction of a large number of these closed-cycle Seehunds or their operational use to be practicable, because they did not possess submerged shapes truly compatible with the higher submerged performance and speeds that closed-cycle drive could supply, and their range was too limited by their small fuel-oil supply and battery capacity (only two troughs).

Having regard to the Seehund hull shape, the ranges ascertained for the OM67/4 and the Büssing Seehund engine were as shown in Table 65. The total range of approximately 200 nautical miles, with an endurance of 24–30 hours was too small for an operational boat of this size. Later calculations, after test-bed closed-cycle consumption measurements had been taken, yielded rather better values.

The development of this closed-cycle Seehund suggested by Kurzak was carried out by the IBG in Blankenburg and was given the designation Type 227. Contracts for test boats along these lines were awarded to GW, Kiel and Schichau, Elbing. By the end of the war, the construction of a further three boats (*U5188–U5190*) had been awarded to GW. These boats were to be given the Seehund diesel engine (Büssing-NAG) converted for closed-cycle operation. In a letter dated 8 September 1944,

Table 65. **Comparative ranges of engines for closed-cycle Seehund**

	submerged, c-c	plus surfaced	plus submerged electric
DB-OM67/4[1]			
n. miles	96	85	21
knots	8	8.5	2.7
Büssing-NAG LDG[2]			
n. miles	78	96	21
knots	7.9	7.75	2.7

[1]100hp at 2,000rpm.   [2]60hp at 1,400rpm.

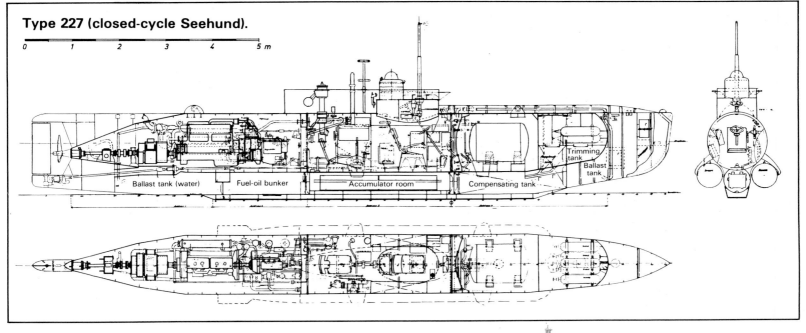

Type 227 (closed-cycle Seehund).

0   1   2   3   4   5 m

Ballast tank (water)   Fuel-oil bunker   Accumulator room   Compensating tank   Trimming tank   Ballast tank

Kurzak had indicated the important advantages that the production and tactical use of the closed-cycle midget U-boat would gain by using the Daimler-Benz OM67/4 engine. However, HAS Chief Otto Merker decided that Büssing engines were to be used because Daimler engines were not available in large quantities. It was therefore decided that a Büssing engine should be given closed-cycle tests alongside the OM67/4 as soon as possible.

On 20 September 1944, test-bed trials of the OM67/4 closed-cycle installation began at the FKFS in Kirchheim. By 1 December 1944, it had been tested for 30 hours in air operation and 52 hours in closed-cycle operation with liquid oxygen; for the last part of these tests, the complete engine installation was incorporated, as for operational use, in the after section of the closed-cycle Seehund,

with the screw replaced by a water brake. During this test, a maximum closed-cycle output of 75hp on the shaft with a fuel consumption of 300g/shp/hr and an oxygen consumption of approximately 1.2kg/shp/hr were obtained. In accordance with the HAS requirement that the Büssing Seehund engine be used for the closed-cycle Seehund, a Büssing-NAG LD6 diesel engine was tested in closed-cycle. These engine tests were carried out likewise by FKFS in Kirchheim, again with success. However, the war situation meant that such units were never incorporated into those hulls under construction.

Biber II and III

The disadvantages of Biber − its petrol engine and the fact that the driver had far too much to do − led the Flenderwerke to develop an enlarged version,

designated Biber II, with a two-man crew who were to take turns regularly in controlling the boat. This changing of duty was intended to facilitate longer operations, but the noteworthy property of the original design, namely the low weight and consequent ease of launching, was lost by the necessary increase in displacement.

The successful closed-cycle tests with smaller vehicle diesel engines led to a change in this project in the autumn of 1944. Designated Biber III, a midget closed-cycle U-boat of 10.34 tons surface displacement (without torpedoes) and with a length of 11.82m was developed in collaboration with the Engineering Office for Ship Construction, Lübeck. Externally it differed from other midget U-boats in its stern shape, rudder arrangement and torpedo attachment. Instead of ending with a vertical stern

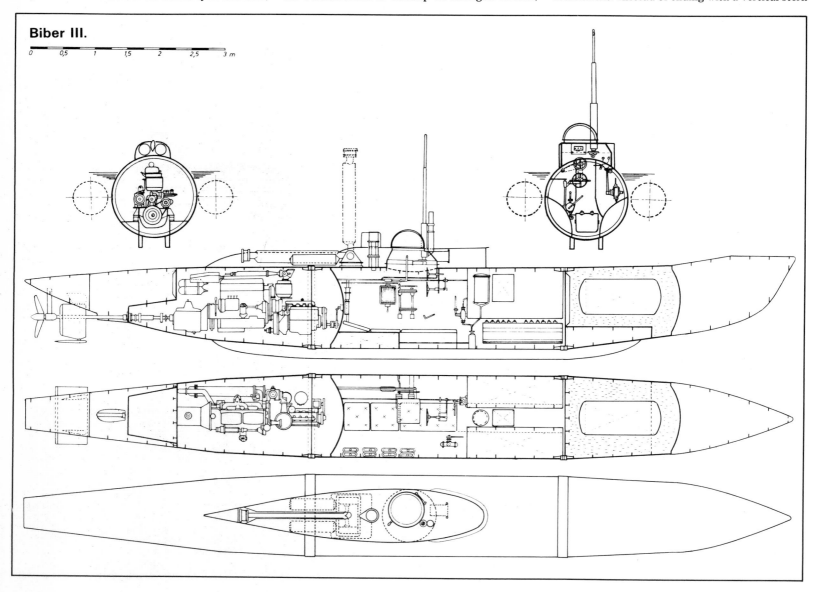

Biber III.

with the screw rotating in a well as was usually the case, the stern ended in an edge almost horizontally, with the screw shaft and screw projecting under the stern in a V-shaped strut. Lateral steering was carried out by a double rudder, and depth keeping by a hydroplane beneath the double rudder. Torpedoes were carried at the same level as the main axis. In a position of flotation they could be secured relatively simply. The transitions between the various compartments of the boat were made very flat, and the fore-ship was given a very full shape at the waterline, with a raised forecastle. The boat was given two strong, shallow keels which allowed secure resting on the bottom.

On 14 November 1944, the HSVA received a request from the TVA at Eckernförde for towing tests to be carried out with this new shape. The tests showed that at quite low speeds, the hull fore-ship produced a dense bow wave that considerably impeded the driver's view, but a wave-diverter fitted at the most forward part of the forecastle pushed the wave to one side and kept it low. The increase in resistance caused by the two lateral rudders and the hydroplane amounted to 8 per cent at a submerged speed of 8 knots, which was regarded as very satisfactory. Submerged results are no longer available. The originally selected central position for the torpedoes meant that, at 7.5 knots, the boat was forced beneath the surface, but putting the torpedoes farther aft improved the trim when in motion so considerably that this enforced submerging no longer occurred.

The Supreme Naval Command did not pursue this design any further because experience with the closed-cycle installation did not justify series production, and the requirement for test boats with closed-cycle engines was being met by the construction of the closed-cycle Seehund. The very stretched position of industry at that time would not have been enhanced by a parallel development. However, at the request of the Midget Weapons Unit, this project was researched further. The FKFS was requested to develop and construct a closed-cycle installation suitable for Biber III. The engine was the Daimler-Benz four-cylinder diesel OM4/65 with a maximum 65hp at 2,200rpm. The construction of the necessary closed-cycle installation corresponded to that already tested for the closed-cycle Seehund, 100hp OM67/4. The engine was to be made suitable by reduction gearing for the different speed stages (1st gear 1:2.5 for endurance travel; 2nd gear 1:4.5 for silent creep; and an additional gear for reversing). Gear changing was hydraulically operated.

In the interests of noise suppression it was intended to line the engine compartment with a 30–40mm layer of cork. Electrical energy was supplied by two lorry lighting dynamos driven by the diesel engine, and by three small vehicle batteries each of 12 volts.

With extra bunkers the surface range was to be 1,500 nautical miles at 6 knots (approximately 250 hours duration!). The 430 litres of oxygen (liquid in the fore-ship), sufficed for additional submerged closed-cycle travel of 100 nautical miles at 5 knots. Without torpedoes, the maximum submerged speed was 7.75 knots, the submerged endurance speed 5

knots and the submerged silent creep speed approximately 2 knots.

Construction of the test installation began in December 1944. The first trials on a test-bed took place in January 1945, but still on an open installation. During endurance tests in air operation, the engine recorded 58hp at 1,800rpm, and in closed-cycle operation corresponding to a water depth of 30m, 45hp with a fuel consumption of 300–350g/hp/hr. By the end of March 1945, the installation had passed its numerous examinations and tests and was ready for incorporation into a boat's hull. At this stage, it was intended to run the engine once again in a completely enclosed cylinder, simulating hull conditions, but the military situation in the Stuttgart area at that time prevented this. The installation was, therefore, partly dismantled, loaded on to lorries and sent, accompanied by its service engineers, to Lübeck, but the planned tests were not possible here, either, and the installation was dismantled once again. At the capitulation, it was hidden in various places. At the end of the war, those parts still available were searched out under the supervision of the British occupation forces and collected together at the Kronshagen Camp.

Delphin

A lesson learned from the use of midget weapons during the Allied landing in Italy was that only midget submarines with a high-submerged speed had much chance of successfully penetrating the strong screening and defensive measures of large concentrations of ships. The designs projected hitherto — Neger, Biber, Molch and Hecht — did not meet these requirements for an adequate submerged speed; long journeys would have made very considerable demands on their operators. It was clear that automatic steering and a suitable direction-finding equipment for use when attacking were absolutely necessary. The most advisable propulsion engine would seem to be a simple, closed-cycle combustion engine. Following successful results obtained with the closed-cycle torpedo engine, an Otto engine also seemed suitable.

At a meeting in May 1944 between the Admiral for Midget Weapons, Vizeadmiral Heye and the Head of the Test Institute for Engine Design at the TH Berlin, Professor E. A. Cornelius, it was decided that the Test Institute should design a new type of midget U-boat. In mind was a high-speed, one-man U-boat with a well-proportioned submerged shape, a displacement of 2.5 tons, a length of 5m and a diameter of 1m, driven by a simple closed-cycle Otto engine.

Dr. K. Haug was given the design task and he worked out an appropriate design during the Whitsun holiday of 1944. The boat had a tear-drop shaped cross-section, with a Plexiglass dome (which served also as a hatch) on the top and a cross-shaped rudder at the stern. The well-proportioned submerged shape was to allow considerable submerged speed at even low engine outputs. Diving and trimming tanks were not provided. The boat was to be able to dive dynamically and, therefore, was given the suggestive name Delphin

(Equipment 205). At the beginning of July 1944, thorough investigation was made into this new 'Haug-shape' by model tests in the wind tunnel and in the towing canal of the HSVA. These showed that, by a slight change in the dome construction, the total resistance could be reduced by 25 per cent. Test results showed the Navy Constants to be extraordinarily large for a midget U-boat; Cw for submerged travel=210. Considerably large, too, was the scepticism of the shipbuilders who had no confidence in outsiders from the automobile industry. It was especially doubted that principles applicable in light industry could be used to give a submerged vessel adequate strength.

The construction of the three test boats was entrusted to the coach-building factory Ambi-Budd in Berlin-Johannisthal, where the bodies for the

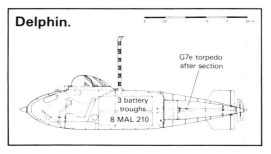

Delphin.

G7e torpedo after section

3 battery troughs
8 MAL 210

long-range V-1 and V-2 missiles were being manufactured. Departing from normal shipbuilding practice, the boats were manufactured there, using propulsion methods from modern coachbuilding techniques. Parts that were curved in two directions (head section, engine compartment and after section) were formed in the stretching/drawing-out process on so-called Az presses, while the cylindrical centre portion and the frames were formed by rollers. The metal used was pressed steel with a thickness of 2.5–4mm. The maximum sheet thickness of 4mm for the cylindrical centre section was dictated by the limited mechanical handling facilities. The use of a pressing machine-tool was planned in the event of mass-production of a large series, and this could be used to produce these parts in two casing-halves.

The connections between sections were: head section with centre part (driver's compartment), welded; centre portion with engine chamber, screwed; engine chamber with after section welded. Frames were rolled in the shape of U-frames: by splitting one U-frame, two L-frames were obtained. During the construction of the first boat, the hull had to be lengthened because the closed-cycle engine, which had been developed meanwhile in the Test Institute, required more room than had originally been calculated.

In order that practical tests could be carried out before completion of this installation, the test boat was fitted first of all with the propulsion component of a normal G7e torpedo. To this end, three battery troughs were fitted in the engine chamber. The first test boat was ready in the autumn of 1944, and its strength was tested in a pressure tank at the Flender-Werke in Lübeck. This showed that the hull had a denting-strength against outward over-pressure of more than 6 atmospheres overload. Prior to testing in the sea, the boat was subjected to basic towing tests at the HSVA. The first submerged test runs in the Trave estuary showed a lack of stability caused by the uncompensated displacement volume of the Plexiglass dome, which projected during surface travel. This problem could be rectified by the incorporation of a small diving tank under the driver's seat. During the test runs, by overloading the electric motor for a short time while submerged, a maximum of 17 knots was achieved. These tests were ended on 18 January 1945 by a collision with the escort vessel.

The original concept of Delphin envisaged a boat purely designed to carry an explosive charge of 500kg in the bow. However, during the design of the boat, an alternative was suggested in the form of a Type Grim towed mine of 500kg. Depth of the towed body was to be controlled by an air-bubble. The use of a towed charge had the advantage that, unlike a suspended torpedo, it did not affect adversely the very good streamlined properties of Delphin, and an attack could be repeated endlessly until a hit on the target was achieved. The direction-finding equipment for Delphin was the same as had been developed for torpedoes: it was screwed into the head section forward, and with it an attacking run could be carried out in a 'pursuit' curve, so that the attacker was head-on to the quarry. A control-stick (which could be used with one hand) was installed for control of depth and lateral movement, but an automatic pilot was also available. For constant speed at schnorkel depth, automatic depth adjustment was provided. During surface travel, air was introduced through a fixed schnorkel, 1.32m long, in the driver's compartment; during schnorkel travel there was a direct connection to the engine — otherwise, with the balancer volume being so small, the submerging of the schnorkel valve would have made conditions unpleasant for the driver. The maximum schnorkel speed was calculated as 14 knots. The schnorkel valve was activated by an electro-magnet. Additionally, mechanical activation by a foot pedal was provided.

Tests on the Otto engine closed-cycle installation commenced in the autumn of 1944 at the TH Berlin under the direction of Chief Engineer Dr. Urbach. As the Junkers KM8 torpedo engine, which had already been tried out, seemed too costly, the 2.5-litre Opel Kapitän four-stroke engine (80hp) was chosen. Initially, work was carried out using the Junkers regulation of the torpedo engine. During a second phase of testing, from the middle of October to the middle of December 1944, the regulators were developed afresh, in a simpler form more appropriate for series production. Additionally, the relatively high consumptions of fuel and oxygen were brought to a lower level and the whole installation was reshaped in a more reliable form. During the last phase, the back-pressure operation, with its frequent failures, was abandoned and a special suction-pump was fitted which made operating conditions in the closed-cycle completely compatible with atmospheric operations. This made the installation still more simple. The performance figures achieved are shown in Table 66.

Table 66. Tests on 2.5-litre Opel Kapitän engine for Delphin

	Air operation	Closed-cycle
Performance	32hp	32.4hp
Revolutions	2,500	2,550
Fuel (g/hp/hr)	422	536
Oxygen (g/hp/hr)	—	1,010

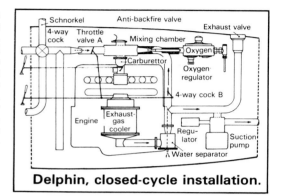

Delphin, closed-cycle installation.

Left: Delphin prior to a pressure test at Flender-Werke, Lübeck. **Right:** Delphin on trials in 1944.

When standing nearby, one could not tell by the noise of the engine whether it was running in air operation or in closed-cycle. The engine ran perfectly over the whole range of revolutions from 1,100rpm (3.3hp=8 knots) to 2,550rpm (32.4hp=17 knots), and could readily be switched, at any number of revolutions, from air to closed-cycle operation and vice versa. After much research, the spark plugs also worked perfectly, but endurance testing involving a very large number of hours was not carried out in view of the shortage of fuel at that time (February 1945). When these tests ended, the installation, apart from the missing suction pump, was quite ready for testing under operational conditions, but no incorporation of the installation in a Delphin hull was ever carried out. On 14–15 April 1945, the two remaining test boats completed at Ambi-Budd were transported on lorries to Pötenitz on the Trave estuary where they were destroyed on 1 May 1945 before occupation by British troops.

In the light of the good towing test results obtained from the Delphin shape, the IBG at the beginning of September 1944 made investigations into the submerged properties that the relatively slow Seehund (C_w=73!!) or the closed-cycle Seehund would have with a similar shape. The resulting design for a high-speed midget U-boat with a displacement of approximately 8 tons and the closed-cycle Seehund propulsion unit was given the designation Delphin II or 'Large Delphin'.

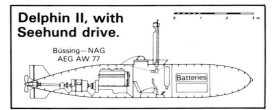

Delphin II, with Seehund drive.

Büssing—NAG
AEG AW 77

Batteries

As with 'Small Delphin', the hull was to be built using light industrial methods as in coach-building. Control and navigational installations were to be similar to those of Delphin and, as with that craft, special diving tanks were not planned: it was intended that she submerge and surface dynamically. As she was to carry out most of her travel submerged, she had a fixed schnorkel, into the housing of which a periscope was incorporated. This meant that a lookout dome, involving a considerable increase in resistance, could be dispensed with. For endurance travel, a schnorkel speed of 14 knots was calculated.

Two versions, with a one-man and two-man crew, were projected. The one-man boat (7.5 tons) was to have a maximum submerged speed of 18 knots and a range of 400 nautical miles; the two-man boat (8.5 tons) a maximum submerged speed of 16 knots and a range of 800 nautical miles. In order that the shape of this new boat could be tested before the closed-cycle propulsion unit had been brought to

the state where it would be ready for series production, it was planned to incorporate a normal Seehund propulsion unit into the first test boat. A greater submerged speed was to be achieved in these boats (as with the 'Small' Delphin) by short-period overloading of the electric motor. Calculations showed that a maximum submerged speed of 14 knots for approximately 10 minutes could be expected. However, no test vessel on these lines was constructed.

Type XXVIIF and Schwertwal

Following the good results obtained from the development of a Walter-turbine installation with sea-water injection, it was anticipated that in a short period of time a corresponding drive would be available for long-range torpedoes. In the light of this, the torpedo-turbine seemed to have additional significance for use as a drive for a high-speed midget U-boat.

In the summer of 1944, 'K' Office designed a small, torpedo-shaped, midget U-boat designated Type XXVIIF, for which this drive was suitable. The torpedo envisaged as a weapon was to be carried in an indentation beneath the hull. The driver sat in the bow section, which had a larger superstructure with a periscope above the control position. Through its consumption of Ingolin, the boat would become lighter during a passage. Nevertheless, a compensating tank was not to be provided, as it was calculated that the difference in

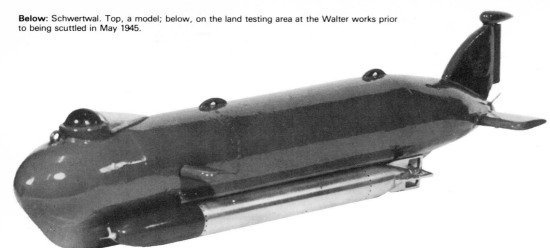

weight could be compensated dynamically at the relatively high speed. Nor was the boat given a diving tank. When starting, the boat was heavier than was appropriate for her displacement. The negative buoyancy was to be equalized by a buoyancy container that could be jettisoned.

As the intended sea-water-injected Walter-turbine was still some way from being ready for series production, the project was postponed when the design had been completed. In its place, a previously suggested version of a high-speed, midget U-boat, using the tested Walter-torpedo turbine with fresh-water injection, was to be designed and embodied into Project XXVIIF2. Because of the necessity for carrying fresh water, the boat would have to be larger than Project XXVIIF. Dynamic compensation of weight difference was not possible when fresh water was used, and compensating tanks had therefore to be provided. This meant that the submerged

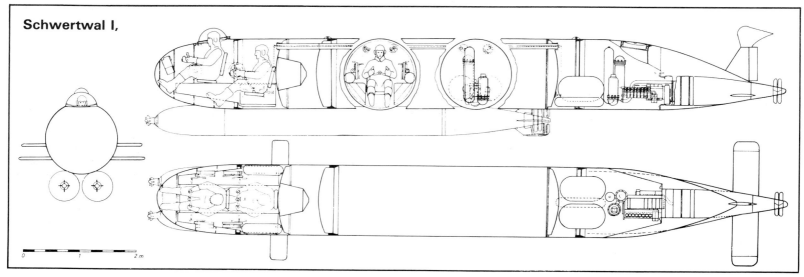

Schwertwal I,

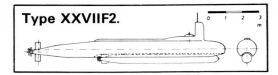

Type XXVIIF2.

displacement rose to 7.9 tons, the length to 11.28m and the beam to 1.5m. Otherwise, the new design was similar to that of Project XXVIIF. Towing tests were carried out on the enlarged shape of Type XXVIIF in August 1944 at the HSVA. These yielded, without a torpedo, a C_W value of 153 and, with a torpedo, a C_W value of 124.

Although the torpedo was recessed into the shaped indentation on the underside of the boat, the increase in resistance caused by the torpedo was considerable. At 20 knots it accounted for 50hp, i.e., one-third of the total resistance of the boat without a torpedo. The basic resistance of the torpedo alone was only 16—17hp. The remaining 34hp could be written down to the unfavourable overall influence of torpedo and boat in the total construction concept. At a propulsion output of 300hp, the boat could achieve a submerged speed of 22.6 knots without a torpedo and 20.4 knots with a torpedo. The restricted range was especially unsatisfactory and, in the light of this together with the unfavourable war and industrial situations, in the autumn of 1944 all non-essential development projects were curtailed and the design was not pursued by 'K' Office.

Despite the official cessation, work continued on the development of a midget U-boat with a Walter drive, with collaboration from Experimental Command 456 of the 'K' Force in the Walter Works. On 1 July 1944, work began on a high-speed, two-man U-boat, with a length of 11.2m, a diameter of 1.26m and a form displacement of 11.25 tons. This project was given the cover-designation 'Schwertwal'.

The first constructional design for Schwertwal I (SW1) was in no sense a final one, but served really as a vehicle for the testing, under sea conditions, of the 800hp installation specially developed for this purpose from the Type 'Wal' torpedo-drive with sea-water injection, and for the testing of the properties of the boat at high submerged speeds. Shaped like an enlarged torpedo, the driver's position and control room lay in the bow section; abaft them were trimming tanks and Ingolin bunker and, finally, the propulsion unit in the stern. The entry hatch above the driver's seat was fitted with Plexiglass as a small observation dome. A tail unit was added at the stern, with a lateral rudder and fixed stabilizing fins, this design being based upon aviation practice. The hydroplane was fitted forward at the same level as the control room.

The hull was tested in the wind tunnel of the Aviation Research Institute in Brunswick, and measurements taken on a 1:3 model in the towing channel at the HSVA; this was so that all influences affecting speeds could be obviated, and the best possible disposition of the proposed two torpedoes could be made. The results showed that, to achieve the intended submerged speed of 30 knots, a performance of 562shp, corresponding to C_W=240,

would be necessary. With the two unsheathed torpedoes positioned to best advantage beneath the boat, however, this dropped to C_W=120. With a streamlined bow sheathing that enclosed the torpedoes, it amounted to 165. The appropriate propulsion efficiencies of 73 per cent, 59.7 per cent and 66 per cent were regarded as satisfactory, but the double propeller available was regarded as very inadequate, enabling the boat to achieve only 350shp (=25.6 knots) without torpedoes (otherwise the resulting large turning moment would have endangered the turbine drive). Initially, therefore, it was necessary to prepare a single-screw propeller suitable for a maximum turning moment of 215mkp and a performance of 500shp.

Schwertwal was to be fast, and as manoeuvrable underwater as an aeroplane in the sky, and was intended also as an underwater hunter of submerged enemy submarines. Consequently, the use of a small rocket-propelled torpedo developed by the firm of Walter was planned. Apart from the two 'K-Butt' torpedoes suggested as the main armament, there was also discussion regarding the use of the Type Grim towed mine, and buoyancy-mines and underwater rockets for use against pursuers.

As the high speed meant that a periscope could not be used, development was initiated on an advanced detection installation to locate the enemy underwater. An orientation device consisting of a gyroscopically-stabilized aircraft compass, made by the firm of Patin (Berlin), with automatic control for lateral movement and depth was incorporated, and this functioned perfectly during tests. The master compass was positioned in a streamlined addition to the rudder assembly unit.

At the beginning of 1945, Schwertwal I was constructionally ready and awaiting practical trials. Test-bed trials of the driving unit had concluded, yielding the requisite endurance performance of 800hp. At the end of the war, the boat, lying in the test area of the firm of Walter at Bosau on the large lake at Plön, where practical tests were to be carried out, was sunk by special command. About two months later it was detected and raised by a British investigation group, but the British were not interested in this small vessel, and it was scrapped in Kiel.

In the light of experience gained in construction of Schwertwal I at the beginning of 1945, an improved Schwertwal II had been projected, the design of which was made even more streamlined. It had a length of 13.5m and a maximum cross-section of 2m with a total weight of 18 tons, of

which 10 tons alone were necessary for carrying Ingolin. Without torpedoes, the submerged range at 32 knots maximum was to be approximately 100 nautical miles. The enlarging of the boat made for a roomier shaping of the driver's compartment and permitted the incorporation of a small electric installation unit, which, including a 25hp electric motor, allowed manoeuvring and silent creep speed of up to 8 knots.

Manta

An additional project worked on jointly by the Walter Works and Experimental Command 456 was the underwater-hydroplane high-speed boat (USG-boat) Manta. She was designed in an effort to unify in one design all the advanced ideas that had gone into the different midget U-boat projects. Among these was the avoidance of the high resistance caused by underslung torpedoes, and the problems of launching such equipment.

Project Manta had a hull similar to a trimaran, consisting of three torpedo-shaped cylinders connected by a platform. The middle cylinder had a cockpit forward for a two-man crew and a diesel generator. The remaining section, like the two side cylinders, contained tanks for Ingolin and fuel. There were also trimming and compensating tanks. The propulsion unit was housed in two side keels beneath the outer cylinders. It consisted of one Schwertwal II installation in each. In addition to a diesel-electric drive for endurance speed, there was discussion of a diesel-hydraulic transmission. Each side keel was to take two large aircraft wheels, to enable the heavy vessel (50 tons total weight, 15 tons empty) to roll of its own accord into the water. Between the side keels, adjustable gliding surfaces for surface hydroplane travel were arranged. The following possibilities were envisaged:
1. Surface gliding travel (maximum 50 knots with Walter-drive).
2. Schnorkel endurance (10 knots with diesel-electric installation).
3. Submerged top speed (maximum 30 knots with Walter-drive).
4. Submerged creep speed (maximum 8 knots with electric motors and a battery of four torpedo troughs).

A maximum range of approximately 1,180 nautical miles was calculated and, at maximum speed, approximately 320 nautical miles. The wing surface between the outer cylinders was to carry four tubes for torpedoes or mines — thus, this midget U-boat had a very strong armament. The automatic and detection equipment was similar to that planned for Schwertwal. Model testing in the towing channel was never carried out, however. Despite many interesting ideas, this project was an especially striking example of how, particularly in times of military disaster, certain designers consciously or sub-consciously lose touch with what is capable of positive realization and take refuge from harsh reality in never-never land. After years in which military circles had shown the utmost lack of understanding and scepticism towards such ideas and accorded their originators only refusal, in the face of a total defeat they now cling to any idea, no matter how fantastic!

Schwertwal II.

Master compass

Driver

1 2 3 4 5 6 7 8 9 10

Engine compartment

Regulating tank   Ingolin Bunkers   Fuel tank
1 — 10

Control room

12 SUBMARINE DEVELOPMENT IN THE GFR FROM 1955 TO 1974

Classes 201 and 202

Under the pressure of the attempt made by the Communist hierarchy to take control of South Korea at the beginning of the fifties, the Western Allies regarded a West German defence contribution as essential. But this German rearmament was, for political and psychological reasons, only possible in the framework of a close relationship with the Western Powers. After the collapse of the 'Pleven' plan, which called for German participation in European military forces (EVG, Europäische Verteidigungsgemeinschaft, or European Defence Community, EDC) the only alternative was for national German armed forces to be created with the Federal Republic being incorporated into NATO by treaty. On 23 October 1954, the so-called 'Paris Treaties' were signed: these both established and limited the German defence contribution, and accorded the Federal Republic the necessary sovereignty required for membership of the WEU (Westeuropäische Union) and NATO. In view of its strategically important situation at the outlet of the Baltic, it was necessary to allow the Federal Republic small submarines for coastal operations. The size of these was restricted by the treaties to a displacement of less than 350 tons.

On 8 March 1955, Dr. Fischer and Engineer Gabler of the Blank Office, forerunner of the later Federal Ministry of Defence, were requested to work out suggestions for an appropriate submarine type. They used information gained from coastal U-boat Type XXIII of the former Navy, and ideas dating back to the last stages of the war. In the light of the restrictive impositions of the Paris Treaties, the abruptly-terminated wartime development work on the closed-cycle and Walterdrive, and the desire that an operationally-sound submarine be quickly available, only the dieselelectric principle with a large electric capacity and schnorkel-charging was considered as a propulsion unit. The resulting suggestion was a single-shaft boat with an electric motor of 1,300–1,350hp, a separate creep-speed electric motor and a diesel engine of 950hp for battery charging, which would provide a maximum submerged speed of 16–16.5 knots. The armament suggested was four bow tubes.

This design was initially designated Type 55, later Class 201, and was to be the pattern for 12

submarines planned as the basis of the first construction programme for the Federal Navy, in 1956. Alongside this, in the summer of 1956, Dr. Grim (Atlas-Werke, Bremen), projected a design for a quickly constructed, coastal-defence midget submarine of 58 tons displacement, 14.3m length, 2.35m beam, with a six-man crew. The drive was to consist of a diesel engine and an electric motor, each of 85hp, permitting a maximum submerged speed of 10.5 knots, a surface range of 400 nautical miles at 10 knots and a submerged range of 270 miles at 5 knots.

Both designs were handed over in 1957 to the Engineering Office Lübeck (Ingenieurkontor Lübeck, or IKL) for further working-out. IKL had been established as early as 28 July 1946, with the collaboration of Ulrich Gabler, as a firm succeeding the former IfS, but, in those early post-war years, concerned itself with the design and production of equipment for agricultural, farming and fisheries use. Now that it was handed the planning contracts for both these submarine types, it could once again take up the work of its predecessor and thus begin a steep ascent to its position today as a leading design office in world submarine design.

Work commenced with the small submarinehunter designated IK6 or Class 202. It was very soon apparent that electronic equipment, regarded

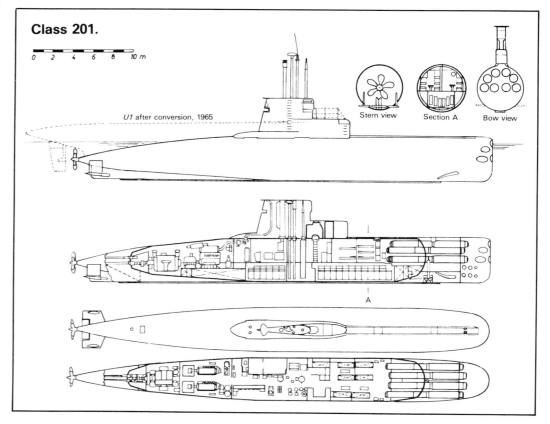

Class 201.

0 2 4 6 8 10 m

U1 after conversion, 1965

Stern view   Section A   Bow view

A

as essential in modern submarine technology, could
not be accommodated in a boat of only
approximately 60 tons, so the displacement was
increased to over 100 tons, the length to 23.1m and
the beam to 3.4m. Obviously the propulsion unit
had to be made more substantial. It was decided,
because of restricted space in the short boat, to
install a diesel engine and electric motor, each of
350hp, next to one another, both connected by
gearing to the shaft. The last designs of the
wartime Navy had envisaged, for silent creep
speed, a special creep-speed electric motor that
could be coupled to the propeller shaft by a V-belt
drive. Next to the switch-couplings between diesel
and gearing, gearing and propeller shaft and V-belt
drive and propeller shaft, it was necessary to fit
three additional elastic couplings on both sides of
the gearing, to reduce the emission of noise and
vibration. The electric motor was operated by a
switch-cam arrangement in the control room, which
formed a roomy unit with the fore-ship. The fore-
ship contained the torpedo installation (two tubes
for submarine hunting torpedoes of 3.5m length)
and two-section batteries placed beneath it. The
submerged detection installations consisted of a
passive bow-array with 144 receivers in three
groups; a passive side-array with 24 crystal
receivers on each side in a slightly curved bulge on
the outer hull; an active equipment with a rotating
base beneath a small dome on the bow; and an
active panorama detection installation positioned
around the entry shaft. Abaft the open bridge,
which could only be protected from wind and spray
by a tarpaulin, a fairly high superstructure enclosed
the extensible items: periscope, radar aerial, rod
aerial, FuMB (radar warning) aerial and schnorkel.
Forward hydroplanes of the conventional kind were
dispensed with. In their place, scoop-shaped fins,
which could be extended outwards, were provided;
by their shape, these imparted an upward moment
to starboard and a downward moment to port. As
in U-boat Type XXIII, the after hydroplanes were
positioned beneath the flow of water to the screw.
Two lateral rudder versions were planned: one was
a movable Kort nozzle, while the other was a lateral
tail unit with two lateral rudders set on the ends of
a horizontal fin.

In February 1959, Bremer Atlaswerke was given
the construction contract for 3 small U-boats of this
type, which were planned as the prototypes of a

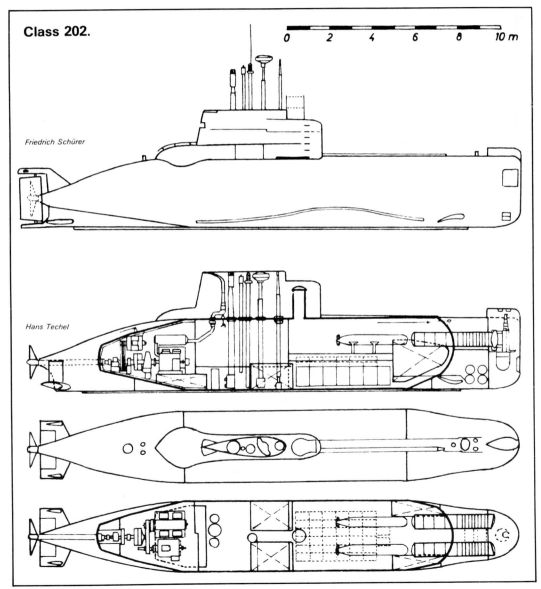

Class 202.

Friedrich Schürer

Hans Techel

large series of approximately 40 units. However, during the following years, the more offensively designed Project 201 was given preferential treatment, so that commencement of building was delayed several times. In the course of further development, it became apparent that a small U-boat would not be large enough to take maximum advantage of the available technical devices and the decision was made that only two boats should be built as experimental acoustic equipment carriers.

Design 201 was developed in line with requirements specified for it in 1957–58 by IKL. Two plans were presented on 29 and 30 January 1958. The first, conforming to instructions, had four torpedo tubes with reload facilities through a special torpedo hatch, forward hydroplanes, a heavy-duty, three-section battery and a propulsion installation that bore some similarity to that of Class 202: two fast-running diesel engines geared on one shaft, a powerful main electric motor (which served as a generator as well as a propulsion unit) and a creep-speed electric motor of 80hp. It was necessary to provide two small diesel engines in place of the originally intended single diesel, because an appropriate large, fast-running diesel was not available at that time. The battery was to be fitted with the available lattice-plate Type MAL 740 made by Varta. The hull was tear-drop shaped to keep resistance to a minimum, and the upper works were kept as small as possible. As in Class 202, the bridge was restricted to a platform, half the height of the fairing provided abaft it, for the extensible items of equipment. Also as in Class 202, the lateral rudder arrangement consisted of a fin beneath the propeller with lateral rudders set on its ends. This version was chosen because it was necessary that the boat make very little noise, and it was desired to use wire-controlled torpedoes. The alternative proposal by IKL for Class 201 investigated the maximum number of torpedo tubes that could be accommodated in a boat of this type. The accommodation of the maximum number of ready-to-fire torpedo tubes was reminiscent of a request from U-boat operational circles in 1943, which led initially to the side-tube idea and later to an arrangement of two quadruple bow tubes in two storeys one above the other. Neither possibility was suitable for a small submarine of only 350 tons. The IKL solution was to put the eight tubes in the upper half of the hull, arranged 2–2–4. Although torpedo tubes of a larger calibre, suitable for torpedoes to be fired from depth, were to be fitted, the closely grouped arrangement of eight tubes was possible because the non-ejecting tubes needed much less in the way of fittings and tanks than ordinary torpedo tubes.

These eight bow tubes made the fore-ship lines bulkier, and the submerged speed dropped by approximately 1 knot for the same power output. The increase in weight was adjusted by a reduction in the engine installation and battery. A special torpedo hatch was now unnecessary, because the two uppermost torpedo tubes were so high that they could by used to introduce the torpedoes without necessity for docking. Instead of conventional forward hydroplanes, as in Class 202,

scoop-shaped blades which could be turned outwards were provided.

The IKL proposal, with the doubled number of torpedoes, was welcomed by the Federal Defence Minister, yet doubts existed concerning their accommodation in the bow compartment. It was decided, therefore, to construct a 1:1 model of the bow compartment. This model was inspected on 4 September 1958, after which the new arrangement was finally authorized. The IKL alternative design, IK10, formed the basis for Class 201.

Meanwhile, the engine installation of the original design had been reshaped. The gearing was dispensed with and the two diesel engines (Daimler-Benz MB820), each of 600hp, 1,450rpm were connected to BBC generators. The main electric motor was now positioned directly on the propeller shaft, and had therefore to be planned as a heavier, low revving (approximately 25–270rpm) motor. Although a saving had been effected with the creep-speed engine, it was believed initially that the weight increase caused by the two generators and the low-revving main electric motor would be very considerable. However, collaboration between IKL and SSW — marked especially by the latter's development of a special 1,500hp electric motor — made possible the provision of an appropriate installation within the intended space and weight requirements. The advantages of this new propulsion unit were obvious: simpler operation, better noise suppression, better resistance to shock. As the boat was now to be driven by only one engine, it was essential that an especially reliable switching method for the propeller engine be provided. A decision was made against an obligatory cam-operated switching, as in U-boat Type XXI, or in the new Class 202. In Class 201, the performance switches were activated solely by compressed-air control. In order to keep noise emission during schnorkel travel as low as possible, the noise suppressors — as, incidentally, were originally planned for U-boat Type XXVI — were re-positioned in the pressure-hull. Housed in a large cylinder above each diesel was a combined noise suppressor and exhaust-gas cooler. It was possible to dispense with a special exhaust-gas mast during schnorkel travel, because the unsupercharged diesel engine had a lower back-pressure sensitivity. Exhaust gases left the upper end of the control-room superstructure and were well-dispersed before entering the water, thus avoiding a strong exhaust trail. (Exhaust gases are cooled better by a larger water column and offer less opportunity for infra-red detection.) The schnorkel mast needed to be designed merely as an air-supply mast. IKL therefore projected a version with an electro-pneumatic head valve which is also in use in the Italian submarines of the *Enrico Toti* class. The extensible schnorkel mast has, in its submerged part, a streamlined fairing and, in that portion where it breaks the surface, a knife-edge, and is thus designed to offer the least possible degree of resistance.

The battery types were also changed. In place of the German lattice-place types, a small tube battery, made by the Swedish firm Tudor, was chosen. It has a larger specific capacity (more

than 20 per cent) and a life 3–5 times that of the lattice-plate battery. The 3×92 cells were arranged as double cells in 138 GFK boxes (glass-fibre strengthened plastic containers). Additionally — and this was in contrast with all previous German U-boat construction practice — the battery ventilation was conceived as compartment ventilation. In this respect, the practice common in foreign countries had been adopted, it having been shown that so long as appropriate measures were taken there was no greater danger for the boat than with individual ventilation; and, on the other hand, there was a substantial reduction in the amount of water lost from the cells. The rather low degree of cooling of cells that occurs in compartment ventilation is unimportant, as it is in any case necessary to have a battery-cooling installation for large batteries with high rates of charging and discharging.

Further improvements in this new submarine type, compared with the last German U-boat designs of the war, consisted of: comprehensive use of automation (automatic diesel cut-out; automatic retraction of all extensible equipment on reaching a determined depth; automatic steering and depth control with also a stationary installation); comprehensive detection installations (GHG (sound-detection), with a large hoof-shaped base beneath the torpedo tubes; an active acoustic detection equipment in the middle frequency range, made by Krupp-Atlas-Elektronik, the base of which could be rotated and inverted and was situated in the control room superstructure; a sonar-warning device; a radar equipment with a parabolic aerial on an extensible mast; a radar warning aerial on an extensible mast); a comprehensive hydraulic system (for control and activation of the entire rudder installation, and all extensible items of equipment, and the outlet hatches of the torpedo tubes). The periscope was designed to have a fixed eyepiece end, which was also an innovation in such a small boat.

On 10 October 1958, IKL presented the completed design for this Class 201, and it was inspected and approved by the Federal Defence Ministry. Here, U-boat construction was dealt with by Sub-Department TV (Marine Technology). Until the end of the sixties, TV was controlled by Dr. Fischer, Dr. Menz and Dr. Waas successively. Howaldtswerke AG of Kiel was decided upon for the construction. From November 1958, IKL was working on building instructions for the construction.

Initially, the well-proved U-boat Steel 52 was intended for the pressure hull. At a discussion on 14 November 1958, for the first time, the comprehensive use of non-magnetic material was demanded. The principal area of operations envisaged for the new boats was in the shallow waters of the Baltic, and the possible dangers there would be magnetically-activated sea-bed mines and detection equipment that could register magnetic impulses. A completely non-magnetic submarine had never been built before, and it was essential to consider carefully all aspects of available materials, and the composition of an electrical installation having a very weak magnetic field. The magnetic effect of those ferrous installation components that were not to be substituted in this way was to be largely obviated by a dipole compensation with probe-controlled automatic MES installation. The final decision concerning the use of non-magnetic steel, and of a building method necessary to minimize the magnetic field in Classes 201 and 202 was made on 13 April 1959.

After an examination of twelve non-magnetic kinds of steel, after weighing up all relevant aspects and costings, those offered by the Austrian firm of Schoeller-Bleckmann Stahlwerke AG of Ternitz, Lower Austria — non-magnetic steels A3CY (later AM 10) and AMCR 1 (later AM 20) were placed on the short list. Wide-ranging tests, carried out in some haste, showed that AM 10 had better strength values, and this steel was chosen for the pressure-hull skin. Through a misinterpretation of test material, it was assumed — wrongly — that AM 10 possessed better resistance to corrosion.

AM 20 was chosen for the parts that would be under less stress, i.e., for the outer hull. Additionally, AM 20 was chosen, for production reasons, for the pressure bulkheads.

In March 1959, the Howaldtswerke AG, Kiel (KHW), received the contract for the proposed 12 Class 201 U-boats. Yard acceptance of the first boats was scheduled for July 1960. As KHW did not have a U-boat construction office, IKL were requested by the Federal Defence Minister, on 25 June 1959, to prepare workshop drawings. This procedure was followed with all subsequent U-boat types. As had been done with the final constructions during the war, section construction methods were projected for the Class 201 series production, and assembly construction was then to follow in two special, sinkable construction pontoons, each of 3,000 tons, a contract for which had already been given to the Nobiskrug Yard in Rendsburg.

Stopgaps: Hai, Hecht and Wilhelm Bauer

In order that the training of permanent submarine crews and the testing of new equipment and methods could commence before the delivery of the first new U-boats, and as the loan of similar types of small boats could not be obtained from the associated countries, particularly the United States, an attempt was made to raise and make seaworthy German Type XXIII U-boats that had been sunk at the end of the war. The Hamburg salvage firm of Beckedorf was given the contract to find and raise *U2365* and *U2367*, which were lying at the bottom of the Kattegat and the Great Belt respectively. In June and August 1956, both U-boats were brought up from a depth of more than 50m. Although they had been rusting at the bottom of the Baltic for eleven years, both boats were still in astonishingly good condition and, in less than a year, Howaldtswerke, Kiel, had overhauled them completely and were able to deliver them almost in

Below: *Hai* (S170) and *Hecht* (S171) after being re-commissioned for the Federal German Navy.

Top: *Hai* and *Hecht* after the 1964 conversion at Blohm & Voss. **Middle:** *Hai* (ex-*U2365*) on manoeuvres after conversion.
Above: The author on the bridge of *Wilhelm Bauer* (ex-*U2540*).

their original condition to the Federal Navy. Only the tip of the bow needed to be changed to receive new active acoustic detection equipment. Additionally, both boats were given an anchor device, which had not been available for Type XXIII. On 15 August 1957, *U2365*, renamed *Hai* ('Shark') and, on 1 October 1957, *U2367*, renamed *Hecht* ('Pike') were commissioned for the second time.

At first, both boats were handed over to the Ship Testing Command and were available to different Command Departments. After the foundation of the U-Boat Education Group at Neustadt on 31 August 1960, *Hai* and *Hecht* became the first training boats of the new German U-boat arm. During the years that followed, both boats were to be twice rebuilt. In 1961 they were given a more streamlined bridge fairing. In early 1964 at B&V, their hulls were cut open and increased in length by 1.2m in order to provide space for a new diesel installation (the diesel generator of Class 201). The boats could only be propelled electrically. At the same time, the diesel air-mast was cut off above the connection with the schnorkel air-mast and was closed with a flange. During surface travel, the diesel engine received its combustion air through the conning-tower hatch, this being fed through special shafts into the engine compartment. The shafts had their outlet in the bilge. Consequently, the engine-compartment door could remain shut, but, with this change, it was necessary for the conning-tower hatch to remain open. Of course, it was also possible to feed air for the diesel through a schnorkel air-supply connection in the engine compartment, but, as the schnorkel was only sealed with the air-intake socket (flange) when fully extended, the danger existed that in a very high sea the opening for the schnorkel shaft, which was only 79cm above the deck, might let water into the boat. As with Class 201, a special exhaust-gas mast could be dispensed with. The diesel exhaust gases were led outside the boat through a fixed tube and, during schnorkel travel, left the boat in well dispersed condition approximately 3m below the surface. After this conversion, which was to reproduce similar running and operating conditions as in Class 201, *Hai* and *Hecht* were given the new designation 'Class 240'.

In the summer of 1957, a large Type XXI U-boat was also raised in the vicinity of the Flensburg Lightship where it had been scuttled. This was *U2540* which, being a large vessel, could not really have played any part in the building-up of the Federal Navy. It is assumed that the initial idea (with special permission from the WEU) was to use this boat, which proved to be well preserved, for training purposes in the same way as the two previously-raised Type XXIII boats. But, in addition, this large and most modern U-boat of the former Navy seemed to be an ideal submarine vessel for possible tests under operational conditions.

Howaldtswerke, Kiel, were requested to restore the boat to its original condition. With very few constructional background details available, this was a much more difficult task for such a large and complicated U-boat than had been the case with

Hai and *Hecht*. In autumn 1958, work was interrupted after a decision had been made that *U2540* was to be used as a special test carrier for the installations that would be used in the new U-boats. The design work appropriate to the conversions was handed over to IKL, which carried them out under the Project No. IK12. A special feature was that, instead of the previous diesel installation, the diesel generators of Class 201 were incorporated. The bridge was reshaped and the anti-aircraft turrets were not restored. The quick-loading installation and two torpedo tubes were not replaced, and the bow compartment was converted to crew's living quarters. The crew's compartment abaft the galley was converted to an NCO's Mess, which left more room in the forward living compartments for detection and measuring installations. Instead of being used as a workshop, the stern compartment was intended to provide access for a frogman lock built above it. On 1 September 1960, the boat, renamed *Wilhelm Bauer*, and with the designation 'Class 241', was commissioned and placed at the service of Test Centre 71 in Eckernförde. During the following years, the bridge fairing was reconstructed many times and, in its forward part, was given Class 201 characteristics (with entry shaft and sonar) and then Class 205 characteristics.

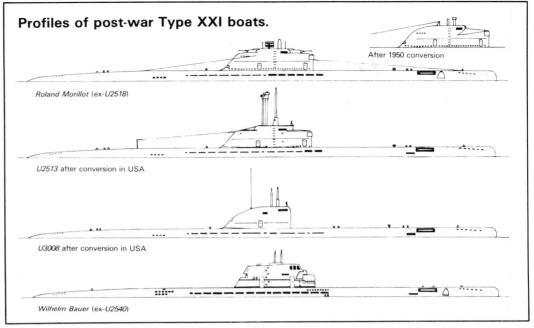

Profiles of post-war Type XXI boats.

After 1950 conversion

Roland Morillot (ex-*U2518*)

U2513 after conversion in USA

U3008 after conversion in USA

Wilhelm Bauer (ex-*U2540*)

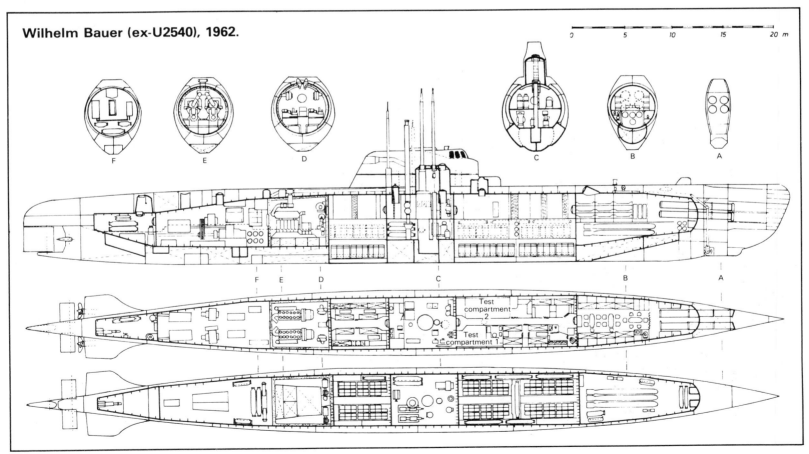

Wilhelm Bauer (ex-U2540), 1962.

0   5   10   15   20 m

F   E   D   C   B   A

F E D   C   B   A

Test compartment 2

Test compartment 1

Construction of Class 205

At the beginning of 1960, KHW had begun section construction for the Class 201 U-boats. The Federal Office for Defence and Technics Procurement (Bundesamt für Wehrtechnik und Beschaffung, or BWB) in Koblenz had set up an outside department in Kiel specially for U-boat construction, under the control of Leading Administrative Construction Director Aschmoneit. Assembly construction could only begin with delivery of the two specially-planned building pontoons from the Nobiskrug Yard — given the names 'Max' and 'Moritz' in February and April 1961. As a protection against the elements, these pontoons had removable roofs which could be pushed aside when it was necessary to manoeuvre sections with a crane. At the same time as work was being commenced on the first Class 201 boats, sea tests of engines and equipment were being carried out in *Wilhelm Bauer*, the resistance to shock of certain parts was being tested with explosive charges, and pressure-tightness was being investigated in a specially-built pressure tank at KHW.

After a building time of approximately eighteen months, the first new German U-boat, which according to tradition was designated *U1*, was afloat on 21 October 1961 and was commissioned five months later on 20 March 1962. *U2* and *U3* followed on 3 May and 10 July 1962. In 1961, Norway had ordered 15 submarines of a similar type from Rheinstahl Nordseewerke, Emden, and, until such time as these should be delivered *U3* was lent to the Norwegians. In the presence of the Commander-in-Chief of the Norwegian Navy, Vice-Admiral Hostvedts, *U3* was named *Kobben* on 10 July 1962.

Class 201 had been designed with the condition in mind that the permitted displacement of up to 350 tons meant the weight of the U-boat in ready-to-dive condition, without fuel and lubricants, fresh water, ballast water or solid ballast. On 10 July 1962, the Armament Control Office of the WEU established precisely the so-called Type displacement (standard displacement in long tons=1,016kg) with reference to the Washington Fleet Disarmament Treaty of 1921–22 and the Anglo-German Fleet Agreeement of 1935; in this, solid ballast could no longer be discounted. Class 201, now being 395 tons, no longer met the conditions imposed by the Paris Treaties. On 19 October 1962 therefore, at German request, the tonnage limit was raised to 450 tons and the construction of 6 larger U-boats of up to 1,000 tons was simultaneously sanctioned.

Even in the initial construction phase of *U1–U3* in 1960, it was requested that these small boats be fitted with a second sonar equipment of greater range. The section construction permitted the necessary enlargement of the boat without great constructional changes in the hull, so that section-rings prepared for subsequent boats could still be used. The central section was increased in length by 1.8m and the bridge superstructure was considerably enlarged. The forward edge was drawn upwards to receive the transducer of this new equipment, and the hitherto-open surface control positions were moved to a place provided in the

Top: *U1* (Class 201) afloat on 21 October 1961. **Above:** *U3* (Class 201) after its return from the Norwegian Navy.

U11–U12 (improved Class 205).

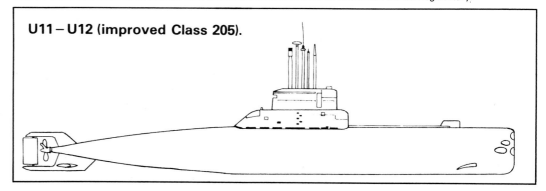

bridge superstructure. There it was better protected from seas breaking over the boat, and observation from it was also improved. All this meant that a military requirement had been met. (The new sonar equipment was also tried out for the first time in *Wilhelm Bauer* and, to accommodate this, the vessel received a new forward section for the bridge in 1962.) A further change was the abandoning of rotary transformers in favour of static Thyristor-alternators, which were more appropriate for the numerous items of electronic equipment in that they had greater frequency constancy and needed less attention. These, too, were accommodated in the enlarged control room. The increase in length brought the standard displacement up to 420 tons, but this was still well below the new maximum of 450 tons.

It was resolved to incorporate these changes from *U4* onwards. The altered design IK10W was given the new designation 'Class 205'. IKL designs for a so-called 'pure' submarine, with an exclusively-electric propulsion or a single-drive not dependent on air, were given the designations 'Class 203' and 'Class 204', but these did not reach the construction stage. Despite the constructional changes and redrafting of workshop drawings, delay was negligible in the delivery of subsequent U-boats up to *U8*. *U4* was afloat on 22 August and *U5* on 20 November 1962; with an assembly construction time of approximately six months, the next two boats followed, *U6* on 22 April and *U7* on 20 May 1963 with, finally, *U8* on 11 October 1963.

In the meantime, something unexpected had become manifest which was to make future planning uncertain and was to have considerable effects on new German U-boat production. While, with the exception of the over-large turning circles, the travelling and diving tests confirmed the predicted offensive qualities of the new boats, within a few months of the commissioning of *U1*, a new kind of corrosion was noticed in the non-magnetic steel. This took the form of inter-crystalline corrosion tension cracks, which became wider and wider and which led, finally, to the laying-up of *U1* and *U2* in the summer of 1963 — a precautionary measure to enable a thorough investigation to be made into this corrosion. The fact that *U3* was in commission constantly until 15 September 1967 (under the Norwegian flag until 20 June 1964) shows that, if appropriate measures were taken with constant surveillance, there was no direct danger for these boats. Following a conversion to the after-ship, *U1* was recommissioned on 4 March 1965 to serve as a test boat for the firing of wire-controlled torpedoes from stern tubes.

U4–U8 were given a protective coating of zinc paint and applications of plastic materials designed to restrict corrosion, but it was not possible to achieve a complete inhibition of corrosion where this had occurred beneath the surface. For reasons of safety, therefore, the boats were taken down deep at regular intervals, off the Norwegian coast, in order to test their pressure-tightness. This was a rather irrational undertaking, and it was then decided, in line with former Navy practice, to have a pressure-dock constructed at the Lübeck

Top and middle: *U1* in the dry dock at HDW, Kiel, in early 1965 after its conversion as a test-carrier for firing wire-guided torpedoes. The container set-up at the stern of the boat carries the firing mechanism. **Above:** *U7* after its new bridge conversion, which was similar to that of improved Class 205.

Flenderwerke and this was to be ready in August 1967.

The total extent of the damage amounted to millions of marks, and both public and parliament reacted with great acrimony. Further U-boat construction was stopped, and deliberations took place as to what should be done with the remaining four Class 205 U-boats that had been ordered. As only non-magnetic materials could be used for Baltic boats, it was essential to carry out lengthy tests on new non-magnetic steels. This had not been done in the case of the first Schoeller-Bleckmann steels, partly because previous experience of steels used in ship construction did not suggest that it was necessary, and partly because when they were chosen time was of the essence. It was further resolved that, in place of the decommissioned *U1* and *U2*, 2 new boats should be built, with the same designation, but using conventional Steel 52 for the pressure hull. The still serviceable installations and engines of *U1* and *U2* were to be used as far as possible. Both boats were built according to the design of Class 205, but with improvements in the electronic equipment, with elastic bedding of certain engines and with a newly-altered control-room superstructure.

The considerably enlarged bridge superstructure of Class 205 not only increased considerably the friction resistance, but also brought about additional shaft resistance at periscope-depth. Now the upper portion of the superstructure could be made narrower because the new longer-ranged sonar equipment was inapplicable. A further change to the outer ship was a streamlined dome on the fore-ship which contained additional detection equipment. The new *U2*, the first boat of this improved Class 205 (IK10Wm) was commissioned on 10 October 1966.

The remaining four boats, *U9–U12*, were also built in line with this changed design, but with new corrosion-resistant, non-magnetic steels. The intention was to make a thorough test in these boats of the suitability and strength of these kinds of steel. Consequently, *U9* and *U10* were built of the new Schoeller-Bleckmann Steeel AM 53, *U11* of PN 18 S2 and *U12* of Amanox 182 M 9. Delivery of these followed at considerable intervals, and it was 14 January 1969 before *U12*, the last boat of the series decided upon in 1956, was commissioned. In *U11* and *U12*, because of the fact that the rudder effect was too slight with the rudder blades of the present arrangement being outside the propeller-wash (a condition most noticeable in slow manoeuvring), a return was made to the classic arrangement of a large balanced rudder abaft the propeller. *U7* was given the new design for the bridge superstructure: in 1965, an exhaust-gas explosion made extensive repairs necessary.

Top, far left: *U10* (improved Class 205) in the floating dock at HDW, Kiel. **Top, middle:** The fast-disappearing bridge fairing of *U10*, which is carrying-out diving manoeuvres. **Top right:** The conning tower of *U9* (improved Class 205) which, as a 'tradition boat' bears the Iron Cross coat-of-arms. **Left:** *U11* (improved Class 205). The photograph on the far left shows it manoeuvring in front of the Laboe Memorial in the Kiel Estuary; and, left, being towed from the sunken construction pontoon, 9 February 1968.

311

In the shadow of the steel fiasco in Classes 201 and 205, construction of the two small Class 202 test U-boats began at the Bremen Atlas-Werke in 1963. As these were likewise to be constructed of non-magnetic steel, different concepts concerning these boats existed between naval technological circles and the Navy, and retrospective changes were requested, which meant that production was delayed until 1963. The first boat, *Hans Techel*, with a rudder arrangement as in Class 201, was not launched by slip-carriage until 15 March 1965, followed by *Friedrich Schürer* (with a movable Kort nozzle) on 10 November 1965. After only a short period of commission at Test Centre 71 in Eckernförde, both boats were taken out of service on 15 December 1966 and laid up at the Naval Arsenal, Kiel, as the Navy felt that there was no area of application for these small U-boats.

The year 1966 was also overshadowed by the loss of the training submarine *Hai*. She was on her way to Aberdeen, together with two other submarines and two escort ships from the Submarine Training Group Neustadt, for a fleet visit, when she ran into a heavy storm on 14 September. The sinking of *Hai*, with only one survivor, is considered to have been the result of an accumulation of various diverse incidents. She was travelling on the surface, and it is assumed that over a period of time breakers drove through the air-intake connections of the retracted schnorkel into the engine compartment bilge. The stern over-heaviness that this caused was accentuated by the after diving tanks which became more and more flooded. Initially, neither of these effects were noticed in the heavy seas. The boat sank deeper and deeper and the quantity of water entering the boat caused a leak into the engine compartment. Ultimately, the flotation of the boat became so poor that water was even able to stream in through the conning-tower hatch. Obviously, when this occurred, the commander, Oberleutnant Wiedersheim, thought the boat was about to sink immediately and he gave the order to abandon ship. But the boat filled rapidly and sank with only some of the crew being able to reach the deck. The fact that no SOS message was sent bears out this supposition.

On 19 September 1966, *Hai* was raised from 47m by the salvage crane *Magnus III* and towed to Emden for investigation. Two years later, on 3 September 1968, *Hecht* was taken out of service and was broken up.

So ended the first decade of the new German submarine arm, which had begun with high expectations and had been marked by considerable reversals, in that five Class 205 boats were only partly operationally-sound because of corrosion in their steel construction, so that they had to be transferred to the U-Boat Training Group; and in which the First U-Boat Squadron was assembled at Kiel consisting of 6 boats of the improved Class 205 including *U1* and *U2* in magnetic steel, and the clearly indestructible, large, test boat *Wilhelm Bauer*.

Friedrich Schürer and *Hans Techel* (Class 202) at the Naval Arsenal in Kiel after de-commissioning.

Classes 206 and 208

For a continuation of U-boat construction following the first series of 12 Class 201 and 205 boats, studies began in 1962 at IKL on a further development, this being given the designation Class 206 (IK34). On completion of its reconstruction, the U-boat fleet was to total 24 small operational boats of up to 450 tons, and six larger submarine-hunter boats (Class 208). The first research work for this new Class 208 commenced in 1966 at IKL; however, these plans were shelved or completely abandoned mainly because of the extra financial outlay occasioned by the steel fiasco (for the rectification of which reconstruction and new constructions were necessary) and by the economic lull at the end of the sixties.

From the very beginning, a standard displacement of 450 tons maximum was established for Class 206. The most important requirement was for an even stronger battery in order to accommodate the demands for an ever-increasing range of electronics without the submerged range suffering. As the fitting-out of the improved Class 205 had already made necessary a standard displacement of 420 tons, a significant increase in battery weight could only be achieved at the expense of stability ballast, which, for safety reasons, had been set at a high figure in the first types.

Further changes as against the present boats were, outwardly, a new bridge shape, a large

passive sonar with a circular base on the fore-ship, a new schnorkel, a two-stage rod aerial and a lateral rudder arrangement as in *U11* and *U12*. The active acoustic detection installation was also improved. The boat was fitted with a long-range section-panoramic-sonar with search-ray operation and computer-controlled guidance, an equipment that can be adjusted to the changing velocity of noise in the water by a checking sweep over a measured distance. The fire-control installation was that developed by the Dutch firm Hollandse Signaal-apparaten, a new version of their well-tried Series M8, which enables simultaneous calculations on different targets to be made. The parabolic radar antenna was replaced by a slotted aerial, which allowed for better installation.

Safety devices for the crew were also improved. It was planned to incorporate a new safety installation, which caused the automatic expulsion of the safety raft when the interior pressure exceeded a certain figure, but this idea was given up. Instead, at several places in the boat, a quick-release mechanism for hatch-opening and ejection was built-in. Additionally, an oxygen-helium mixture could be taken from an emergency air-breathing installation, which was made in the form of a ring-duct.

In Class 206, for the first time, a departure from self-controlled to wire-controlled torpedoes was made. The question was debated as to whether stern tubes would not be more suitable for this

application, and during 1963 different projects designated 206H were worked on. Numerous problems were encountered, and these made it essential that large-scale testing be carried out. To this end, in 1964 the original *U1* (no longer in commission) was rebuilt and subjected to tests at KHW. Two years later, this line of research was finally discontinued, and the well-tried bow torpedo-tube arrangement was retained.

After final approval of the new design, construction planning commenced in the autumn of 1966 and concluded approximately in the summer of 1967. However, it was 1968 before 12 new Class 206 boats were contracted among four yards with, subsequently, HDW and RNSW being given an increase of 6 boats each.

In consequence of the difficulties that had been experienced following the delivery of the first boats, from 1967, the Federal Defence Minister had developed a new concept in the acceptance and maintenance of submarines. The testing of individual functions when boats were handed over to the Navy was no longer adequate in the light of the complicated and complex weapon systems now obtaining in U-boats. The Navy also lacked personnel able to cope with the testing and running-in of new boats. This overall undertaking was, in future, to be handed over to a suitable yard, designated 'General Contractor' (Generalunternehmer, or GU), which would take over full responsibility, even for all subcontractors, provide proof of current functioning of all U-boat equipment with its own personnel, and would establish supply systems for spare parts. When finally handed over, boats should then be instantly ready for operational use. To the objections of the yards that the risk of held-up deliveries was too high or too incalculable, a final determination of the mandate and responsibilities of the GU was made on 12 September 1966; the GU could guarantee that the deliveries would fulfil the prescribed performances. It was agreed, furthermore, that this new system would not apply completely to *U13–U24*, the design of which had already been determined. In April 1969, HDW was designated General Contractor of the various Class 206 boats. The contract was enlarged in the autumn of 1970

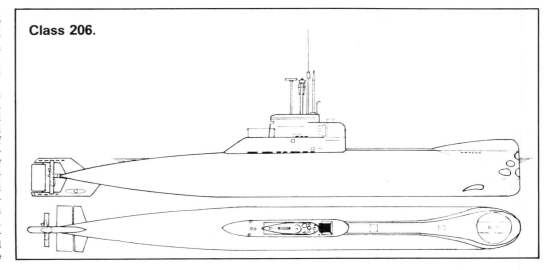

Class 206.

Table 67. Summary of U-boats built for the German Federal Navy after 1960

U-boat	Class	Nato Code	Construction No.	Construction began	Launched	Commissioned	Decommissioned
U1	201	S 180	H 1150	8 June 1960	21 Oct 1961	20 Mar 1962	22 June 1963
	201			11 April 1964[1]	29 Jan 1965	4 Mar 1965	25 Mar 1966
	205 improved		H 509	1 Feb 1965	17 Feb 1967	26 June 1967	
U2	201	S 181	H 1151	1 Sept 1960	25 Jan 1962	3 May 1962	15 Aug 1963
	205 improved		H 508	1 Sept 1964	15 July 1966	11 Oct 1966	
U3	201	S 182	H 1152	12 Oct 1960	7 May 1962	10 July 1962[2]	
						10 July 1965	15 Sept 1967
U4	205	S 183	H 1153	1 April 1961	25 Aug 1962	19 Nov 1962	1 Aug 1974
U5	205	S 184	H 1154	1 June 1961	20 Nov 1962	4 July 1963	17 May 1974
U6	205	S 185	H 1155	8 Nov 1961	30 Jan 1963	24 July 1963	23 Aug 1974
U7	205	S 186	H 1156	1 Feb 1962	10 April 1963	16 Mar 1964	
						22 May 1968[3]	12 July 1974
U8	205	S 187	H 1157	20 Mar 1962	19 June 1963	22 July 1964	9 Oct 1974
U9	205 improved	S 188	H 1158	10 Dec 1964	20 Oct 1966	11 April 1967	
U10	205 improved	S 189	H 1159	15 July 1966	5 June 1967	28 Nov 1967	
U11	205 improved	S 190	H 1160	1 April 1966	9 Feb 1968	21 June 1968	
U12	205 improved	S 191	H 1161	1 Sept 1966	10 Sept 1968	14 Jan 1969	
U13	206	S 192	H 31	15 Nov 1969	28 Sept 1971	19 April 1973	
U14	206	S 193	N 441(32)	1 Mar 1970	1 Feb 1972	19 April 1973	
U15	206	S 194	H 33	1 June 1970	15 June 1972	17 July 1974	
U16	206	S 195	N 442(34)	1 Nov 1970	29 Aug 1972	9 Nov 1973	
U17	206	S 196	H 35	1 Oct 1970	10 Oct 1972	28 Nov 1973	
U18	206	S 197	N 443(36)	1 April 1971	31 Oct 1972	19 Dec 1973	
U19	206	S 198	H 37	5 Jan 1971	15 Dec 1972	9 Nov 1973	
U20	206	S 199	N 444(38)	3 Sept 1971	16 Jan 1973	24 May 1974	
U21	206	S 170	H 39	15 April 1971	9 Mar 1973	16 Aug 1974	
U22	206	S 171	N 445(40)	18 Nov 1971	27 Mar 1973	26 July 1974	
U23	206	S 172	N 450(51)	5 Mar 1973	25 May 1974	2 May 1975	
U24	206	S 173	N 446(42)	20 Mar 1972	26 June 1973	16 Oct 1974	
U25	206	S 174	H 41	1 July 1971	23 May 1973	14 June 1974	
U26	206	S 175	N 447(48)	14 July 1972	20 Nov 1973	13 Mar 1975	
U27	206	S 176	H 47	1 Oct 1971	21 Aug 1973	16 Oct 1974	
U28	206	S 177	N 448(50)	4 Oct 1972	22 Jan 1974	18 Dec 1974	
U29	206	S 178	H 49	10 Jan 1972	5 Nov 1973	27 Nov 1974	
U30	206	S 179	N 449(52)	5 Dec 1972	4 April 1974	13 Mar 1975	
Hans Techel	202	S 172			15 Mar 1965	14 Oct 1965	15 Dec 1966
Friedrich Schürer	202	S 173			10 Nov 1965	6 April 1966	15 Dec 1966

[1]Commencement of conversion. [2]*Kobben*. [3]After repair and conversion. Yards: H=Howaldtswerke Deutsche Werft AG-Werk, Kiel Sud. N=Rheinstahl Nordseewerke GmbH, Emden.

Left and right: *U23* (Class 206) being towed to the slipway at Rheinstahl Nordsee Werken, Emden.

Left: Two of the German-built Class 206 boats for the Norwegian Navy. Top, *U24* undergoing trials. Below, *U14* on yard trials in the summer of 1972. The boat is seen here in front of the construction yard of NSW Emden.

for a further 6 boats of this class (as replacement for *U3–U8*): now, HDW was to manufacture 8 and RNSW, as subcontractor of HDW, 10 boats.

At the end of 1969, construction work began on these U-boats in the newly-built yard, Kiel South, of HDW. In March 1970, similar work began at RNSW in Emden. As they had done previously, HDW assembled its boats from five sections on pontoons that could be sunk, while RNSW assembled its boats on a flat keel in a building hall. Here, on completion, the boat was towed from the hall over the quay-wall into a floating dock (slipway tow) and undocked after being named. A similar process for putting boats into the water had already been used at the Kaiserliche Werft, Danzig. (The RSNW had decided on this method because Slipway 1, used hitherto for U-boat construction, was not currently available because of reconstruction work.)

The first Class 206 boats to be afloat were *U13* on 18 September 1971 at HDW in Kiel, and *U14* on 1

February 1972 in Emden. Even with the new GU system, certain sea tests had still to be carried out by the yards, and it was not until 18 April 1973 that the boats were delivered, although they were now in a full state of operational readiness. On 2 May 1975, *U23*, the last boat of this series, was commissioned for the Third U-Boat Squadron.

Over a period of time many deliberations had been made regarding Class 208, and studies carried out without final decisions being taken. A considerable increase in size over present Class 201 and Class 205 boats had been estimated, as a result of the even more comprehensive acoustic detection installations and the desired increased submerged speed necessary in a submarine-hunter. In order that nothing should inhibit planning from the onset, the WEU had been requested in 1962 to allow a displacement of up to 1,000 tons for the type, although obviously, efforts would be made to achieve a smaller vessel.

In the meantime, improvements in acoustic detection devices meant that smaller boats were now suitable for submarine hunting. The principal disadvantage — lack of speed — as compared with the nuclear submarines of the Great Powers, was

something that could not adequately be made good by an increase in displacement. It was therefore resolved in 1971 to postpone Class 208 until a suitable submerged propulsion unit had been developed. The restrictions imposed by the Paris Treaties with regard to unconventional propulsion methods had been lifted on 3 October 1968 — with the exception of nuclear propulsion.

Export submarines: Classes 207 and 209

To secure the defence of the important northern flank of NATO, it was necessary to supply a small, but offensively-effective submarine fleet for Norway. The submarines that were available (of wartime German and British construction) were out of date at the end of the fifties and needed replacing by new boats. The United States was ready to bear half the cost of this, and a decision was made in favour of a type of boat being developed in the Federal Republic at this time; it was relatively small, but had good offensive and operational capabilities. A governmental agreement between Norway and the Federal Republic decided that 15 boats suitable for use in Norwegian waters should be designed and built in the Federal Republic as a

Table 68 Submarines built for foreign countries in the German Federal Republic after 1960

Country	Submarine	Class	Designation	Construction No.	Construction began	Launched	Delivery
Norway	*Kinn*	207	S 316	N 351	18 Mar 1963¹	30 Nov 1963	8 April 1964
	Kya	207	S 317	N 352	26 May 1963¹	20 Feb 1964	15 June 1964
	Kobben	207	S 318	N 353	9 Dec 1963¹	25 April 1964	17 Aug 1964
	Kunna	207	S 319	N 354	3 Mar 1964¹	16 July 1964	29 Oct 1964
	Kaura	207	S 315	N 355	19 May 1964¹	16 Oct 1964	5 Feb 1965
	Ula	207	S 300	N 356	21 Aug 1964¹	19 Dec 1964	7 May 1965
	Utsira	207	S 301	N 357	1 Jan 1964	11 Mar 1965	8 July 1965
	Utstein	207	S 302	N 358	1 April 1964	19 May 1965	15 Sept 1965
	Utvaer	207	S 303	N 359	1 July 1964	30 July 1965	1 Dec 1965
	Uthaug	207	S 304	N 360	1 Sept 1964	3 Oct 1965	16 Feb 1966
	Sklinna	207	S 305	N 361	20 Dec 1964	21 Jan 1966	27 May 1966
	Skolpen	207	S 306	N 362	1 Feb 1965	24 Mar 1966	17 Aug 1966
	Stadt	207	S 307	N 363	15 April 1965	10 June 1966	15 Nov 1966
	Stord	207	S 308	N 364	1 July 1965	2 Sept 1966	14 Feb 1967
	Svenner	207	S 309	N 365	15 Oct 1965	27 Jan 1967	12 June 1967
Greece	*Glavkos*	209	S 110	H 1221	1 Sept 1968	15 Sept 1970	6 Sept 1971
	Nereus	209	S 111	H 1222	15 Jan 1969	7 June 1971	10 Feb 1972
	Triton	209	S 112	H 1223	1 June 1969	19 Oct 1971	8 Aug 1972
	Proteus	209	S 113	H 1224	1 Oct 1969	1 Feb 1972	23 Nov 1972
Argentina	*Salta*	209	S 31	H 29	30 April 1970	9 Nov 1972	7 Mar 1974
	San Luis	209	S 32	H 30	1 Oct 1970	3 April 1973	24 May 1974
Peru	*Islay*	209	S 45	H 53	15 May 1971	11 Oct 1973	29 Aug 1974
	Arica	209	S 44	H 54	1 Nov 1971	5 April 1974	21 Jan 1975
Colombia	*Pijao*	209	S 28	H 61	1 April 1972	10 April 1974	18 April 1975
	Tayrona	209	S 29	H 62	1 May 1972	16 July 1974	16 July 1975
Turkey	*Atilay*	209	S 347	H 65	1 Dec 1972	23 Oct 1974	23 July 1975
	Saldiray	209	S 348	H 66	2 Jan 1973	14 Feb 1975	21 Oct 1975
Venezuela	*Sabalo*	209	S 21	H 67	2 May 1973	1 July 1975	6 Aug 1976
	Caribe	209	S 22	H 68	1 Aug 1973	6 Nov 1975	11 Mar 1977
Ecuador	*Shyri*	209	S 11	H 91	5 Aug 1974	6 Oct 1976	5 Nov 1977
	Huancavilca	209	S 12	H 92	2 Jan 1975	15 Mar 1977	16 Mar 1978
Turkey	*Batiray*	209	S 349	H 95	11 June 1975	24 Oct 1977	20 July 1978
	Yildiray	209	S 350	H 96	1 May 1976	20 July 1977	
Greece	*Poseidon*	209	S 350	H 106	15 Jan 1976	21 Mar 1978	21 Mar 1979
	Amfitriti	209	S 350	H 107	26 April 1976	14 June 1978	3 July 1979
	Okeanos	209	S 350	H 108	1 Oct 1976	16 Nov 1978	15 Nov 1979
	Pontos	209	S 350	H 118	15 Jan 1977	21 Mar 1979	
Peru	*Casma*	209		H 131	15 July 1977	31 Aug 1979	
	Antofagasta	209		H 132	3 Oct 1977	19 Dec 1979	
	Pisagua	209		H 133	15 Aug 1978		
	Blume	209		H 134	1 Nov 1978		
Indonesia	*Cakra*	209		H 135	25 Nov 1977		
	Nanggala	209		H 136	14 Mar 1978		

¹Commencement of assembly in building hall. Yards: H=Howaldtswerke Deutsche Werft AG-Werk, Kiel Süd. N=Rheinstahl Nordseewerke GmbH, Emden.

development of Class 201. On 16 January 1961, therefore, IKL received a development contract from the Norwegian Navy. The proposed new design was to be based on Class 205 (the improved version of 201) but, instead of using non-magnetic steel for the pressure hull, a high-tension steel (HY80), especially suitable for greater diving depths, was to be used. The increase in weight necessitated by greater pressure tightness was compensated by a rather larger diameter (4.65m instead of 4.55m). The boat was 90cm longer than Class 205, a consequence of a different lateral fin installation (a simple balanced rudder abaft the propeller). The shape of the bridge and certain items of equipment were also changed. However, in its basic features, especially that of drive and armament, the new design corresponded to Class 205.

The governmental agreement laid down that Norwegian interests, especially in the sphere of construction supervision, should be looked after by the outside office of the BWB (Bundesamt für Wehrtechnik und Beschaffung, or Federal Office for Defence Technics and Procurement) in Kiel (BWB-MS24) with a Norwegian liaison officer with full powers working in collaboration. The IKL design was submitted to this office in the summer of May 1961, and was approved after a four-week examination. After confirmatory approval had been received from the Norwegians, there followed in the autumn of 1961 the advanced orders for engines and components that would determine delivery dates.

The design was then offered to three German yards for construction, and RNSW received the award. On 21 December 1961, an initial contract was made with the Nordseewerke and, on 19 January 1962, a final construction contract was concluded. Building instructions were ready in April 1962. Once again, IKL were entrusted with the preparation of workshop drawings. At Norwegian request, the new design (IK29), which now had the German designation 'Class 207' was given, despite its section method of construction, a special diesel assembly hatch — a so-called 'French hatch' — with a conical top fixed by bolts. This created further strength problems.

Although certain workshop drawings for Class 207 had to be redrawn, the construction was able to commence in Emden during the summer of 1962. As had been the case with Classes 201 and 205, section construction was chosen, but with assembly on this occasion at a covered-over building slip. The speedy construction of all 15 boats was ensured by the fact that important components had been ordered in the autumn of 1961. Assembly of the first boat began on 13 March 1963, and of the second on 26 May. Assembly time amounted to eight months, but this was shortened to between four and five months in the following 13 boats. The

last boat Svenner, was lengthened by the distance between two frames, in order that a second periscope could be accommodated to aid in the training of commanders. She was delivered to the Norwegian Navy on 12 June 1967, and was commissioned on 1 July, only 3¼ years after Kinn, the first boat of the type. These 15 boats were to prove themselves splendidly in the Norwegian Navy, and carried out demanding operations even under the most difficult weather conditions in the North Atlantic.

Following the delivery and successful tests of the first Class 207 boats, Denmark also decided to acquire two submarines on the lines of Class 205, but to be built in their own country. The State Yard at Copenhagen, which had already built submarines for Denmark at an earlier date, acquired the licence from the Federal Defence Minister to build 2 boats from the IKL plans for the improved version of Class 205, but in magnetic form. Further changes were necessitated by the desire to use Danish items of equipment.

The construction of these 2 boats, named Narhvalen and Nordkaperen, began in 1965. Despite help from KHW, however, deliveries did not take place until February and December 1970 — clearly the juxtaposition of Danish equipment with German designs and specifications created more difficulties for Danish yards than had been originally estimated. Such building by the Danes could hardly be justified economically.

The summer of 1967 looked as if it would be the start of a lean period for the German U-boat industry: the last Class 207 submarine was

delivered to Norway, the construction of Class 206 was postponed indefinitely, and a start on Class 208 was simply not in prospect. Considerable developmental design and construction capacity had by now been assembled, so strenuous efforts were made to obtain further export orders. The small Class 205 being no longer wanted, it seemed profitable to offer a larger submarine as a replacement for obsolescent fleet submarines, especially in those Latin-American countries that had received submarines from the large wartime complement of the United States. In other countries, Britain's *Oberon* class (Canada, Australia, Brazil and Chile) and France's *Daphné* class (Pakistan, South Africa, Portugal and Spain) were well entrenched.

The legitimate possibility of building submarines of up to 1,000 tons in the Federal Republic came when permission was granted by the WEU for 6 boats of Class 208. In 1966, IKL in common with KHW, had already developed a larger electro-boat for export purposes, which corresponded roughly to Class 205 in shape, construction and armament, but with increased dimensions, much larger battery capacity and a stronger propulsion unit. As with Class 207, the pressure-hull material was planned to be of the high-tensile, magnetic, special steel HY80. During the early part of 1967, a design was worked out to the construction stage and was later designated Class 209.

The new design was for an ocean-going submarine with a standard displacement not exceeding 1,000 tons, planned to have a maximum endurance of 50 days, but which, on account of its relatively short

Right: Svenner (Class 207) being launched at NSW Emden on 27 January 1967. The boat was towed from the construction hangar into a floating dock. **Far right:** The launching of Stadt (Class 207) at Rheinstahl Nordseewerke, Emden, on 10 June 1966.

length of approximately 54m, could also be employed successfully in coastal work. As with the smaller IKL types, good submerged properties were given top priority. The boat was completely smooth, with the shape of the bridge similar to the improved version of Class 205. Once again, in place of the conventional forward hydroplanes, this design had scoop-shaped fins that could be swung out. The after rudder installation, however, was changed and had been assembled with a fin-cross in front of the screw. The considerably enlarged, submerged propulsion installation was designed to provide a maximum submerged speed of 22 knots — this meant that the boat had a submerged speed that, apart from special designs, had never hitherto been achieved by submarines of this displacement with diesel-electric propulsion. The well-tried Daimler-Benz MB820 diesel engines were used and, to obtain doubled power output, a total of four of these units were arranged in the spacious engine compartment. It was proposed that two larger diesels be used in later boats.

The boat had two periscopes, but the other extensible items of equipment were similar to those in the earlier smaller boats. To assist in the evaluation of RT signals received by the various aerials, and in place of the earlier piecemeal arrangement of different items of equipment disposed wherever space was available in the radio compartment, a special communications centre, from the firm of Collins Radio Co., was installed in the shape of a single large desk. The larger boats permitted the accommodation of additional installations, such as reserve torpedoes, effective

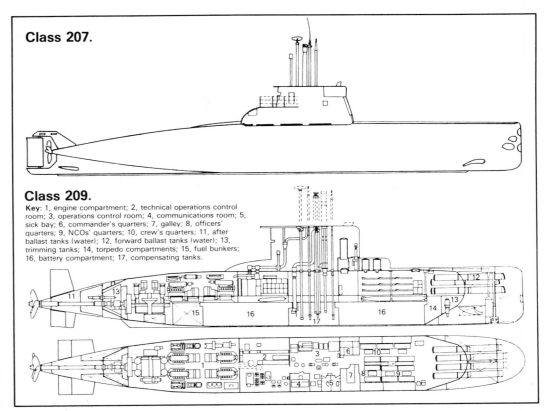

Class 207.

Class 209.

Key: 1, engine compartment; 2, technical operations control room; 3, operations control room; 4, communications room; 5, sick bay; 6, commander's quarters; 7, galley; 8, officers' quarters; 9, NCOs' quarters; 10, crew's quarters; 11, after ballast tanks (water); 12, forward ballast tanks (water); 13, trimming tanks; 14, torpedo compartments; 15, fuel bunkers; 16, battery compartment; 17, compensating tanks.

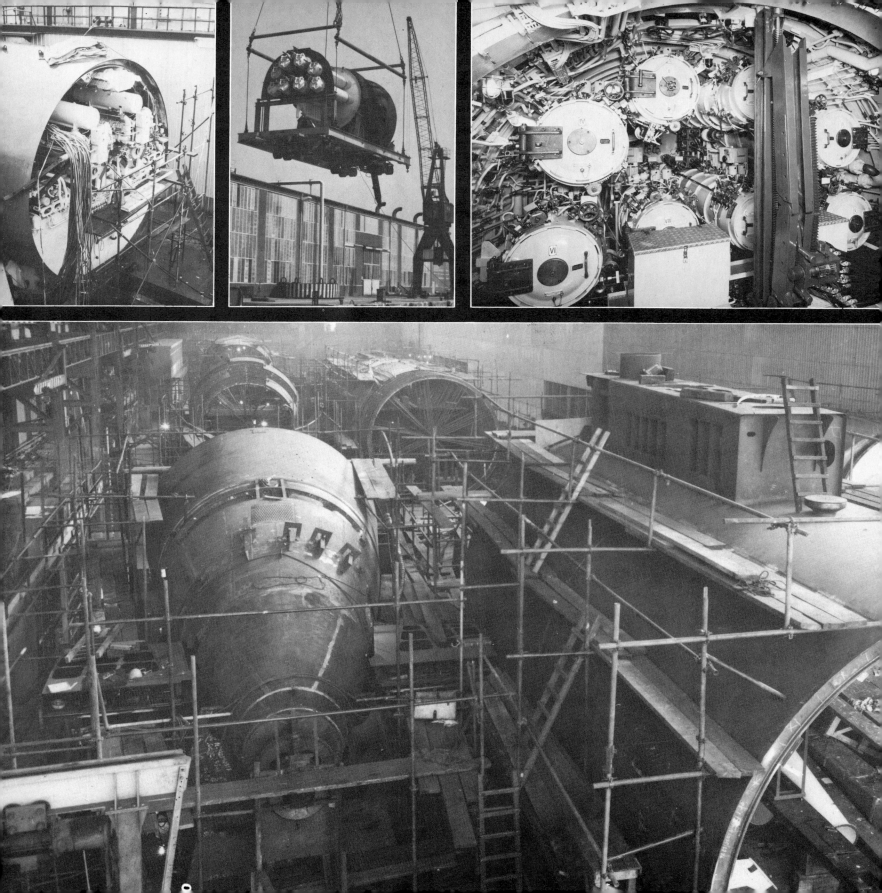

Left, top: Some of the assembly processes for a Class 209 export submarine. The photograph on the far left shows a midships section in the floating dock at HDW; middle, the torpedo tube section being transferred to the assembly hall at HDW, Kiel-Sud from the manufacturer MAK in Kiel-Friedrichsort; and, left, the torpedo tube installation in a completed boat. **Below:** Three phases of series production of sections for Class 209 in the large assembly hangar at HDW, Kiel-Sud. In the foreground may be seen, left, stern sections, middle, centre sections and, right, bow sections; in the background, pressure hull construction for boats to follow. **Right:** *Islay* (Class 209) in the floating dock at HDW, Kiel.

air-conditioning, two WCs and showers, two life-rafts and other items, made necessary by the enlarged range of operations for which the boat was intended.

The first four boats of this Class 209 in the IK36 version were ordered in 1967 by NATO-member Greece. When military forces took over political power in that country, the contract caused political repercussions in the Federal Republic to the extent that, for some time, there was suggestion that German yards should only build sections, with the boats being completed subsequently in Greece. However, in 1970, assembly began in HDW's floating dock at Kiel. Between November 1971 and November 1972, the submarines *Glavkos*, *Nereus*, *Triton* and *Proteus* were delivered to the Greek Navy. For all these submarines and the following orders, financial problems had a special significance, so IKL (development and design) and KHW/HDW (construction) collaborated closely with the special export company, Ferrostaal Essen (Sales).

Two additional submarines in improved versions (56m length) were ordered by each of the following: 1968 Argentina (IK68); 1969 Peru and Colombia (IK62 and IK78 with 35-man crews); 1970 Turkey (IK14 with a 33-man crew). For Venezuela, a further improved version, with a length of 59.5m and a large detection dome located in the bow (similar to Class 206) was developed under the IKL designation IK81. Two boats of this type were placed in contract at HDW in 1972. Additional orders followed from Ecuador, Turkey, Greece, Peru, Indonesia and Iran. There were, therefore, 34 boats of this export Class 209 and its modifications firmly ordered.

In view of the very different requirements of foreign interests, and in order to offer as wide a range as possible, IKL worked-out a number of other different designs:
1. With reference to TOURS 170 (page 325) a small military submarine of 70 tons for genuine coastal operations, with a length of 18m, a submerged speed of 11 knots, diving depth of 100m and two torpedo tubes.
2. A 'warm water' submarine of 380 tons, designed in 1969 especially to meet Mediterranean conditions.
3. A submarine of 450 tons, designed from data of Class 206, but with magnetic steel for the special requirements of the Turkish Navy.
4. An enlarged version of No. 3 above, of 540 tons, with additional electronic equipment, stronger propulsion, reserve torpedoes and, for the first time, the proposed incorporation of the new Vickers anti-aircraft missile SLAM.
5. In 1972, an additional design for a boat of 740 tons, with numerous innovations, but with conventional drive, was included in the list of possibilities.
6. Finally, a variation from Class 209 was projected to serve as a carrier for a 17-ton midget submarine.

However, important business with foreign countries in the sphere of larger submarines was inhibited by the restrictive clauses of the Paris Treaties. The exception that had been made concerning the building of six 1,000-ton submarines

for NATO had been taken up completely by the construction of the four Greek, and the proposed construction of the two Turkish boats. Consequently, both the Argentinian boats had to be built in sections at HDW with assembly following in Argentina (at the Tandanor Yard in Buenos Aires). This unsatisfactory position was ended, however, on 27 September 1973, by the WEU decision to permit the Federal Republic of Germany to build submarines up to 1,800 tons.

In the summer of 1972, an agreement for co-operation was concluded between Vickers Ship-building Group (VSG), HDW and IKL for develop-ment, design, construction and delivery of sub-marines. At the centre of this agreement was the construction under licence of the internationally recognized German submarine designs at the Vickers Yard. These IKL submarines that Vickers would offer could be specially equipped with British weapon systems and thus be more appropriate for

the British market. The first result of this co-operation is that, beginning in 1974, 3 submarines of IKL Project 540 were built for Israel at Vickers Ltd. at Barrow-in-Furness. According to details in the fleet handbooks, this was a smaller version of Class 209 for warm-water operation, with the following main specifications:

Length:	48m.
Beam:	4.7m.
Displacement:	approx. 540 tons.
Propulsion:	two × 600hp diesel generators.
	one × 1,800hp SSW electric motor.
Armament:	eight bow tubes (plus reserve supplies).
	1 SLAM rocket missile for six anti-aircraft rockets with a range of 3,000m.
Crew:	22.

One of the boats of IKL Project 540 built at Vickers, Barrow-in-Furness.

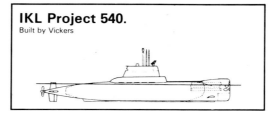

IKL Project 540.
Built by Vickers

Meanwhile, Nordseewerke, Emden, participate in German submarine exports to South America too. In 1978, they concluded a deal to supply Argentina with four 1,750-ton boats and two of 1,400 tons; all, except one of the 1,750-ton boats, to be built in Argentina. A further considerable export order for the German submarine industry will be to replace in the next few years the Norwegian *Kobben* class (Class 207) by a more modern and larger design, which is currently in the design stage at IKL under the designation Class 210.

Postwar single-drive propulsion schemes

While the very successful tests carried out on the Walter-drive and the closed-cycle drive during the last years of the war brought a new generation of 'pure' submarines within measureable reach, neither of these methods of propulsion was persevered with after the war. This was partly because of the increased costs involved, and partly because of the lack of experience that prejudiced a worthwhile foreign development of what had been achieved in Germany. It was ten years after the war before Britain succeeded in commissioning two test boats of the Walter type, which had been under construction in Germany in 1945. The United States finally by-passed this development phase by the introduction of nuclear drive, and the other great sea powers, the Soviet Union, Britain and France, followed her example. However, because of the considerable weight of the reactor shielding, this drive was initially feasible only for very large boats of more than 2,000 tons and, the expense being so high, was only appropriate for boats of a very offensive nature, with missile armament.

For coastal defence of the smaller sea powers especially, the conventional submarine with diesel-electric drive remained standard. Sweden took the initiative in the development of new types of propulsion drives: initially, tests were carried out to develop further closed-cycle drive for her boats. Test-bed experiments with an eight-cylinder diesel engine of approximately 1,500hp, in an exhaust-gas closed-cycle, using liquid oxygen, were so successful that it was decided to convert 6 submarines of the U class to closed-cycle drive. The boats were already partly cut up for this when, at the beginning of the 1960s, the plan was suddenly shelved; the *Abborren* class boats, rebuilt from the old wartime U-boats $U4-U9$, were once more given a conventional propulsion installation. At this time, it was believed in Sweden that the fuel cell represented a better solution for the single-drive, for it avoided the disadvantages of the diesel engine (a limited capacity for being regulated and considerable noise) and it seemed, therefore, pointless to invest further capital in closed-cycle experiments.

A purely electrical propulsion is ideal for a submarine in respect of high efficiency and lack of noise, and because cooling problems are fewer than in thermal engines. Not so favourable is the relatively low energy output provided by the electric accumulators. In the small-tube, lead accumulators of a modern submarine battery amount to approximately 20W/hr/kg at a one hour discharge, or 55W/hr/kg at a 100 hour discharge, as compared with 1,730W/hr/kg when fuel (Dekalin) is burned with H_2O_2. If silver-zinc batteries were used, the theoretical maximum capacity at high discharge would be trebled and at low current usage doubled, but silver-zinc batteries have only a short life and are very expensive. Additionally, they can only be charged at relatively low current strengths, which means a lengthy charging time. At present, therefore, they are used only as primary batteries for torpedoes and midget submarines.

It has long been desired to be able to charge batteries by the direct supply of fuels, which, in the

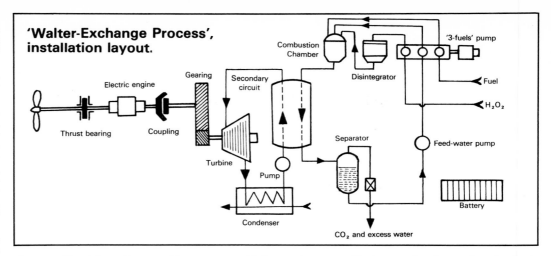

'Walter-Exchange Process', installation layout.

absence of heat formation, would mean a very high coefficient of efficiency. The requirements of space travel gave a great impetus to the development of this 'fuel cell'. In the still most frequently used H_2-O_2cell, the production of current is brought about by a kind of reversal of the water disintegration that takes place in electrolysis: both gases are fed under pressure to two porous electrodes in a potash lye. This causes the gases to ionise, which has the effect of charging the electrodes. This is, therefore, a 'cold' oxy-hydrogen gas combustion in which, instead of heat, electrical energy results. Water is produced as a residue, and this has to be removed constantly from the cell when current is being used.

The theoretical voltage between the electrodes amounts to 1.23 volts. However, under load this value drops considerably in practice. At $100mA/cm^2$ related to the outer surface of the electrodes, the voltage amounts to only 0.75–0.80 volts. For high performance, one would require a multiplicity of cells connected in parallel. The contract placed by the Swedish Navy to the Allgemen Svenska Elektrizitets Aktiebolaget (ASEA) for such a submarine battery called for eight fuel-cell groups, each of 25kW.

In recent years it has been possible to reduce considerably the original very heavy performance weight and performance volume — in the case of a 30kW installation with $NaBH_4$ from 125kg/kW (1968) to 45kg/kW (1973) and from 80 1/kW (1970) to 46 1/kW (1973) — but there are still difficulties in the preparation of fuel. The Swedish installation suggests the manufacture of H_2 from ammonia and the obtaining of O_2 from H_2O_2 or from liquid oxygen.

At this time, work was also being done in the Federal Republic of Germany in connection with a single-drive for submarines. Professor Hellmuth Walter had offered the Federal Defence Minister a further development of his indirect propulsion method designated 'Walter-Exchange Process' and, in 1960, received a contract to build and test a 3,000hp installation in a version suitable for small boats. The new process differed principally from the indirect method by using an efficient heat-exchanger. Post-war development of heat-exchangers, particularly in the sphere of atomic power-stations, has made it possible to work with lower temperatures of the primary heating gas, which makes the installation safer and cheaper. The primary cycle can now take place with water injection in the combustion chamber, as in the direct process. After passing through the heat-exchanger, this injected water is removed from the exhaust-gas mixture into a separator and fed once again into the combustion chamber, so that only the fuel and Aurol (H_2O_2), led into the boat from the bunkers, leaves the boat again in the form of CO_2 and excess water. As fuel and Aurol material in Walter-boats are carried for convenience in exterior bunkers, where they are comprehensively compensated by sea water, there is no great trimming problem.

While it was necessary, during the last war, to use a stowage wheel-pump with a subordinated mixture regulator for three materials (H_2O_2, fuel and water), in the new process it was decided to use a displacement pump which could simultaneously supply and measure exactly. This had been developed and tried out as early as 1944 for the Walter 'Steinwal' torpedo with sea water injection.

Although in 1965–66 this installation came up to the required performance on the test-bed, and for tests of its performance aboard ship the construction of a third Class 202 boat was already under consideration, no Walter U-boat was built. Also further IKL designs for small submarines with single drive (Class 203 and 204) remained paper concepts. The factors that called a halt to further development were, one supposes, the same as in Sweden: excessive costs and the prospect of a better solution being supplied by the fuel cell. However, there is no doubt that the amount of time needed to develop a suitable high-performance fuel cell for use in a vessel had been considerably underestimated, so the heat-exchange Walter-drive was suggested once again in about 1970 for the submarine-hunting boats of Class 208. At present it seems to be the only non-nuclear single drive that offers a sufficiently high output to yield speeds equalling those of atomic submarines. As in all turbine propulsion units, it is specially noteworthy that the efficiency decreases considerably with output; hence, in the medium cruising speeds, the ranges that can be achieved are too small and too uneconomic. A way round this could be the use of a pre-switched turbine, or the distribution of the unit output to several turbines, but this would necessitate a much greater allocation of space. Obviously certain problems remain to be solved before a Walter-exchange-process can be used, and certain elements of the new Walter-installation do not seem to have been quite sufficiently developed as yet. Extremely comprehensive tests carried out by IKL have shown that the Walter-drive is hardly likely to be available any earlier than the variants that are independent of outside air, and which are being given parallel development. A decisive factor could well be that there is simply not the same capacity being applied to Walter development as to the variants — indeed, it seems at present, as if there is no serious desire to build Class 208 at all, in view of the considerable costs that its realization would entail. Very possibly there is speculation as to the development of atomic drives, with lower output and dimensions, involving less cost. This, of course, would represent the best solution of the propulsion problem in smaller submarines.

At the end of the 1960s, there was discussion on the feasibility of the Stirling hot-gas engine made by Philips for submarine propulsion. In this particular engine, external heating and cooling produces a heat incline in a cylinder, which can be used to bring about periodic expansion of a working gas and can, therefore, be used to drive a piston. The uniform combustion and the possibility of completely balancing the engine enables the small, hot-gas engine to run quietly, without oscillation and in a way that resembles the running of an electric motor. Its coefficient of efficiency is very satisfactory in atmospheric combustion, and approximates to the values of a diesel engine. Further advantages are that it can use different fuels, has fewer exhaust-gas problems and is capable of simple performance control by the changing of pressure of the working gas. These properties, especially that of silent running, could make the hot-gas engine of great interest as a charging component in schnorkel submarines. (There was, in fact, discussion about the possibility of testing such an installation on the test boat *Wilhelm Bauer*, but so far as can be ascertained, nothing has yet come of this.)

The hot gas engine would also be very suitable — possibly in connection with a Walter-turbine installation — for the 'independent of air' submerged-cruising drive, but there would still be further problems to be solved involving the heat supply from the combustion chamber to the cylinders. In air operation, the high heat level of the exhaust gas can be used for pre-warming the atmospheric combustion air, which facilitates a high degree of efficiency. This, of course, does not apply in combustion that is independent of air.

Further, mainly theoretical, possibilities of energy production in submarines using so-called heat accumulators and through chemical heat production are a long way from practical realization. Only considerable investment could enable one of the various suggested processes to be brought to the stage of a breakthrough. Although it is acknowledged that underwater research is of considerable significance in the ever more acute power and food crises on our 'Spaceship Earth', it seems that the acceptable time has still not arrived.

Non-military submarines

During the last twenty years, there has been considerable international development of underwater installations and submarines for submerged research, impetus for this being supplied especially by the International Geophysical Year 1957/58. The deep-sea diving-boat occupied the centre of the stage — Piccard's *Trieste*, for example — in which a depth of 10,916m was reached in the Marianas Trench in January 1960, and later the submerged habitats for lengthy visits on the sea bed of the European continental shelf. In this way began a development period that one day — as has already happened with air travel — will shift the emphasis of submerged travel from a military application to a civilian and commercial one.

The spectrum of applications for diving-boats includes submersibles for research, general purposes, cargo and tourism. While there could be many uses for research and general-purpose submarines, peacetime cargo submarines would have an application only for passing under the Arctic region — for example, in the transportation of crude oil from Alaska — while in the near future, because of the considerable technical outlay and the special safety problems involved, the use of submarines for tourism is hardly likely to be an economic proposition.

In Germany at the present time, only the firms of Dräger (underwater habitats), IKL (TOURS diving-boats), Bruker-Physik AG (MERMAID diving-boat) and Hellmuth Walter GmbH (project for a deep-sea diving-boat) have done much research or presented plans for underwater installations. The IKL diving-boat developments and those of the firm of Walter merit rather more description.

At the end of the 1960s, IKL, following their considerable success in the field of medium submarines, projected a small, robust type of boat, in the hope of filling a gap in the submarine market. An initial version, designated 'TOURS 60' (Tourist Observation and Underwater Research Submarine, length 60dm!) was a two-man submarine with many applications. Its weight was 10 tons, and it was suitable for use in oceanic research, fisheries research, underwater archaeology, salvage and inspection and supervision of underwater installations (e.g., dams, quays and pipelines). It was developed in three versions, designed for a diving depth of 100m (TOURS 60/100), 200m (TOURS 60/200) and 300m (TOURS 60/300). The pressure hull consisted of a steel cylinder with two hemispherical pressure bulkheads welded on, plus an entry shaft on top that served also as a driver's cockpit and had five observation windows. The forward pressure bulkhead had four extra Plexiglass windows. Two strong keel skids (or runners) were fastened to the pressure hull, and

these aided stability besides providing a surface on which the boat could rest when on the bottom. The outer ship consisted mainly of two saddle tanks, a deck superstructure housing a magnetic compass in a nose made of non-magnetic steel, which could be read by electrical impulse in the driver's position, and a spindle-shaped after ship with stabilizing fins in the shape of a cross and a lateral rudder at the end of the vertical fin.

Two propellers were disposed at the sides of the small boat. Each was connected to a 6hp electric motor inside the boat, and were given vertical movement by hand operation, which made movement possible in all directions. The electrical installation of the boat was supplied by one battery with 2×58 cells, allowing submerged ranges of 19 nautical miles at 5.5 knots (maximum speed) or 60 nautical miles at 3 knots (cruising speed). For special applications, this boat could be fitted with a larger battery and a diesel generator for battery charging. An air renewing system allowed an uninterrupted diving time of 30 hours. Special emphasis was laid on the simplest possible operation and safety, by simplified engines and systems, and by providing a maximum of life-saving devices: for example, automatic blowing of diving cell in the saddle tanks if the permitted depths were exceeded or if the crew failed to activate the safety controls in the prescribed manner.

An enlarged version of this basic concept, one with five- or six-man crew and which would also be suitable for underwater tourism, is available under the designation TOURS 73 (8m long, 12.7 tons weight). In this design, the propeller is positioned at the point of the stern, in a Kort nozzle that functions simultaneously as a lateral rudder and hydroplane. It is driven by a 16.3hp electric motor, which can be controlled by a Thyristor installation in both turning directions from 50—480rpm without intermediate gearing. The radius of action quoted is 20 nautical miles at 6 knots (maximum speed) and 55 nautical miles at 3 knots (cruising speed). The diving tanks, which in TOURS 60 are positioned at the sides, have been displaced upwards and are incorporated in the deck superstructure, thus providing observation for passengers through pressure-tight 'bullseyes' in the sides. In the course of time, a series of further designs for small and midget submarines has followed, as shown in Table 69. Few of these designs aroused interest, however. On the one hand, the lack of financial support given by the German Federal Government meant that most institutions with small budgets could not acquire such diving-boats for research tasks of limited scope; on the other hand, from a mercantile-profit point of view, the productiveness was a doubtful factor.

In 1969, this situation changed when the Kuo Feng Ocean Development Corporation of Taipei, Taiwan, ordered a general-purpose diving-boat developed from TOURS 60/300 for the collecting of precious corals, and this vessel was given the new designation TOURS 64. The new type differs from TOURS 60/300 mainly in having a hydraulic grab, capable of carrying out six functions and with a maximum reach of 1.9m, and a gyro compass replaces the planned magnetic compass. The boat uses the hydraulic system to activate propeller direction, movement of the trimming weights and use of the outer searchlight. TOURS 64 is rather larger than TOURS 60, has a length of 6.93m, a beam of 3.65m and weighs approximately 14 tons. The pressure hull consists of 13mm high-tensile steel G 36. An MWM diesel engine D202, of 15kW/3,000rpm charges the 1.9-ton battery, which consists of 120 cells (210Ah at a 5 hour's discharge). This gives an enlarged radius of action of 400

nautical miles at 4.5 knots. The coral is collected in a freight net, weighing 200kg, beneath the grab; this net can be released from within. The cost is quoted at 1.2 million marks. The boat (Construction No. 001) was built in 1970 in the IKL-affiliated factory Maschinenbau Gabler GmbH (MG), Lübeck, and carried out her trials successfully at the end of 1970. She was named *Argus I* and was despatched to Taiwan in March 1971 by the Nationalist Chinese freighter *Ling Yung*.

Another diving-boat for the same purpose was ordered in 1971 by the Sarda Estrazione Lavoratione Prodotta Marini S.p.A., Cagliari, Italy. This two-man submarine was given the type designation TOURS 66/300. She is rather larger than her predecessor, has a length of 7.3m, a beam of 3.8m and weighs a quoted 14.5 tons: there is, therefore, space for a maximum of three persons. In other respects, she is similar to TOURS 64. Shortly before the tenth anniversary of the founding of MG,

Table 69. Main specifications of TOURS-type projects

Designation	Diving depth	Crew	Weight (tonnes)	Length	Range submerged (nautical miles at knots)	Range surfaced	Features
48 TDL/200	200m 656ft	1+2	8.2	4.8m 15.7ft	Dependent upon power supply of tender		L,G,E,UT,R,S
60 DC/300	300m 984ft	2+2	9.5	6.4m 21ft	8 at 5 15 at 3		L,G,E,UT,R,S
64 DGK/300	300mm 984ft	2	14	6.9m 22.6ft	10 at 5 21 at 3	400 at 4.5	D,M,G,E,UT,R,S
66 DGK/300	300m 984ft	2	14.5	7.3m 23.9ft	10 at 5 21 at 3	400 at 4.5	D,M,G,E,UT,R,S
66 DGK/500	500m 1,640ft	2	14.5	7.3m 23.9ft	10 at 5 21 at 3	400 at 4.5	D,M,G,E,UT,R,S
66 BK/100	100m 328ft	2/3	14.5	7.3m 23.9ft	17 at 5 33 at 3		M,G,E,UT,R,S
76 DCD/300	300m 984ft	2+2[1]	20.1	8.6m 28.2ft	8 at 5 20 at 3	400 at 4.5	D,L,M,G,E,UT,R,S
76 DCD/500	500m 1,640ft	2+2[1]	20.1	8.6m 28.2ft	8 at 5 20 at 3	400 at 4.5	D,L,M,G,E,UT,R,S
80 DCD/300	300m 984ft	2+2[1]	19	8.9m 29.2ft	8 at 5 20 at 3	400 at 4.5	D,L,M,G,E,UT,R,S
80 DCD/500	500m 1,640ft	2+2[1]	19	8.9m 29.2ft	8 at 5 20 at 3	400 at 4.5	D,L,M,G,E,UT,R,S
73/300	300m 984ft	2+4	15.5	8m 26.2ft	18 at 3		G,E,UT,R,S
170 DGK/100	100m 328ft	5+8	77	18m 59ft	51 at 5[2] 61 at 3[2]	800 at 4.5	D,L,G,E,UT,R,S
110/50	50m 164ft	2+10	32	11.4m 37.4ft	7 at 5 12 at 3		G,E,UT,R,S
180/50	50m 164ft	2+28	57	18.8m 61.6ft	11 at 5 25 at 3		G,E,UT,R,S
430/500	500m 1,640ft	8+3/5	690	42.5m 139.4ft	115 at 5 120 at 3	4000 at 4.5	D,L,M,G,E,UT,R,S
DSWS/300	300m 984ft	6+2	107	16.4m 53.8ft	Dependent upon power Supply of buoy		L,M,G,E,UT,R,S
DSWS/600	600m 1,968.5ft	6+2	225	22.2m 72.8ft	Dependent upon power Supply of buoy		L,M,G,E,UT,R,S

Note:[1] One passenger. [2] Maximum speed submerged: 11 knots. **Key to features:** D, diesel generator; E, echo-sounder; G, gyro-compass; L, driver's lookout; M, manipulator; R, radio; S, searchlight; UT, underwater telegraphy.

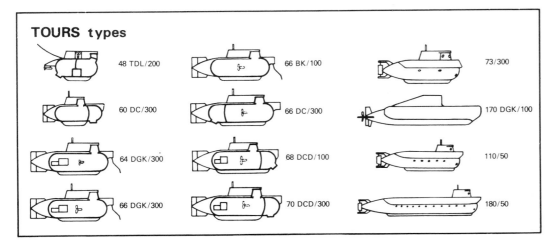

TOURS types

48 TDL/200
60 DC/300
64 DGK/300
66 DGK/300
66 BK/100
66 DC/300
68 DCD/100
70 DCD/300
73/300
170 DGK/100
110/50
180/50

Above and below: TOURS 66 boat *Antonino Magliulo*.

Above: *Antonino Magliulo* on completion. Note the apparatus for breaking off and collecting coral, and the observation windows.

TOURS 64.

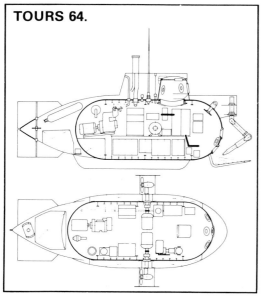

Deep-sea midget submarine Project Stint.

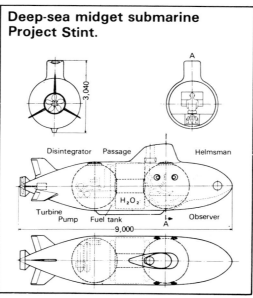

this boat, Construction No. 002, was put into the water on 17 July 1972, after a building time of 13 months. The cost is said to have been 1.5 million marks. Following a pressure test in the HDW pressure tank to a maximum of 30 atmospheres overload, she was delivered to her purchaser in the summer of 1972 and named *Antonino Magliulo*. The construction of these two general-purpose boats and their great profitability in the coral business aroused world-wide interest. An option for a further 6 midget submarines of this type is already with MG.

Another German project, the deep-sea research diving-boat *Stint* of Hellmuth Walter GmbH, is still seeking a corresponding success. She was developed in about 1967 for the new 'independent of depth' Walter-exchange system. The stable storage of H_2O_2 in plastic bags with appropriate sea-water pressure makes possible the convenient accommodation of a large energy supply, adding a considerable submerged range to a relatively high submerged speed, which is unusual in a research submarine. To achieve this, the hull was given a much more streamlined shape than is usual in deep-sea submarines. The boat is 9m long with an overall form displacement of 24 tons. The pressure hull consists of two spheres, each of 2m diameter, connected by a cylindrical panel: the forward sphere contains control and observation positions for both crew members; the after sphere contains the drive unit with disintegrator, steam producer (heat-exchanger), turbo-generator and condenser.

With the propulsion installation giving 50hp, in the so-called cold process (without combustion of energy material), approximately 350 nautical miles at 5 knots or 100 nautical miles at 10 knots (maximum) can be achieved; in the so-called hot process (with combustion of fuel-oil), approximately 750 nautical miles at 5 knots or 200 nautical miles at 10 knots can be obtained. The first of these alternatives has the advantage that the oxygen released in the disintegration process can be used in the operation of the boat. 2kg H_2O_2 produces 0.8kg oxygen, 1.2kg fresh water and approximately 1,200kcal of heat — in other words, all the essential requirements for a lengthy underwater operation. The total 3,000kg of H_2O_2 is arranged in plastic containers above the connecting cylinder. The fuel-oil is stored in plastic tubes forward and aft of it. Below the connecting tunnel, a battery is stored as an energy buffer and to increase stability. Should the boat be in danger, this, like the keel, can be jettisoned to give the boat the necessary positive buoyancy to rise immediately.

In terms of performance, *Stint* would be matched currently by no other two-man submarine. However, the relatively complicated propulsion installation and the use of relatively untried processes make her, for the time being, suitable only for scientific or military applications with highly-qualified specialist personnel. Despite the undeniably unique qualities of this boat, her very considerable development and construction costs have so far deterred any possible purchaser. It is to be hoped that this interesting project will not remain just the drawing of a model as shown at the Inter-Ocean Exhibition of 1970 in Düsseldorf.

Appendices

Below: A Type IXC boat undergoing trials.

U-Boat Specifications, 1906–1918

Type:	U1	U2	U3	U5	U9	U13	U16	U17	U19	U23	U27	U31	Ms	Ms
UI Project No.	GW development	7	12	—	—	—	—	20	—	—	—	—	25	—
Builder	GW	KWD	KWD	GW	KWD	KWD	GW	KWD	KWD	GW	KWD	GW	KWD	GW
Boats ordered	*U1*	*U2*	*U3–4*	*U5–8*	*U9–12*	*U13–15*	*U16*	*U17–18*	*U19–22*	*U23–26*	*U27–30*	*U31–41*	*U43–50*	*U51–56*
Displacement (tons)														
Surfaced	238	341	421	505	493	516	489	564	650	669	675	685	725	715
Submerged	283	430	510	636	611	644	627	691	837	864	867	878	940	902
Length (m)	42.4	45.4	51:3	57.3	57.4	57.9	57.8	62.4	64.2	64.7	64.7	64.7	65.0	65.2
Beam (m)	3.8	5.5	5.6	5.6	6.0	6.0	6.0	6.0	6.1	6.3	6.3	6.3	6.2	6.4
Draught (m)	3.2	3.1	3.1	3.6	3.1	3.4	3.4	3.4	3.6	3.5	3.5	3.6	3.7	3.6
Propulsion (no. × hp)														
Main	2×200 Körting	2×300 Daimler	2×300 Körting	4×225 Körting	2×300, 2×225 Körting	2×350, 2×250 Körting	2×342, 2×258 Körting	4×350 Körting	2×850 MAN	2×900 GW	2×1,000 MAN	2×925 GW	2×1,000 MAN	2×1,200 MAN
Electric	2×200	2×315	2×515	2×520	2×580	2×600	2×600	2×560	2×600	2×600	2×600	2×600	2×600	2×600
Fuel capacity (tons)	22	46	48	52	52	64	64	74	54+22	53+30	54+44	56+55	57+75	57+46
Speed (knots)														
Surfaced	10.8	13.2	11.8	13.4	14.2	14.8	15.6	14.9	15.4	16.7	16.7	16.4	15.2	17.1
Submerged	8.7	9.0	9.4	10.2	8.1	10.7	10.7	9.5	9.5	10.3	9.8	9.7	9.7	9.1
Range (n. miles/kn)														
Surfaced	1,500/10	1,600/13	1,800/12	1,900/13	1,800/14	2,000/14	2,100/15	6,700/8	7,600/8	7,620/8	9,770/8	8,790/8	11,400/8	9,400/8
Submerged	50/5	50/5	55/4.5	80/5	80/5	90/5	90/5	75/5	80/5	85/5	85/5	80/5	51/5	55/5
Armament														
Bow torpedo tubes	1	2	2	2	2	2	2	2	2	2	2	2	4	2
Stern torpedo tubes	—	2	2	2	2	2	2	2	2	2	2	2	2	2
Torpedoes carried	3×45cm	6×45cm	6×45cm	6×45cm	6×45cm	6×45cm	6×45cm	6×45cm	6×50cm	6×50cm	6×50cm	6×50cm	8×50cm	8×50cm
Guns	—	—	—	—	—	—	—	—	1×8.8cm	1×8.8cm	1×8.8cm	1×8.8cm	2×8.8cm	2×8.8cm
Mines	—	—	—	—	—	—	—	—						
Crew	12	22	22	29	29	29	29	29	35	35	35	35	36	35
Notes					Paraffin-fuelled						With one additional 8.8cm gun	With one additional 8.8cm gun		Improved Type *U41*

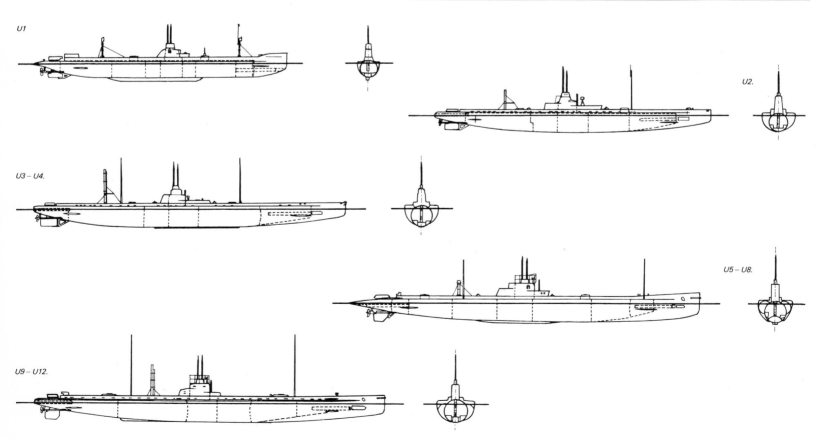

U1

U2.

U3 – U4.

U5 – U8.

U9 – U12.

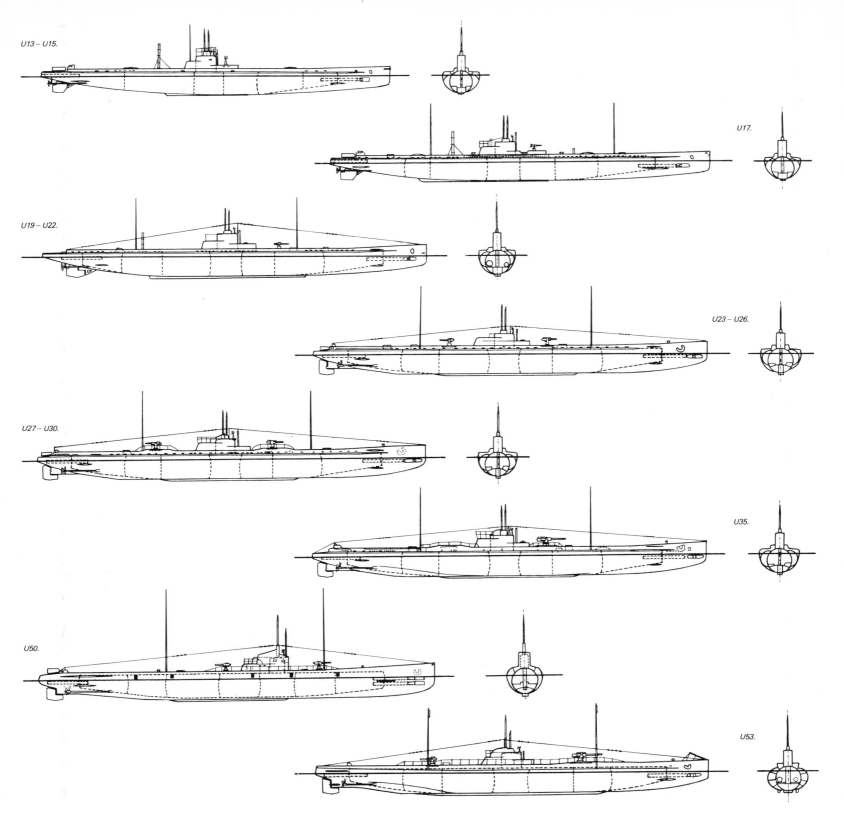

U13 – U15.

U17.

U19 – U22.

U23 – U26.

U27 – U30.

U35.

U50.

U53.

Type:	Ms	Ms	Ms	Ms	Ms	Ms	Ms	Ms	Ms	Large Ms	Large Ms	UD	UE
UI Project No.	—	—	—	—	25	—	43	—	—	42	42a	GW development	38
Builder	AG Weser	AG Weser	GW	GW	KWD	GW/Br. Vulkan	Schichau	KWD	GW/Br. Vulkan	KWD,GW, AG Weser	KWD,AG Weser,B&V	GW	Vulkan, KWD
Boats ordered	U57–59 Similar: U99–104	U60–62	U63–65	U81–86	U87–92	U93–95 Similar: U96–98, U105–114, U160–172, U201–212	U115–16 U263–276	U158–159	U229–246 Similar: U247–262	U135–138 Similar: U127–130, U131–134	U213–218 Similar: U219–224, U225–228	U66–70	U71–72, U75–80 Similar: U73–74
Displacement (tons)													
Surfaced	787	768	810	808	757	838	882	811	908	1,175	1,135	791	755
Submerged	954	956	927	946	998	1,000	1,233	1,034	1,192	1,534	1,830	933	832
Length (m)	67.0	67.0	68.4	70.1	65.8	71.6	72.3	71.2	74.0	83.5	88.1	69.5	56.8
Beam (m)	6.3	6.3	6.3	6.3	6.2	6.3	6.5	6.2	6.7	7.5	7.9	6.3	5.9
Draught (m)	3.8	3.7	4.0	4.0	3.9	3.9	4.0	3.9	4.3	4.3	4.0	3.8	4.9
Propulsion (no. × hp)													
Main	2×900 MAN	2×1,200 MAN	2×1,100 GW	2×1,200 MAN	2×1,200	2×1,200	2×1,200 MAN	2×1,200 MAN	2×1,450	2×1,750, 2×450gen	2×1,750, 2×450gen	2×1,150 GW	2×450
Electric	2×600	2×600	2×600	2×600	2×600	2×600	2×600	2×600	2×615	2×845	2×845	2×630	2×400
Fuel capacity (tons)	78+41	76+52	78+30	81+38	54+79	47+60	68+65	58+87	71+67	53+138	53+138	47+40	80+10
Speed (knots)													
Surfaced	14.7	16.5	16.5	16.8	15.6	16.8	16.0	16.0	16.5	17.6	18.0	16.8	10.6
Submerged	8.4	8.4	9.0	9.1	8.6	8.6	9.0	9.0	9.0	8.1	9.0	10.3	7.9
Range (n. miles/kn)													
Surfaced	10,500/8	11,400/8	9,170/8	11,220/8	11,380/8	9,020/8	11,470/8	12,370/8	11,400/8	10,000/8	12,000/8	7,370/8	7,880/7
Submerged	55/5	55/5	60/5	56/5	56/5	52/5	50/5	55/5	50/5	50/4.5	90/4.5	115/5	83/4
Armament													
Bow torpedo tubes	2	2	2	2	4	4	4	4	4	4	4	4	1
Stern torpedo tubes	2	2	2	2	2	2	2	2	2	2	2	1	1
Torpedoes carried	7×50cm	7×50cm	8×50cm	8×50cm	12×50cm	12×50cm	12×50cm	12×50cm	12×50cm	14×50cm	16×50cm	12×45cm	4×50cm
Guns	2×8.8cm	2×8.8cm	2×8.8cm	2×8.8cm	1×10.5cm	1×10.5cm	1×10.5cm	1×10.5cm	1×10.5cm	2×10.5cm	1×15cm	2×8.8cm	1×8.8cm
Mines	—	—	—	—	—	—	—	—	—	—	—	—	34 UE150
Crew	35	35	35	35	36	36	36	39	39	46	46	36	32
Notes	Improved Type U27	Improved Type U27	Improved Type U56	Improved Type U65	Improved Type U50	—	—	Improved Type U92	—	—	Improved Project 42	Originally intended for Austro-Hung Navy	Minelaying U-boat

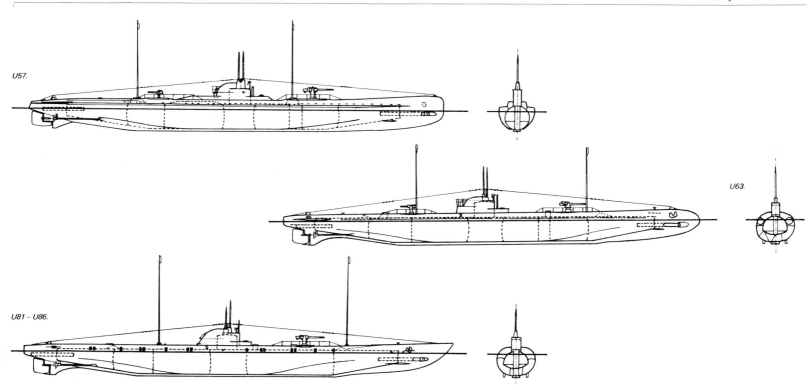

U57.

U63.

U81 – U86.

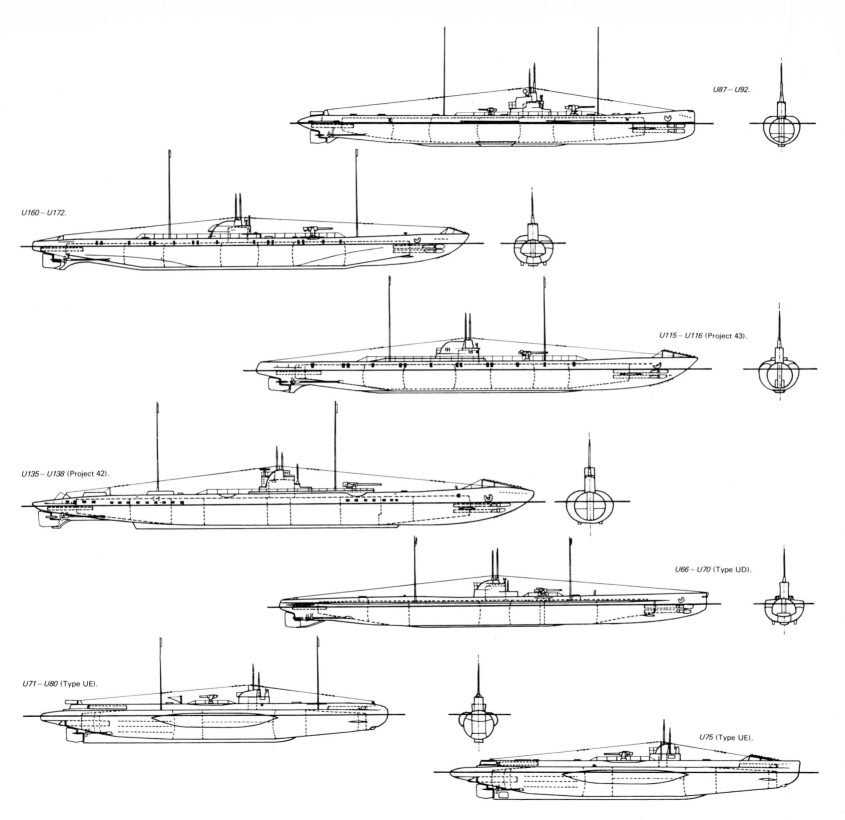

U87 – U92.

U160 – U172.

U115 – U116 (Project 43).

U135 – U138 (Project 42).

U66 – U70 (Type UD).

U71 – U80 (Type UE).

U75 (Type UE).

Type:	Large Minelaying U-boat	U-cruiser	U-cruiser	U-cruiser	UBI	UBII	UBIII	UCI	UCII	UCIII	UF
UI Project No.	45	46	46a	GW development	34	39	44	35a	41	41a	48a
Builder	Vulcan, B&V	GW	GW, Vulcan, AG Weser, B&V	GW	GW, AG Weser	B&V, AG Weser	B&V, AG Weser, Vulcan, GW	Vulcan, AG Weser	B&V, Vulcan, GW, KWD, AG Weser	KWD, AG Weser, B&V	Schichau, Tecklenborg, Atlas, Neptun, Seebeck
Boats ordered	*U117–121* Similar: *U122–126*	*U139–141*	*U142–144* Similar: *U145–150, U173–200*	*U151–157*[1]	*UB1–8 UB9–17*	*UB18–23* Similar: *UB24–47*	*UB48–53* Similar: *UB54–249*	*UC1–10* Similar: *UC11–15*	*UC16–24* Similar: *UC25–79*	*UC80–86* Similar: *U87–152*	*UF1–92*
Displacement (tons)											
Surfaced	1,164	1,930	2,158	1,512	127	263	516	168	417	474	364
Submerged	1,512	2,483	2,785	1,875	142	292	651	183	493	560	381
Length (m)	81.5	92.0	97.5	65.0	28.1	36.1	55.3	34.0	49.4	56.1	44.6
Beam (m)	7.4	9.1	9.1	8.9	3.2	4.4	5.8	3.2	5.2	5.5	4.4
Draught (m)	4.2	5.3	5.4	5.3	3.0	3.7	3.7	3.0	3.7	3.8	4.0
Propulsion (no. × hp)											
Main	2×1,200	2×1,650–1,750, 1×450 gen.	2×3,000, 1×450 gen.	2×400	1×60	2×142	2×550	1×90	2×250	2×300	2×300
Electric	2×600	2×845	2×1,300	2×400	1×120	2×140	2×394	1×175	2×230	2×385	2×310
Fuel capacity (tons)	95+96	103+283	120+330	148+137	3.5	22+6	35+36	3.0	41+15	55+11	—
Speed (knots)											
Surfaced	14.7	15.3–15.8	17.5	12.4	6.5	9.2	13.6	6.2	11.6	11.5	11.0
Submerged	7.0	7.6	8.5	5.2	5.5	5.8	8.0	5.2	7.0	6.6	7.0
Range (n. miles/kn)											
Surfaced	12,500/8	12,630/8	20,000/6	25,000/5.5	1,650/5	6,500/5	8,500/6	750/5	9,430/7	8,400/7	3,500/7
Submerged	35/4.5	53/4.5	70/4.5	65/3	45/4	45/5	55/4	50/4	55/4	40/4.5	64/4
Armament											
Bow torpedo tubes	4	4	4	2	2	2	4	—	2	2	4
Stern torpedo tubes	0	2	2	0	0	0	0	1	1	1	1
Torpedoes carried	12×50cm	19×50cm	24×50cm	18×50cm	2×45cm	4×50cm	10×50cm	—	7×50cm	7×50cm	7×50cm
Guns	1×15cm	2×15cm	2×15cm 2×8.8cm	2×15cm 2×8.8cm	1 MG	1×5cm	1×8.8cm	—	1×8.8cm	1×10.5cm	1×8.8cm
Mines	42 UC200 plus 30 mines in deck containers	—	—	—	—	—	—	12 UC120 mines	18 UC200 mines	18 UC200 mines	—
Crew	40	66+20	66+20	56+20	14	22	34	14	26	32	30
Notes	—	—	—	Converted cargo U-boats	—	—	—	—	—	—	—

Note: Constructional diving depth: *U1–U4*, 30m; Project 42, 42a, 45, 46, 46a, 48a, 75m; others, 50m. **Key to abbreviations**: gen.=generator. [1]*U155* had 6 surface torpedo tubes.

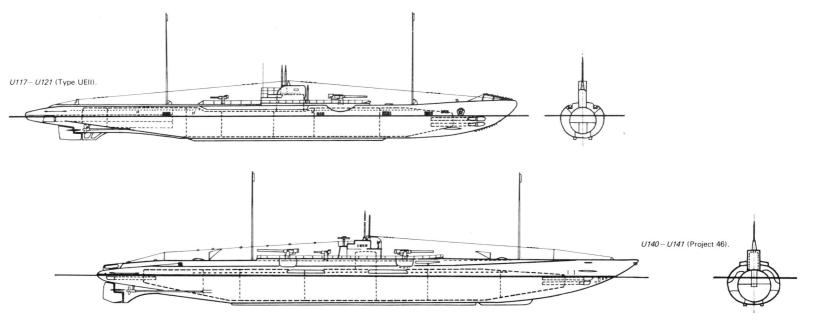

U117–U121 (Type UEII).

U140–U141 (Project 46).

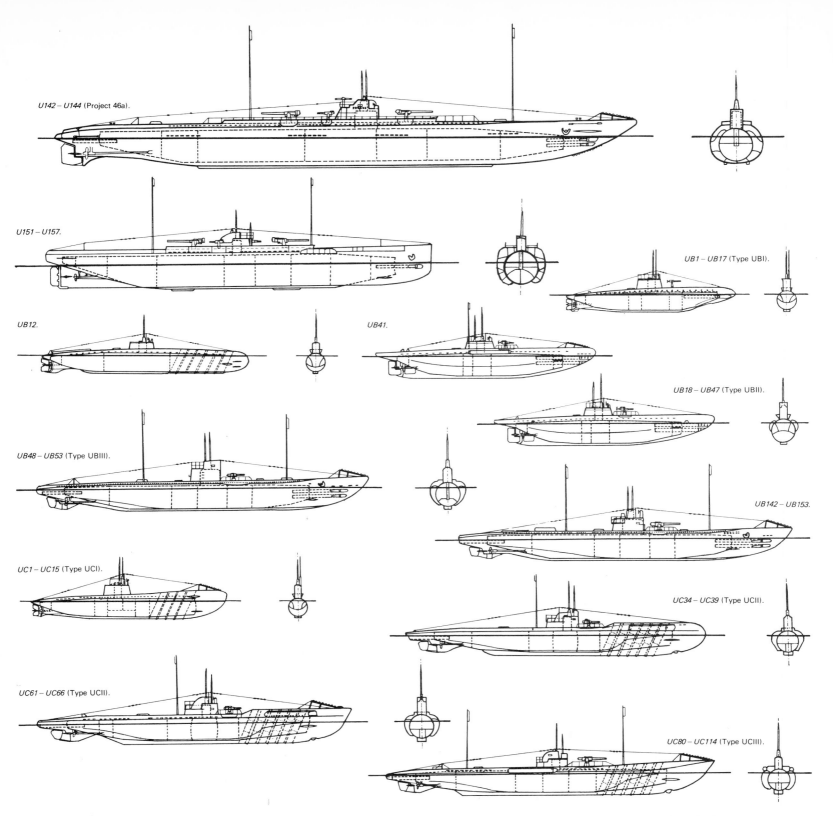

U142 – U144 (Project 46a).

U151 – U157.

UB1 – UB17 (Type UBI).

UB12.

UB41.

UB18 – UB47 (Type UBII).

UB48 – UB53 (Type UBIII).

UB142 – UB153.

UC1 – UC15 (Type UCI).

UC34 – UC39 (Type UCII).

UC61 – UC66 (Type UCII).

UC80 – UC114 (Type UCIII).

U-Boat Specifications, 1935–1945

Type:	IA	IIA	IIB	IIC	IID	III	IV	V
Boats ordered	*U25–26*	*U1–6*	*U7–24, U120–121*	*U56–63*	*U137–152*	Project	Project	Project
Displacement (tons)								
Surfaced	862	254	279	291	314	1,500	2,500 (max)	300
Submerged	983	303	329	341	364	2,000		320
Length (m)	72.4	40.9	42.7	43.9	44.0	78		32
Beam (m)	6.2	4.1	4.1	4.1	4.9	7.4		3.2
Draught (m)	4.3	3.8	3.8	3.8	3.9	5		4
Propulsion (no.×hp/type)								
Diesel	2×1,540 MAN	2×350 MWM	2×350 MWM	2×350 MWM	2×350 MWM	2×1,540 MAN		2×2,400
Electric	2×500	2×180	2×180	2×205	2×205	2×500		2×3,750c-c
Fuel capacity (tons)	96	12	21	23	38	100		36 (+74 H_2O_2)
Speed (knots)								
Surfaced	17.8	13.0	13.0	12.0	12.7	15.5		26
Submerged	8.3	6.9	7.0	7.0	7.4	7		30
Range (n. miles/kn)								
Surfaced	6,700/12	1,050/12	1,800/12	1,900/12	3,450/12	7,500/10		2,000/15
Submerged	78/4	35/4	43/4	43/4	56/4			500/15
Armament								
Bow torpedo tubes	4	3	3	3	3	4		2[1]
Stern torpedo tubes	2	—	—	—	—	2		—
Torpedoes carried	14	6	6	6	6	14		—
Guns	1×10.5cm 1×2cm	1×2cm	1×2cm	1×2cm	1×2cm	1×10.5cm 1×2cm		
Crew	43	25	25	25	25			
Notes						To carry 2 small MTBs and 48 TMA mines	Supply and workshop U-boat	Walter-boat

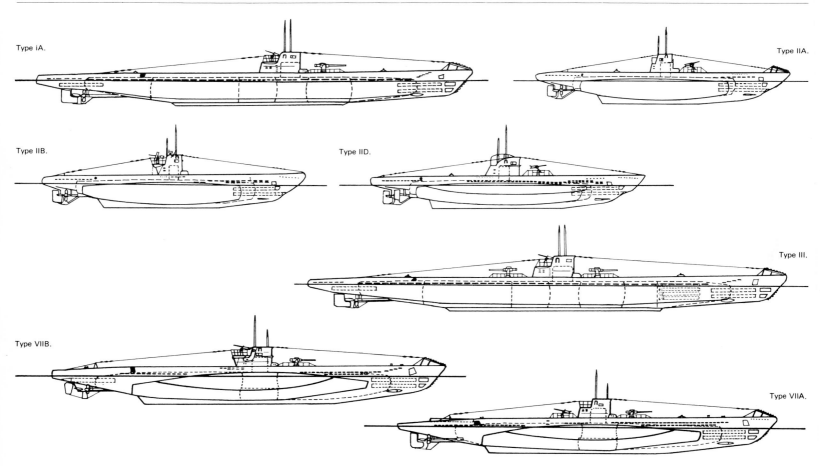

Type iA.

Type IIA.

Type IIB.

Type IID.

Type III.

Type VIIB.

Type VIIA.

Type:	VI	VIIA	VIIB	VIIC
Boats ordered	Project	U27–36	U45–55, 73–76, 83–87, 99–102	U69–72, 77–82, 88–98, 132–136, 201–212, 221–232, 235–291, 301–316, 331–458, 465–486, 551–686, 701–722, 731–782, 821–828, 901–908, 929–930, 951–994, 1051–1058, 1063–1065, 1101–1106, 1131–1132, 1161–1162, 1191–1210
Displacement (tons)				
Surfaced	850 (max)	626	753	761
Submerged		745	857	865
Length (m)		64.5	66.5	67.1
Beam (m)		5.8	6.2	6.2
Draught (m)		4.4	4.7	4.8
Propulsion (no.×hp/type)				
Diesel		Single-drive Schmidt/Hartmann steam process	2×1,160	2×1,400	2×1,400
Electric		2×375	2×375	2×375
Fuel capacity (tons)		67	108	113
Speed (knots)				
Surfaced		16.0	17.2	17.0
Submerged		8.0	8.0	7.6
Range (n. miles/kn)				
Surfaced		4,300/12	6,500/12	6,500/12
Submerged		90/4	90/4	80/4
Armament				
Bow torpedo tubes		4	4	4
Stern torpedo tubes		1	1	1
Torpedoes carried		11	14	14
Guns		1×8.8cm 1×2cm	1×8.8cm 1×2cm	1×8.8cm 1×2cm
Crew		44	44	44
Notes	Shape identical to Type IA			Guns, from 1944: 1×3.7cm, 2×twin 2cm

Type:	VIIC/41	VIIC/42
Boats ordered	U292–300, 317–330, 687–698, 703–705, 723–730, 829–840, 909–912, 931–936, 995–1050, 1107–1114, 1133–1146, 1163–1190, 1211–1214, 1271–1285, 1301–1312, 1331–1338, 1401–1404, 1417–1422, 1435–1439, 1801–1804, 1823–1828	U699–700, 783–790, 913–918, 937–942, 1069–1080, 1093–1100, 1115–1120, 1147–1152, 1215–1220, 1286–1297, 1313–1318, 1339–1350, 1423–1434, 1440–1463, 1805–1822, 1901–1904, 2001–2004, 2101–2104, 2301–2318
Displacement (tons)		
Surfaced	759	999
Submerged	860	1,099
Length (m)	67.2	68.7
Beam (m)	6.2	6.9
Draught (m)	4.8	5.1
Propulsion (no.×hp/type)		
Diesel	2×1,400	2×2,200 MAN
Electric	2×375	2×375
Fuel capacity (tons)	113	159
Speed (knots)		
Surfaced	17.0	18.6
Submerged	7.6	7.6
Range (n. miles/kn)		
Surfaced	6,500/12	10,000/12
Submerged	80/4	80/4
Armament		
Bow torpedo tubes	4	4
Stern torpedo tubes	1	1
Torpedoes carried	14	16
Guns	1×8.8cm 1×2cm	1×quad 2cm 2×twin 2cm
Crew	44	45
Notes	Guns from 1944: 1×3.7cm, 2×twin 2cm	

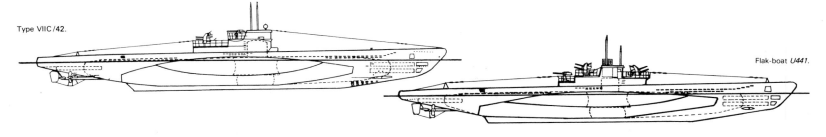

Type VIIC/42.

Flak-boat U441.

Type:	VIID	VIIE	VIIF	VIII	IXA	IXB	IXC	IXC/40
Boats ordered	*U213–218*	Project	*U1059–1062*	Project	*U37–44*	*U64–65, 103–111, 122–124*	*U66–68, 125–131 153–166, 171–176, 501–525*	*U167–170, 183–194 526–550, 801–816, 841–846, 853–858, 865–870, 877–882, 889–894, 1221–1262, 1501–1503*
Displacement (tons)								
Surfaced	965	—	1,084	—	1,032	1,051	1,120	1,144
Submerged	1,080	—	1,181	—	1,153	1,178	1,232	1,257
Length (m)	76.9	—	77.6	—	76.5	76.5	76.8	76.8
Beam (m)	6.4	—	7.3	—	6.5	6.8	6.8	6.9
Draught (m)	5.0	—	4.9	—	4.7	4.7	4.7	4.7
Propulsion (no.×hp/type)								
Diesel	2×1,400	2×V-12 Deutz two-stroke	2×1,400	—	2×2,200 MAN	2×2,200 MAN	2×2,200 MAN	2×2,200 MAN
Electric	2×375	2	2×375	—	2×500	2×500	2×500	2×500
Fuel capacity (tons)	169	—	199	—	154	165	208	214
Speed (knots)								
Surfaced	16.0	—	16.9	—	18.2	18.2	18.3	18.3
Submerged	7.3	—	7.9	—	7.7	7.3	7.3	7.3
Range (n. miles/kn)								
Surfaced	8,100/12	—	9,500/12	—	8,100/12	8,700/12	11,000/12	11,400/12
Submerged	69/4	—	75/4	—	65/4	64/4	63/4	63/4
Armament								
Bow torpedo tubes	4	—	4	—	4	4	4	4
Stern torpedo tubes	1	—	1	—	2	2	2	2
Torpedoes carried	14	—	14+27	—	22	22	22	22
Guns	1×8.8cm 1×2cm +15SMA	—	1×8.8cm 1×2cm	—	1×10.5cm 1×3.7cm 1×2cm	1×10.5cm 1×3.7cm 1×2cm	1×10.5cm 1×3.7cm 1×2cm	1×10.5cm 1×3.7cm 1×2cm
Crew	44	—	46	—	48	48	48	48
Notes	Minelayer	Test boat developed from Type VIIC to test new engines	Torpedo supply boat	—	Guns: from 1944, 1×3.7cm, 2×twin 2cm			

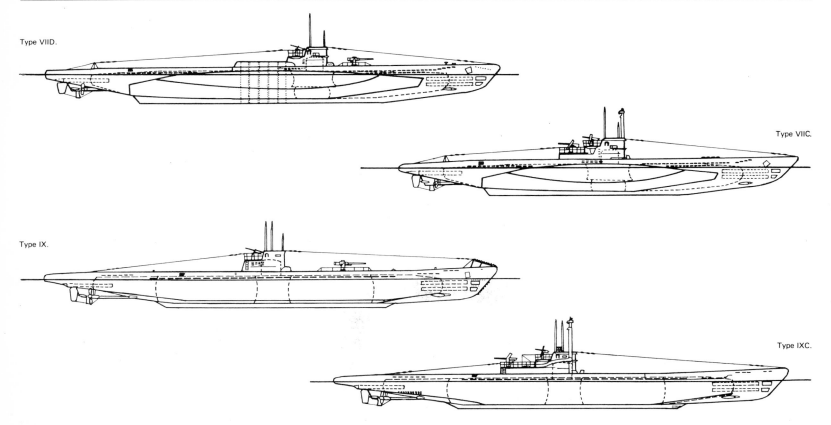

Type VIID.

Type VIIC.

Type IX.

Type IXC.

Type:	IXD$_1$	IXD$_1$ converted to transport boat	IXD$_2$	IXD/42	XA	XB	XI
Boats ordered	*U180; U195*	*U180; U195*	*U177–179, 181–182, 196–200, 847–852, 859–864, 871–876*	*U883–888, 895–900, 1531–1542*	Project	*U116–119, 219–220, 233–234*	*U113–115*
Displacement (tons)							
Surfaced	1,610	1,610	1,616	1,616	2,500	1,763	3,140
Submerged	1,799	1,799	1,804	1,804	—	2,177	3,930
Length (m)	87.6	87.6	87.6	87.6	103	89.8	115
Beam (m)	7.5	7.5	7.5	7.5	9.5	9.2	9.5
Draught (m)	5.4	5.4	5.4	5.4	4.4	4.7	6.2
Propulsion (no.×hp/type)							
Diesel	6×1,500	2×1,400 GW	2×2,200 MAN	2×2,200 MAN	2	2×2,100 GW	8×2,200 MWM
Electric	2×500	2×500	2×580 MWM 2×500	2×580 MWM gen. 2×500	2	2×550	2×1,100
Fuel capacity (tons)	—	203	442	442	—	368	500
Speed (knots)							
Surfaced	20.8	15.8	19.2	19.2	14	16.4	23.0
Submerged	6.9	6.9	6.9	6.9	—	7.0	7.0
Range (n. miles/kn)							
Surfaced	—	9,900/12	23,700/12	23,700/12	—	14,450/12	15,800/12
Submerged	—	115/4	57/4	57/4	—	93/4	50/4
Armament							
Bow torpedo tubes	4	—	4	4	4	—	4
Stern torpedo tubes	2	—	2	2	—	2	2
Torpedoes carried	24	—	24	22	—	11	12
Guns	1×10.5cm 1×3.7cm 1×2cm	1×3.7cm 2×twin 2cm	1×10.5cm 1×3.7cm 1×2cm	1×10.5cm 1×3.7cm 1×2cm	1×10.5cm, 1×3.7cm, 1×2cm +SMA	1×10.5cm, 1×3.7cm, 1×2cm +66 SMA	2×twin 12.7cm, 2×3.7cm, 1×2cm +Ar231 aircraft
Crew	57	57	57	57		52	110
Notes		252 tons of cargo			Minelayer	Minelayer	Artillery boat

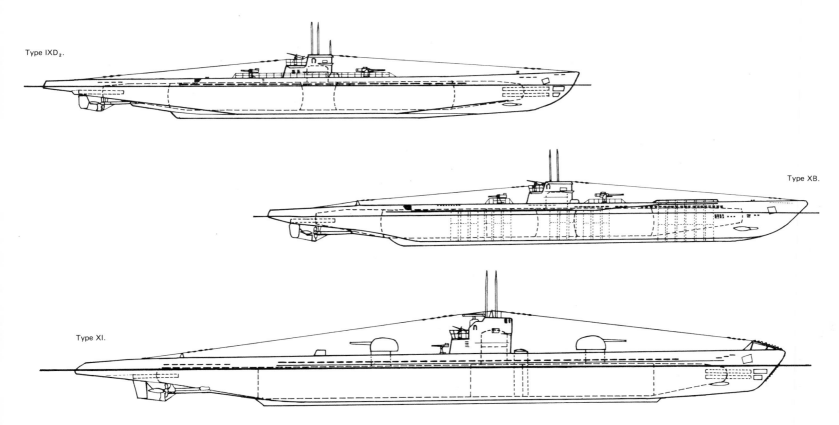

Type IXD$_2$.

Type XB.

Type XI.

Type:	XII	XIII	XIV	XIVB	XV	XVI	V80	V300	Wa201
Boats ordered	9 planned	Project	*U459–464, 487–500, 2201–2204*	Project	Project	Project	*V80*	*U791*	*U792, U793*
Displacement (tons)									
Surfaced	2,041	400 approx.	1,688	1,895	2,500	5,000	73	610	277
Submerged	—	—	1,932	—	—	—	76	655	294
Length (m)	92.4	—	67.1	70.9	—	—	22	52.1	39
Beam (m)	8.5	—	9.4	—	—	—	2.1	4.0	3.3
Draught (m)	5.4	—	6.5	—	—	—	3.2	5.5	4.3
Propulsion (no.×hp/type)									
Diesel	2×3,500 GW	2	2×1,400 GW	2×1,400 GW	2×1,400	2×1,400	1×2,000 Walter	2×150 MWM 2×2,180 Walter	2×210 Deutz 2×2,500 Walter
Electric	2×840	2	2×375	2×375	2×375	2×375		2×75	1×77
Fuel capacity (tons)	—	—	203	—	—	—	20 H_2O_2	34+98 H_2O_2	18+43 H_2O_2
Speed (knots)									
Surfaced	22.0	15	14.4	—	—	—	—	9.3	9.0
Submerged	10.0	—	6.2	—	—	—	28	19.0	25.0
Range (n. miles/kn)									
Surfaced	20,000/12	—	9,300/12	—	—	—	—	2,330/9	—
Submerged	—	—	55/4	90/4	—	—	50/28	205/19	117/20
Armament									
Bow torpedo tubes	4	4	—	—	—	—	—	2	2
Stern torpedo tubes	2	—	—	—	—	—	—	—	—
Torpedoes carried	22	—	4	4	—	—	—	6	4 [1]
Guns	1×10.5cm 1×3.7cm 1×2cm	1×2cm	2×3.7cm 1×2cm	1×3.7cm 2×twin 2cm	—	—	—	—	—
Crew	—	—	53	53	—	—	4	25	12
Notes	Fleet boat		Fuel supply boat with 432 tons oil	Doubled battery capacity	Supply and workshop boats		Walter test boat		*U793* only 1 Walter turbine

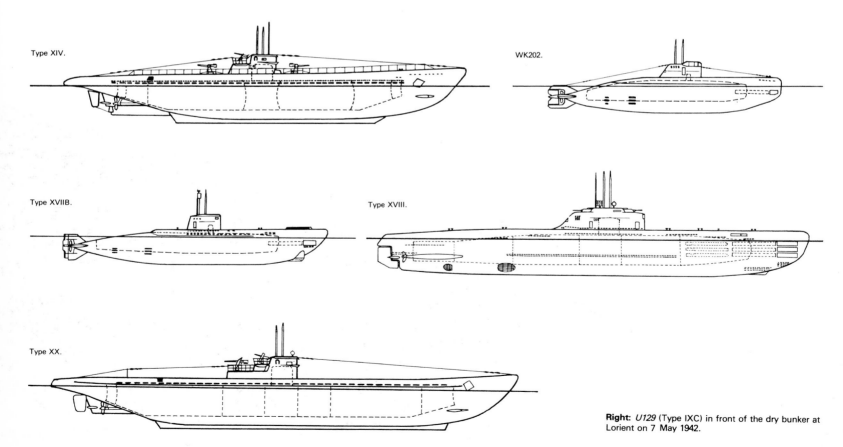

Type XIV.

WK202.

Type XVIIB.

Type XVIII.

Type XX.

Right: *U129* (Type IXC) in front of the dry bunker at Lorient on 7 May 1942.

Type:	WK202	XVIIB	XVIIE	XVIIG	XVIIK	XVIII	XIX	XX	XXB
Boats ordered	*U794, 795*	*U1405–1416*	Project	*U1081–1092*	*U798*	*U796; 797*		*U1601–1615 1701–1715*	Project
Displacement (tons)									
Surfaced	236	312	340	314	301	1,485	2,000	2,708	—
Submerged	259	337	—	345	340	1,652	—	2,962	—
Length (m)	34.6	41.5	43.9	39.5	40.7	71.5	—	77.1	—
Beam (m)	3.4	3.3	3.3	3.4	3.4	6.2	—	9.2	—
Draught (m)	4.6	4.3	4.3	4.7	4.9	6.4	—	6.6	—
Propulsion (no.×hp/type)									
Diesel	1×210 Deutz 2×2,500 Walter	1×210 Deutz 1×2,500 Walter	1×900	1×210 Deutz 1×2,500 Walter	1×1,500 c-c	2×2,000 MWM 2×7,500 Walter	—	2×1,400	2×1,400
Electric	1×77	1×77	1×1,160	1×77	1×68	2×198	—	2×375	2×375
Fuel capacity (tons)	14+40 H_2O_2	20+55 H_2O_2	40	19+45 H_2O_2	23+9.2 O_2	124+204 H_2O_2	—	471	—
Speed (knots)									
Surfaced	9.0	8.5	11.5	8.5	14.0	18.5	—	12.5	—
Submerged	24.0	21.5	14.5	21.5	16.2	24.0	—	5.8	—
Range (n. miles/kn)									
Surfaced	1,840/9	3,000/8	6,000/8	3,000/8	2,400/12	5,200/12	—	13,100/12	—
Submerged	—	150/20	224/4	114/20	120/16	250/20	—	49/4	88/4
Armament									
Bow torpedo tubes	2	2	2	2	—	6	—	—	
Stern torpedo tubes	—	—	—	—	—	—	—	—	
Torpedoes carried	4[1]	4[1]	4[1]	4[1]	—	23	—	—	—
Guns	—	—	—	—	—	2×twin 3cm	—	1×3.7cm 2×twin 2cm	1×3.7cm 2×twin 2cm
Crew	12	19	—	19	18	52	—	58	58
Notes	*U795* only 1 Walter turbine				Closed-cycle test boat			Transport boat (800 tons cargo)	Transport boat (800 tons cargo)

Type:	XXI	XXIB	XXIC	XXID	XXI V	XXIE	XXIT	XXII
Boats ordered	*U2501–2762, 3001–3295, 3501–3695*	Project	Project	Project	Project	Project	Project	*U1153, 1154*
Displacement (tons)								
Surfaced	1,621	1,621 approx.	—	1,949	1,621 approx.	2,809	1,621 approx.	155
Submerged	1,819	—	—	—	—	—	—	—
Length (m)	76.7	76.7	83	76.7	76.7	78	76.7	27.1
Beam (m)	6.6	6.6	6.6	7	6.6	9 approx.	6.6	3.0
Draught (m)	6.3	6.3	6.3	—	6.3	—	6.3	4.2
Propulsion (no.×hp/type)								
Diesel	2×2,000 MAN 2×2,500	2×2,000 MAN 2×2,500	2×2,000 MAN 2×2,500	2×2,000 MAN 2×2,500	2×2,000 MAN 2×2,500	2×2,000 MAN 2×2,500	2×2,000 MAN 2×2,500	1×210 Deutz 1×1,850 Walter
Electric	2×113 S	2×113 S	2×113 S	2×113 S	2×113 S	2×113 S	2×113 S	1×77
Fuel capacity (tons)	250	—	—	—	—	—	—	12+30 H_2O_2
Speed (knots)								
Surfaced	15.6	15	14	15.3	—	14	15.5	7
Submerged	17.2	—	—	15.5	—	10.5	14.5	20.1
Range (n. miles/kn)								
Surfaced	11,150/12	—	—	11,300/10	—	20,000/10	20,000/8	1,550/6.5
Submerged	285/6	—	—	155/6	—	75/6	135/6	96/20
Armament								
Bow torpedo tubes	6	6	6	2	2	2	2	2
Stern torpedo tubes	—	— (+6 side)	— (+12 side)	—	—	—	—	1
Torpedoes carried	23	12	18	2	2	2	2	3
Guns	2×twin 2cm	2×twin 3cm	2×twin 3cm	2×twin 3cm	2×twin 3cm	2×twin 3cm	2×twin 3cm	
Crew	57	—	—				46	12
Notes		Development of Type XXI with addition of side torpedo tubes		Fuel supply boat with 430 tons oil	As Type XXID, but with lesser payload	Transport boat (665 tons cargo)	As Type XXIE but with lesser payload[2]	

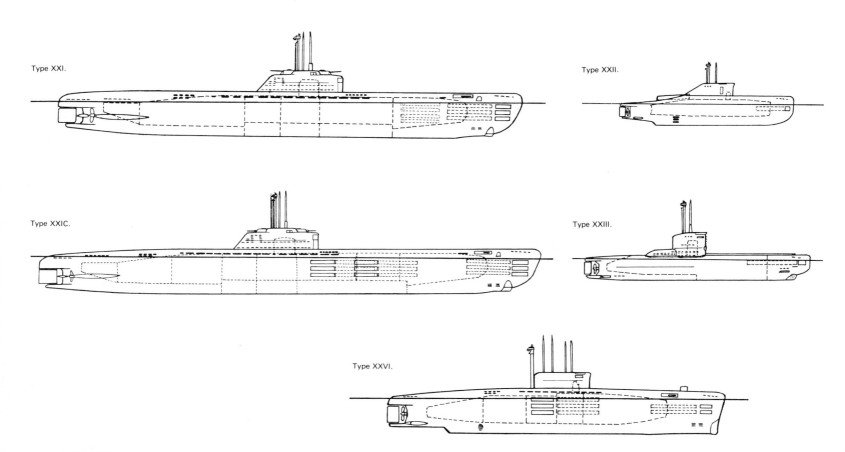

Type XXI.

Type XXII.

Type XXIC.

Type XXIII.

Type XXVI.

Type:	XXIII	XXIV	XXV	XXVIA	XXVIB	XXVIW	XXVII	XVIII	XXIXA
Boats ordered	U2321–2460, 4701–4891	Project	Project	Project	Project	U4501–4600	Midget boat (see page 343)	Project	Project
Displacement (tons)									
Surfaced	234	1,800	160	950	1,050	842		200 approx.	681
Submerged	258	—	—	—	926			—	—
Length (m)	34.7	—	28	58	61.3	56.2		32	53.7
Beam (m)	3.0	—	3	6.7	6.7	5.4		—	4.8
Draught (m)	3.7	—	—	6.5	6.5	5.9		—	5.1
Propulsion (no.×hp/type)									
Diesel	1×580 MWM	2×1,000 MWM 2×7,500 Walter	—	1×2,200 Deutz 1×100 MAN gen. 1×7,500 Walter	1×2,200 Deutz 1×100 MAN gen. 1×7,500 Walter	1×580 MWM 1×265 MAN gen. 1×7,500 Walter		1×250 Walter	1×750 MWM 1×265 MAN gen.
Electric	1×580 1×35 S	2×198 2×70 S	1×160	1×1,670 1×75 S	1×1,670 1×75 S	1×536 1×71 S		1×70 S	1×1,400 1×70 S
Fuel capacity (tons)	18	—	—	(H$_2$O$_2$)	(H$_2$O$_2$)	65+97 H$_2$O$_2$		(H$_2$O$_2$)	—
Speed (knots)								—	12
Surfaced	9.7	14	—	15.5	14.5	11.0		10	13.8
Submerged	12.5	21	9.0	22.5	21.5	24.0			
Range (n. miles/kn)									
Surfaced	2,600/8	15,000/10	—	—	8,000/10	7,300/10		—	7,100/10
Submerged	175/4	—	400/6	—	130/21[3]	158/24		2,000/6	125/6
Armament									
Bow torpedo tubes	2	6	2	6	6	4		4	8
Stern torpedo tubes	—	— (+8 side)	—	+6 side	+6 side	+6 side		—	—
Torpedoes carried	2	14	2	12	12	10		4	8
Guns	—	2×twin 3cm	—	2×twin 3cm	2×twin 3cm	—		—	—
Crew	14		—	—		35		—	—
Notes		Development of Type XVIII with added side torpedo tubes						Project for indirect Walter process	

Type:	XXIXB	XXIXB2	XXIXC	XXIXD	XXIXE (XXVI E1)	XXIXF	XXIXGK
Boats ordered	Project	Project	Project	Project	Projects	Project	Project
Displacement (tons)							
Surfaced	753	790	825	1,035	785	880	1,000
Submerged	—	—	—	—	—	—	—
Length (m)	57.5	57	61.3	66.7	60	57	57.8
Beam (m)	4.8	4.8	4.8	5.4	5	5.4	6.7
Draught (m)	5.1	5.6	5.1	5.3	6.4	6.4	6
Propulsion (no.×hp/type)							
Diesel	1×750 MWM 1×265 MAN gen.	1×1,400 MAN 1×265 MAN gen.	1×750 MAN 1×265 MAN gen.	1×2,000 MAN 1×265 MAN gen.	1×1,400 MAN 1×265 MAN gen.	1×750 MWM 1×750 MAN gen.	1×750 MWM 1×750 MWM gen.
Electric	1×2,100 1×110 S	1×2,400 1×120 S	1×2,800 1×140 S	1×2,100 1×110 S	1×2,400 1×50 S	1×2,100 1×110 S	1×2,800 1×140 S
Fuel capacity (tons)	—	—	—	—	—	—	—
Speed (knots)							
Surfaced	11.9	15.3	11.8	15	13	13.5	12
Submerged	15.4	16.6	16.7	14.8	16	15	16.5
Range (n. miles/kn)							
Surfaced	7,100/10	7,100/10	7,100/10	7,100/10	6,000/10	6,500/10	10,000/10
Submerged	175/6	235/6	250/6	150/6	175/6	—	225/6
Armament							
Bow torpedo tubes	8	8	8	8	4	4	6
Stern torpedo tubes	—	—	—	+4 side	4	+4 side	+6 side
Torpedoes carried	8	8	8	12	12	8	16
Guns	—	—	—	—			
Crew	—	—	—	—	—	—	35
Notes	'K' Office developments					IBG developments	

Type:	XXIXH	XXIXK1	XXIXK2	XXIXK3	XXIXK4	XXXA	XXXB
Boats ordered	Project	Project	Project	Project	Project	Project	Project
Displacement (tons)							
Surfaced	715	915	1,060	930	1,060	1,180	1,170
Submerged	—	—	—	—	—	—	—
Length (m)	52	57.8	64.5	51.8	64.5	68.9	65.7
Beam (m)	6.4	—	—	—	—	5.4	5.4
Draught (m)	4.7	—	—	—	—	6.2	—
Propulsion (no.×hp/type)							
Diesel	1×580 MWM 1×580 MWM gen.	2×1,100 MWM c-c	4×1,100 MWM c-c	4×1,500 DB c-c	2×2,000 MWM c-c	1×2,000 MAN 1×265 MAN gen.	1×2,000 MAN 1×265 MAN gen.
Electric	1×1,400 1×70 S	1×110 S	1×127 S	1×127 S	1×127 S	1×2,800 1×140 S	1×2,800 1×140 S
Fuel capacity (tons)	—	(O₂)	(O₂)	41 O₂	(O₂)	—	—
Speed (knots)							
Surfaced	13	16.7	18.0	17.6	—	14.6	14.6
Submerged	15.5	14.8	18.2	21.5	—	15.6	15.8
Range (n. miles/kn)							
Surfaced	9,000/10	7,200/10	7,200/10	7,200/10	7,200/10	15,500/10	15,500/10
Submerged	120/6	694/6	800/6	1,000/6	—	210/6	215/6
Armament							
Bow torpedo tubes	6	8	8	8	8	8	8
Stern torpedo tubes	—	2	2	—	2	+4 side	—
Torpedoes carried	10	18	18	8	18	12	16
Guns	—	—	—	—	—	—	—
Crew	27	—	—	—	—	—	—
Notes			Closed-cycle developments				

Type:	XXXI	XXXII	XXXIII	XXXIV	XXXV	XXXVI	Tümmler
Boats ordered	Project	Midget boat (see page 343)	Project	Project	Project	Project	Project
Displacement (tons)							
Surfaced	1,200		360	90	1,000 approx.	1,000 approx.	200
Submerged	—		—	—	50 approx.	61.2	32
Length (m)	54		40	23	—	5.4	—
Beam (m)	6.2		4.0	2.5	—	6.0	—
Draught (m)	7.0		4.2	2.6			
Propulsion (no.×hp/type)							
Diesel	1×2,000 MAN 1×265 MAN gen.		1×580 MWM c-c	1×1,500 DB c-c	1×2,000 MWM 1×7,500 Walter	1×580 MWM 1,265 MAN gen. 1×7,500 Walter	1×2,000 MAN 1×60 gen.
Electric	1×2,800 1×140 S		1×30 S	1×16 S	1×175 S	1×536 1×71 S	1×35 S
Fuel capacity (tons)	—		24+26 O₂	4+6 O₂	65 O₂	(O₂)	20
Speed (knots)							
Surfaced	14.3		9.5	12	—	—	—
Submerged	16.4		11.5	21	22	22	17.0 (schnorkel)
Range (n. miles/kn)							
Surfaced	15,500/10		1,550/9.5	>1,000/12	7,000/10	7,000/10	3,000/8
Submerged	245/6		1,600/6	80/21	160/22	110/22	40/5
Armament							
Bow torpedo tubes	8		4	—	8	4	4
Stern torpedo tubes	4		—	—	—	+6 side	—
Torpedoes carried	24		6	2	12	10	4
Guns	—		—	—	—	—	—
Crew	—		—	3	—	—	6
Notes			Closed-cycle developments		Oxygen-fuelled		

[1]Torpedoes of 5m length. [2]160-ton cargo with normal batteries; 275 tons with half batteries. [3]Running on electric motor, 160/4. **Note:** Constructional diving depths (safety factor 2½): Type II 80m; Type VIIC/41, XI and XIV 135m; Type VIIC/42 200m; otherwise, up to Type IX, 100m. The designed diving depths of Types XXI and XXIII later were found to have been set too large. **Key to abbreviations:** c-c=closed-cycle; gen.=generator; H₂O₂=Hydrogen Peroxide (Aurol) fuel for Walter-turbine; S=silent electric motor; SMA=Sonder-Mine A, a special anchor mine; Walter=Walter-turbine.

Midget U-Boat Specifications 1944–1945

Type:	Neger	Marder	Hai	Molch	Biber	Biber II	Biber III	XXVII (Hecht)	XXVIIB	XXVIIF	XXVIIK
No. boats delivered	200 approx.	300 approx.	1	383	324	Project	Project	53[1]	Project	Project	Project
Displacement (tons)	2.7	3	3.5 approx.	11.0	6.3	—	12	11.8	15.6	9.2	17.3
Length (m)	7.6	8.3	11 approx.	10.8	9	—	11.8	10.4	10.6	11.2	13.9
Beam (m)	0.5	0.5	0.5	1.8	1.6	—	2.5	1.7	1.7	1.0	1.7
Propulsion (no.×hp)	1×12 ET	1×12 ET	1×12 ET	1×13 ET	1×32 Otto 1×13 ET	1 Otto 1×13 ET	1×60 D (40 c-c)	1×12 ET	1×22 D 1×12 ET	1×200 WT	1×100D (80 c-c) 1×8 S
Fuel capacity (tons)	—	—	—	—	0.11	—	1.4+0.3 O_2	—	—	(H_2O_2)	0.5 (0.65 O_2)
Speed (knots) Surfaced	4	4	—	4.3	6.5	—	8	—	5.5	—	9.5
Submerged	—	—	—	5.0	5.3	—	5	6	6.9	22.6	10
Range (n. miles/kn) Surfaced	48/4	48/4	—	50/4	130/6	—	1,100/8	—	—	—	180/9.5
Submerged	—	—	—	50/5	8.6/5	—	100/5	38/4	—	—	60/10+34/2
Torpedoes	1	1	1	2	2	2	2	1	2	1	2
Crew	1	1	1	1	1	2	2	2	2	1	2

Type:	XXXII	127 (Seehund)	227	Schwertwal	Seeteufel	Delphin I	Delphin II
No. boats delivered	Project	285[2]	Project	1	1	3	Project
Displacement (tons)	20 approx.	14.9	17.0	11.3	20	2.8	7.5
Length (m)	—	11.9	13.6	11.3	13.5	5.5	8.7 approx.
Beam (m)	—	1.7	1.7	2.4	2.8	1.0	1.3
Propulsion (no.×hp)	1×25 E	1×60 D 1×25 E	1×100 D (80 c-c) 1×25 E	1×500 WT	1×80 Otto 1×30 E	1×32 Otto	1×100 D (32 c-c) (80 c-c)
Fuel capacity (tons)	—	0.5	0.6 (+0.72 O_2)	5 H_2O_2	—	—	—
Speed (knots) Surfaced	—	7.7	8.0	—	10	10	—
Submerged	—	6.0	10.3	26	8	17	18
Range (n. miles/kn) Surfaced	—	300/7	340/8	—	300/10	—	—
Submerged	—	63/3	71/10+17/4	108/15+27/22	80/8	300/10	400/10
Torpedoes	2	2	2	2	2	1	2
Crew	2	2	2	2	2	1	1

[1] Allocated numbers: *U2111–2113, 2251–2300*. [2] Allocated numbers: *U5501–6442*. **Key to abbreviations:** c-c=closed-cycle; D=diesel; E=electric motor; ET=motor from electric-powered torpedo; Otto=Otto motor; S=silent electric motor; WT=Walter torpedo turbine.

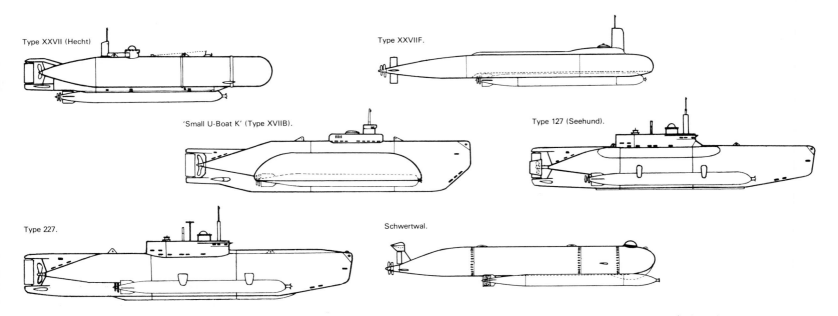

Type XXVII (Hecht)

Type XXVIIF.

'Small U-Boat K' (Type XVIIB).

Type 127 (Seehund).

Type 227.

Schwertwal.

Torpedo Types of the Imperial German Navy at the beginning of the First World War

Designation:	C35/91	C45/91 Bronze standard	C45/91 Steel	C45/91 Steel	C/O3 AV	C/O3 AVK	C/O3 D	C/O6 AV	G/O6 AVK	C/O6D	G/6 AV	G/6 AVK	G/6 D	G/7	H/8
Diameter (cm)	35.55	45	45	45	45	45	45	45	45	45	50	50	50	50	60
Length (cm)	475.15	511	515	515	515	515	515	565	565	565	600	600	600	702	800
Propulsion	AV 3-cyl	AV 3-cyl	AV 3-cyl	AV 3-cyl	AV 3-cyl	AV 3-cyl	Steam 3-cyl	AV 4-cyl	AV 4-cyl	Steam 4-cyl	AV 4-cyl	AV 4-cyl	Steam 4-cyl	Steam 4-cyl	Steam 8-cyl
Fuel	Alcohol	Alcohol	Alcohol	Alcohol	Alcohol	Paraffin	Paraffin	Alcohol	Paraffin	Paraffin	Alcohol	Alcohol	Paraffin	Paraffin	Paraffin
Boiler pressure (psi)	1,371	1,428	1,428	1,428	2,143	2,357	2,143	2,286	2,500	2,286	2,286	2,500	2,286	2,428	2,428
Boiler capacity (litres)	121.5	200	275	275	300	300	300	396	396	396	540	540	540	635	—
Range (n. miles/knots)	500/27	1,000/27	1,500/27	1,600/27	3,000/26	3,500/27	5,000/27	3,600/27	4,200/27	5,900/27	5,000/27	5,500/27	8,400/27	9,800/27	14,000/27
Charge (kg)	40.5	87.5	129	141	147.5	147.5	147.5	122	122	122	160	160	164	195	210–250
Notes	Bronze torpedo with and without gyroscopes	Bronze torpedo	Steel torpedo	Steel torpedo	—	—	First torpedo with water injection	—	—	—	—	—	—	—	—

Note: C/O3 and C/O6 in their steam torpedo versions, had sea-water injection; subsequent larger torpedoes had fresh-water injection. The old C35/91 and C45/91 torpedoes were allocated at the beginning of 1915 for U-boat commerce raiding. G/6 AV torpedoes, adapted specially for U-boat use, were designated K, KI and KII. G/7 was not used until 1918, H/8 not at all for U-boats. All torpedoes after C/O6 had a ±90° angled shot device. The G and H torpedoes had a so-called double gyroscope which imparted smoother running qualities.

Key to abbreviations: AV=Anwärm-Vorrichtung (pre-heat device); AVK=Anwärm-Vorrichtung und erhöhter Kesseldruck (pre-heat device and increased boiler pressure) only for war use, but in no circumstances for use in torpedo-boats and U-boats; cyl=cylinder.

53cm Torpedoes up to 1945

Designation:	T I	T I Fat I	T I Lut I/II	T II	T III	T III Fat II	T IIIa Fat II	T IIIa Lut I/ Lut II	T IIIb	T IIIc	T IIId	T IIIe
Type	G7a	G7a	G7a	G7e	G7e	G7e	G7e	G7e	G7e	G7e	G7e	G7e
Apparatus No.	12	12	12	20	20	20	20	20	20	20	20	20
Code name	—	—	—	—	—	—	—	—	—	—	Dackel	Kreuzotter
Intended use	—	—	—	—	—	—	—	—	Marder	Seehund and others	Special operations	Seehund and others
Diameter (cm)	53.34	53.34	53.34	53.46	53.46	53.46	53.46	53.46	53.46	53.46	53.46	53.46
Length (cm)	716.3	716.3	716.3	716.3	716.3	716.3	716.3	716.3	716.3	716.3	1,100	716.3
Weight (kg)	1,538	1,538	1,538	1,608	1,608	1,620	1,760	1,760	1,352	1,342	2,220	1,345
Negative buoyancy (%)	21	21	21	21	21	21	32	32	1.5	0.75	1.5	0
Propulsion												
Motor	4-cyl gas/steam	4-cyl gas/steam	4-cyl gas/steam	E	E	E	E	E	E	E	E	E
Battery	—	—	—	2×13T	2×13T	2×13T	2×17T	2×17T	1×13T	1×13T	4×17T	1×13T special
Output												
hp	350	350	350	100	100	100	100	100	30	30	7 approx	32
rpm	1,470	1,470	1,470	1,700	1,700	1,700	1,700	1,700	1,100	1,100	500 approx	1,125
Speed (knots)	40	40	40	30	30	30	30	30	18.5	18.5	9	20
Range (km)	75	75	75	50	50	50	75	75	40	40	570 approx	75
Warhead [1]	Ka, Kc	Ka, Kc	Ka, Kc	Ka	Kb	Kb	Kb	Kb	Kb2	Kb 2	Kb 2	Ke 1
Charge (kg)	280	280	280	280	280	280	280	280	280	280	280	280
Detonator	Pi 1 or TZ3 with Pi 3	Pi 1 or TZ3 with Pi 3	Pi 1 or TZ3 with Pi 3	Pi 1	Pi 2	Pi 2	Pi 2	Pi 2	TZ 2 with Pi 2f	TZ 2 with Pi 2f	Pi 2	TZ 25 with Pi 4c
Steering/programme	—	Fat programme	Lut programme	—	—	Fat programme	Fat programme	Lut programme	—	—	Lut programme	

Key to abbreviations: c-c=closed cycle; cyl.=cylinder; E=electric; Fat=Federapparat (spring-loaded); Lut=Lagen unabhängiger Torpedo (independent torpedo).

Table continues on next page.

Designation:	T IV	T V	T Va	T Vb	T VI	T VII	T VIII	T IX	T X	T XI	T XII	T XIII	T XIV
Type	G7es	G7es	G7es	G7es	G7e	G7ut	G7ut	G5ut	G7e	G7es	G5e	G7ut	G7a
Apparatus No.	37	45	45	45	20	30	30	26	43	46	20	30	12
Codename	Falke	Zaunkönig	Zaunkönig I	Zaunkönig I	—	Steinbarsch	Steinbutt	Goldbutt	Spinne	Zaunkönig	—	K-Butt	—
Intended use	—	—	For MTBs	For U-boats	—	—	—	—	NYE	—	—	—	Seehund and others
Diameter (cm)	53.46	53.46	53.46	53.46	53.46	53.46	53.46	53.46	53.46	53.46	53.46	53.46	53.34
Length (cm)	716.3	716.3	716.3	716.3	716.3	716.3	716.3	550	716.3	716.3	550	716.3	(boiler 52.7)
Weight (kg)	1,400 approx.	1,495	1,495	1,495	1,760	1,730	1,730	—	1,620	1,495	1,260	1,309	1,352
Negative buoyancy (%)	—	11 approx.	11 approx.	11 approx.	32	24.4	24.4	—	21	11 approx.	40 **approx.**	0	1.5
Propulsion													
Motor	E	E	E	E	E	Walter turbine	Walter turbine	Walter turbine	E	E	E	Walter turbine	4-cyl gas/steam
Battery	1×13T	1×13T special	1×17T plus 2 extra troughs	2×17T plus 2 extra troughs	2×17T	—	—	—	2×13T	1×13T	1×9 T	—	—
Output													
hp	32	55	40	40	100	430	430	390	100	55	100	425	165
rpm	1,125	1,350	1,210	1,210	1,700	1,640	1,640	—	1,700	1,350	1,700	1,590	1,120
Speed (knots)	20	24	21.5	21.5	30	45	45	45	30	24	30	45	34
Range (km)	75	57	80	80	75	80	80	38	50	57	30	28	25
Warhead[1]	Kd	Ke 1	Ke 1	Ke 1	Kf	Kb 2, Kf	Kb 2, Kf	Kb 2	Kb	Ke 1	Kb	Kb 2	Kc
Charge (kg)	274	274	274	274	300	280	280	—	280	274	280	280	280
Detonator	Pi 4a	TZ 5 with Pi 4c	TZ 5 with Pi 4d	TZ 5 with Pi 4c	TZ 6 with Pi 6	TZ 2, TZ 6	TZ 2, TZ 6	TZ 2	Pi 2	TZ 5 with Pi 4c	TZ 2 with Pi 2	TZ 2 with Pi 2	TZ 3 with Pi 3
Steering/programme	Acoustic self-steering	Acoustic self-steering	Acoustic self-steering	Acoustic self-steering	Lut programme	Lut programme	Lut programme	—	Wire-guided	Acoustic self-steering	—	—	—

Designation:	—	—	—	—	—	—	—	—	—	—
Type	G7as	G7es	G7es	G7ut	G7ut	G7m	G7d	G7p	G7uk	G5uR
Apparatus No.	12	47	48	30	30	—	—	—	29	32
Codename	Möwe	Geier	Lerche	Schildbutt	Steinwal	—	—	—	Klippfisch	Hecht
Intended use	—	—	—	—	—	—	—	—	—	—
Diameter (cm)	53.34	53.46	53.46	53.46	53.46	53.34	53.46	53.46	53.34	53.46
Length (cm)	716.3	716.3	716.3	716.3	716.3	716.3	716.3	716.3	716.3	550
Weight (kg)	—	—	—	1,730	1,730	—	—	—	—	—
Negative buoyancy (%)	—	—	—	—	—	—	—	—	—	—
Propulsion										
Motor	Further development of Zaunkönig II for G7a	E	E	Walter turbine with sea-water injection	Walter turbine with sea-water injection	c-c motor KM8	Walter turbine with pure oxygen	E	G7a piston engine based on Walter process	Rocket propulsion
Battery	—	1×13 T special	1×13 T special	—	—	—	—	MG-C Primary battery	—	—
Output										
hp	—	55	55	430	430	425	435	220	—	approx. 1,200
rpm	—	1,350	1,350	1,640	1,640	4,500	—	—	—	thrusts
Speed (knots)	—	—	—	40	45	40	—	40	40	—
Range (km)	—	—	—	180	210	120	—	—	65	—
Warhead[1]	—	Ke 1	Ke 1	—	—	—	—	—	—	—
Charge (kg)	—	274	274	—	—	—	—	—	—	—
Detonator	—	—	—	—	—	—	—	—	—	—
Steering/programme	Acoustic self-steering	Active acoustic self-steering	Wire guided based on positive acoustic detection by torpedo	Long-range torpedoes with varying guidance systems, used by Fasan and Kondor						

[1] K=Kopf (head)

U-Boat Specifications, 1960-74

Class:	201	202	205	206	207	209	209	209
Boats ordered	3	2	5+6+2	18	15	4	8	4
Displacement (tons)								
Standard	395	100	419	450	435	960	980	1,000 approx.
Surfaced	433	137	455	approx. 520	485	1,105	1,185	1,285
Length (m)	42.4	23.1	44.3	48.0	45.2	54.3	56.0	59.5
Beam (m)	4.6	3.4	4.6	4.7	4.7	6.3	6.3	6.3
Propulsion (no.×hp/type)								
Diesel	2×600 Daimler	1×330	2×600 Daimler	2×600 MTU	2×600 Daimler	4×600 MTU	4×600 MTU	4×600 MTU
Electric	1×1,500	1×350, 1×27S	1×1,500	1×1,500	1×1,500	1×2,700	1×2,700	1×2,700
Fuel capacity (tons)	—	—	—	23.5	—	50+14	50	—
Speed (knots)								
Surfaced	10	6	10	10	10	10	10	10
Submerged	17.5	13	17	17	17	22	22	22
Battery wt/disp (%)[1]	19.2	16.8	19.8	18.8	18.1	22.6	21.7	20
Armament								
Bow torpedo tubes	8	2	8	8	8	8	8	8
Stern torpedo tubes	0	0	0	0	0	0	0	0
Torpedoes carried	8	2	8	8	8	14	14	14
Crew	21	6	21	22	17	32	32	33

Key to abbreviations: S=silent motor. [1] Derived from Type VII.

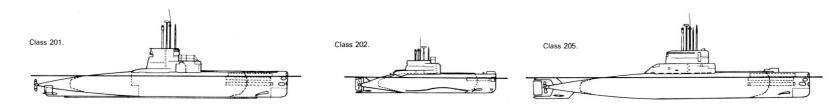

Class 201.   Class 202.   Class 205.

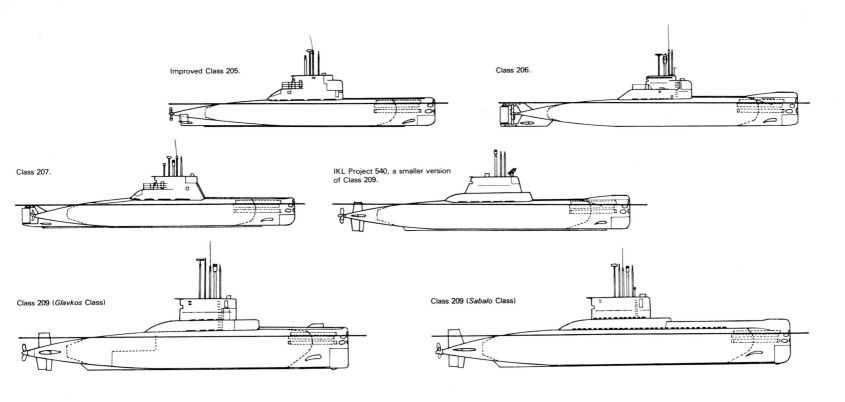

Improved Class 205.

Class 206.

Class 207.

IKL Project 540, a smaller version of Class 209.

Class 209 (*Glavkos* Class)

Class 209 (*Sabalo* Class)

Below, left: *U13* (S192), *U17* and another Class 206 boat at the HDW construction yard, Kiel-Gaarden. **Below:** The HDW yard at Kiel-Süd, summer 1974. In the foreground are the Class 206 boats *U21* and *U27*, moored with the Class 209 export boats *Islay, Arica, Pijao* and *Tayrona*. In the background, a completed middle section for a Class 209 lies outside the large assembly hangar; it is ready for transportation by floating crane to the final assembly point, which may be either construction pontoons or a dock.

Type VIIB (1940), outboard profile and plan.

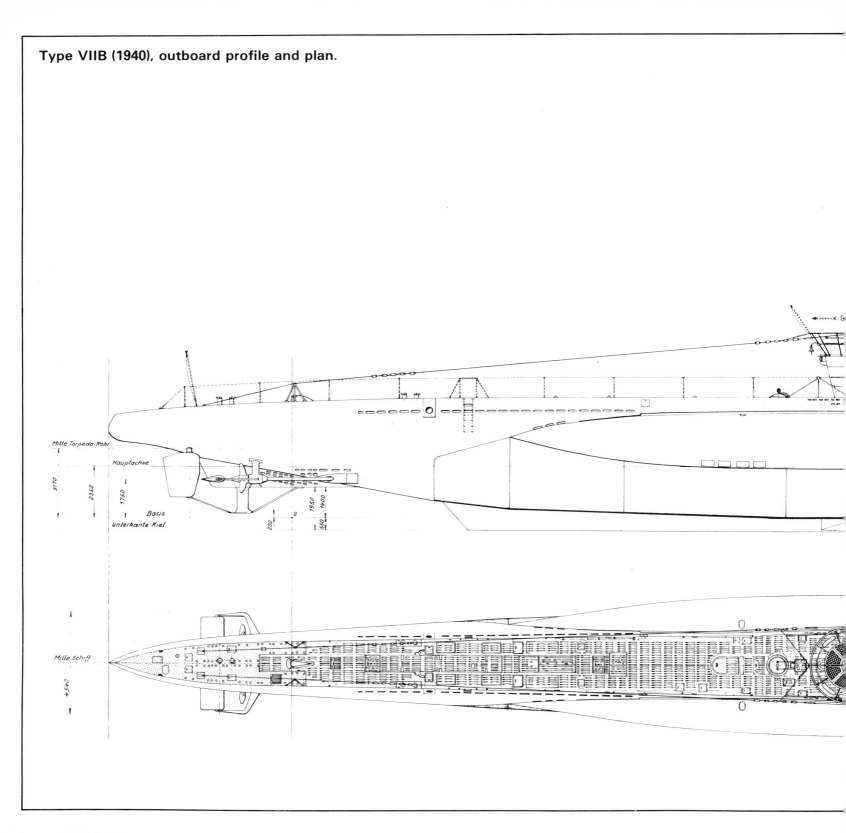

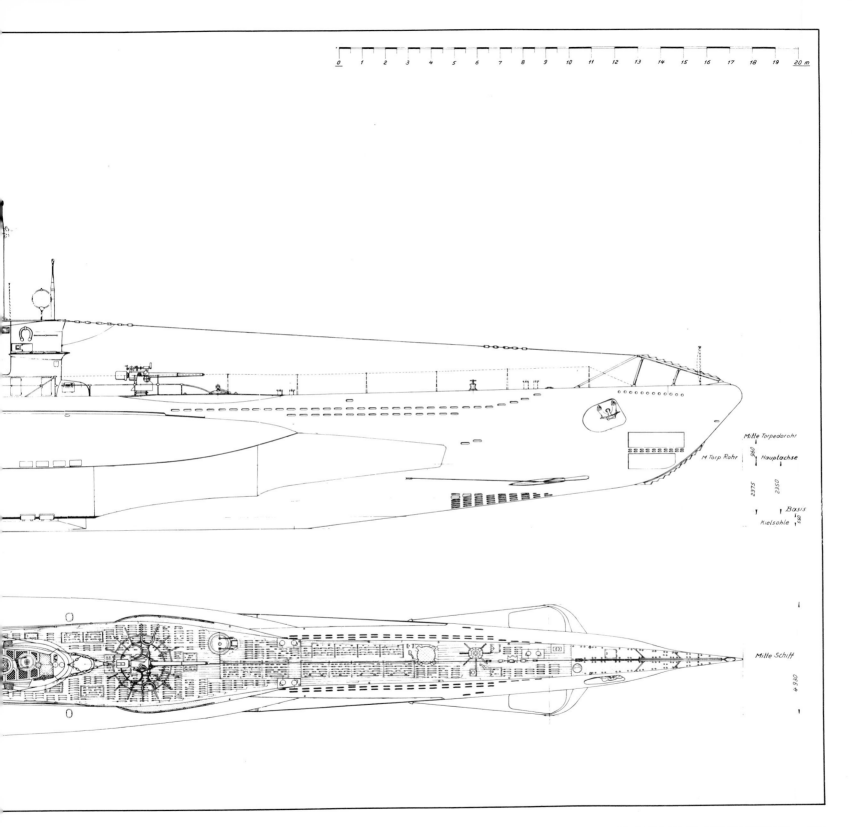

Mitte Torpedorohr
M Torp Rohr
960
Hauptachse
2375
2350
Basis
550
Kielsohle

Mitte Schiff

4 930

Type VIIB, inboard profile and deck plan.

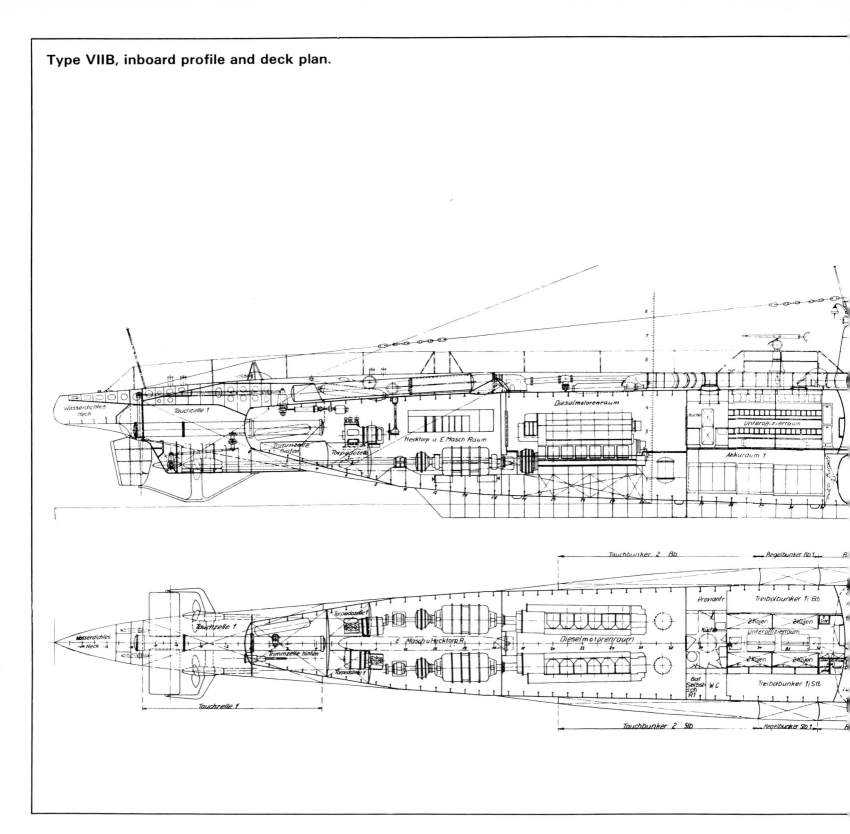

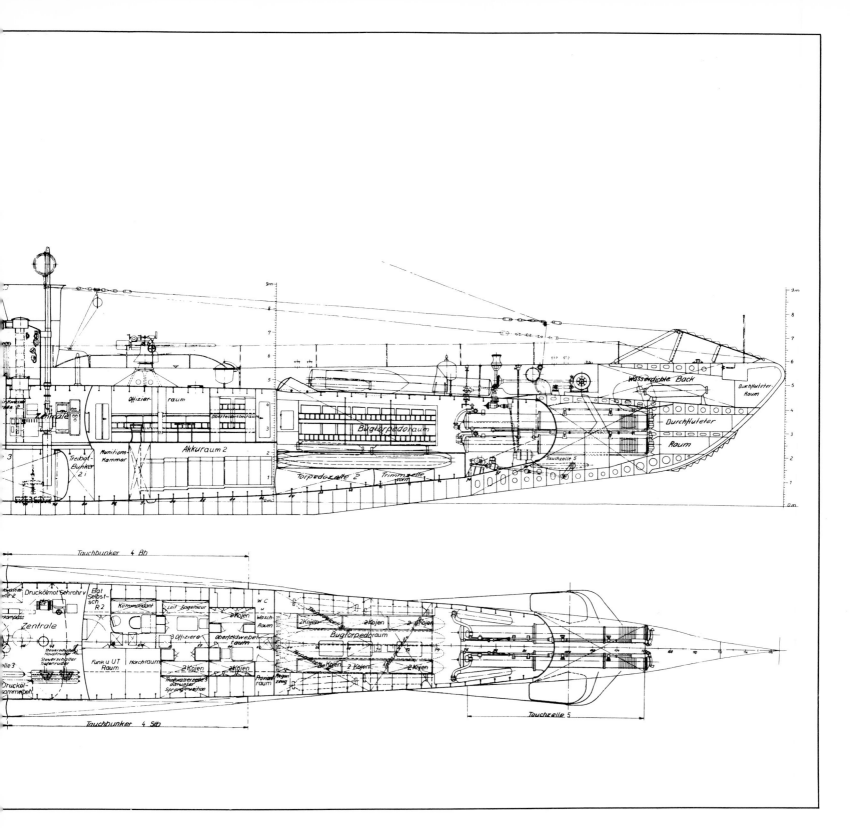

Type VIIC (1944), inboard profile and outboard deck plan.

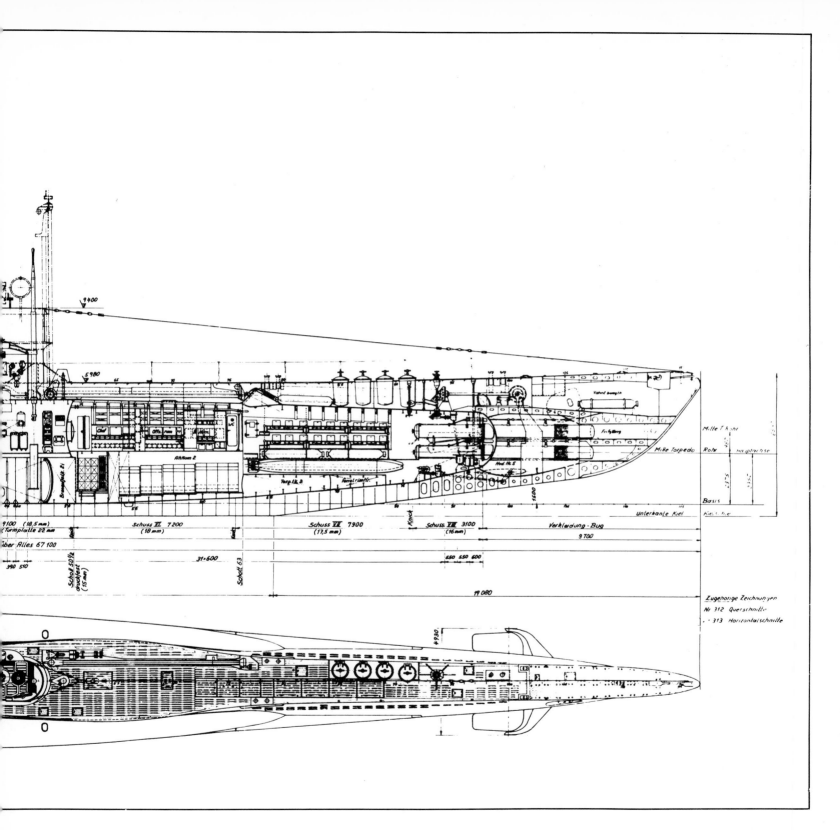

Type VIIC (1944), deck plans.

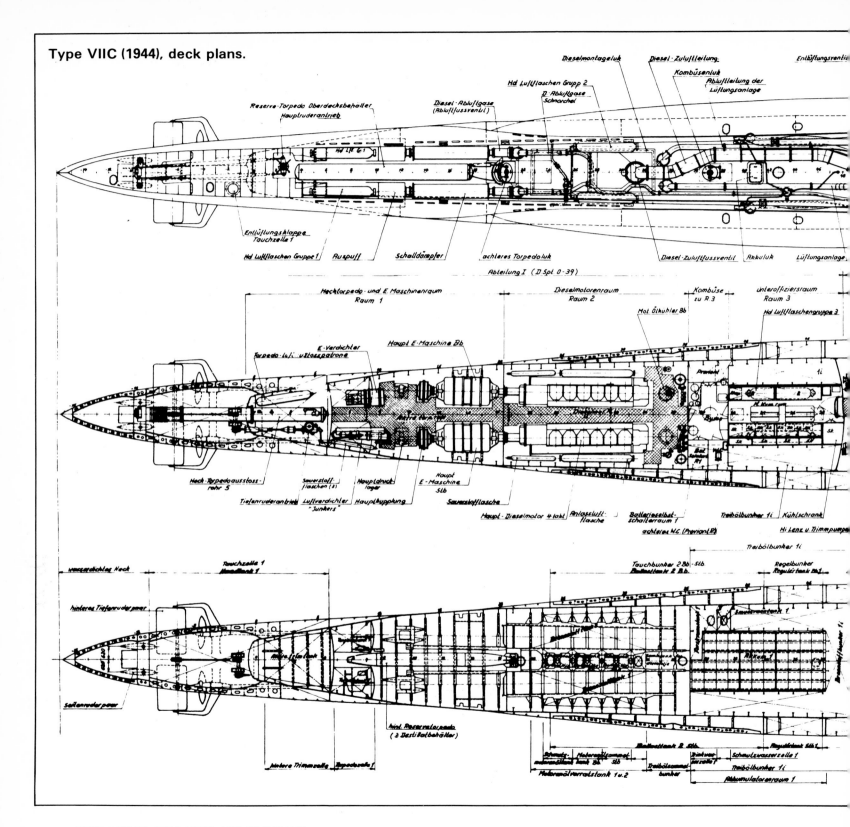

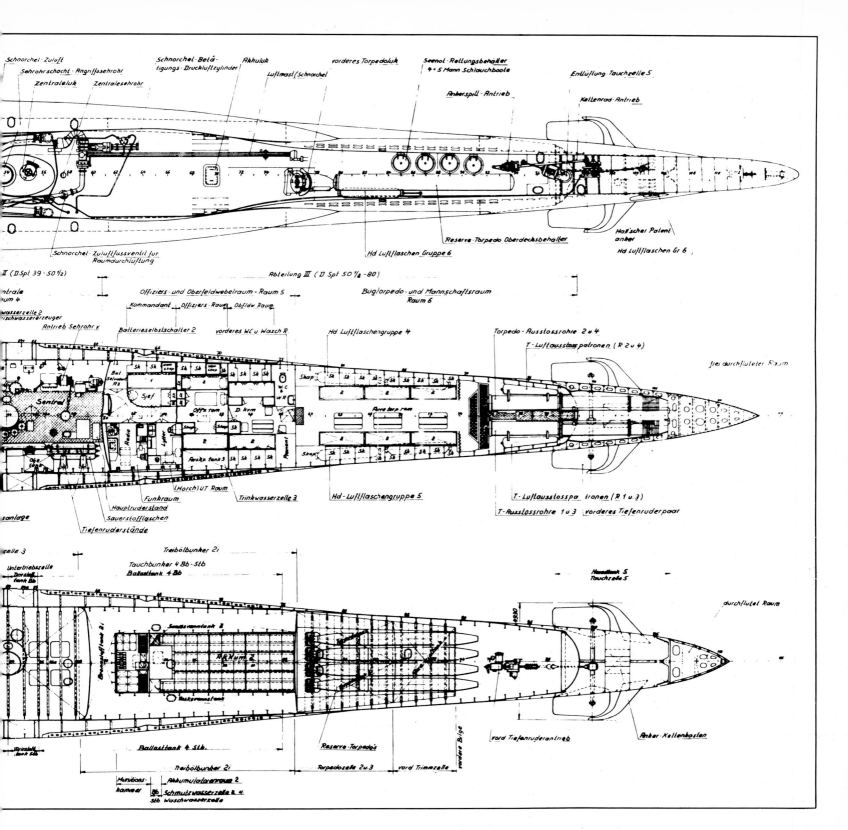

Schnorchel-Zuluft
Sehrohrschacht · Angriffssehrohr
Zentraleluk
Zentralesehrohr
Schnorchel · Belä-
tigungs · Druckluftzylinder
Akkuluk
Luftmast (Schnorchel)
vorderes Torpedoluk
Seenot · Rettungsbehälter
4 × 5 Mann Schlauchboote
Ankerspill · Antrieb
Entlüftung Tauchzelle 5
Kettenrad · Antrieb
Schnorchel · Zuluftfussventil für
Raumdurchlüftung
Reserve Torpedo Oberdecksbehälter
Hall'scher Patent
anker
Hd Luftflaschen · Gruppe 6
Hd Luftflaschen Gr 6

II (D Spt 39 - 50 ½)
Abteilung III (D Spt 50 ½ - 80)
Zentrale
Raum 4
Offiziers · und Oberfeldwebelraum - Raum 5
Buglorpedo · und Mannschaftsraum
Raum 6
wasserzelle 2
Frischwassererzeuger
Kommandant
Offiziers · Raum
Obfdw Raum
Antrieb Sehrohr v.
Batterieselbstschalter 2
vorderes WC u. Wasch R.
Hd Luftflaschengruppe 4
Torpedo · Ausstossrohre 2 u. 4
T · Luftausstosspatronen (R 2 u 4)
frei durchfluteter Raum
Zentral
(Horch)UT Raum
Funkraum
Hauptruderstand
Sauerstofflaschen
Tiefenruderstände
Trinkwasserzelle 3
Hd · Luftflaschengruppe 5
T · Luftausstosspatronen (R 1 u 3)
T · Ausstossrohre 1 u 3   vorderes Tiefenruderpaar
sanlage

zelle 3
Treibölbunker 2i
Untertriebszelle
Drucköff
tank Bb
Tauchbunker 4 Bb - Stb
Ballasttank 4 Bb
Hauptank 5
Tauchzelle 5
durchflutet Raum
Akku Raum 2
Reserve · Torpedo's
vord Tiefenruderantrieb
Anker · Kettenkasten
Ballasttank 4 Stb.
Treibölbunker 2i
Torpedozelle 2 u 3
vord Trimmzelle
vordere Bilge
Munitions ·
kammer
Akkumulatorenraum 2
Schmutzwasserzelle 2 u. 4.
Stb Waschwasserzelle

Type IXD₂ inboard profile, deck plans and sections.

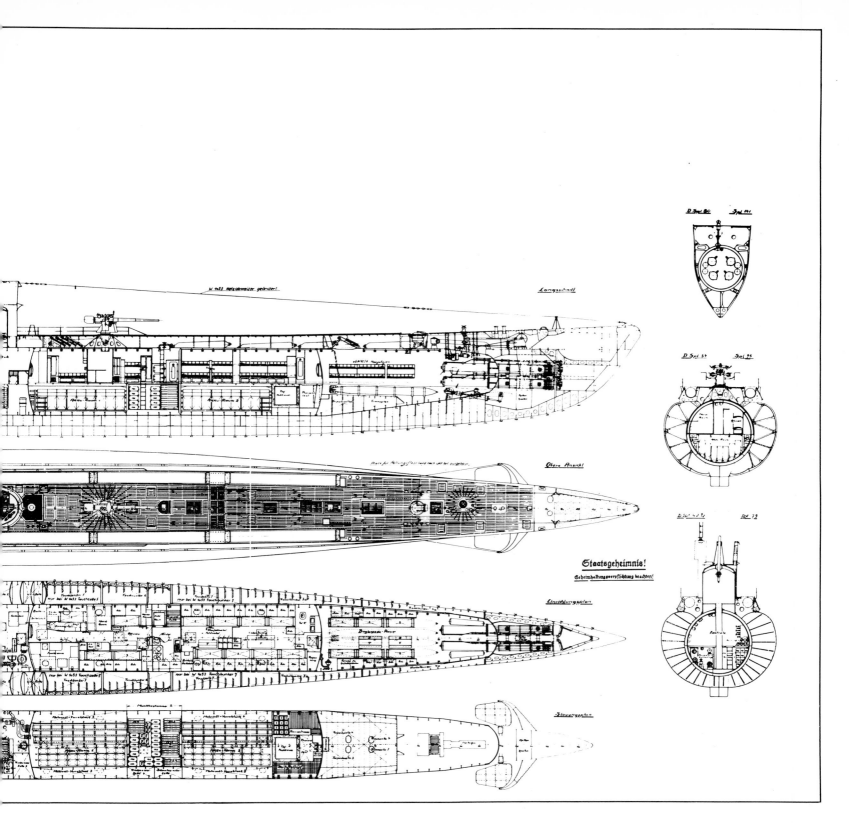

Staatsgeheimnis!

Geheimhaltungsverpflichtung beachten!

Type XVIIG, inboard profile and deck plan.

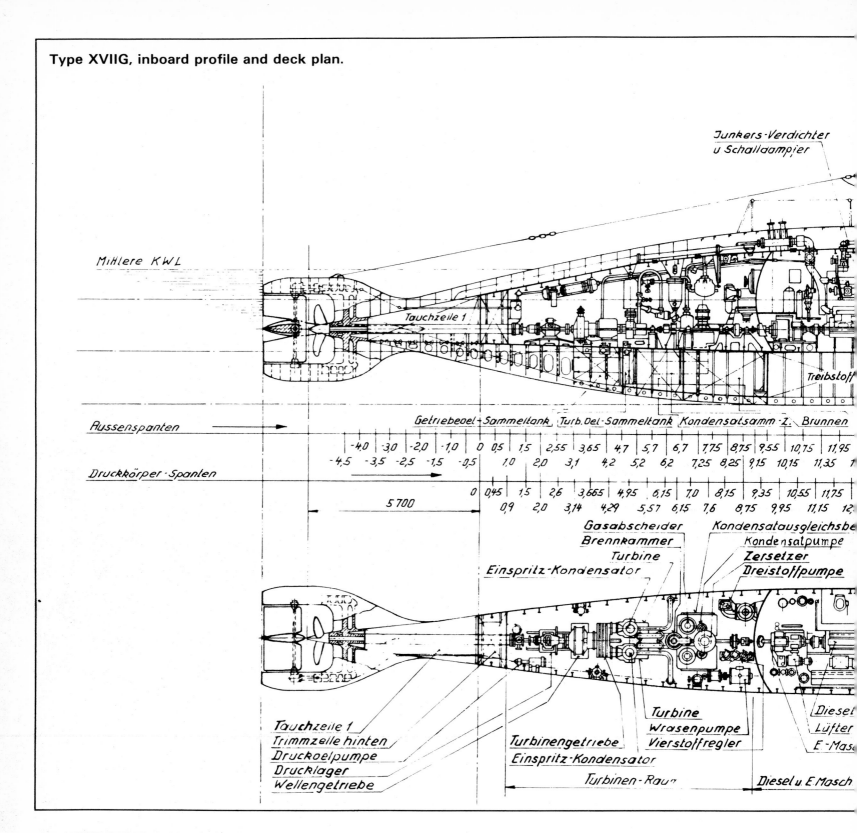

Junkers-Verdichter
u Schalldampfer

Mittlere KWL

Tauchzelle 1

Aussenspanten

Getriebeoel-Sammeltank, Turb.Oel-Sammeltank, Kondensatsamm.-Z. Brunnen

Treibstoff

| -4,0 | -3,0 | -2,0 | -1,0 | 0 | 0,5 | 1,5 | 2,55 | 3,65 | 4,7 | 5,7 | 6,7 | 7,75 | 8,75 | 9,55 | 10,75 | 11,95 |
| -4,5 | -3,5 | -2,5 | -1,5 | -0,5 | | 1,0 | 2,0 | 3,1 | 4,2 | 5,2 | 6,2 | 7,25 | 8,25 | 9,15 | 10,15 | 11,35 |

Druckkörper-Spanten

| | 0 | 0,45 | 1,5 | 2,6 | 3,665 | 4,95 | 6,15 | 7,0 | 8,15 | 9,35 | 10,55 | 11,75 |
| 5 700 | | 0,9 | 2,0 | 3,14 | 4,29 | 5,57 | 6,15 | 7,6 | 8,75 | 9,95 | 11,15 | 12, |

Gasabscheider
Kondensatausgleichsbe
Brennkammer
Kondensatpumpe
Turbine
Zersetzer
Einspritz-Kondensator
Dreistoffpumpe

Turbine
Wrasenpumpe
Vierstoffregler

Diesel
Lüfter
E-Masc

Tauchzelle 1
Trimmzelle hinten
Druckoelpumpe
Drucklager
Wellengetriebe

Turbinengetriebe
Einspritz-Kondensator

Turbinen-Raum

Diesel u. E. Masch

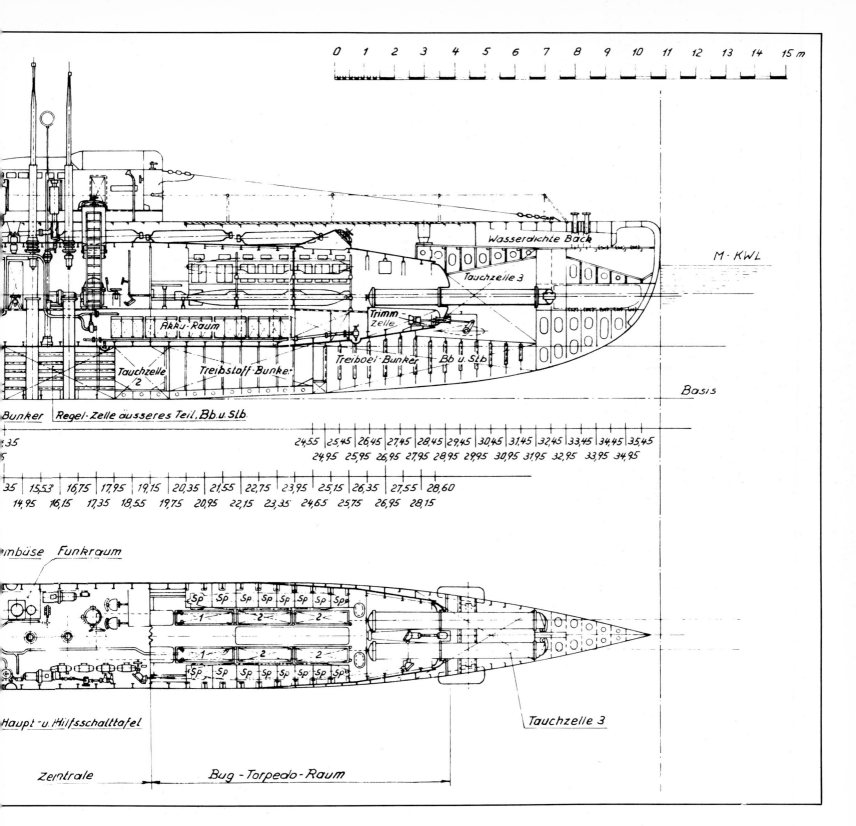

0 1 2 3 4 5 6 7 8 9 10 11 12 13 14 15 m

Wasserdichte Back

M·KWL

Tauchzelle 3

Trimm Zelle

Akku·Raum

Treiböl·Bunker Bb u. Stb

Tauchzelle 2

Treibstoff·Bunker

Basis

Bunker | Regel·Zelle ausseres Teil, Bb.u.Stb.

:35   24,55 |25,45 |26,45 |27,45 |28,45 |29,45 |30,45 |31,45 |32,45 |33,45 |34,45 |35,45
5   24,95 25,95 26,95 27,95 28,95 29,95 30,95 31,95 32,95 33,95 34,95

35 | 15,53" | 16,75 | 17,95 | 19,15 | 20,35 | 21,55 | 22,75 | 23,95 | 25,15 | 26,35 | 27,55 | 28,60
14,95 16,15   17,35   18,55   19,75   20,95   22,15   23,35   24,65   25,75   26,95   28,15

mbüse Funkraum

Sp Sp Sp Sp Sp Sp Sp Sp
1   -2-   -2-
1   2   2
Sp Sp Sp Sp Sp Sp Sp

Tauchzelle 3

Haupt·u.Hilfsschalttafel

Zentrale   Bug·Torpedo·Raum

Type XXI, inboard profile and deck plan.

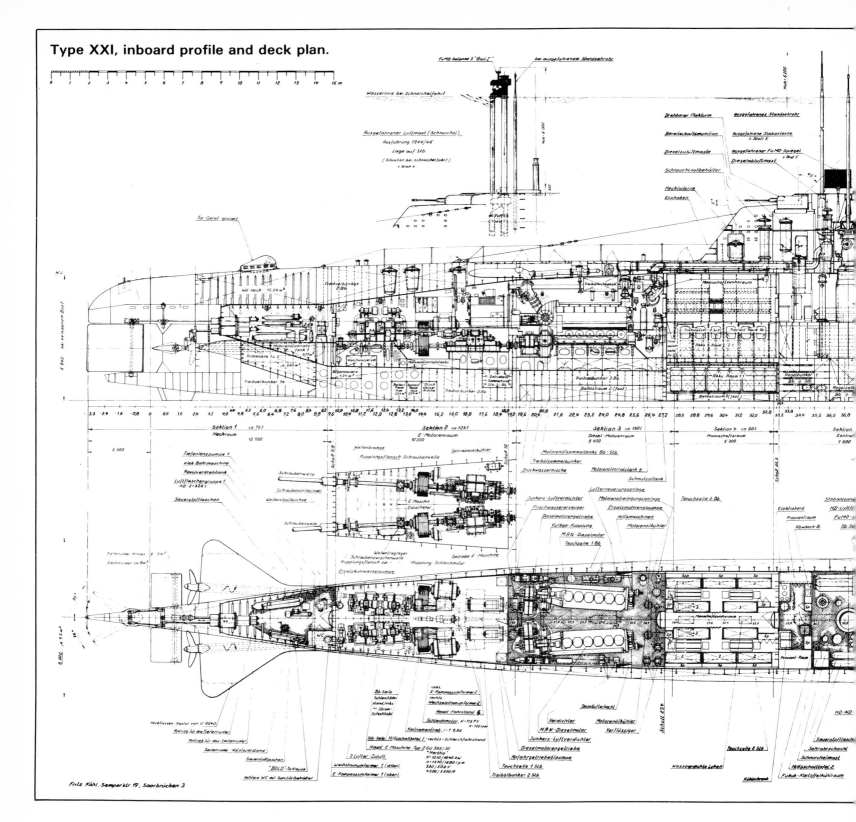

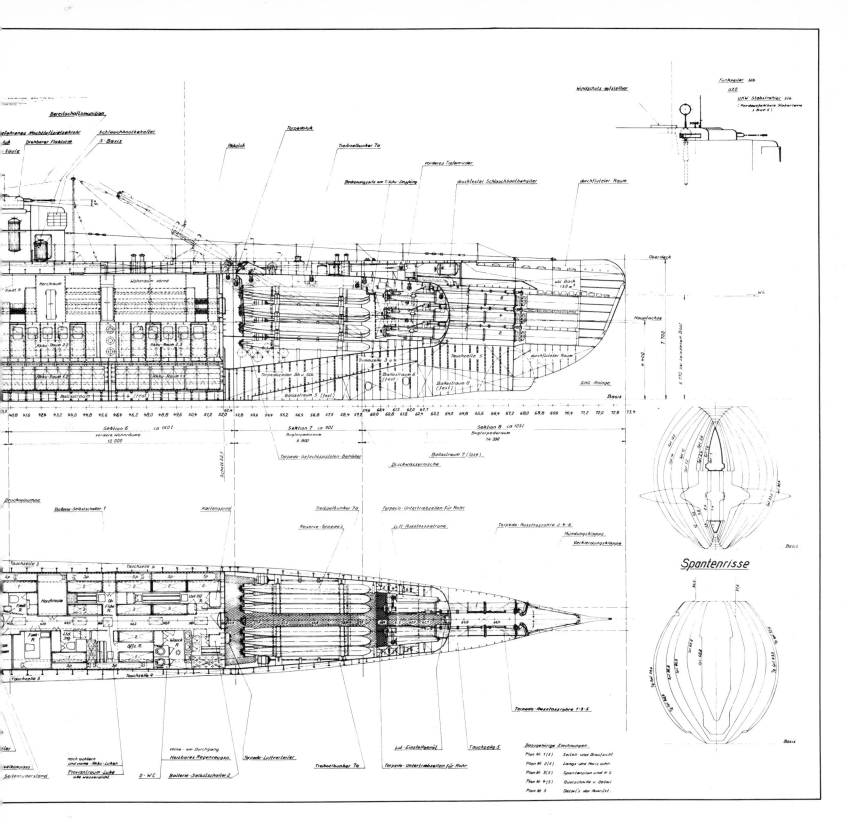

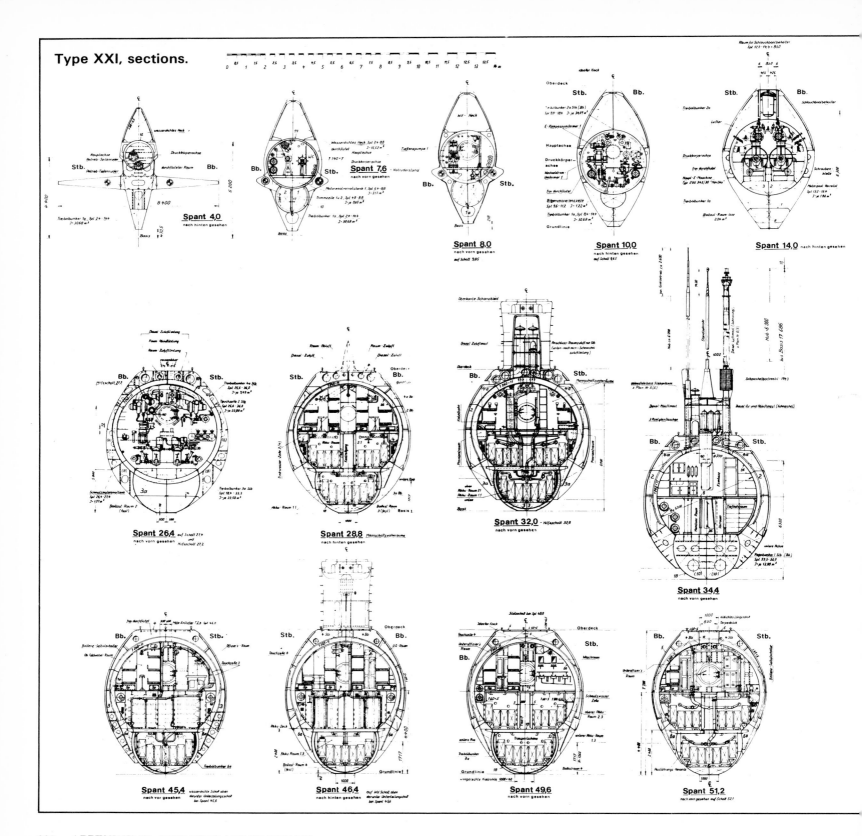

Type XXI, sections.

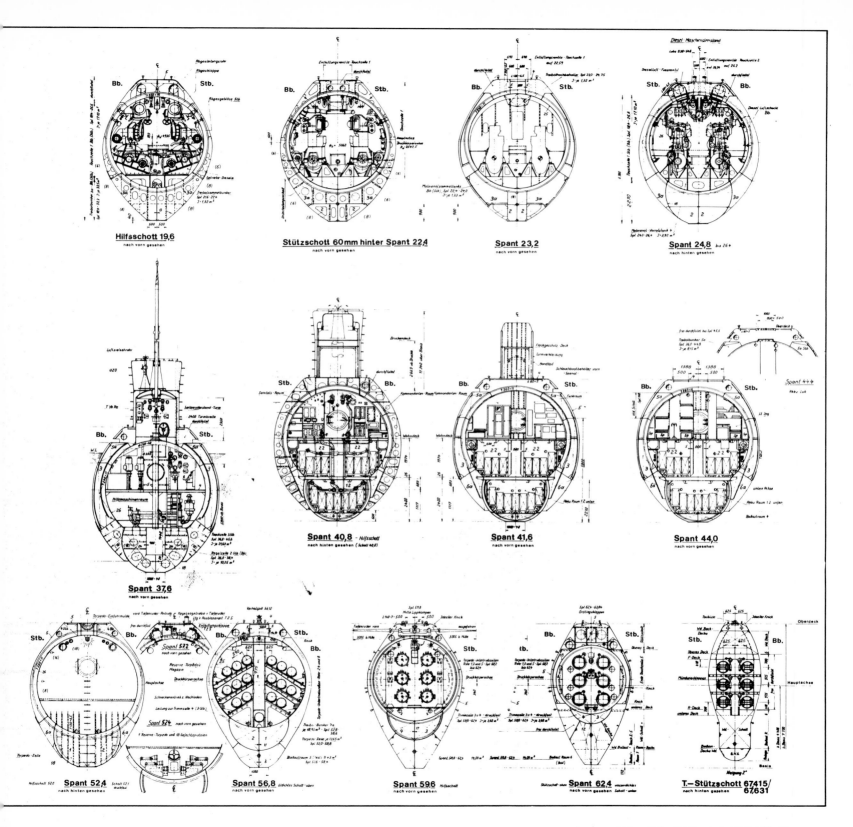

Type XXI, hull form.

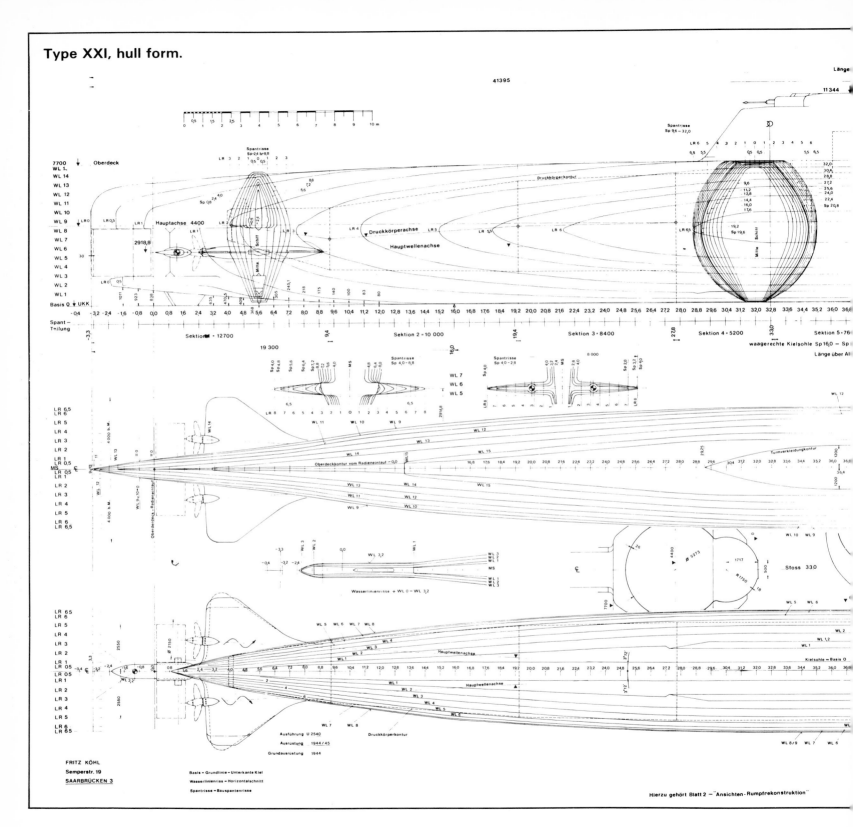

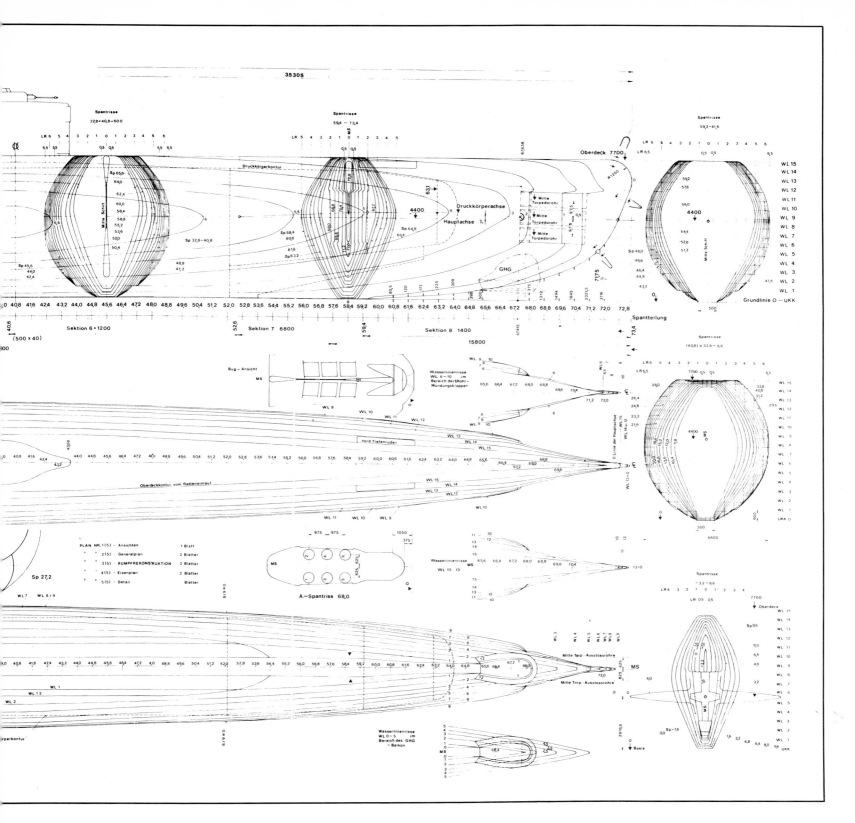

Type XXIII, inboard profile, deck plans and sections.

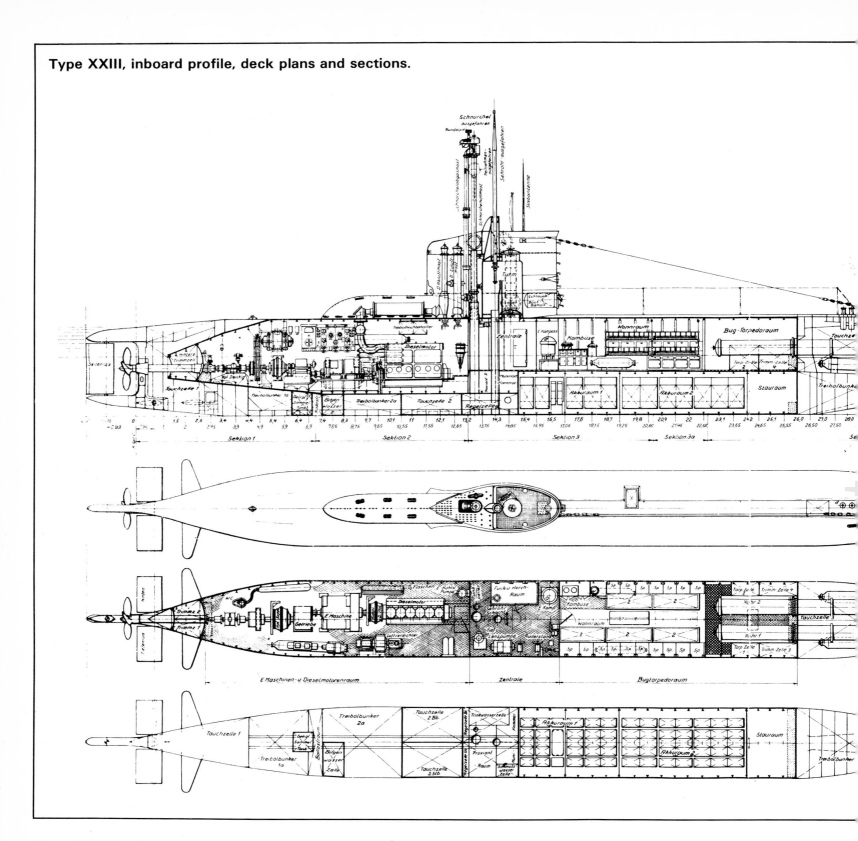

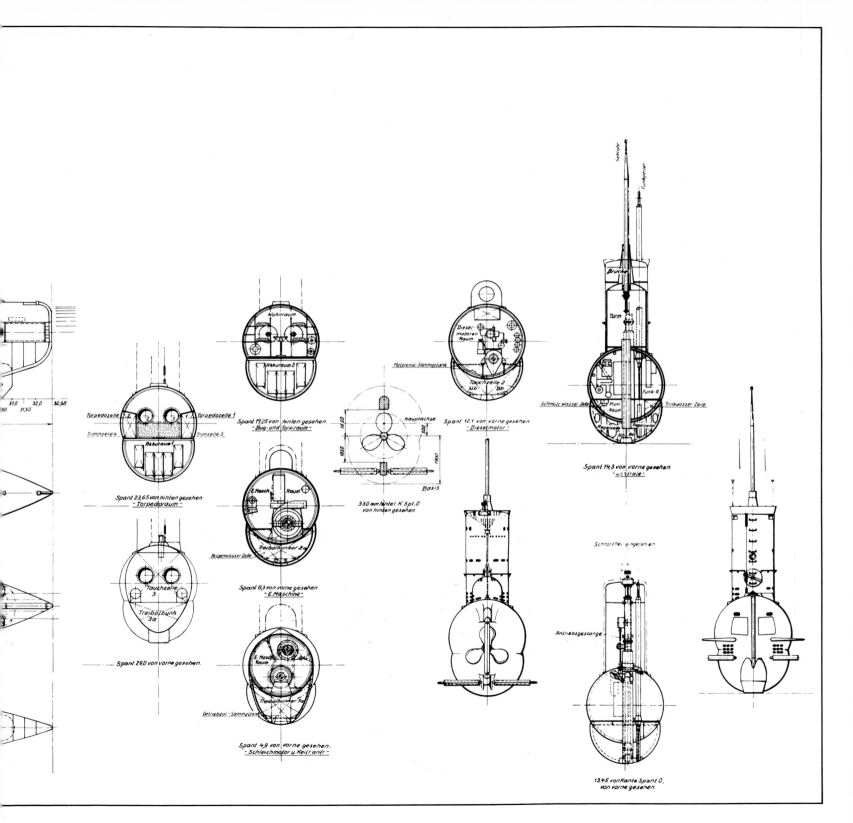

Torpedozelle 2   Torpedozelle 1

Trimmzelle 4   Trimmzelle 3

Akkuraum 1

Spant 23,65 von hinten gesehen.
- Torpedoraum -

Wohnraum

Akkuraum 2

Spant 19,25 von hinten gesehen.
- Bug- und Torpedoraum -

Motorenöl-Sammeltank

Diesel-
motoren
Raum

Tauchzelle 2
Stb   Bb

Spant 12,1 von vorne gesehen
- Dieselmotor -

Hauptachse

Basis

330 mm hinter K.Spt.0.
von hinten gesehen

E.Masch.   Raum

Bilgenwasser Zelle

Treibölbunker 2a

Spant 8,3 von vorne gesehen.
- E.Maschine -

Tauchzelle
3

Treibölbunk
3a

Spant 29,0 von vorne gesehen.

E.Masch.
Raum

Treibölbunker 1a

Getriebeöl-Sammeltank

Spant 4,9 von vorne gesehen.
- Schleichmotor u. Keilr.antr. -

Sehrohr

Lumpanier

Brücke

Turm

Schmutz Wasser Zelle

Funk R.

Trinkwasser Zelle

Regelzelle
Stb Bb

Spant 14,3 von vorne gesehen.
- Zentrale -

Schnorchel eingefahren

Antriebsgestange

13+5 von Kante Spant 0,
von vorne gesehen.

Class 240, inboard profile and deck plans.

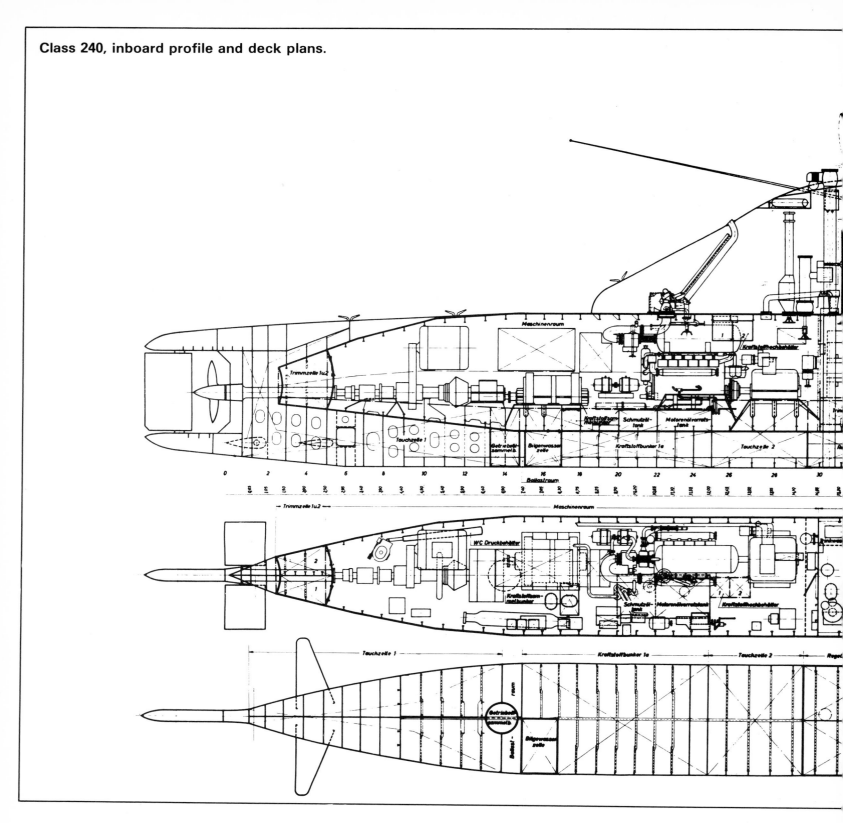

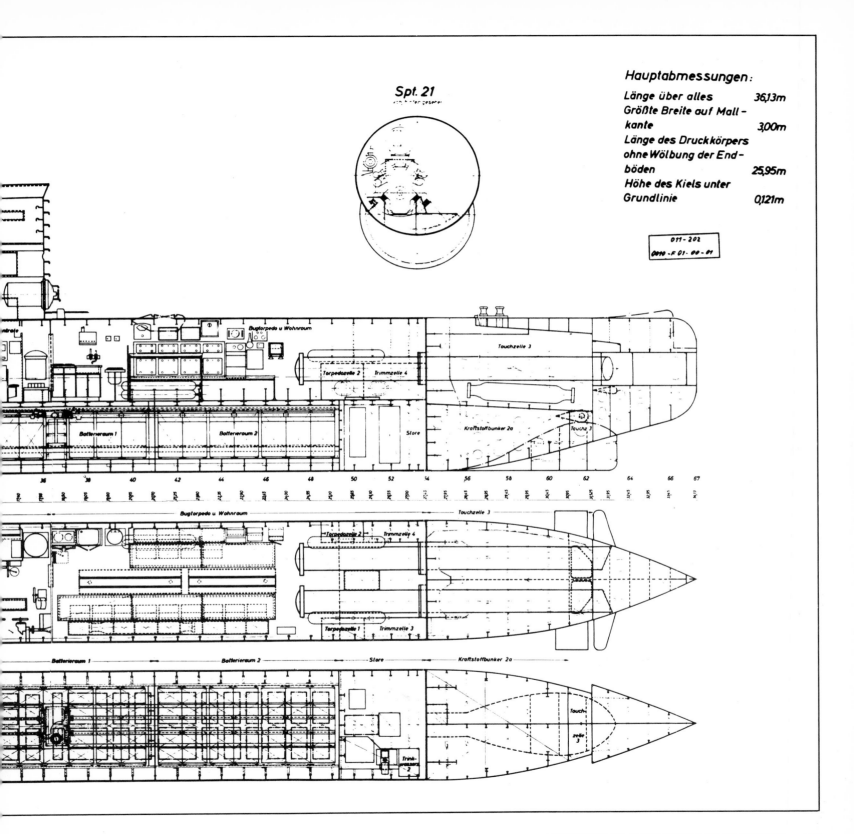

Spt. 21
von hinten gesehen

Hauptabmessungen:

Länge über alles	36,13m
Größte Breite auf Mall- kante	3,00m
Länge des Druckkörpers ohne Wölbung der End- böden	25,95m
Höhe des Kiels unter Grundlinie	0,121m

011-202
0010-F 01-00-01

Bugtorpedo u Wohnraum

Torpedozelle 2   Trimmzelle 4

Tauchzelle 3

Batterieraum 1   Batterieraum 2   Store   Kraftstoffbunker 2a   Tauchz. 3

36 38 40 42 44 46 48 50 52 54 56 58 60 62 64 66 67

Bugtorpedo u Wohnraum   Tauchzelle 3

Torpedozelle 2   Trimmzelle 4

Torpedozelle 1   Trimmzelle 3

Batterieraum 1   Batterieraum 2   Store   Kraftstoffbunker 2a

Trink-
wasser-
2

Tauch-
zelle
3

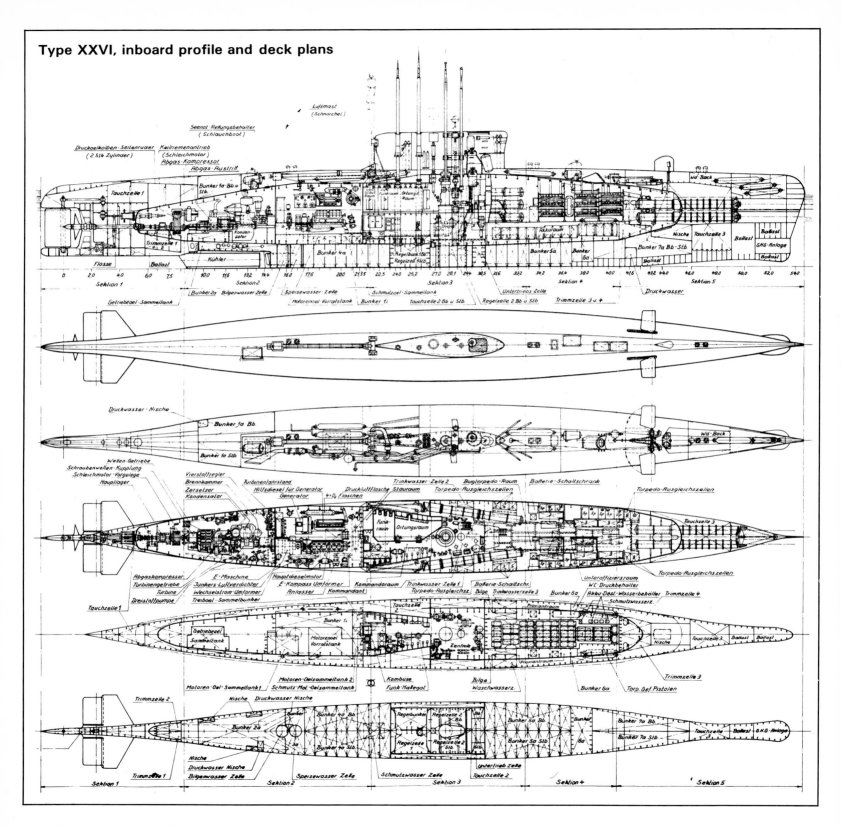

Type XXVI, inboard profile and deck plans

LIST OF ABBREVIATIONS

Abbreviation	Full term	Translation
A	Marinekommandoamt mit seinen Unterabteilungen A I, A II usw.	Naval Command Office with sub-divisions A I, A II etc.
AEG	Allgemeine Elektricitäts-Gesellschaft	—
AdK	Admiral der Kleinkampfverbände	Admiral of Midget Units
AFA	Accumulatoren-Fabrik Aktiengesellschaft, Berlin-Hagen	—
Agru Front	Ausbildungsgruppe für Front-Unterseeboote	Training Group for Operational U-Boats
Asdic	—	Early form of radar (initials for Allied Submarine Detection Investigation Committee)
ASEA	Allgemen Svenska Elektrizitets Aktiebolaget	—
Au bzw.AII u	Ubootreferat im Marinekommandoamt	U-boat section in the Naval Command
AZ	Aufschlagzündung	Impact fuze
B	Allgemeines Marineamt mit den Unterabteilungen B St, BW usw.	General Naval Office with sub-divisions B St, BW, etc.
B I, B III	Abteilungen des Admiralstabes (1916–18)	Departments of the Admiralty Staff (1916–18)
B V	Abteilung für Torpedowesen und Funkentelegraphie (Ubootabteilung) im Werftdepartement B des Reichs-Marine-Amtes	Department for Torpedo Affairs and Wireless-Telegraphy (U-Boat Branch) in Yard Department 'B' of the Imperial Naval Office
BAK	Ballon-Abwehr-Kanone (Flak)	Balloon defence gun (Flak)
BBC	Brown, Boveri & Cie	—
BdU	Befehlshaber der Unterseeboote	Commander-in-Chief of Submarines
BKC	Brückner, Kanis & Co	—
BMdVg	Bundesminister der Verteidigung (Verteidigungsministerium)	Minister of State for Defence
BN	Abteilung Technisches Nachrichtenwesen von 'B'	Communication Department of 'B'
BR	Baurat	Construction Adviser
Br.V.	Bremen Vulkan	—
BS	Seetransportabteilung im Allgemeinen Marineamt	Sea-Transport Department in the General Naval Office
BU	Ubootabteilung im Allgemeinen Marineamt 'B'	U-Boat Department in the General Naval Office
B & V	Blohm & Voss	—
BW	Waffendepartement für 'B'	Weapons Department of 'B'
BWB	Bundesamt für Wehrtechnik und Beschaffung	Federal Office for Defence Technics and Procurement
BWi	Amt für Rüstung und Wehrwirtschaft	'B' Department for Economics
C_e, C_w		Official German Navy coefficient used to compare the form/propulsion efficiency of boats.*
Danz.W.	Danziger Werft AG	—
DB	Daimler Benz AG	
DE	(höchste) Dringlichkeitsstufe	(highest) Priority Designation
Dete-Gerät	Deutsches Technisches (Funkmess-) Gerät	German Technical (Radar) Equipment
DW	Deutsche Werft AG, Hamburg	—
DWK	Deutsche Werke Kiel AG	—
EAU	Erprobungsausschuss für Unterseeboote	Test Committee for Submarines
EGRU	Erprobungsgruppe für Unterseeboote	Test Group for Submarines
Elac	Electroacustic Kommanditgesellschaft, Kiel	—
Eto	Elektro-Torpedo	Electric-torpedo
EVG	Europäische Verteidigungsgemeinschaft	European Defence Community (EDC)
Fat	Federapparat (Torpedo)	Spring-loaded (torpedo)
FdU	Führer der Unterseeboote	Chief of Submarines
Fla(k)	Flugzeugabwehr-(Kanone)	Anti-aircraft Defence (Guns)
Flensb.SBG	Flensburger Schiffbau-Gesellschaft	—
Fl.W	Flender Werke, Lübeck	—
FKFS	Forschungsinstitut für Kraftfahrwesen und Fahrzeugmotorenbau an der TH Stuttgart	Research Institute for Motor Transport and Motor Vehicle Engine Construction at the TH Stuttgart
FT	Funk(en)-Telegraphie	Wireless Telegraphy
FuMB	Funkmess-Beobachtungsgerät	Radar Observation Equipment
FuMO	Funkmess-Ortungsgerät	Radar Detection Equipment
g/shp/hp	—	grams per shaft horsepower per hour
GB Chem	Generalbevollmächtigter für Chemie im Rüstungsministerium	—
GBT	Geräuschboje T	Acoustic Buoy T
GEMA	Gesellschaft für elektro-Akustische und mechanische Apparate	—
GFK	Glasfaserstärkter Kunststoff	Glass-fibre strengthened plastic containers
GHG	Gruppen-Horch-Gerät	Group Listening Apparatus
GHH	Gutehoffnungshütte, Oberhausen	—
GU	Generalunternehmer	General Contractor
GW	Germaniawerft, Kiel	—
HAS	Hauptausschuss Schiffbau	Main Committee for Ship Construction
hp/hr	—	Horsepower per hour
HDW	Howaldtswerke Deutsche Werft AG	—
HSVA	Hamburgische Schiffbau-Versuchsanstalt GmbH	Hamburg Shipbuilding Test Institute
IBG	Ingenieurbüro Glückauf	Engineering Officer, Glückauf
IfS	Ingenieurbüro für Schiffbau, Lübeck	Engineering Office for Ship Construction, Lübeck
Igewit	Ingenieurbüro für Wirtschaft und Technik GmbH	Engineering Office for Economics and Technics, GmbH (Company)
IKL	Ingenieurkontor Lübeck	—
IvS (Inkavos)	Ingenieurskaantor voor Scheepsbouw	Engineering Office for Shipbuilding
K bzw.K-Amt	Konstruktionsamt bzw. Hauptamt Kriegsschiffbau bzw. Amt für Kriegsschiffbau	Construction Office, or Head Office for Warship Construction, or Office for Warship Construction
kg/shp/hr	—	kilograms per shaft horsepower per hour
K I U, K II U	Ubootabteilungen im K-Amt	U-boat department (sub-divisions) in the K Office
KdH	Kommando der Hochseeflotte	High Seas Fleet Command

* Where D represents the form displacement in cubic metres, v the speed in knots, N_e the towed power in horsepower and N_w the shaft horsepower,

$$C_e = \frac{D^{2/3}.v}{N_e} \quad \text{and} \quad C_w = \frac{D^{2/3}.v}{N_w}.$$

GLOSSARY OF GERMAN TECHNICAL TERMS

German	English	German	English	German	English
Abblaseventil	Escape valve	Akkumulator(en)	Battery(ies) or accumulator(s)	Anlasser	Starter
Abgas	Exhaust gas			Anlassflaschen	Starting air bottles
Abluft	Exhaust air	Anfahrgetriebeölpumpe	Oil pump for starting gear	Antennenmastwinde	Winch for aerial masts
Abmessungen	Dimensions			Antennenschacht	Shaft for aerials
Abort	W.C.	Angriffssehrohr	Attack periscope	Antrieb	Propulsion
Abscheider	Separator	Anker	Anchor	Antriebsgestange	Propulsion rod
Achse	Axis	Ankerspill	Anchor capstan	Arzneischrank	Medicine chest
Achter, achtern	Abaft, after	Anlage	Installation	Assistent(en)	Assistant(s), Clerks

Aufwasch	Scullery
Aufzug	Hoist, lift
Ausbau	Extension
Ausblase	Exhaust
Ausblasekästen	Exhaust cases
Ausführung	Completion, realization
Ausgleichstank	Compensating tank
Auspuff	Exhaust
Auspufftöpfe	Silencers
Ausrüstung	Armament
Aussen	Exterior
Ausstossrohr	Exit tube, ejection tube
Austritt	Exit
Azetylenflaschen	Acetylene cylinder
Back	Forecastle
Backbord (abbr. BB, Bb)	Port
Behälter	Container(s)
Bereich	Region, range, near
Bereitschaftsmunition	Ready-use ammunition
Betrieb	Operation, plant
Bilgenwasser, Schmutzwasser	Bilge water
Blech	Sheet metal
Blende	Shutter
Bodentank	Floor tank
Bohrmaschine	Drilling machine
Boje	Buoy
Breite	Breadth, width
Bremse	Brake
Brennkammer	Combustion chamber
Brücke	Bridge
Brunnen	Well
Bug	Bow
Bunker	Bunker
Deck	Deck
Deplacement	Displacement
Destillatbehälter	Distilling chamber
Dieselmotor (DM)	Diesel engine
Draufsicht	View from the top
Drehbar	Revolving
Dreistoffpumpe	'3-fuels' pump
Druckbehälter	Compression tank
Druckfest	Pressure tight
Druckkörper	Pressure hull
Drucklager	Thrust bearing
Druckluft	Compressed air
Druckwasser	Pressurized water
D-Spant	Pressure-hull frame
Durchfluteter Raum	Flooding compartment
Durchfluten	To flood
Durchgang	Corridor
Echolotbehälter	Echo-sounding compartment
Einführmulde	Entry trough
Einrichtungsplan	Installations layout
Einspritz	Injection
Einspritzflaschen	Injection bottles
Einsteige	Entry
Einsteigeluke	Entry hatch
E-Kompass	Electric compass
Elektrizitätsmaschine	Electricity supply generator
Elektroherd	Electric source
Elektro-Maschine (EM)	Electric engine
E-Motor	Abbreviation for electric (main) motor
Entlüftung	Exhaust
Entlüftungsventil	Exhaust valve
Entwässerung des Sehrohrbocks	Drainage for periscope jack
Ersatz	Reserve
Etwa	Approximate
Fahrbühne	Control platform
Fahrstand	Control position
Fenster in der Netzabweiserstütze	Porthole(s) in the stanchion supporting the net jumping wires.
Flansch	Flange
Flasche(n)	Bottle(s), air bottle(s), cylinders
Flosse	Fin
Flurboden	Floor
Flurgräting	Floor Grating
Flutklappe(n)	Flooding doors, flooding hatches
Flutschlitzen	Flooding slits
Freiflütend	(Free) floodable
Frischluft	Fresh air
Frischwasser	Fresh, Drinking water
Fundament	Base, floor
Funk	Radio
Funkentelegrafie	Wireless telegraphy (W/T)
Fuss	Foot
Gang	Passageway, corridor
Gasförmig	Gaseous
Gefechtskopf	Warhead
Gefechtspistolen	Contact pistol
Gefechtstorpedoköpfe	Torpedo warheads
Gerät(e)	Equipment(s)
Gesehen	Looking
Gestrichelt Linie	Painted line
Getriebe	Gearing
Gewehr	Gun
Gewicht	Weight
GHG-Anlage	Group listening apparatus installation
Glocke	Bell
Grösste Breite	Max. beam
Grösster Durchmesser	Max. cross-section
Grundausrüstung	Basic fitting-out
Grundlinie	Base line
Gummischlauchboot	Rubber dinghy
Halle	Hall, hangar
Handrad	Handwheel
Handrad für Betätigung der Drehtflügelschraube	Handwheel for moving wing screw
Handsteuer	Hand steering
Haupt	Main
Hauptkompressor	Main compressor
Hauptwellenachse	Main shaft axle
HD abbrev. for Hochdruck q.v.	
Hebehaken	Lifting hooks
Heck	Stern
Heizer	Stoker(s)
Hilfs-	Auxiliary-
Hilfsluftmast	Auxiliary air mast
Hinten, Hinter	After (usually followed by nouns i.e. adjectival)
Hinteres Tiefenruder	After hydroplane
Hinterschiff	After body
Hochdruck (HD)	High pressure
Höhe	Elevation, height
Holzbelag	Wooden sheathing
Horch-	Listening
Ideeller	Hypothetical
Ingenieur	Engineer
Innen	Interior
Kabelbahn	Cable path
Kalipatronen	Potash fitter
Kalt	Cold
Kanister	Canister/container
Kammer	Chamber
Kanone	Gun
Kartenspind	Map locker
Kartoffel	Potato
Kasten	Casing, box
Kegelrad	Bevel wheel
Keilriemantrieb	Wedge-shaped driving-belt
Kettenkasten	Chain cover
Kettenrad	Sprocket wheel
Kiel	Keel
Kielsohle	Keel bottom
Klampe	Clamp
Klappbar	Collapsible, folding
Klappen	Flap
Knick	Break
Kojen	Berths
Kolben	Piston
Kombüse	Galley
Kommandoelemente	Controls
Kommandoturmfenster	Conning tower portholes
Kommandoturmluke	Conning tower hatch
Kondensator	Condenser
Kontur	Contour, outline
Körper	Body, casing
Kraftstoff	Fuel
Kraftstoffhochbehalter	Gravity fuel container
Kreiselkompass	Gyro-compass
Kristall-Basisgerät (KDB)	Crystal base-hydroplane
K. Sehr	Main periscope
K-Spant	Constructional frame
Küche	Galley
Kühler für Haupt E-Motoren	Cooler(s) for main electric motors
Kühlwasser	Cooling water
Kupplung	Coupling, clutch
Lade	Cargo
Ladeluke	Cargo hatch
Lagerraum	Store-room
Länge	Length
Länge über alles (Lu.a.)	Overall length
Längschnitt	Longitudinal section
Lasche(n)	Fish-plate
Laterne	Lantern
Lederzeug	Leather equipment
Leit. Ing.	Chief engineer
Leitung	Leading, direction, guidance
Lenz	Bilge
Leuchtboje	Light buoy
Lichtbildübertragung	Photographic transmission, Photographically transmitted
Lippe	Lip, edge
Lot	Sounding
Lotapparat	Depth-sounder, depth-finder
Luft	Air
Lüfter	Ventilators
Lufterneuerungsanlage	Air renewal system
Luftkühler	Air cooler
Luftpatronen	Air cartridges
Luftreiniger	Air purifier
Luftschacht	Air shaft
Lüftungsanlage	Ventilating system
Lüftungsmaschinen	Ventilation motors
Luftverdichter	Air compressor/condenser
Luftzielsehrohr	High-altitude periscope
Luke	Hatch
Magnetkompass	Magnetic compass
Mannschaft	Crew
Markierungsboje	Marker buoy
Maschinengewehr	Machine-gun
Maschinenraum	Engine room
Maschinentelegraf	Engine telegraph
Maschinistenstand	Engine control platform
Maschinist	Engine-room artificer

Mastwinde	Mast winch
Matrose(n)	Sailor(s), rating(s)
Meerestiefenmesser	Depth gauge
Messe	Wardroom
Mitte	Middle
Montage	Assembly
Motor	Motor, engine
Motor für Ankerwinde	Anchor engine
Mündungsklappen	Opening flaps
Munitionsaufzug	Ammunition hoist
Mutterkompass	Master compass
ND, abbrev. for Niederdruck q.v.	
Neben	Shunt
Nebenschaltafel	Shunt switchboard, switchpanel
Netzabweiser	Net protector
Niederdruck (ND)	Low pressure
Niedergangsluke	Companion hatch
Nische	Recess
Not	Emergency
Notsteuer	Emergency steering
Ober	Head
Obere Ansicht	View from above
Oberkante	Above the head
Öl, Oel	Oil
Öldicht	Oil tight
Ölmotor	Oil engine
Ortung	Position-finding, detection
Patronen	Cartridge
Peiler-funk	Radio beam, radar direction-finding
Peilrahmen	D/F frame, aerial
Petroleum-Motor (PM)	Paraffin engine
Petroleumbunker	Paraffin bunker
Pistole (Pi)	Pistol
Platte	Sheet (of metal)
Platz	Site, location
Pressluft	Compressed air
Proviant	Stores
Pumpe	Pump
Querschnitt	Cross-section
Raum	Compartment, e.g. 'Wohnraum' living-compartment or -quarters
Rechenstelle	Control point
Regelbunker	Compensating fuel tank (water or fuel)
Regelzelle	Compensating tank (water)
Regenzeug	Oilskin
Regler	Regulator
Reglertank(s)	Regulating tank(s)
Reibungskupplung	Friction clutch
Reinigung	Cleansing, purifying
Reserve	Spare, reserve
Rettungsbehalter	Escape compartment
Rettungsfloss	Recovery float
Revolverdrehbank	Revolving lathe
Rohr	Tube, usually torpedo tube
Ruder	Rudder
Rudermaschine, Ruder-motor	Steering motor, steering engine
Rumpf	Hull
Runddipol	Round dipole
Sammeltank	Collecting tank
Sanitär	Hygenic
Sauerstoff	Oxygen
Sauerstofflaschen	Oxygen bottles
Säule	Column, post, pillar
Schacht	Shaft
Schalldämpfer	Silencer
Schaltafel	Switch panel
Schalter	Switch
Schanzkleid	Bulwark cladding
Schiff	Ship
Schlauchboot	Rubber dinghy
Schleichmotor	Creep motor
Schleuse	Sluice, lock
Schlippvorrichtung für Schlepptrosse	Device for jettisoning towing hauser
Schmieröl	Lubricating oil
Schmieröltank	Lubricating oil tank
Schmierölverbrauchstank	Lubricating oil consumption tank
Schmutzöl	Waste (used) oil
Schmutzwasser, Bilgenwasser	Bilge water
Schneckenantrieb	Worm-drive
Schnitt	(Cross) section
Schnorchelfahrt	Schnorkel traverse
Schott	Bulkhead
Schrank	Locker
Schraube	Propellor
Schraubenschutz	Propellor protection
Schraubenwelle	Propellor shaft
Schuss	Round/section
Schutz	Protection
Seenot	Distress at Sea
Seeröhr(e)	Periscope(s)
Seerohrfahrstuhl	Periscope control seat
Seerohrwinde	Periscope winch
Seiltrommel für Funkentelegrafiemast	Cable drum for W/T mast
Seitenruder	Side rudder
Sicherheitsgewichte	Safety weights
Signalpatronen	Signal cartridges
Signal-Schleuse	Signalling lock
Sliphaken	Slip hooks, hauling hooks
Spant (abbr. Sp.)	Frame
Spantenriss	Frame lines
SP-Gerät	Echo-ranging equipment
Speicher	Storage battery
Speisewasser	Feed water
Spinde	Cupboard
Sprengmunition	Explosive ammunition
Stabantenne	Dipole
Stand	Station, position, as at
Stauungsplan	Stowage (layout)
Steuer	Helm, steering
Steuerbord, Abbrev. Stb.	Starboard
Steuerstand	Control platform
Stopfbuchse	Piston-rod collar
Stoss	End, thrust
Strom	Current (elec.)
Stützschott	Support bulkhead
Tank	Tank
Tauchbunker	Ballast tank (water or fuel)
Tauchtank(s)	Diving tank(s)
Tauchzelle	Ballast tank (water)
Taukluse	Hawser hole
Telefonboje	Telephone buoy
Tiefenmesser	Depth gauge
Tiefenruder	Hydroplane(s)
Tiefgang	Draught
Tief-Kühlraum	Deep freeze
Tochterkompass	Repeater compass
Torpedoausstoss-patrone	Torpedo-firing cartridge
Torpedoausstossrohr	Torpedo tube
Torpedoeinführluke	Torpedo loading hatch
Torpedoluk	Torpedo hatch
Torpedomunitionsbehälter	Torpedo stowage
Torpedorohr(e) (TR)	Torpedo tube(s)
Transformator	Transformer
Transportschiene	Transport rail
Treibölbunker	Fuel-oil bunker
Treibölverbrauchsbunker	Fuel-oil consumption bunker
Treibstoff-Bunker	(Motor) fuel bunker
Trimm	Trimming
Trimmpumpe	Trimming pump
Trimmtank/Trimmzelle	Trimming tank
Trinkwasser	Drinking water
Trinkwasserzelle	Drinking water compartment/tank
Trockenraum	Drying room
Trog(e)	Trough(s)
T-Stoff	Abbr. for hydrogen peroxide
Turbogebläse	Turboblower
Turm	Conning tower
Turmluk	Turret hatch
Übernahmepumpe	Loading (i.e. 'taking-in') pump
Übungskopf	Practice (war) head
Umformer	Transformer
Unteroffizier	Petty Officer, NCO
Unterteil	Lower part, base
Untertrieb	Negative buoyancy
UZO (Uboot-Zieloptik)	U-boat target optical apparatus
Ventil	Valve
Verdampfer	Vaporizer
Verdichter	Compressor
Verdrängung	Displacement
Verflüssiger	Liquefier
Vergaser	Carburettor
Verholspill	Warping capstan
Verkleidung	Covering, facing
Versenkbar	Retractable
Verteiler	Distributor
Vertikalruder	Vertical rudder
Vertikalrudermaschine	Vertical rudder engine (motor)
Vierstoffregler	'4-fuels' regulator
Vorder	Forward
Vorderer Trimmtank	Forward trimming tank
Vorderes Tiefenruder	Forward hydroplane
Vorn	Forward
Vorrat, Vorräte	Supplies, stores
Waagerechte	Horizontal, level
Waschwasser	Washing water
Wasserdicht (Wd.)	Watertight
Wasserlinie (WL)	Waterline
Wechselstrom	Alternating current
Wellenbremse	Shaft brake
Wellengetriebe	Shaft, gearing
Winde	Winch
Windschutz	Windscreen
Wohnraum	Living quarters
Wrasen	Vapour
Zeichnungen	Drawing, sketch
Zelle(n)	Cell(s) (of batteries), tanks
Zentrale	Control room
Zersetzer	Disintegrator
Zielsehrohr	Target (attack) periscope
Zu-und Abluftmast	Inlet and exhaust air mast
Zugehörige	Accompanying
Zuluft	Air intake
Zusatz	Extra, booster
Zusatzkompresor	Booster compressor
Zwischenwand	Bulkhead
Zwischenwelle	Main drive shaft
Zylinder	Cylinder

Select Bibliography

UNPUBLISHED SOURCES

a. Bundesarchiv- Militärarchiv, Freiburg (Federal-Military Archives).
Documents in the Reichs-Marine Office and Admiralty (British PG Numbers) quoted on account of incomplete nature): PG 62026, 65314, 65877–8, 65981–4, 69292, 69294, 69499–503, 69509, 69511, 69514–5, 69523, 69713, 69714–6, 77496, 77903, 77907, 78284–5.
Naval documents with the inventory designation of the Militärgeschichtlichen Forschungsamtes (MGFA, or Military History Research Office): II M3, 13, 14/1–2, 22, 23/1–2, 27, 34/1, 34/3–4, 34/6–7, 62/1–2, 90/5, 110/2, 111/23, 112/7–16, 112/19, 112/21–25, 112/27–28, 112/30, 113/1, 113/5–8, 113/11–12, 114/4–5, 114/8–9, 114/11–13, 114/20–26, 114/28–29, 116/1. II M(A) 4, III M(A), 42, III M(A) 47, III M 151/3.
Case documents from the German Federal Navy: GE 889, 1504, 1510, 1522–6, 1528.
Documents from the collection of Grand Admiral Erich Raeder: 6, 12–14, 19.
Documents from the collection of Grand Admiral Karl Dönitz: 19 and BdU War Diary.
Unclassified technical data (documents, projects and sketches) with the provisional designation TS: TS 1–412.
b. Bibliothek für Zeitgeschichte (History Library), Stuttgart.
Report from the U.S. Strategic Bombing Survey (USSBS): Report Number 92–100, IBG and AFA-Hagen.
Saville, A. W. 'The Development of the German U-Boat Arm 1919–1935' University of Washington, 1963.
c. Archives of N.V. Nederlandsche Vereenigde Scheepsbouw Bureaux, Den Haag.
Unclassified documents from the former IvS.
d. Archives of Ingenieurkontor Lübeck (IKL):
Miscellaneous plans and data.
e. Unpublished reports
Aschmoneit, C. 'Nachweis der in der Typenreihe der deutschen Kriegsmarine nicht zum Fertigbau gelangten Uboot projekte'. Eckernförde, 1945.
—'Über Kleinst-U-Boote und U-Boot-ähnliche Kleinkampfmittel der deutschen Kriegsmarine'. Eckernförde, 1945.
Beuter/Diestelmeier. 'Übersicht über die Entwicklung deutscher Ubootentwürfe', 21 Sept 1946.

Kurzak, K. H. 'Der Dieselmotor mit Sauerstoffbetrieb', 29 March 1947.
Oelfken, H. and Mitarbeiter. 'Ausarbeitungen über Grundsatzund Einzelfragen des deutschen Ubootbaus im Zweiten Weltkrieg'. Kressbronn, 1946–1948.

PUBLISHED WORKS
General
Gabler, U. *Unterseebootsbau.* Wehr & Wissen, Darmstadt, 1964.
Gröner, E. *Die deutschen Kriegsschiffe 1815–1945.* 2 vols., Lehmanns, Munich, 1966/1968.
Herzog, B. *60 Jahre deutsche Uboote 1906–1966.* Lehmanns, Munich, 1968.
Jeschke, H. *U-Boottaktik. Zur deutschen U-Boottaktik 1900–1945.* Rombach, Freiburg, 1972.
Rössler, E. *Geschichte des deutschen Ubootbaus.* Lehmanns, Munich, 1975.
– Die deutschen U-Boote und ihre Werften. 2 vols., Bernard & Graefe, Munich, 1979/1980.
Sahlin, Ch. 'Ubåtens utveckling i typhänseende före under och efter andra världskriget'. *Tidskrift i Sjöväsendet,* 5/1954.

To 1900
Bethge, H.-G. *Der Brandtaucher. Ein Tauchboot – von der Idee zur Wirklichkeit.* Hinstorff, Rostock, 1968.
Busley, C. *Die modernen Unterseeboote.* Schiffbautechnischen Gesellschaft Volume 1, 1900.
Hauff, L. *Die unterseeische Schiffahrt, erfunden und ausgeführt von Wilhelm Bauer.* C. C. Buchner, Bamberg, 1859.
Hofmann, F. 'Die unterseeische Schiffahrt und W. Bauer's Küstenbrander'. *Die Gartenlaube,* Book 35, 1864.
Lawrenz, H.-J. *Die Entstehungsgeschichte der U-Boote.* Lehmanns, Munich, 1968.
Röhr, A. *Wilhelm Bauer.* Oldenbourg, Munich/Verein Deutscher Ingenieure Düsseldorf, 1975.

1900–1918
Berling, G. *Die Entwicklung der Unterseeboote und ihrer Hauptmaschinenanlagen.* Schiffbautechnischen Gesellschaft Yearbook, Volume 14, 1913.
Gröner, E. 'UD 1 (UK 50), ein Turbinen-U-Kreuzer'. *Marine-Rundschau,* 4/1956.

Docter, H. 'Geschichte des U-Bootbaues'. *Die Kriegsmarine,* 1935.
Flügge, G. 'Die Entwicklung, Bauart, Zweck und Verwendung der deutschen Unterseeboote'. *Schiffbau,* 27/28, 1920.
Küster, J. *Das U-Boot als Kriegs- und Handelsschiff.* Klasing, Berlin, 1917.
Lohmann, W. 'Die Entwicklung des Unterseebootes, sein Wesen und seine Verwendung'. *Die Wehrmacht,* 1934/35.
Rössler, E. 'Die Auslieferung der deutschen U-Boote nach dem Ersten Weltkrieg und ihre Hintergründe'. *Marine-Rundschau,* 1/1979.
Scheer, R. *Deutschlands Hochseeflotte im Weltkrieg.* Scherl, Berlin, 1920.
Schürer, F. 'Deutsche U-Boote für Küstengewässer (B-Klasse)'. *Schiffbau,* 18/1919.
Spindler, A. *Der Handelskrieg mit U-Booten.* 5 vols., Mittler, Berlin, 1932–1941, and Frankfurt, 1966.
Stegemann, B. *Die Deutsche Marinepolitik 1916-1918.* Duncker & Humblot, Berlin, 1970.
Techel, H. *Der Bau von Unterseebooten auf der Germaniawerft.* Verein Deutscher Ingenieure, Berlin, 1922.
— 'Die Entwicklung des Unterseebootes bis zum Beginn des Weltkrieges'. *VDI-Zeitung,* 47/1937.
— 'Die Entwicklung des Unterseebootes während des Weltkrieges und bis zur Jetztzeit'. *VDI-Zeitung,* 5/1938.
Vogel, H. 'Das moderne Unterseeboot'. *VDI-Zeitschrift,* 7/9, 1911.
Werner, F. 'Deutsche Unterseeminenleger für Küstengewässer (C-Klasse)'. *Schiffbau,* 1/1919.
—'Das Hochsee-Minenunterseeboot'. *Schiffbau,* 3/1919.
German Imperial Navy List for 1914.

1918–1935
Dülffer, J. *Weimar, Hitler und die Marine.* Droste, Düsseldorf, 1973.
Güth, R. *Die Marine des Deutschen Reiches 1919–1939.* Bernard & Graefe, Frankfurt, 1972.
Rahn, W. *Reichsmarine und Landesverteidigung 1919–1928.* Bernard & Graefe, Munich, 1976.
Rössler, E. 'Die deutsche U-Bootausbildung und ihre Vorbereitung 1925–1945'. *Marine-Rundschau,* 8/1971.
— 'Das Projeckt Liliput.' *Marine-Rundschau,* 3/1972.

1935–1945

Aschoff, V. 'Physikalische Probleme des Unterwasserkrieges erläutert am Beispiel eines zielsuchenden Torpedos'. *Wehrtechnische Monatshefte*, 6/1961.

Brennecke, J. *Jäger — Gejagte! Deutsche U-Boote 1939–45*. Köhlers, Jugenheim, 1956. English-language edition *The Hunters and the Hunted*. Burke, 1958.

— *Haie im Paradies*. Gerdes, Preetz, 1961.

Dinechin, G. de 'Technique de Sous-Marin pendant la Dernière Guerre'. *Revue Maritime*, 1949.

Dönitz, K. *Zehn Jahre und zwanzig Tage*. Athenäum, Frankfurt, 1958. English-language edition *Ten Years and Twenty Days*. Weidenfeld & Nicolson, London, 1959; World Pub. Co., 1959.

Fahrmbacher, W. and Matthiae, W. *Lorient. Entstehung und Verteidigung des Marine-Stützpunktes 1940/1945*. Prinz-Eugen-Verlag, Weissenburg, 1956.

Fock, H. *Marinekleinkampfmittel*. Lehmanns, Munich, 1968.

Giessler, H. *Der Marine-Nachrichten- und Ortungsdienst*. Lehmanns, Munich, 1971.

Gröner, E. *Die Schiffe der deutschen Kriegsmarine und Luftwaffe 1939–45 und ihr Verbleib*. Lehmanns, Munich, 1972.

Grützemacher, K. W. 'Der Schnorchel und sein Einsatz'. *Marine-Rundschau*, 2/1956.

Heggstad, K. M. 'Noen tyske ubats-konstruksjoner i krigen 1939-45'. *Norsk Tidskrift for Soevaesen*, 1949.

Janssen, G. *Das Ministerium Speer. Deutschlands Rüstung im Krieg*. Ullstein, Berlin, 1968.

Kruska, E. 'Das Walter-Verfahren, ein Verfahren zur Gewinnung von Antriebsenergie'. *VDI-Zeitschrift*, 3, 9, 21 and 24, 1955.

Kruska, E. and Rössler, E. *Walter-U-Boote*. Lehmanns, Munich, 1969.

Kurzak, K. H. 'German U-Boat Construction'. U.S. Naval Institute Proceedings, 4/1955.

Kurzak, K. H. and Rössler, E. *Unterseeboote und Torpedos mit Kreislaufantrieb*. Kiel, 1969.

Lenton, H. T. *German Submarines*. 2 vols., Macdonald, London, 1965.

Lohmann W. and Hildebrand, H. H. *Die deutsche Kriegsmarine 1939–1945. Gliederung-Einsatz-Stellenbesetzung*. 3 vols., Podzun, Dorheim, 1956–1964.

Michaux, Th. 'Rohstoffe aus Ostasien. Die Fahrten der Blockadebrecher'. *Wehrwissenschaftliche Rundschau*, 11/1955.

Neuerburg, O. K. W. 'Der Landtransport von U-Booten zum Schwarzen Meer. *Marine-Rundschau*, 1955.

Popp, F. 'Overland transport of German ships during World War II'. U.S. Naval Institute Proceedings, 1/1955.

Price, A. *Aircraft versus Submarine*. Kimber, London, 1973.

Reuter, F. *Funkmeß. Die Entwicklung und der Einsatz des RADAR-Verfahrens in Deutschland bis zum Ende des Zweiten Weltkrieges*. Westdeutscher Verlag, Opladen, 1971.

Rohwer, J. *U-Boote. Eine Chronik in Bildern*. Stalling, Oldenburg, 1962.

— *Die U-Boot-Erfolge der Achsenmächte 1939–1945*. Lehmanns, Munich, 1968.

— *Der U-Bootkrieg und sein Zusammenbruch 1943 In: Entscheidungsschlachten des Zweiten Weltkrieges*. Bernard & Graefe, Frankfurt, 1960.

— *Geleitzugschlachten im März 1943*. Motorbuch Verlag, Stuttgart, 1975.

Rohwer, J. and Hümmelchen, G. *Chronik des Seekrieges 1939–1945*. Oldenburg, 1968. English-language edition *Chronology of the War at Sea*. Ian Allan, Shepperton, 1974; Arco, New York, 1975.

Rössler, E. *U-Boottyp XXI*. Lehmanns, Munich, 1967.

— *U-Boottyp XXIII*. Lehmanns, Munich, 1967.

— 'Die U-Kreuzerentwürfe des Flottenbauprogramms 1938/39. *Marine-Rundschau*, 3/1970.

— 'Entwicklung des U-Boottyps VII C'. *Marine-Rundschau*, 11–12/1970.

— 'Erprobung des Walter-U-Bootes U 792'. *Marine-Rundschau*, 12/1971.

— 'Die Bauvorbereitungen für den Walter-U-Boottyp XXVI 1944/45'. *Marine-Rundschau*, 9/1972.

— 'The type XXIII'. *Aviation & Marine International*, Interconair, No. 7 (January), 1974.

— 'V80. The first Walter submarine'. *Aviation & Marine International*, September, 1974.

Rössler, E. 'The Legendary XXI's'. *Aviation & Marine International*, June/July, 1976

— 'Entwicklung und Erprobung von deutschen Unterwasser-Schleppkörpern für den Versorgungseinsatz im Zweiten Weltkrieg'. *Marine-Rundschau*, 1/1977.

— 'Das Walter-Verfahren'. *Marine-Rundschau*, 2/1981.

Sahlin, Ch. 'Utvecklingen av radar och högfrekvent radio och deras utnyttjande i kriget till sjöss 1939–1945, med särskild hänsyn tagen till ubatskriget'. *Tidskrift i Sjövasendet*, 4/1957.

Salewski, M. *Die deutsche Seekriegsleitung 1935–1945*. 2 vols. Bernard & Graefe, Frankfurt, 1970 and 1975.

Schade, H. A. 'German Wartime Technical Developments'. Transactions of the Society of Naval Architects and Marine Engineers (SNAME), 1946.

Spachmann, F. 'Versuchskommando 456 des Kleinkampfverbandes der Kriegsmarine und die zukunftsweisenden Entwicklungen "Schwertwal" und "Seeteufel" mit den dazugehörigen Spezialwaffen sowie dem Tiefsee-Tauchgerät "Grundhai".' *Marine-Rundschau*, 3/1970.

— 'Das Projekt "Manta" des Versuchskommandos 456'. *Marine-Rundschau*, 3/1972.

Speer, A. *Erinnerungen*. Ullstein, Frankfurt, 1969.

Starks, J. F. 'German U-Boat Design and Production'. Paper No. 5 from Inst. of Naval Architects, 1948.

Trenkle, F. *Deutsche Ortungs- und Navigationsanlagen (Land und See 1935–1945)*. Ausschuß für Funkortung, Düsseldorf, 1964.

Wagner, G. *Lagevorträge des Oberbefehlshabers der Kriegsmarine vor Hitler 1939–1945*. Lehmanns, Munich, 1972.

1954–1980

Abels, F. 'Einfluß schiffstechnischer Arbeiten auf Entwurf und Konstruktion von Ubooten'. *Schiff und Hafen*, 9/1973.

Arendt, K. 'Der U-Boots-Bau der Rheinstahl Nordseewerke GmbH, Emden'. *Hansa*, 7/1976.

Bachmann, H.-G. and Ritterhoff, J. 'Landerprobung der Hauptantriebs- und Hilfsmaschinenanlage der Uboote Klasse 206'. *Schiff und Hafen*, 9/1973.

Breyer, S., Koop, G. and Mrva, F. *Die Schiffe und Fahrzeuge der deutschen Bundesmarine 1956–1976*. Bernard & Graefe, Munich, 1976.

Büttner, G. 'Stand und Entwicklungsmöglichkeiten der elektronischen Ausrüstungen konventionell angetriebener Uboote'. *Schiff und Hafen*, 9/1973.

— 'Zwanzig Jahre U-Boot-Entwicklung in Lübeck. Rückblick und Ausblick'. *Marine-Rundschau*, 9/1979.

Gabler, U. 'Einhüllen- oder Zweihüllen-Bauweise im Untersee-bootbau?' *Marine-Rundschau*, 9/1979.

Gierschner, N. *Tauchboote*. Transpress, Berlin, 1980.

Jablonsky, W. 'Ubootbau in der Bundesrepublik Deutschland'. *Marineforum*, 5/1974.

Koldewijn, A. 'Weapon Systems for Submarines'. *International Defence Revue*, 4/1973.

Kayser, P. 'Erfahrungen mit schnellaufenden Dieselmotoren in Unterwasserfahrzeugen'. *Schiff und Hafen*, 9/1973.

Krüger, P. 'Einfluß des Ubootbaus auf Fahrzeuge und Geräte der Meerestechnik'. *Schiff und Hafen*, 9/1973.

Kruska, E. 'Neuzeitliche U-Boots-Antriebe'. *Wehrtechnik*, 12/1969.

Lawrenz, H.-J. 'Bleiakkumulatoren als Fahrbatterie im U-Boot'. *Marine-Rundschau*, 9/1980.

Nohse, L. 'Der Antrieb von Unterseebooten, augenblicklicher Stand und Entwicklungsmöglichkeiten'. *Wehrtechnik*, 9/1969.

— 'The German 1000 ton Export U-Boat'. *International Defence Revue*, 5/1972.

— 'Entwurf und Konstruktion von Ubooten in der Bundesrepublik Deutschland nach dem Zweiten Weltkrieg'. *Schiff und Hafen*, 9/1973.

Nohse, L. and Rössler, E. *Moderne Küsten-Uboote*. Lehmanns, Munich, 1972.

Ramsauer, U. 'Torpedoentwicklung in Deutschland'. *Internationale Wehrrevue (International Defence Revue)*, 1/1976.

Rössler, E. 'U-Bootantriebe heute und morgen'. *Marine-Rundschau*, 4/1970.

— 'Die neuen U-Boote der griechischen Marine'. *Marine-Rundschau*, 9/1974.

Totzek, F. W. 'U-Boote gestern und heute — ein Vergleich'. *Marine*, 9/1969.

— 'Die besonderen Beanspruchungen unserer U-Bootsbesatzungen'. *Truppenpraxis*, 13/1970.

Ude, U. and Nohse, L. 'Die deutschen Kampf-Uboote der Bundesmarine'. *Internationale Wehrrevue (International Defence Review)*, 3/1968.

Waas, H. *Rückschläge im Ubootbau und die daraus zu ziehenden Folgerungen*. Schiffbautechnischen Gesellschaft Yearbook, Volume 61, 1967.

Werf, P. H. *Die U-Boote der deutschen Marine*. Wehrtechnik Yearbook, 1973.

Index

INDEX OF U-BOATS

GENERAL INDEX

Below: *U17* and *U18*.

Photograph acknowledgments
Boman, 96 (bottom); Bundesarchiv/Militärarchiv, 135 (right), 197; BV-Fotoarchiv, 138 (top); Claviez, 132 (top left), 245; Deutsches Museum München, 13, 30, 34, 45 (bottom right); Dressler/Rohwer, 106, 190 (bottom), 209, 222 (top), 228 (right), 241, 289 (top); Druppel, 22, 45 (top), 62, 82; Friese, 55, 306 (centre); Greger, 43 (centre and bottom); Gröner, 195 (top); Grützemacher, 225; HDW, 224 (top), 309 (top), 320 (top right); Hellmuth Walter GmbH, 300 (bottom); Herold, 11 (top); Imperial War Museum, 229 (top), 289 (bottom); Illies, 270; Jung, 109, 293; Köhl, 196, 189 (right), 201; Krupp, 138 (bottom); Kludas, 58, 64; Kurzak, 295; Lawrenz, 11 (bottom); 15 (bottom left and right), 95; Lennart Lindberg, 130; Marinearsenal Kiel, 95, 155, 312; Nerlich, 320 (top left); Oelfken, 291; RNSW, 314; Sahlin, 189 (left), 230; Selinger, 16, 18 (top), 42 (left), 43 (top), 71, 111, 128, 133 (bottom left), 141 (bottom), 164, 171 (top), 190 (top), 192 (bottom), 195 (bottom), 200 (top), 299; Stegemann, 53.

Line drawing acknowledgments
Ahme, 38; Boman/Köhl, 348, 352, 354; Bundesarchiv/Militärarchiv, 23, 24, 28, 29, 111, 116, 284, 350; BWB MS, 150, 277, 279, 287, 288, 291; Fock, 79; Gröner, 74, 279; IKL, 319, 325, 370; Köhl, 94, 113, 118, 148, 151, 163, 186, 201, 205, 209, 323, 356, 358, 360, 362, 364, 366; Kruska, 295; Kurzak, 368; Lawrenz, 14 (bottom); Marinearsenal Kiel, 14 (centre); Schürer (*Deutsche U-Boote für Küstengewässer*), 41, 50, 51, 56; Techel (*Der Bau von Unterseebooten auf der Germaniawerft*), 16, 19, 22, 23, 29, 37, 39, 68, 69, 70; Werner (*Deutsche Unterseeminenleger für Küstengewässer, Das Hochsee-Minenunterseeboot*), 44, 46, 47, 52, 59, 60, 77, 78.